BBC In Tou[ch]

1995-96 HAN[DBOOK]

LATE SUPPLEMENT
and ORDER FORM

June 30 1995

Legislation latest

4 Your rights to help

4.3 The Disability Discrimination Bill

The Bill has now completed the Committee Stage in the House of Lords and the next step will be the Report Stage on July 18th and 20th 1995. The Third Reading in the Lords is unlikely before mid October, with the bill receiving Royal Assent possibly in late October 1995.

Timescales may change again, but at present implementation dates have been postponed to late 1996. The employment section will be introduced first, followed by access to goods and services. Access to information may be implemented in 1997. Improved access to buildings and transport will be developed over a period of time.

On June 15th a reassurance was given that service provided to a child is also service provided to a parent, guardian or carer, and a vote was won extending the provision of the bill to cover people without obvious disabilities.

On June 26th an amendment was introduced to give the **National Disability Council** statutory powers to investigate discrimination and help disabled people to enforce their rights. It was withdrawn with no vote called, which was a disappointing lack of progress at this stage. Parliament and its services are now covered by this Bill, clarification is being sought to ensure that the services provided by MPs both in parliament and in their constituencies will be covered.

Disability organisations still hope that, whether it be called a council or commission, the National Disability Council will be able to operate on the same level as the Commission for Racial Equality and the Equal Opportunities Commission, independent of the government, adequately resourced, capable of advising individuals and businesses, and with the power to investigate and take action in cases of discrimination.

Key to media of publication ⓟ clear print ⓛ large print ⓑ braille ⓣ tape Ⓜ Moon ⓓ disk

5 Benefits

5.4.2 Disability Living Allowance: the middle rate care component

The Secretary of State lost the appeal. On June 15th 1995 the Court of Appeal ruled that 'there is nothing in [the relevant section], or the statutory provisions generally, which leads to the conclusion that only attention which is necessary to maintain life itself is reasonably required'. Lord Justice Glidewell said that attention required to carry out a reasonable level of social activity **was** relevant when adjudication officers were considering whether a claimant needed 'frequent attention'.

This ruling should mean that visually impaired people should have taken into account the help they need to enjoy a reasonable level of social activity - such as going for a walk, shopping, attending a club or other similar activities.

Although the Court of Appeal refused the Department of Social Security leave to appeal to the House of Lords, the DSS is now asking the House of Lords itself for leave to appeal. As a result, visually impaired people whose applications were successful because their social activity needs were taken into account, continue to have their payments suspended.

This continued uncertainty should not deter visually impaired people from applying for DLA and describing in detail their need for help both with social activities and domestic activities.

Further developments will be covered as and when they happen on the **In Touch Programme** on BBC Radio 4 and on the **In Touch Gateway**.

26 Helping older, frailer people

26.11 Help for Carers

Carers (Recognition and Services) Bill

This Bill will receive Royal Assent in July, and will come into force in April 1996. It places a duty on local authorities in England and Wales to assess the ability of a carer to sustain an appropriate level of care, plus a duty to take this assessment into account when deciding what services should be provided for the person needing care.

A carer is defined as someone providing a substantial amount of care on a regular basis, and includes children under the age of 18. Those caring for children with disablities will be able to ask for a separate assessment when the child is being assessed for services under the Children Act 1988.

These provisions will also apply to Scotland. In Northern Ireland directions will be issued to the Health and Social Services Boards asking them to apply the main policy intentions of the Bill to Northern Ireland.

The **Carers National Association** will be issuing leaflets for carers later in 1995.

Other late news

2 What went wrong?

2.3.4 Retinitis Pigmentosa

The British Retinitis Pigmentosa Society now has a welfare worker attached to the RP clinic in Glasgow Western Infirmary. ℘ 0141 338 3823.

5 Benefits

5.2 Incapacity benefit

An additional leaflet **Incapacity Benefit: information for new customers** (IB 204) is now issued in braille, as is the **Guide for registered medical practitioners** (IB 202).

5.3 Severe disablement allowance

The NI252 claim form has been updated and is now called SDA1. A braille version can be obtained from the *Benefits Enquiry Line*.

5.16 Getting information

The **Benefits Enquiry Line** (freephone 0800 882200) stock all braille benefits leaflets produced by RNIB and can, on request, supply other leaflets in braille using their own transcription equipment. Audio tapes **Out of work? Information on social security benefits for the unemployed** and **Benefits for working people: information on social security benefits for those in employment** can be supplied in English, Welsh, Chinese, Gujerati, Hindi, Punjabi, Somali, Sylheti, Turkish, Urdu and Vietnamese.

    Money for pensioners with sight problems ⓛⒷⓣ (Free. RNIB) concentrates on eligibility for attendance allowance and what to consider when making a claim. It includes a claim card.

6 Parents and children

6.15 Further reading

Play it my way: learning through play with your visually impaired child ⓣ (HMSO/RNIB. 1995. £9.95). A resource book for parents, teachers, play leaders and health professionals working with visually impaired children, including children with multiple disability.

    RNIB: Services for children is a free audio cassette from *RNIB Education Information Service* in Bengali, Chinese, English, Greek, Gujerati, Hindi, Punjabi, Turkish, Urdu and Welsh.

7 Extra help for extra problems

7.3.1 Sources of help

Movement, Gesture and sign: an interactive approach to sign communication for children who are visually impaired with additional disabilities. Mary Lee and Lindi MacWilliam. (RNIB. 1995. £7.50). This book is based on work at Canaan Lodge and Barrie House, Royal Blind School, Edinburgh.

8 Education

8.1 The 1993 Education Act

A Special Partnership: A practical guide for Named Persons and parents of children with special educational needs. Linda Kerr, Liz Sutherland and Joyce Wilson. (HMSO. 1994. £3.95). This book is of special interest for parents in Scotland where the **Statementing** process (known as Recording of Special Needs) is slightly different to elsewhere in the UK. See 8.2.2 for details of the role of the 'Named Person'.

10 Finding a job
10.7.4 Access to work

Amendments accepted by the government to the **Disability Discrimination Bill** include these examples of 'reasonable adjustments' - the steps an employer may have to take in order to comply with the Act:

(a) making adjustments to premises;

(b) allocating some of the disabled person's duties to another person;

(c) transferring him to fill an existing vacancy;

(d) altering his working hours;

(e) assigning him to a different place of work;

(f) allowing him to be absent during working hours for rehabilitation, assessment or treatment;

(g) giving him, or arranging for him to be given, training;

(h) acquiring or modifying equipment;

(i) modifying instructions or reference manuals;

(j) modifying procedures for teaching or assessment;

(k) providing a reader or interpreter;

(l) providing supervision.

It will be noted that (h) and (k) are services currently financed by **Access to work**. It is unclear at present whether the intention is that in future this help should be funded by employers. The Access to work scheme is currentlly under review, and a report is expected at the end of 1995. The **In Touch Gateway** will carry up-to-date information.

10.8 Setting up in business

RNIB Small Business Unit is now known as the **Self Employment Development Unit**

12 Getting about safely
12.3.4 Roller tips

A new design of roller tip which will fit RNIB canes will be available from *Cobolt Systems*, price approximately £7.00, from July 1995. The ball spins on all its axes, rather than only rolling.

12.6 Maps

A cassette giving details of facilities at **Glasgow Central Station** is available free from the Station General Manager's Office ℘ 0141 335 4799.

12.8.1 Public buildings

Building Sight (RNIB. 1995. £25) shows how the needs of visually impaired people can be met in the design of all types of building and how simple, low-cost solutions can make the environment a more friendly place for everybody. The book is aimed especially at architects, designers, planners and access officers. A set of 21 **Technical bulletins** covering subjects such as tactile paving, kitchen design, direction signs, bathrooms and staircases is issued by RNIB/GDBA Joint Mobility Unit, Price £3.00.

Access for All (Owlion Audio Programmes. £15.75 inc p&p) is an audio-cassette to help surveyors appreciate the difficulties faced by people with disabilities, including visual impairment. Visually impaired people joining a local

Access Group would find this tape helpful as it contains a clear description of the current legislative position in England and Wales as well as the function of local authority access officers - and where they may be found. Mail order from *RICS Books, Surveyor Court, Westwood Way, Coventry CV4 8JE* ℘ 0171 222 7000.

Project Rainbow is a two year research project begun in April 1995 by the Department of Construction Management and Engineering and the Department of Psychology at the University of Reading. It aims to establish how colour can best be used, primarily in interior environments, to help people with very poor sight to get about. The research will be based on information provided by visually impaired people. Other projects being undertaken by the research team include emergency lighting, escape route lighting and wayfinding provision for visually impaired people as well as design considerations for automatic and manually operated doors. More details from Foz Gillespie, Department of Construction Management and engineering, University of Reading, Whiteknights, PO Box 219, Reading, RG6 2BU ℘ 01734 316734 (24 hour answerphone), or lo-call 0345 023153.

14 Health
14.9 Health care information
Incontinence ☎, a pamphlet issued free by Help the Aged. It explains how bladders and bowels work, how people can help themselves and the services and equipment available.

16 In the kitchen
16.6 Microwave ovens
Cobolt Systems are now marketing a **talking microwave oven**. It is an adapted Goldstar MA892TE, the control panel having been removed and a talking keypad substituted. Taped instructions included. £185 including postage and packing.

17 Labelling and identification
17.1.1 Identifying clothes
Colour indicating buttons (Sladecolour buttons) are now stocked by RNIB in two different packs, each costing 95 pence. Pack DH97 contains one button of each of the eight primary range of colours; DH98 consists of one each of the eight fashion colours.

18 Reading and writing
18.1.2 Other large print publications
The Select Quarterly (£2.50 per issue. Watson publishing) is a new large print quarterly magazine. It includes well-known stories as well as previously unpublished work by authors in the Glasgow Blind Writers Group and a crossword. It is produced in 18 point Helvetica print. Contact *Watson Publishing, PO Box 12206, Edinburgh, EH4 3YU* ℘ 0131 220 4204.

21 Recreations
21.7.2 Golf
The telephone number of **English Blind Golf** has been changed to ℘ 0181 505 2085.

23 Physical disabilities

23.3.5 Sources of information

The **British Diabetic Association** has a **Careline** ℘ 0171 636 6112 which can help with general questions on living with diabetes, including visual impairment, but cannot give specific individual medical advice.

24 Deafblindness

24.1.3 Using the telephone

Hasicom users can now access police, fire and ambulance services. By dialling Freephone ℘ 0800 112 999 in an emergency they can contact a Typetalk operator who will pass on the details directly to the relevant emergency service. Users should make sure their equipment is compatible with the new emergency service by ringing the Technical Helpline Freephone ℘ 0800 592 600.

24.6 Equipment and publications

The **British Deaf Association** and **Sense**, supported by the Department of Health, have issued three attractive booklets on Usher syndrome in strip cartoon form. **Usher and You** gives tips on how to help young people with Usher, whilst **Usher in the Family I** and **Usher in the Family II** is especially helpful for parents. Designed originally for signing deaf people, they have proved to be popular with a much wider readership. Contact: *British Deaf Association, 38 Victoria Place, Carlisle CA1 1HU* ℘ 01228 48844. Each title is sold in multiple copies of five, price £4. Single copies available on application. Cheques payable to the Big D Co., Ltd.

'**Oh really, you have Usher?**' is a new video due to be released towards the end of 1995. Details of availability from *Sense*.

The Young Usher Group has now merged with Usher Syndrome Link Groups to form **Usher UK**. Contact Gillian Winstanley (Chair) via *Sense Headquarters*.

25 Adults with complex needs

25.9 Further reading

What's it like to be a parent? ❶❷❸ (Sue McGaw. £10. British Institute of Learning Disabilities) is an introduction to all aspects of parenting for people with learning disabilities. Further books will be addressing specific topics in detail. Contact *BILD, Wolverhampton Road, Kidderminster, Worcs DY10 3PP* ℘ 01582 850251.

Planning individual leisure activities for adults with visual and learning disablties (50p. RNIB Information and Practice Development Service on Multiple Disability) is a new addition to the Focus Factsheet collection.

26 Helping older, frailer people

26.6.5 Avoiding Accidents

Home Safety leaflets entitled **Safety in Your Home**, **Keep out the Cold**, **Security in your Home** and **Fire** are issued free on cassette by Help the Aged.

A LIBRARY OF VISUAL IMPAIRMENT INFORMATION FROM
In Touch Publishing

101 PRACTICAL HINTS
Everyday living   **CARE GUIDE**

Everyday tasks made easier with nothing more elaborate than a paper clip or a rubber band. Practical help for everyone with poor sight. Tape version read by Annette Crosbie and David Rintoul.

WAITING TO SEE
Cataract   **CARE GUIDE**

With 330 cataract operations every day, timely answers to haunting questions: What does the operation involve? What is a lens implant? Will I need thick glasses? When can I see again? How to reduce anxiety at a difficult time.

COPING AGAIN
Macular disease   **CARE GUIDE**

The commonest cause of sight loss in elderly people. Here are many ways to make the most of remaining sight to see better, plus exercises and illustrations to help choose and use a magnifier. Catherine Cookson describes how the disease has not stopped her writing.

SPORT AND LEISURE
Recreation   **CARE GUIDE**

Try new activities, regain those enjoyed pre-sight loss. Tape read by Peter White.

PLEASURES OF LISTENING
Spoken word   **CARE GUIDE**

A guide to easy-to-use equipment including pre-set radios, sound-only TV sets. Libraries with a wide range of recorded books for adults and children.

GETTING ABOUT SAFELY
Mobility   **CARE GUIDE**

How anyone with very poor sight can relearn to move about safely.

OPENING BOOKS
CATALOGUE

for visually impaired readers, carers and professionals

An exciting new catalogue for all print handicapped readers:

* all existing and new **In Touch** publications
* selected top titles from **BBC Books** with readability ratings by our low vision panel
* selected audio titles from the **BBC Collection** complete with braille labelling
* important **titles for professionals** working in visual impairment

order form overleaf

BBC
In Touch Publishing

IN TOUCH CARE GUIDES

		PRINT	TAPE	BRAILLE
		Number of Copies		
Opening Books	free with this form	☐	☐	☐
101 Practical Hints	£2.50	☐	☐	☐
Coping Again (macular)	£3.50	☐	☐	☐
Waiting to See? (cataracts)	£2.50	☐	☐	☐
Pleasures of Listening	£1.95	☐	☐	☐
Sport and Leisure	£1.95	☐	☐	☐
Getting About Safely	£1.75	☐	☐	☐
Partners or Helpers	£1.75	☐	☐	☐

	PRINT	DISK	BRAILLE
IN TOUCH 1995-96 HANDBOOK £19.95	☐	☐ *	☐

I enclose a cheque for £_____ made payable to
In Touch Publishing

☐ * Registered blind or partially sighted readers **only**. Please supply VAT exemption certificate, **or** tick for us to supply one for signature.

Name _____

Organisation _____

Address _____

_____

_____ Post Code _____

Phone _____ Date _____

Post to: **In Touch Publishing**, 37 Charles Street, Cardiff CF1 4EB

ITHB95

BBC In Touch

1995-96 HANDBOOK

The BBC Radio 4 guide to services for
people with a visual impairment

Margaret Ford
and
Thena Heshel

**Updated with the help of
Anne Theakstone**

In Touch
Publishing

Published by In Touch Publishing
in association with BBC Network Radio

Published by In Touch Publishing
37 Charles Street, Cardiff CF1 4EB
in association with BBC Network Radio

First Published 1973
Twelfth edition July 1995

© **In Touch Publishing** 1995

Print edition: ISBN 0 9526130 0 X
Braille edition: ISBN 0 9526130 1 8
Disk edition: ISBN 0 9526130 2 6

Produced at Pia, 37 Charles Street, Cardiff CF1 4EB

Publisher, Mike Joseph
Production Manager, Gail Chester
Artwork manager and production software, Mike Southern
Editing and indexing, Lyn Hooper
Cover design, Andy Dark

Cover photograph Martin Keene, Press Association
(HRH Princess of Wales visiting seeABILITY, January 17th 1995)

Photographs by Michael Blackburn 28, 29, 237, Richard Copsey 335,
Larry Croker 25, 26, 27, Guide Dogs Adventure Group 24, Taira Iqbal 23,
Lancashire Evening Post 30, Jens Nielsen 31, Chris Rushton 24.

In Touch Publishing is an imprint of Gwasg Pia cyf.

In Touch Handbook   DIRECTORY

Tables and illustrations

The BBC In Touch Programme

'Good Evening. Tonight ...' Oh, sorry, it's such an instinct to start a script with those time honoured words! If they ring a bell, you'll know they signal 30 minutes of your news, your views, and very often your answers to other listeners' questions raised in earlier programmes. That's why we call the programme *In Touch*: the key to living with little or no sight is so often to get in touch with others who've been round the course before.

As we sort through your questions and suggestions for the programme in the office, the chances are that you, the audience have your own answers. So when Christine said on *In Touch* that she fancied a day's rock climbing to build her self-confidence, we were only a bit surprised to get three calls from climbing instructors by ten pm – all, naturally, blind or partially sighted themselves.

The **In Touch Handbook** is of course the storehouse of all these facts and tips, and we probably use it as much in the office as you do at home or work. As Mike Joseph explains opposite, the Handbook is now live 'on line' for the ever-growing bunch of computer literate listeners. This will make it even easier to keep in touch with the answers to tricky situations, but how do we generate new questions? It's obvious by now, isn't it – you tell us. Well, you didn't expect us to do the work did you?!

Every Tuesday you can phone us for an hour after the programme, on the number most of you could recite in your sleep: 0171 580 4444 (9.30 – 10.30pm). You can write to us in braille or, if you must, print. You can send a cassette and you can even send a floppy disk with the usual rubber band indicating a message (3.5″, double density please, and we use WordPerfect in the office if you do). If we could answer every listener personally, we'd be worried we weren't getting enough mail, so sorry if you don't always get a personal response. We can say though that everything goes in the pot and comes out on air eventually! If you miss the programme which finally dealt with your query, of course it'll be in the Handbook, in all its forms, before long.

Despite all the wonderful modern media though, there's one thing for which you must rely on the wireless: talking to the decision makers. Ask London Underground, or Stagecoach (one of the hopeful bidders for the BR franchises), or even the dear old Braille Authority of the UK. They'll tell you how vocal *In Touch* listeners have been when they ventured into the studio to defend their policies or, in BAUK's case, take soundings on capitalisation in English Braille (letters please, direct to BAUK now!). This year, as last, we'll deliver you the people whose decisions affect your lives – whenever we can lure them in!

Dave Harvey

The BBC In Touch Gateway

A live computer information service

The **In Touch Handbook** has both the virtues and the vices of being a book. It seeks to be comprehensive and authoritative. Whatever the topic of interest, there is something between its covers to extend and deepen knowledge. Complex topics will be presented clearly and methodically. Linked subjects will be well flagged and cross-indexed. The book is an orderly view of a disorderly world.

The Handbook has virtues: but its vices cannot be denied. The world is not orderly. It is full of people with opinions, feelings, criticisms, ambitions, hopes and fears: as testified weekly on the *In Touch* programme. Moreover, it is awash with change. Once it was enough to have an edition of the Handbook every four or five years. Then in the mid-80s, with the increasing pace of change, the book became an annual, simultaneous publication in print, braille and tape. Even that is no longer enough.

Satisfaction at the Handbook being up to date in all media on launch is tempered by the knowledge that by next morning it is a day out of date. This 1995-96 Handbook has taken nine months to research and edit. Yet comprehensive though it is, in the time it has taken to reach your hands the world has moved on.

Can there be a medium as all-embracing and authoritative as the book, as up-to-date and personal as a broadcast? The **In Touch Gateway** may be the answer: a live computer information service, launched during the currency of this Handbook.

To discover the In Touch Gateway for yourself, plug your computer and modem to a phone line and dial 01 222 222099. During 1995 (the research year), give your first name as **GUEST USER**, press [RETURN] at 'password', and follow the prompts.

The public Gateway service will be launched early in 1996. From then, give your name as **TRIAL SUBSCRIBER**. This will give a free trial period to test the service. If you have difficulties with either method, phone *In Touch Publishing* on 01 222 222456.

At the core of the In Touch Gateway service is the complete In Touch Handbook, with automated subject search and instant cross-reference links. Next are News areas, where the BBC In Touch Programme and In Touch Publishing newsrooms provide an ever changing view of the diverse world of visual impairment.

The Directory sections deliver information and publications from the leading blind welfare organisations: at a glance you can check and obtain the most relevant information from a range of publishers. Imagine being able to list all the information on any visual impairment topic from many different welfare organisations in an instant: you are imagining the Gateway. Later we aim to offer an order-by-computer facility for courses, events, services, and products, so that information can lead directly to action.

Already Gateway Messages enable subscribers to talk back – like the *In Touch* phone-in – sharing notes, news, queries and opinions on all topics of concern.

The In Touch Gateway is not exclusive to one publisher. It is a forum for all concerned with visual impairment, for research, rapid updating and exchange of views and information. How it develops is very much in your hands. As you read this, these words will be out of date. That is inevitable when we are pioneering a new medium. This is our warm invitation for you to join us.   *Mike Joseph*

How to use this book

Structure

The **In Touch Handbook** is published in four editions: print, braille, disk and online via the **In Touch Gateway**.

The Handbook is made up of units, chapters, sections and subsections. The ten **Units**, lettered A – J, are thumb-indexed in the print edition, and comprise the ten volumes of the braille edition. Each unit covers a major subject area, and starts with a detailed Unit contents listing. The **Unit directory** is at the front of the Handbook.

The **34 chapters** are numbered 1 – 34, and the contents of each chapter is broken down to numbered section and subsection levels. The numbering for every section and subsection starts with the chapter number, so all references are unambiguous.

The same numbers are used in all four editions to assist cross-referencing. Except only for the page indexes in the print and braille editions, references throughout are to the section/subsection, not to the page number.

Contents

A **summary** of the contents by unit is at the front of the Handbook. **Chapter contents** are listed in detail at the head of each unit. A **page index** appears at the back of the print and braille editions. Addresses not given in the text are listed alphabetically in **32 Useful addresses**. **Resource Centres** are fully listed in **34**. **NEW** This symbol indicates material new in the 1995-96 edition.

Publication dates

This Handbook is published July 1995. The main book is updated to May 1995. Yellow pages are updated to June 1995. Latest developments are on the In Touch Gateway.

Accessible publications

Symbols used to indicate titles available in alternative media: **P** clear print **L** large print **B** braille **T** tape **M** Moon **D** disk. Most titles are also available in standard print. If no symbol or details are given, assume that it is available in standard print.

Prices

Prices quoted are current at press time. Unless otherwise indicated, postage, packing and VAT are included where applicable (see 15.5.4). RNIB and Partially Sighted Society prices are quoted at the subsidised or concession rate (see 29.1).

Accuracy and endorsement

Whilst all efforts have been made to ensure accuracy and comprehensiveness, the inclusion of a product or service in the Handbook should not be read or quoted as an endorsement by the authors or publishers, who give no warranty as to accuracy, inaccuracy or omission in matters of fact or opinion. Inclusion of information in the In Touch Handbook is at the sole discretion of its authors and publishers.

As and when information can be usefully updated, readers are encouraged to pass details and comments to the publishers: see In Touch Publishing and In Touch Gateway listings in 32.

Foreword

Robin SeQueira
President, Association of Directors of Social Services,
Director of Social Services, Dorset

Rarely a week goes past without the publication of a report which somewhere highlights the importance of information to people with disabilities, their families or carers. No matter how much effort individuals or organisations put into producing material, the messages suggest the need for information which is accurate, up to date and accessible.

In order that information is relevant, information providers need to address a number of issues and questions. When was it produced? Does it still have legitimacy? Is the timing for its publication appropriate? Often the right information is delivered but its timing is wrong. The information giver may not know of all the specialist sources which provide assistance, perhaps not surprising when considering that this edition of *In Touch* refers to 20 different conditions which may impair eyesight, almost all of which have their own society, support group or helpline. There may not be any reference material available for the information user to take away and so a large proportion of what has been learned is lost. The material may be available but not in the format that meets individual needs; print is of little help to a braille user.

In a rapidly changing environment it is essential that people who are visually impaired as well as those who set out to assist them (whether they are workers in statutory or independent agencies, volunteers, carers or friends) have access to the material which can, if used properly, reduce errors of fact or omission.

In Touch is unique in its approach. It combines a comprehensive handbook, covering the essential basic detail, with a regular radio programme. Whilst not compulsory for workers in the field, the programme has developed into compulsive listening. Taking these parts together there can be no excuse for visually impaired people to be put in a position to say, "I didn't know about that; it would have made such a difference."

This edition of the handbook has been expanded to provide additional information for visually impaired people who have other disabilities. Information for carers, particularly those with responsibility for elderly, frail blind people is also included. Both areas are of importance as Community Care results in increasing numbers in these groups being able to remain in their own homes, leading to new demands on carers and on those who provide support.

In Touch is an important source of assistance which I unreservedly commend to you. It is up to us all to make sure that the information it contains is well used.

Acknowledgements

We are indebted to over 100 organisations and individuals concerned with visual impairment whom we consulted for guidance on ways to improve this new edition of the Handbook. Those who took part in the consultation are too numerous to mention individually, but we hope that they will recognise that we have benefited from their advice. The changes they suggested have resulted in a new presentation of the benefits chapter which we hope makes a complex system as simple as possible for the non-specialist. We have also expanded the information for families and carers of frail and multiply disabled people with visual impairments.

Like our colleagues who produce the BBC Radio 4 In Touch programme we are indebted to visually impaired listeners whose comments and suggestions constantly challenge and inform us all, and whose experiences are quoted throughout this book.

Additional advice has been generously given by *Duleep Allirajah, Neil Anderson, Bill Aylward, Ros Constable, John Crosland, Lis Grundy, John Keast-Butler, Peng Khaw, Chris Macmillan, Robert Orr, Gordon Plant, Peter Raine, Nick Rumney, Nick Sarkies, Valerie Scarr* and *Stephen Tuft.* Staff in the Departments of Education, Employment, Health and Social Security have supplied advice, information and encouragement. Our thanks are due again for the continued help and co-operation we have received from both senior and junior staff in nearly every department of RNIB. *Jane Copsey, Jessica Finch* and *Andrea Llewellyn* updated the chapters on computers, labelling and the kitchen respectively.

We are also indebted to *Dr. Michael Wolffe* for his advice on the sight simulation pictures and to the *British College of Optometrists* for their contribution towards the costs of these. *Patricia Capon's* illustrations and *Jane Fallow's* diagrams enliven the text.

The publishers acknowledge with thanks the financial support of *BBC Network Radio* towards the In Touch Handbook, and of the *Guide Dogs for the Blind Association* towards the work of In Touch Publishing. Their indispensable support enables the Handbook to maintain its central role of informing and advising everyone concerned with sight loss.

Margaret Ford, Thena Heshel, Anne Theakstone

Coping with sight loss A

1 Learning to live with sight loss 12

2 What went wrong? 33

3 Making the most of remaining sight 44

1 Learning to live with sight loss

Folklore has it that people who lose their sight are brave and cheerful, despite living in a world of darkness. They tend to be fond of dogs. They develop a sixth sense (though this is rarely identified) and, undisturbed by the visual vanities of the sighted world, live on a higher plane than the rest of us. Biographies of high achieving blind people tend to support this view. The reality is different.

Folklore also has it that services for blind people in this country are unparalleled for excellence. Extra money to compensate for lack of sight is quickly forthcoming (though the source is rarely identified) and the sympathy, understanding and sheer kindness that everyone shows towards blind people makes them a privileged minority. The reality is different.

Most people lose their sight late in life and so are also likely to have absorbed these ideas. Separating fact from fantasy is one of the painful processes which begins when sight deteriorates to blind registration level. Anyone who loses a significant amount of vision is likely to think, 'If blind people are so brave and cheerful, why do I feel so depressed? Far from having a sixth sense, my remaining four do not seem to be particularly efficient. Why do I have a seemingly built-in ability to create a disaster area with every unguarded movement? Why do I feel so ready to murder rather than thank the kindly friend who has given up his time to read the newspaper to me?' And above all, 'Why have I been registered blind? My sight's pretty bad, but I can still see. Is the future, literally, black?'

Nearly everyone who is registered as blind is told by their eye specialist that it is very unlikely that they will lose all their sight. Even if the legal niceties have been explained (as in 4.7), at two in the morning doubts creep in. For a minority, registration as blind does indeed mean a total loss of vision. In 1983 it happened to John Hull. 'The last light sensations faded and the dark discs finally overwhelmed me. It was then I began to sink into the deep ocean, and finally learned how to touch the rock on the far side of despair.'[1]

'On the far side' implies a journey. 'Finally' implies the passage of time. Perhaps the idea of a journey is a helpful way for people who have lost part or all of their sight, and those who want to help them, to think about their new situation, rather than measuring themselves against a blind superman or superwoman. No two people will experience or describe the journey in exactly the same way, but the milestones will be similar for many. The destination – the incorporation of this devastating loss into their life, or as Lennart Dahl, a Swedish poet whose sight began to fail when he was thirty five, puts it, 'a new self under way' – will be reached by most. But the journey will take time.

Most people begin their journey when an eye specialist breaks the bad news to them. It is an unenviable task. The tension and distress felt by the patient are likely to be felt by the specialist as well. All the efforts made to improve vision have been

---

1. Hull, John M. *Touching the Rock: An Experience of Blindness.* Available in braille (National Library for the Blind), as a talking book (RNIB Talking Book Service) and on cassette (Calibre).

'Little simple everyday things are so aggravating ... like the mail dropping through the letter box.

I go and pick up the mail and I feel it – that's a large envelope, that's a small envelope – but what's inside it? I feel very frustrated, sometimes angry because I can't get to the contents of the envelope and have to wait for someone to read it for me.'

frustrated, or medical knowledge cannot suggest any form of treatment. The hopes centred on the specialist's skill and profession have proved to be in vain. In such a situation, in our culture, both parties will tend to cope by exercising extreme self-control. So it is not unusual for the patient to return home, feeling the specialist was curt and uncaring, whilst the specialist hurriedly calls in the next patient, whom he can help, thinking again how well people cope with loss of sight.

Loss of sight is sometimes thought to have much in common with bereavement (see 14.3). A period of numbness is followed by a period of mourning when it is difficult to think of anything except what could be done in the past and what now seems to be impossible. The unanswerable question, 'Why should it happen to me?' throbs in the background. At this time most people do have a great need to talk about their loss, and the question, 'How much can you see?' is rarely considered tactless or prying. It gives an opportunity to put into words what has happened. The confused impressions of the consulting rooms, the anxious waits for treatment – would things have gone better if appointments had been made earlier – talking about these things helps to impose an order and pattern on those events, and this in itself gives some reassurance. At this stage in the journey, it may well be that blame for the failure of the treatment is attached to an entirely innocent person, or loss of sight may be attributed to an innocuous event many years ago, but identifying a scapegoat is one way of dealing with resentment and anger. Pointing out the illogicalities in the argument is no help at all. At this time, listening is better than action. The listener does not need to be an expert. 'She cried and I cried. What else could I do?' said one listener, untrained in counselling skills but with a gift of warm sensitivity. 'I like these women', says Dahl, referring to 'ladies with voices vacant as school corridors in summer'. 'I like these women, their clumsy friendliness. It's harder with the others, the professional care people. The voices of those who have had a course in pedagogy, experts with views on what's good for you.'[2]

Not everyone is fortunate enough to have a good listener at their time of need. Even the closest relative or friend may themselves be so distressed at what has happened that it may not be felt possible, or kind, to talk frankly. Everyone may try bravely to 'rise above it' and nurse their sorrow in secret. It is here that the opportunity to talk things over with someone who has personal experience of the difficulties being

2. Dahl, Lennart. *The House of Darkness*. Mexico, Costa-Amic Editores, 1986.

faced often helps. The telephone is an obvious way to make contact. **It is surprising that no national organisation for blind people has a freephone telephone service for this purpose, although some of them are amongst the wealthiest charities in the country**. Listed in chapter 2, however, are small self-help groups for people with particular eye conditions. All have telephone contacts and welcome calls. The **British Retinitis Pigmentosa Society** and the **Behçet's Syndrome Society** have designated helplines (see 2.3.4 and 2.7).

The parent support groups listed in 31 are also local contact points. The organisers only ask that callers should be thoughtful about the time of day that they telephone, as they also are parents. One voluntary agency provides a 24 hour telephone counselling service for families with a visually impaired child: **Vision Aid** on ✆ 01204 31882 (see 6.13.4).

How long the grieving lasts depends on the individual. For some, it seems to be only the briefest prelude to their journey; for others it may take weeks or many months. For some, registration may come almost as a relief – it represents the end of years of apprehension, of hopes raised and dashed again, of life measured out in terms of visits to the eye clinic. But when hopes are extinguished, even those years of anxiety can be yearned for as being more desirable than the present. For the very elderly, where loss of vision has gradually accompanied the slow fading of other faculties and is accepted as part of an inevitable ageing process, the blow is softened. A very few, especially those who were already having to cope with daunting mixes of both physical and emotional problems before loss of sight overwhelmed them, may need skilled psychiatric help at this time.

That people do move on is a great tribute to the human spirit. It is at this next stage that **good solid information is the prime need**. 'Blindness is different', said one man who had experienced severe paralysis and, later on, almost total loss of sight. 'When they told me I could never walk again, I knew that if I kept fighting and working on exercising my leg, eventually I would get those muscles going again. And I did. But when I lost my sight, it was different. There was no way in which I could fight it, and get my sight back. I had to rely on what other people could tell me of what was possible and how to achieve it before I could do anything.' It is sad that at this stage of their journey, so many newly blind people find such help difficult to get. **That is the major reason why this book is crammed with practicalities**.

However, loss of sight is rather more than the inability to read print, the impossibility of crossing busy roads, cooking the dinner and running the house, the feelings of helplessness. There are ways out, round or under all these problems.

Snapshot

'We put on a brave face and tell ourselves that we have come to terms with our condition. Then comes the moment when the loss is brought to our notice again. And it is not only a personal loss to ourselves, it is also a daily loss for those whom we love and who love us. It is then we appreciate a firm handclasp of encouragement, an arm around the shoulder or a tight embrace.'
▶ **Doris Easter.** *Sideview*, October 1992

Perhaps the most difficult part of the journey occurs when people find they are being treated differently now they have lost much of their sight. 'Nowadays, everybody makes me sit down as soon as they see me' said a fit and active 50 year old who had started to use a white cane. Lennart Dahl put it more vividly in his account of his early

'Actually I felt I'd been taken over. I didn't feel like me any more. I felt like a "could you just" or a "do you mind"; I stopped being a person'

days as a blind man. 'With toil, tears and assistance I fashion a lantern. It is an exaggerated success in the family circle. Exaggerated attention like that given a two-year-old the first time he's able to sit on the potty.'[3]

It is extremely hard, but unfortunately true, that to survive at a practical level it is essential to become organised, methodical and adaptive. Similarly, to survive socially one needs, if not to become an extrovert, at least to stop being a shrinking violet. At the same time, difficult though it may be to accept help, there are situations when it is necessary or diplomatic to do so.

It is not surprising that blind people increasingly find that **assertion training** helps them become more self-confident. Learning to cope with the sighted world, with people who see the handicap rather than the person, is a skill that can be acquired (see 10.12). Another step in the journey is accomplished when a balance is struck between accepting help and rugged independence. Instead of mentally murdering the kindly newspaper reader who seems to have rustled pages endlessly and then said, 'You won't be interested in that', it becomes possible to say, 'Just read me out all the headlines on the front page, and then we'll decide which bits to read.'

The alternative is to accept passively whatever help is offered. Because it is true that most people have the kindest and most generous feelings towards what they perceive as the plight of anyone with a severe visual loss, it is very easy to slip into a cocoon of dependency. It has been argued that blindness is a learned social role, that blind people behave in the way expected of them and if everybody expects them to be helpless and dependent, then they will be. Being waited on hand and foot is certainly a way of life for some sighted people, and blindness can give it an excellent cosmetic justification. If relying heavily on their partner has always been a feature of a person's life, then loss of sight is likely to confirm that reliance totally. It is sad, however, when more independent souls are diverted down the cul-de-sac of dependency by over-protective friends and relatives.

One way of keeping on the right track is to join a **rehabilitation** group. Often rehabilitation workers in social services departments run short courses, or there may be special day courses offered by local voluntary societies. Special one day courses and occasional weekend residential courses for carers and people who have recently lost their sight are run by an independent advisor and consultant who is herself blind. Contact *June Bretherton, Blind Business Association Ltd.* Meeting other people

---

3. Ibid.

with the same eye condition is often very helpful, and the self-help groups listed in 31 can provide this type of opportunity.

Professional help on the journey is also described throughout this book. It can be excellent and easy to obtain. On the other hand, it may need the methods of Sherlock Holmes and the tenacity of Bulldog Drummond to get any help at all. It is hoped that this book will provide some useful signposts in the search and give some indication of what it is reasonable to expect. Admittedly, when it comes to cash (see chapter 5) the beatitude for most blind people is, 'Blessed is he who expecteth nothing, or at least very little, for he will not be disappointed.'

But many people would say that they have been helped and supported most by people who are treading the same path. That is why joining with other people with similar problems can be so helpful. It is a difficult first step to take, for it is an admission that one is crossing the great divide – the divide between the world of sighted people and the shadowy, seemingly forbidding world of the blind. Having taken the step, most people find it helpful. Much of course, depends on the group joined. But it is significant that the majority of younger people who have joined a residential course at, for example, **RNIB Manor House**, look back on those weeks as a period of great enrichment and the start of a 'new life'. It works for older people as well.

'It helps to talk to anybody but I think it's really important to talk with somebody who went through it too. They feel that they are no different. They're on even ground, you know? Yes, I think it's very important that it should be someone that has gone through it. Somebody else might be able to help you but it's not the same.'[4] That comment was made by an elderly American, but it would be echoed by many British voices. For very elderly people who have outlived friends and family, the local group for blind people can give a sense of security, the feeling that they have a 'hot-line' to people who care and to people who understand. And this in itself can give courage to continue the journey and cope with the problems of daily life.

Does the journey ever end? Perhaps not, in the sense that all life is a journey. But most people with a severe sight loss will say that there is a time of resolution which has stolen upon them, perhaps almost unawares, perhaps only after a long and painful struggle. It is a big leap to go from saying, 'Why did this happen to me?' to, 'It's happened to better people than me – what's so special about me?' But it is a leap that ordinary mortals do take. They have not become superhuman, but have brought their unique strengths and experience of life to come to terms with it in their own unique way. 'Well, he always was an obstinate old devil', was the percipient comment of a wife when congratulated on her husband's mobility expertise. Her husband had remained himself, but added a new dimension. Many others place their experience of blindness in a religious context, and gain comfort and strength from so doing. That is the way for John Hull. 'If a journey into light is a journey into God, then a journey into darkness is a journey into God. That is why I go on journeying, not through, but into.'

---

4. Ainlay, Stephen Charles. *Day Brought Back My Night. Ageing and New Vision Loss.* Routledge, 1989.

16

Street scene as seen by someone with normal vision

Sight simulations
What does a 'blind' person see?

To be registered as blind does not mean total loss of sight. These simulated views show how a street scene might be seen by people with different eye conditions who could be registered as blind. The portrayals must only be regarded as an approximate indication.

The view of a busy street includes adults, children, a dog, street furniture, traffic and parked cars, completely filling the field of sight at all levels, high and low, and across from left to right. The scene is full of vivid colour and diverse shapes, each telling a different story. It is a picture of people recognising each other and engaging each other by sight and voice. Even you are being watched by someone – but can you see her?

On a crowded town centre pavement, cluttered with stationary groups deep in conversation, it takes skill for even a fully sighted person to navigate without bumping into, or disrupting the people interacting on all sides. For a person with a visual impairment, the challenge becomes apparent as you study each simulated view.

Above all, consider the very different problems thrown up by each sight condition. How might you have to compensate? Would you feel more at risk of accident with the central vision loss of maculopathy, or the tunnel vision of glaucoma? And which condition might most seriously impair your ability to recognise and exchange greetings with friends?

How to use the simulations

To gain the best impression, **keep your attention at the centre of each view**. This will show you what you can see in the centre of your field of vision, and what you can see out of the corner of your eye. If you allow your gaze to wander, you permit yourself to build a picture that is not available as such to the person with that condition.

We suggest you look at each picture first, assess the lost vision, then check the following notes to see what was immediately apparent, and what less so.

The simulations are an interpretation. Remember that the experience of visual impairment is very individual, and even two people with identical clinical conditions may see differently.

Cataract 2.4.1

A fogged, grey world, as if through a dirty window. The overall effect is of a general loss of colour, a loss of definite outlines, and trouble from glare, particularly in sunshine. But there are variations to the picture. In the centre of vision, where loss of definition and colour is greatest, objects merge into each other or into their background. The dog has all but disappeared into the pavement. The short lady cannot be distinguished. All colours are dulled, though red tends to be retained and identified. A few highlights remain – the child's bicycle wheels, and most noticeably the contrasting white walls and black paintwork of the hotel in the background. **Contrast is vital in the world perceived through cataract**.

Diabetic retinopathy 2.3.2

Patches of vision are lost across the visual field, corresponding to the areas of damaged retina. Within such a patch, all detailed vision is lost or degraded, yet outside, vision remains normal. Is the short lady standing gazing into a shop window? She doesn't seem to be talking to anyone, like everyone else. But before you bump into the invisible man with the laundry bag, watch out for that dog.

Macular disease 2.3.3

An eye condition largely of old age, macular disease removes central vision and leaves you with a sideways view. There is no point in averting your gaze to the periphery where vision is apparently clear, because your central vision loss will avert with you. To move ahead through this crowd, you will need compensating techniques. **People who suffer from macular disease must learn how to make active use of remaining peripheral sight**. With practice and persistence, much can be achieved.

Glaucoma 2.4.4

As if looking ahead through a telescope while walking along a pavement, though your distant goal remains clearly in view, you are at risk of hitting something long before you get there. Just as people with normal sight are usually unaware of the amount they see in the peripheral view, so glaucoma sufferers are often not conscious that their vision is restricted to a narrow central area.

This simulation demonstrates another apparent anomaly: enlarging a page of print to a large size would do this person little good if only a few letters stay visible in the remaining visual field. **Techniques and aids which widen the angle of sight available to the remaining field are required**.

This simulation can also be used to demonstrate the effect of **retinitis pigmentosa** (2.3.4) on vision.

Hemianopia 2.5, 23.7

The straightforward and dramatic sight loss from stroke: one half normal, the other half lost. Unlike glaucoma, the patient is usually acutely conscious of the lost visual field, but will not necessarily know how to compensate. Retraining is necessary and can be successful.

CMV retinitis 2.6.1

This condition has similarities with both cataract (front of eye) and retinal (back of eye) disorders: and indeed there has been corresponding damage to both parts of the eye. If red tends to be the last colour retained in cataract, then colours such as yellows and blues remain longer in the general loss of colour vision experienced by this group. This is a complex condition which can have diverse effects.

Normal sight?

You have been considering how people with abnormal sight might see the world. But how 'normal' is your sight? Turn to page 32 now for a few questions about what you have just been seeing.

Production

The street scene was directed by *Thena Heshel*, photographer *Jonathan Dumbrell*. The simulations were produced by *Mike Southern* using Adobe Photoshop 3 software on a Pentium processor. Consultant for the sequence was *Dr Michael Wolffe, FBCO*. The dog is *Sophie*.

In Touch Publishing will be releasing the sight simulations as a teaching and demonstration aid, **Seeing Differently**, in the form of colour slides. Details from the publisher.

Mike Joseph

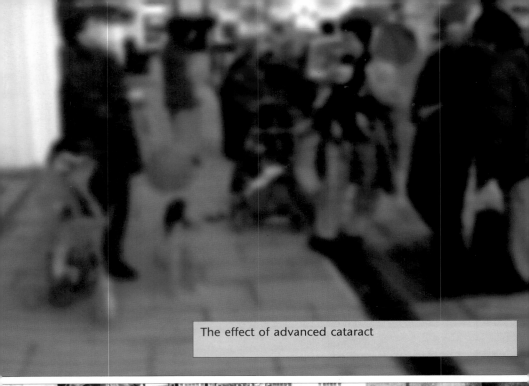

The effect of advanced cataract

Haemorrhages suffered by some people with diabetes obscure vision

In ageing maculopathy central vision is lost, though peripheral sight remains

Tunnel vision as experienced by someone suffering from severe glaucoma

The effect of a stroke can be to lose one half of the field of vision

CMV retinitis is a complex AIDS-related condition which produces varied sight disorders

Toys and equipment

A Vision Aid worker demonstrates some of the toys and equipment that can be used to stimulate a child's sight. See 7.4

Adapted pram
Guide dog owner Kathy Bailey using the pram adapted by the GDBA. See 11.4.1

Aquaplaning is one of the activities offered by the Guide Dog Adventure Group. See 22.5

Invisible and visible food Meals are easier to see and eat when served on dishes that contrast in colour to the food on them. Distinctive shapes distinguish the salt from the pepper pot, and contrasting coloured place mats or serviettes also help to make a meal visible. See 26.8.1

A shoe tidy is useful for keeping things separate and handy on the side of an armchair or bed

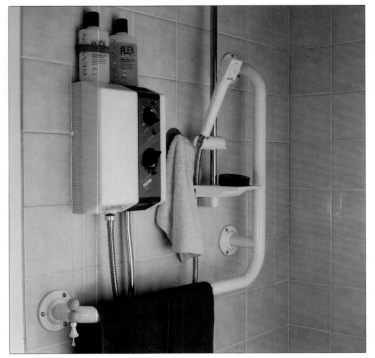

Colour contrast helps to locate soap, towel and flannel. A Bump-On marks the essential setting on the shower control. A distinctive toggle makes the shower cord easy to find and the shampoo is distinguished from the conditioner by a rubber band

The Easiplay cassette recorder stands on a non-slip mat. Large print patience cards are available from the *Partially Sighted Society*. See 26.8.4

A

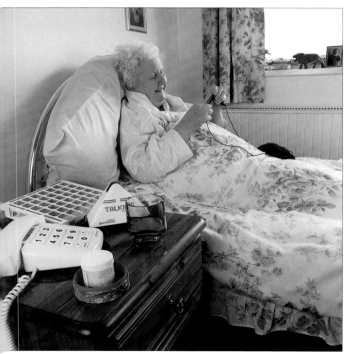

The bedside table has room for an extra large Dosette pill container (see 14.8), the Pyramid talking clock and a large button telephone (see 15.4.3). The pot of cream stands in the base of a colourful box to make it easier to find, and the coloured glass has a shape that is easy to hold. See 26.8.3

Photos taken at Lotte Hobson Home, Salford, run by Henshaw's Society for the Blind

Getting into a car

Many blind people can get into a car unaided once they have been shown the handle of the car door and told which way the car is facing

Putting a hand on the car roof enables a blind person to gauge the height of the door and so prevent them from banging their head as they get in

The technique for
helping a blind person
into a car is described
in 28.3

Bubble tube
A bubble tube is very interesting
... but simpler options are also
described in 7.1

A little room
A 'little room' designed by Lilli Nielsen, provides a safe, compact space which encourages the child to reach out to a world outside himself. See 7.4

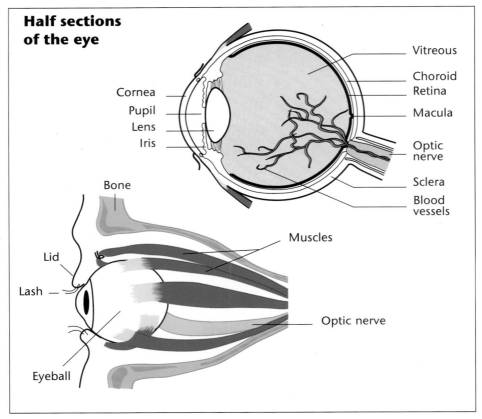

Half sections of the eye

Cornea
Pupil
Lens
Iris

Vitreous
Choroid
Retina
Macula
Optic nerve
Sclera
Blood vessels

Bone

Muscles

Lid

Lash

Optic nerve

Eyeball

Sight simulation quiz

Try to answer these questions quickly with your first response, without turning back to the sight simulations until you have completed the quiz.

Normal sight

1 There are twelve people visible on the street: True or false?

2 What is the girl doing to see you better?

3 How many bicycles are there on the pavement?

4 Which of these objects are blue: teddy, taxi, bus, laundry bag?

5 What does the dog's gaze suggest about the bag in the man's hand?

Sight loss

6 If you had macular disease, might you see the man with the laundry bag if you looked to the right?

7 If you had hemianopia, might you see that man if you looked left?

8 What might help you to see the dog if you had cataract?

9 What might help you to spot the bus if you had glaucoma?

10 If you had cataract, what might help you to negotiate this crowd?

Answers at the end of the Index.

2 What went wrong?

We have all shut our eyes and told ourselves, 'That's what it's like to be blind'. A cold shiver runs down our spines. It is not surprising, therefore, that when meeting anyone carrying a white stick we immediately assume he or she cannot see at all.

In fact, the great majority of so-called blind people are, as one 'blind' lady put it, 'neither one thing nor another'.

That chill of fear experienced by most people only in their imagination does, however, become a reality if they are told by an eye specialist that they are being certified as blind or partially sighted. Such is the shock that, on leaving the clinic, they can recall only snatches of the conversation.

This chapter aims to help patients recall the explanation given by their eye specialist and to suggest ways of getting further information and meeting people in similar situations. It also shows sighted readers, through pictures and anecdotes, that people who need to use a white stick or a guide dog actually 'see' in many different ways. And sometimes seeing a confused version of the world is just as frightening and handicapping as not being able to see at all.

2.1 Why did it happen?

Most people have a deep need to know why they have developed a particular eye condition. It may be linked to a medical condition such as long-standing diabetes. But no-one yet knows the cause of cataracts or age-related maculopathy, the two most common reasons for very poor sight among elderly people. So at present there is often no answer that can be given to this question. It is, however, known that 'eye-strain', reading in a bad light, much fine sewing in the past, are most unlikely to affect eyesight in later life. **The sad conclusion that poor sight must therefore be a retribution for the misdeeds of youth is equally misguided. If that were so, who would escape?**

The nearest source of reassurance is often overlooked. The patient's own family doctor will have received a report from the eye specialist and should be able to explain the diagnosis more fully.

2.2 How the eye works

The eye has much in common with a camera. The retina, a tissue which responds to light, lines the back of the inside of the eye, and is similar to the photographic film in a camera. With a badly damaged film it is impossible to take good pictures. In the same way, anyone with a badly damaged retina will not see very well.

The messages received by the retina are transmitted by the optic nerve to the brain, which translates them into pictures. If the optic nerve is damaged, the messages will be confused or perhaps not transmitted at all, and again the result will be impaired vision.

Key to media of publication   **P** clear print   **L** large print   **B** braille   **T** tape   **M** Moon   **D** disk
Where a full address is not given in the text, see 32 (Useful addresses)

If the lens of the camera is damaged, it is again impossible to take a clear photograph. Similarly, if the lens or the cornea of the eye become cloudy, sight is blurred.

A simple way of getting to grips with 'what went wrong' is to divide the main causes of visual impairment into three: problems at the back of the eyes, problems at the front of the eyes, and neurological problems.

It is cheering to know that 'problems at the front of the eyes' are now treated very successfully. Corneal grafts (see 2.4.2) and lens implants enable many people to see again. Recent advances in surgery have resulted in repairs being done today 'at the back of the eyes' which would have been thought impossible only a few years ago. This is particularly true for patients who suffer from **detached retinas** or various forms of **retinopathy**, including diabetic retinopathy, where speedy treatment can restore sight, or at least limit the damage. Some forms of macular disease also respond to treatment nowadays.

Neurological disorders present a continuing challenge to doctors and patients.

2.3 Problems 'at the back of the eyes'

2.3.1 Retinal detachment

The retina is loosely attached to the inside of the eye at the back, a bit like the lining of a jacket. For various reasons it can develop little holes at the edge. Fluid can pass through these holes from the inside of the eye, allowing the retina to peel off from the edge towards the centre. This is known as a retinal detachment. The retina does not work when detached and when it has completely peeled off, all vision in the eye is lost.

If the holes can be detected before fluid has begun to pass through, they can be sealed off using either laser treatment or freezing treatment (cryotherapy). This can be very successful, but in many cases there is too much fluid and a surgical operation is required. There are several types of repair operations. Some involve introducing a bubble of gas, air or silicone oil into the eye to push up against the hole and close it. If gas is used the patient will need to sit or lie with one side of their face down on a pillow almost constantly for a few days after the operation. Other surgical techniques involve stitching on fine bands of silicone rubber or sponge so that they push in against the hole in the retina. These bands are left in place and usually do not cause any trouble. Whichever operation is used, the procedure is successful in about four out of five cases. This means that 1 in 5 people will need more than one operation to repair the detachment, and some of them will need several operations. Sometimes even when the retina has been successfully re-attached, the vision in the eye may not be so good. This is particularly true if the detachment has included the central part of the retina (the macula) which is used for detailed vision. The vision may then never return to its previous level, though it should usually be better than it was before the operation. Sight can continue to improve for up to one year after the retina is re-attached.

2.3.2 Diabetic retinopathy

Diabetic retinopathy is the major cause of visual impairment amongst adults of working age. Yet there is evidence that if all diabetic patients were systematically referred to their family doctor, specialist or optometrist for a retinal examination, such screening would detect most patients with serious retinopathy and most of those cases would be treatable. Early treatment could reduce the risk of blindness by an estimated 50%.

The exact cause of diabetic retinopathy is not fully understood. However, after fifteen years of diabetes, most insulin-dependent people, and over half of those whose condition is controlled by tablets, will show some evidence of diabetic retinopathy. After thirty years, the proportion rises to 90% of all people with diabetes.

The earliest changes in the retina are referred to as 'background retinopathy' and consist of minute retinal haemorrhages which can only be identified by an eye specialist or optometrist when examining the eyes with an ophthalmoscope. They do not usually cause any loss of vision, unless they occur near the centre of the retina, when vision is affected in much the same way as happens in age-related maculopathy. Although these tiny haemorrhages may clear up by themselves, they are likely to recur if not treated. This is why regular eye examinations are so important and why people suffering from diabetes are among those entitled to free NHS sight tests (see 5.13.2).

Proliferative retinopathy, a more acute but fortunately much rarer sight-threatening form of the condition, is often found in people who have been insulin dependent for 15-20 years. New blood vessels form in the retina. These are particularly likely to bleed and they may grow into the vitreous jelly (see eye diagram in the colour section) and can cause retinal detachment.

The encouraging news is that **laser therapy**, using a beam of high-intensity light which can be focused with extreme precision, has over recent years transformed the prospects of patients. Laser photocoagulation is used to reduce the leakage of fluid or other substances into the retina and to prevent or reduce the growth of new vessels. The earlier the treatment is given, the greater the likelihood of success. It can certainly prevent the total blindness which faced some patients not many years ago.

When proliferative retinopathy is no longer thought to be suitable for laser therapy, there is the possibility of **vitreous surgery**. Some haemorrhages may remain in the vitreous and dense membranes may form around them to such an extent that the clear jelly of the vitreous becomes cloudy so that light can no longer reach the retina. A vitrectomy operation removes the haemorrhage and the clot it has formed and can restore useful vision.

The **British Diabetic Association** has branches in Glasgow and Edinburgh for visually impaired people with diabetes. Both hold regular meetings and circulate a newsletter and magazine to members. The Edinburgh group is raising funds to provide equipment such as talking blood glucose meters (see 23.2.2) for patients living in Edinburgh and South East Scotland. Contact *Horace Dempster, 78 Glenview Crescent, Moodiesburn, Glasgow G69 0NL* ✆ *01236 873357; Robert Hunter, c/o 4 Coates Crescent, Edinburgh EH3 7AP* ✆ *0131 557 1004.*

The **National Diabetic Retinopathy Network** is a voluntary organisation run to help diabetics, carers and professionals with advice, support and information on living with diabetic retinopathy. Members receive a newsletter **L T**. Contact:

South of England, Midlands, Wales: *Miss Jude Andrews, c/o 7 Shore Close, Hampton, Middlesex TW12 3XS ℘ 0181 941 5821, and Marc Moss, White House Farm, Danegate, Eridge, East Sussex TN3 9HX ℘ 01892 853302 (home) ℘ 0171 278 6601 (work)*

*eye*OPENER

'One sees a pretty girl in the peripheral vision and the eye automatically turns to focus on her when, lo and behold, she vanishes into the mist. Quickly, back to the sideways glance!'

Alfred Stock
Sideview October 1991

North of England, Scotland and Northern Ireland: *Judith Jordan, 38 Gloster Park, Amble, Northumberland NE65 0JQ ℘ 01665 711636.*

2.3.3 Macular disease

Age-related macular disease (often known as macular degeneration or ageing maculopathy) affects elderly people. At the eye examination, it may be described as 'age changes at the back of the eyes' or 'some bleeding at the back of the eyes' or 'the eyes are wearing out'. It never results in total loss of sight. Only the macula, a minute area in the central part of the retina, is affected. However, it is the area which enables detail to be seen, so that patients with this condition have great difficulty in recognising faces, seeing print, threading a needle and identifying coins. Colour perception may also sometimes be affected. As side vision is unaffected, patients are often helped by using low vision aids (see 3.3).

An *In Touch* Care Guide **Coping again L B T** (£3.50. In Touch Publishing. 1993) describes the condition, the treatment available and ways of using remaining vision to the best advantage.

The Macular Disease Society has almost 3000 members nationwide. It encourages mutual support and independence through local self-help groups. The Society has a dedicated eye donor scheme and sponsors its own Research Fellow working at London University on the underlying mechanisms which contribute to the condition. The £5.00 annual subscription includes a quarterly newsletter **Side View P T** (£10 for both versions). Contact ℘ 01932 829331.

2.3.4 Retinitis Pigmentosa

This is the name applied to a group of diseases which attack the light sensitive cells of the retina. It is an inherited disease and, in one of the three inheritance patterns, autosomal recessive, it is difficult to trace any evidence of the disease in recent ancestors. It is progressive, although the rate of progress in an individual is not readily predictable. The symptoms are a reduction in the field of vision which can start either from the centre or from the periphery. In the case of peripheral loss, this is usually preceded by varying degrees of night blindness. One unhappy combination

'If I go into Marks & Spencer alone, I'm aware of the spaciousness of the store and my limited field of vision. I seem unable to get an overall view of the place. There seem to be glimpses of bits of bodies coming towards me, either side of me, to and fro and across me, as well as blazes of colour, mirrors and background noise, all of which confuse me'.

Ann Phyall, describing how retinitis pigmentosa affects her sight in Visability, Summer 1992

is Usher Syndrome, where around 5% of people who are born deaf or become deaf at an early age, later develop RP.

Research has shown that although the symptoms of RP vary very little, the causes of the deterioration of the retina are many. The fundamental causes are inherited genetic defects and to date, thirty different genes have been identified as responsible in all or in part for various categories of RP. Work is now progressing well in identifying the proteins produced by these faulty genes and comparing their chemical structures with those produced by healthy genes of the same type. Some progress has been made with the generation of corrected genetic material and the final stage of the research will involve the development of successful methods of introducing the corrected genetic material into positions where it can reverse the detrimental work of the faulty genes.

It is accepted that, due to the many causes, there will not be a single treatment for RP, but hopes are now high that the first treatment could be on test before the end of this decade.

The **British Retinitis Pigmentosa Society** was founded in 1975 to promote research into RP. It has 3000 members in 36 branches and has raised over two million pounds for research. It has an active welfare service offering advice and guidance to its members. A range of publications include **A Guide to RP, Genetics and RP, Young People and RP** and **Mobility and Communication Skills ⓑⓣ**.

A member, who is a trained social worker, attends the weekly RP clinic at Moorfields Eye Hospital to provide a counselling service.

BRPS is a registered charity (membership subscription £5). A quarterly newsletter **Fighting Blindness ⓛⓑⓣ** covers developments in research, articles on day to day living with RP and news from the branches.

Contact *BRPS Helpline* ✆ 01280 860363 any weekday evening from 6.00 p.m. to 10.00 p.m. or telephone Lynda Cantor on this number during the daytime.

2.4 Problems 'at the front of the eyes'

2.4.1 Cataract

This, the best known of all the eye conditions, is often thought to be found literally 'at the front of the eye' as it is widely believed that it consists of a skin growing over the eye. In fact, the word 'cataract' refers to a clouding of the lens of the eye, which is found just behind the pupil (see eye diagram in the colour section).

The Care Guide **Waiting to See? ⓁⒷⓉ** (In Touch Publishing. 1993. £2.50) describes the condition, explains what the operation involves, and suggests ways of making life easier whilst waiting for treatment.

It is sad, but true, that not every patient with cataracts is fit enough for surgery, though with more sophisticated techniques, improvements in local anaesthesia and day surgery this is becoming relatively rare. Cataracts are also, unfortunately, often a complicating factor linked with other eye conditions. Patients with long-standing **diabetes** are more likely to develop cataracts, and if they suffer from retinopathy as well, the decision if and when to operate is a matter of clinical judgement. Similarly, patients who have had surgery for **glaucoma** are slightly more at risk of developing cataracts, whilst advanced macular disease and cataracts may make an eye surgeon reluctant to subject a very elderly patient to surgery.

2.4.2 Corneal problems

The cornea is the window at the front of the eye. In the normal eye the cornea is clear so that light can enter and pass through the lens to focus on the retina at the back of the eye. When the cornea is deformed or damaged by injury or disease light cannot pass freely through the eye and so the picture that the retina passes to the brain is not clear, and sight becomes distorted or patchy. If corneal problems cannot be overcome by treatment with eye drops, drugs, contact lenses or spectacles, a **corneal graft** may be undertaken. This involves an operation in which a central piece of the diseased cornea is replaced with a clear cornea from a donor's eye. This is sewn into place with very fine stitches which are not removed until one or two years after the operation, as the cornea takes a long time to heal completely. During the healing process vision tends to fluctuate. It is unrealistic to expect clear and useful sight immediately after a corneal graft operation. Also, as the shape of the donor cornea may be different from the original one, it may be necessary to prescribe glasses or a contact lens to correct the difference. But these also cannot be given until the healing process is complete, and patients must be prepared to put in eye drops for 6 months or more after the operation to help prevent infection or rejection.

Patients are told to report any symptoms such as pain, decrease in sight or redness in the eye promptly as these may indicate the rejection of the corneal graft, which is more likely to be controlled if treated immediately. A rejection can occur at any time, but is most likely in the first year after the operation.

2.4.3 Keratoconus

NEW **Keratoconus** is a rare condition which occurs when the cornea becomes thin towards its centre causing the thinned area to bulge forward. This results in distortion of vision which in the early stages may be corrected with glasses, but the most usual treatment is specially designed, rigid, gas permeable corneal contact lenses. Some people need a corneal transplant to improve their sight. While the condition does not lead to total blindness, the distortion of vision can become extreme. **A self-help group** was set up in March 1994 to raise awareness of the condition, its effect and treatment, as well as to assist with research. For more details and an explanatory booklet (£1.25 inclusive of p&p) contact *Anne Klepacz, Keratoconus Self Help and Support Association, 58 Twyford Avenue, London W3 9QB* ℘ 0181 993 4659.

2.4.4 Glaucoma

Glaucoma is a major cause of sight loss, much of which can be prevented by early detection and treatment. Everyone over the age of 40 years, and especially people of Afric-Caribbean origin or people with a history of glaucoma in a close relative, should have an annual sight test, which includes measurement of the eye pressure (tonometry), the appearance of the optic nerve examined through an ophthalmoscope, and their visual field checked (perimetry). Glaucoma patients and their close relatives are entitled to free NHS sight tests (see chapter 5).

The most common form of glaucoma, **chronic glaucoma**, usually affects middle-aged or elderly people. Normally, the front part of the eye is filled with watery fluid which is constantly produced by the eye to nourish itself. In glaucoma, this fluid does not drain away at the same rate as it is produced, and, slowly and painlessly, pressure builds up. The optic nerve is deprived of nutrition. Damage to the head of the nerve and the outer edges of the retina follow. At first, this will not be noticed as only side vision is affected.

Treatment for chronic glaucoma is generally by the use of drops (beta blockers) which reduce the amount of fluid produced within the eye and thus reduce the pressure within it. Failure for any reason to use the treatment regularly as prescribed allows the disease to progress. Drops that aid fluid escape from the eye (pilocarpine) are much less frequently used these days as are tablets (diamox) which reduce fluid production. Laser treatment has been used in the endeavour to make new passages to aid fluid escape from within the eye but has not lived up to its early promise, so that if eye drops fail to adequately control pressure, drainage operations (trabeculectomy) are the other main treatment.

Carefully supervised treatment will usually either arrest or materially slow down the progress of chronic glaucoma. Sight is thus normally retained throughout life, but unfortunately treatment cannot restore sight which has been lost.

In the much rarer **acute glaucoma**, the pressure builds up to a very high level very rapidly and causes severe pain. It is a medical emergency. However, sight will often be restored fully if treated immediately, though if there is delay in relieving the very high pressure permanent severe damage may result.

The **International Glaucoma Association** (membership subscription £7.50) issues twice yearly newsletters plus updates. Other publications include a **Guide for Patients** which answers the questions most frequently asked, and leaflets on laser treatment and surgery. Meetings are arranged and members can be put in contact with each other if they wish. There is a professional membership for health care staff. An annual **FROG (For Relief Of Glaucoma)** week publicises the fact that glaucoma is a major cause of sight loss, much of which can be prevented by early detection and treatment. Contact *Betsy Wright* ℘ 0171 737 3265.

2.5 Neurological conditions

A

The optic nerve is rather less than the width of a little finger, yet it consists of 1.2 million nerve fibres conveying electrical impulses from the retina to the brain. The optic nerve is part of the brain itself, and in common with many nerve cells within the central nervous system, the optic nerve does not regenerate if cells are damaged. Trauma to the optic nerve may occur in head injury, most commonly in Britain to-day as a result of a road traffic accident. Fortunately up to half of the nerve fibres may be lost without a demonstrable loss of sensitivity in the visual field. Loss of vision may also be caused by a tumour compressing the optic nerve behind the eyes; this can sometimes be relieved by surgery. Congenital defects, inflammations and strokes can also cause optic nerve damage, or **optic atrophy**, which is a significant cause of registrable blindness in adults under 65.

If damage to the brain causes visual loss, the extent and nature of the defect depends upon the area of the brain damaged. The right hand side of the brain processes the visual information received from the left side of each eye, and vice versa. So that if someone has suffered damage to the left hand side of the brain (as in a stroke), this causes a loss of vision (field loss) on their right (see the colour section). This also causes particular problems when reading from left to right, though there are some techniques which can help to overcome this (see 3.9.2). Injuries to the visual cortex on both sides of the brain may result in a substantial field loss so that the patient is left with tunnel vision and night blindness.

Leber's Optic Neuropathy is a rare form of inherited optic atrophy which mainly affects young men, causing them to lose central vision. **Leber's Optic Neuropathy Trust** is a registered charity aiming to provide mutual support both for those suffering from this condition and for their families. An annually updated information pack on the medical and social aspects of the condition is issued. The Trust has contacts all over the country prepared to talk with those similarly affected. Contact *Mrs. T. Handscombe, 13 Palmar Road, Maidstone, Kent ME16 0DL* ℘ 01622 751025.

Damage to the cortex of the brain can also affect vision in various surprising and complicated ways. This is because visual information is analysed in a number of different areas of the brain which deal with different aspects of the visual image, such as colour or movement. Thus it is known that people who have had a stroke, or a head injury, or who are affected by some types of Alzheimers disease, may lose something very specific such as their colour vision. Such patients are frequently not diagnosed as having a visual disability but continue to present bizarre symptoms which baffle their carers. The visual disabilities experienced vary greatly. Some people lose the ability to identify faces and cannot even recognise their own face in the mirror. Perhaps the most devastating disability is 'visual disorientation', in which people find that although they can see and identify objects they cannot localise them in space. They can see a cup of coffee set down on a table in front of them but are unable to reach accurately to pick it up. Out in the street they could not judge their distance from a lamp post or another pedestrian, and therefore cannot avoid bumping into them. Very little work has been done on the use of visual aids or other rehabilitation techniques for such patients (but see 23.7).

2.5.1 Dystonia

Dystonia is the term used to describe neurological disorders dominated by involuntary spasms of muscular contraction. These spasms may affect only one part of the body, such as the eyes. **Blepharospasm** is a dystonia of the muscles around the eyes. It causes uncontrolled blinking and sometimes spasms become prolonged, and may become so frequent that it is not possible to see, although the eyes and vision itself are normal. A treatment, using injections based on botulinum toxin, has been approved by the Department of Health. These injections are very helpful to many people.

The **Dystonia Society** (annual subscription £10; low income membership £5) provides advice on available treatments, and publishes a newsletter three times a year. It has self-help groups and area contacts offering local support and activities. Contact *Jutta Mason, Weddel House, 13-14 West Smithfield, London EC1A 9JJ* ✆ 0171 329 0797.

2.6 Aids related sight loss

The ways in which Aids related vision loss occurs are varied. The most common is **cytomegalovirus (CMV) retinitis** which primarily affects the retina but can also harm other parts of the eye. But people with Aids may also lose sight because of brain damage caused by infections or tumours, and in these cases sight loss may be accompanied by neurological disorders including memory loss, irrationality and hallucinations. Kaposi's sarcoma, a cancer common in people with Aids, can also cause vision problems when skin tumours interfere with the eyelid's function of protecting the eye and keeping it moist. This leaves the surface of the eye very vulnerable to infections. Other infections that can cause vision problems in people with Aids include toxoplasmosis and herpes simplex (though these infections can also affect people who are not HIV positive).

2.6.1 CMV retinitis

Until fairly recently vision problems were only experienced after someone had been affected by Aids for some time. Now, not least because treatment for other Aids related problems has improved, sight loss may be one of the first signs that someone who is HIV positive has developed Aids. This underlines the importance of regular eye tests for people who are HIV positive, as it is estimated that up to 40% of them may develop CMV retinitis. CMV is a member of the herpes family of viruses which is common in the general adult population, but it is only when a person's immune system is damaged that CMV causes serious problems in different parts of the body, and the retina is particularly vulnerable. At-risk individuals should alert their doctor or optometrist to their condition when having eye examinations, as the initial symptoms of floaters or blurred vision are not unique to CMV retinitis.

It is extremely important if sight is to be retained that diagnosis and treatment are sought without delay because although no drug currently available can eradicate the virus, the available medication can slow down the progression of the disease. The two drugs Foscarnet and Ganciclovir which are effective against CMV are usually given intravenously, which means that after the initial period of hospital treatment to get the infection under control, most patients are provided with a permanent catheter into their chest to enable them to continue medication at home. In March 1995 a tablet version of Ganciclovir became available. This is only suitable for long term maintenance treatment and involves taking about 20 tablets a day. It is not suitable for treating the initial infections or coping with any relapses, but it should improve the quality of life for people with CMV retinitis, who will need to continue to take medication continuously to slow down the progression of the disease and give them the best chance to retain some sight. Unfortunately Ganciclovir cannot be taken at the same time as AZT, the drug most usually given to prolong life for people with Aids, as both suppress the body's ability to produce white blood cells. Foscarnet can be taken together with AZT but there is a risk of kidney damage, so that medication has to be carefully balanced to provide the best possible quality of life for the patient. See also 23.1.

2.7 Behçet's Syndrome

Behçet's Disease is a chronic, multisystem disorder. There is as yet no clear understanding of the disease which is characterised by unpredictable outbreaks of inflammation in small blood vessels and sometimes in larger ones (vasculitis). It tends to start in the 20–40 year age group. People experience recurrent mouth ulcers and these are coupled with inflammatory problems in other body areas, most commonly skin, eyes and joints. Inflammation in the interior of the eye can lead to blindness.

The **Behçet's Syndrome Society** (annual subscription £5) provides a contact and support system for affected people and their families, financial aid in cases of hardship caused by the syndrome, and an information service for sufferers and the medical profession. Explanatory leaflets are issued and newsletters are circulated by *Mrs G. Seaman, 3 Church Close, Lambourn, Newbury, Berks. RG16 7PU.* Contact telephone helplines ℘ 01488 71116, ℘ 0116 289 1356 and ℘ 0151 644 6909.

2.8 Marfan's Syndrome

This syndrome causes weakness of those connective tissues subject to mechanical stress, such as tendons, heart valves and large blood vessels. Those affected tend to be very tall. Often they may be either mildly or severely short-sighted. Some have poor sight due to dislocation of the lens and are prone to retinal detachments. Despite this, it is now often possible to replace the lens of older patients. Early diagnosis is important to prevent unnecessary visual loss.

The **Marfan Association UK** (family membership subscription £10, waived in cases of hardship) exists to advise individuals and their families who are affected by this inherited disorder. Meetings are held and newsletters circulated. The Association publishes a pamphlet on the Marfan Syndrome for the ophthalmic and optometric professions as well as a booklet for patients. Contact *Diane Rust,*

6 Queen's Road, Farnborough, Hants. GU14 6DH ✆ 01252 547441 (office hours) or ✆ 01252 617320 (answerphone).

2.9 The professionals: who are they?

Unregistered spectacle sellers without qualifications are not allowed to sell spectacles for children, or to any customer who is known to be registered blind or partially sighted.

Anyone with poor sight will see at least some of the following professionals:

Dispensing opticians FBDO, FADO, FFDO, MFDO, SMC (Disp.) or BOA (Disp.) are qualified to fit and supply spectacles, low vision aids and other optical appliances, and, after further training, contact lenses, but not to examine eyes. They work in their own high street premises or in hospital eye departments.

Ophthalmic medical practitioners are doctors who have chosen eyes and eye care as their area of work. They are qualified to examine eyes, identify abnormal conditions and to prescribe corrective lenses and other optical appliances. They invariably work with dispensing opticians but may also work as clinical assistants in a hospital eye department.

Ophthalmologists and ophthalmic surgeons FRCS, FRCOphth, DO or DOMS are medically qualified, and specialise in eye disorders and their treatment. They may prescribe corrective lenses although they do not fit and supply spectacles. They usually work in association with eye hospitals or hospital eye departments.

Optometrists (ophthalmic opticians) FBCO, MBCO, FBOA, FSMC or FSAO are qualified to examine eyes, recognise abnormal eye conditions, advise on eye care, and to prescribe, fit and supply spectacles, contact lenses and other vision aids. They are also qualified in orthoptic treatment. They work in their own high street premises and in hospital eye departments.

Orthoptists DBO usually work in association with ophthalmologists. They are trained to deal with the treatment of squint and other disorders of binocular vision and with abnormal eye movements.

Low vision therapists are usually orthoptists (see above) who have done additional training in the area of low vision.

3 Making the most of remaining sight

This chapter aims to help people to see better. Although it is written with adults in mind, its message is equally relevant to the needs of visually impaired children.

The more sight is used the more useful it is likely to become. Using it will not cause strain or damage, or make it deteriorate more quickly. Sitting in a dimly lit room with eyes half closed will not preserve vision, and there is no need to deny oneself the pleasure of watching television.

*eye*OPENER

'If people can read headlines at a very close distance and are motivated, ready to adapt and to change the way they do things, then those are good indicators for success with low vision aids.'
Optometrist, Dr. Susan Leat, speaking on an In Touch programme

No miracle cures for poor sight will be found here. The prescriptions are much more down to earth. Good ophthalmic advice, correct equipment, correct technique, good lighting, and good contrast plus determination are the chief ingredients. The last factor is the most important – even more important than the amount of remaining vision.

3.1 Remaining vision

'Remaining vision' is the phrase used to describe the sight retained by blind and partially sighted people whose eyes have been examined by an ophthalmologist and who have been told 'nothing further can be done'. This examination is essential. Without it, visually impaired people run the risk of solving their immediate problem by, for example, purchasing a magnifier, when the best answer is a new pair of spectacles. Even more seriously, it could mean that the eye condition causing the poor sight is not treated and they might be in danger of losing their sight, whereas early diagnosis and treatment would save it.

The sight simulations in the colour section show how vision is variously affected in the great majority of people who are registered as 'blind'. Total loss of sight is very rare indeed. Most people retain some vision, but how useful it is depends on how well they are able to use it and the circumstances in which they find themselves. People with a central vision loss walking down the high street are far less likely to bump into passers-by than people who have a field loss, who might well be terrified to find themselves in such a situation. A good 'field of vision' is the ability to see above, below and alongside the object being viewed, and retaining it is much more vital than is generally appreciated by people with good sight. It enables us to locate ourselves.

Yet people with a peripheral (side) vision loss, as happens in glaucoma and often in retinitis pigmentosa, may still be able to read ordinary print. Ironically, they would be

Key to media of publication **P** clear print **L** large print **B** braille **T** tape **M** Moon **D** disk able to help anyone with maculopathy (characterised by central vision loss) to read the prices in the supermarket – as long as their friend with maculopathy helped them find the supermarket in the first place.

3.2 Ways to see better

The first step in seeing better is to visit an optometrist for an eye examination. Many elderly people think, mistakenly, that poor sight in old age is inevitable and it is useless to seek professional help. Yet a new pair of spectacles, or even improving the fit of existing ones, may make all the difference.

3.2.1 Fresh help with old problems

People registered as blind or partially sighted (see 4.7) should take advantage of their eligibility for a free NHS sight test and have a yearly eye examination by an optometrist. **In Touch listeners who have been registered blind for many years and have long since given up 'bothering' an optometrist, have found, through a chance encounter, that it might be worth having a check-up.** As a result, a cataract operation has restored some useful vision. Talking through sight problems with an optometrist may also suggest new ways to make life easier, perhaps by improving the lighting.

NEW Excimer Laser Photorefractive Keratectomy (PRK) is a relatively new procedure to correct myopia (short sight). **Excimer Laser Photorefractive Surgery: Patient Information** (single copies free) is a booklet issued by the *Royal College of Ophthalmologists, 17 Cornwall Terrace, London NW1 4QW* ✆ 0171 935 0702. It describes the operation, indicates the risks involved and the levels of myopia most likely to respond successfully to treatment. It includes a sample 'Statement of Informed Consent' which all patients should be given to read and sign before having treatment. This surgery is not available through the NHS, and private treatment may cost over £1,000. People under 21, or people suffering from diabetes, glaucoma, keratoconus and connective tissue disorder (see 2.8) are not considered suitable for treatment.

3.3 Low vision aids

When conventional spectacles can no longer help and surgery or medical treatment is not appropriate, or very prolonged, then it is time to consider **low vision aids**. These come in a bewildering array of strengths and designs. They range from simple hand-held lenses to electronic devices. Different ones are needed for different visual tasks. They do not enable everything to be seen clearly and easily. They are based generally on the type of magnifying lens that Sherlock Holmes used, or a miniature version of the telescope Lord Nelson put to his blind eye. Low vision aids require practice and good technique to get the best out of them, though some people seem to adapt instinctively and use their remaining vision to the full almost immediately. Others find it a struggle, but the reward of increased independence makes the effort worthwhile.

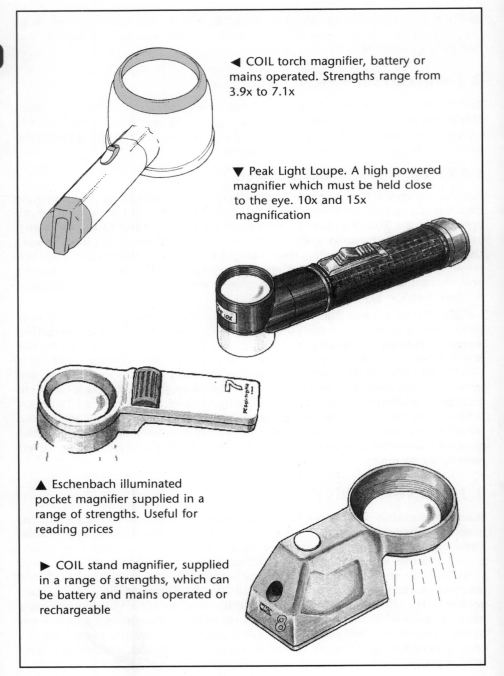

◄ COIL torch magnifier, battery or mains operated. Strengths range from 3.9x to 7.1x

▼ Peak Light Loupe. A high powered magnifier which must be held close to the eye. 10x and 15x magnification

▲ Eschenbach illuminated pocket magnifier supplied in a range of strengths. Useful for reading prices

► COIL stand magnifier, supplied in a range of strengths, which can be battery and mains operated or rechargeable

I read my wine bottle labels with my 'hedgehog' magnifier. The curve fits the bottle beautifully.

3.3.1 Hand magnifiers

These simple magnifiers come in a wide range of powers and shapes and are a deservedly popular choice. They may have round, oblong or square lenses of glass or plastic. Glass is heavier than plastic, but the latter is more likely to scratch. A strong magnifier may distort unless it has a specially curved (aspheric) lens. This is only possible with plastic lenses and accounts for their higher cost compared to simple hobby magnifiers.

Some resemble torches, having their own illumination, and are either battery-powered or rechargeable from mains electricity. Others are lit by a halogen or xenon bulb which gives a particularly bright, white light. Some are small, and designed to slip into purse or pocket and, when high-powered, are very useful for reading price labels if held close to the eye. An irritating disadvantage of hand magnifiers is that they do not leave the hands free. One solution is to use a holder. A **double-ended clamp** with a bulldog type clip on either end (Partially Sighted Society. £14.50) allows a hand magnifier to be converted into a stand magnifier. It makes it easier to write a signature in the correct space on a form or do various jobs around the house.

3.3.2 Stand magnifiers

Another solution to the 'hands free' problem is the stand magnifier. Both high and low power lenses are mounted on stands. They have the added advantage that the focus is fixed. This overcomes the difficulty of holding the magnifier steady at the correct distance from the text.

Variants on the stand magnifier design include hobby/magnifier lamps. The magnifier, surrounded by a circular fluorescent tube, is mounted on an adjustable arm. These lamps are useful for craft work and may help visually impaired typists. Magnification is low although there are models which, with auxiliary clip-on lenses, give about 3.5 times. Details can be obtained from the *Partially Sighted Society*. Another type of stand magnifier is designed to hang round the neck, resting on the chest. It is generally used for needlework, but again the magnification is very low.

Bar magnifiers are yet another variant. They resemble rulers and are intended to be placed on the text to enlarge an entire line of print, such as a telephone directory entry. But the magnification is low and the print is only elongated. The 'hedgehog' magnifier (Eschenbach 1435/1436) is designed so that when placed on an uneven surface of a book, the print remains in focus.

3.3.3 Spectacle mounted magnifiers

These are a more sophisticated way of solving the 'hands free' problem, though they should be regarded as a supplement rather than a replacement to a hand magnifier. A magnifying lens is mounted in the user's spectacles or on a special headband. The disadvantage is that the text being read has to be held very close to the lens (see illustration in 18.1.2). Children accept this quite happily, but adults can find it much more difficult. Older people may well find that although reading a book in this way is too slow and demanding, it is a great help for reading correspondence or sections of the newspaper.

3.3.4 Spectacle mounted telescopes

For work where the reading matter must be at a set distance, as happens when playing music, a near-vision telescope can be mounted on a spectacle frame (see picture in 21.3). This gives a longer working distance, although less can be seen at a time because the field is necessarily restricted. Similarly, telescopic lenses can be spectacle mounted for watching television. For longer distances, spectacle mounted telescopes similar to those sometimes used by racegoers may be an option, but it is dangerous to walk about wearing them.

I'm never going to read 'War and Peace' with these spectacle magnifiers. But I can read my business letters – and that's such a relief. Now if only my daughter learned to type ...

3.3.5 Hand-held telescopes

For distance use, such as spotting the name of a street, reading the departure board at a railway station or seeing the detail of a picture in an art gallery, a miniature monocular or binocular telescope can be the answer. With practice, and preferably training, they can be used to follow moving objects.

Some monoculars have the option of a short focus so they can be adjusted for both near and distance viewing. They can be extremely useful for consulting the timetable at the railway station and then checking the departure board. See also illustration in 23.2.

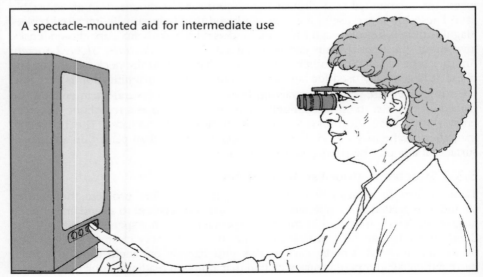

A spectacle-mounted aid for intermediate use

3.3.6 Electronic aids

The low vision aids described so far all have the advantage that they are convenient, easy to carry around, and can be used at a moment's notice. But they can be very tiring to use, especially when a high magnification is needed for reading. Electronic aids such as **closed-circuit television** provide excellent contrast, higher magnification (5 to 35 times is common), and a much more relaxed reading position. Some are portable, some can be linked to a computer, others can be used with a typewriter.

A hand-held telescope for distance use

With this type of equipment, the user sits comfortably in front of the set and the material to be read is displayed on a screen in enlarged print, either black on a white ground or as a white print on a black ground, though some models have other colour options. A camera is mounted vertically above a moveable platform on which the reading matter is placed. The user moves the platform to and fro so that the camera scans the print. Some models have a small hand-held camera which the user moves along the line of text.

Television readers require the user to have a television set tuned into a spare channel. A hand-held scanner is connected to a box into which the TV aerial is plugged. The scanner is run over the material to be read, which then appears, greatly enlarged, on the television screen. One portable version is now available which has its own 7 inch monitor and rechargeable battery. Another system also uses a television set as a monitor but the camera is mounted on an adjustable arm so it can be pointed in any direction. As it leaves both hands free and a good working distance between the lens and the

I had to sell my car, so I lashed out and bought a CCTV. It's given me back my independence ...

...... Leatherhd 376
.... Farnham 712
.... Guildford 38
.... Woking 765
.... Guildford 579
............Woking 727

A television reader may enable small print to be read wherever there is a TV. It is especially useful for reading the 'small print', such as instructions on food packets

object, it is particularly useful for hobbies. Most CCTVs are priced at between £1,300 and £2,500. Using an existing television set as a monitor, the cost can be around £995. Television readers, at around £300, are a popular choice for people who need a low cost aid to read the 'small print' in telephone directories, food packets, and medicine labels. A home trial before purchase should always be requested.

CCTVs are supplied by *AlphaVision, Dixey of Wigmore Street, Horizon CCTV, Professional Vision Services, Pulsedata International (UK) Ltd, Sensory Systems* and *Sight & Sound Technology.*

Television readers are supplied by *Force Ten Co. Ltd* (the Eezee Reader), *183 Boundary Road, Woking, Surrey GU21 5BU* ✆ 01483 762711 and *Horizon CCTV* (Horizon TV Reader) and *Scantec Vision Aid* (Angle-Scan), *6 Ellenborough Close, Bracknell RG12 2NB* ✆ 01344 425096

A free factsheet **Closed-circuit televisions** ❶ describes the television readers and closed-circuit televisions available in the UK and lists suppliers and prices. Contact *RNIB Employment Development and Technology Unit.*

3.4 Where to get low vision aids

Many low vision aids can be obtained on loan through the Hospital Eye Service, or can be purchased privately through an optometrist or dispensing optician. Closed-circuit televisions, television readers and some industrial magnifiers can be supplied through the Employment Service **Access to Work** scheme when they are essential for work (see 10.7.4) or through the LEA when they are essential for school use.

3.4.1 Hospital eye service

Consultant ophthalmologists can refer patients for assessment for low-vision aids, though sometimes it may be necessary for the patient to ask them to do this. Apart from closed-circuit television, low vision aids can be prescribed on loan through the **Hospital Eye Service**, generally at a low-vision clinic. These clinics are often attached to eye hospitals. Where there is no hospital clinic, patients may be referred by their consultant to private dispensing opticians or optometrists who specialise in low-vision work. This arrangement may be made through the Hospital Eye Service.

3.4.2 University optometry departments

During term time, university optometry departments have low-vision clinics and accept self-referrals as well as people referred by their eye specialist. People referring themselves are normally asked to pay a consultation fee (this does not apply at Aston or Glasgow Caledonian University) as well as the cost of the aid prescribed. Contact:

Aston University, Department of Vision Sciences, Aston Triangle, Birmingham B4 7ET ℘ 0121 359 8487

University of Bradford, Department of Optometry, Richmond Road, Bradford BD7 1DP ℘ 01274 384649

Glasgow Caledonian University Eye Clinic, Department of Vision Sciences, Cowcaddens Road, Glasgow G4 0BA ℘ 0141 331 3377/8

UMIST Low Vision Clinic, Department of Optometry and Vision Sciences, PO Box 88, Manchester M60 1QD ℘ 0161 200 3860

Clinics open all year round are:

City University, Department of Optometry and Visual Sciences, 311-321 Goswell Road, London EC1V 7DD ℘ 0171 477 8000 ext. 4338

Department of Optometry and Vision Sciences, University of Wales College of Cardiff, Redwood Building, King Edward VII Avenue, Cardiff CF1 3XF ℘ 01222 874357.

3.4.3 Optical practices ('high street opticians')

Some optometrists and dispensing opticians specialise in low vision work. When expensive low vision aids are prescribed, it is usual for a trial period to be offered. Some spectacle mounted aids can be modified if eyesight changes. Unfortunately, the voucher scheme (see 5.13.3) does not apply to low vision aids. There may also be an examination fee in addition to the usual sight test fee as several visits may be needed.

Prices range from £5 to £40 for a simple hand or stand magnifier. Spectacle mounted aids cost between £50 and £200. A hand-held telescope costs around £65 whilst one which also has a short focus could cost between £70 and £80.

People who wish or need to take a do-it-yourself approach, will find that magnifiers can be purchased in places as diverse as multiple stores and stationery or photographic shops. The magnification is generally marked on the box or on the magnifier itself (2x, 5x, 7x etc). Sometimes, instead, the power is expressed in dioptres. Divide the number of dioptres by 4 and add 1 to establish the magnifying strength. It could also be worth trying conventional binoculars or opera glasses to solve distance problems.

3.5 Information sources

Selections of aids can be found at many resource centres (see 34). An increasing number of voluntary societies and social services departments have staff who are knowledgeable about low-vision aids, keep samples and can give some advice on using them.

3.5.1 Personal advice

The Partially Sighted Society's low vision advisor, who is an optometrist, is always willing to help enquirers identify their nearest source of help and advise on low-vision aids generally. A low vision advisor at RNIB is also pleased to help.

3.5.2 Publications

The **Directory of Low Vision Services in the United Kingdom** (Partially Sighted Society, 1991, £3.25) lists hospital low-vision clinics, optometrists and dispensing opticians either giving low vision assessments privately, or providing a selection of simple magnifiers.

Catalogues which indicate the range of magnifiers on sale include those issued by *Associated Optical, Unit 2, 64 High Street, Burnham, Bucks SL1 7JT ℘ 01628 605433; Combined Optical Industries Ltd., 200 Bath Road, Slough, Berkshire SL1 4DW ℘ 01753 575011; Edward Marcus Ltd., 14 Goswell Road, London EC1M 7AA ℘ 0171 490 5915 and Specialist Optical Source Ltd., 57 Dukes Wood Drive, Gerrards Cross, Buckinghamshire SL9 7LJ ℘ 01753 888411.*

A mail order catalogue with exceptionally clear line drawings of a very wide range of magnifiers is issued by *LVA Ltd., 24 Regent Street, Nottingham ℘ 0115 947 4011.*

3.6 Choosing a magnifier

Professional help is by far the best way to obtain a suitable low vision aid, but for many people self-help is the only option. Simple guide lines can make the task easier. **Large size and high magnification never go together**, and a sheet which magnifies a whole page gives a very low magnification indeed. The **Keeler word chart** at the end of this book helps people identify the magnification needed in order to read print. It is important to use it when sitting in a good light, with reading spectacles if worn. Then decide which line has the smallest print that can be read correctly. It may only be possible to identify the letters of each word, rather than whole words on the line. Underneath that line will be found the approximate magnification needed for ordinary print to be read.

Unfortunately, this does not necessarily mean that a magnifier of that strength will enable a newspaper to be read easily. It is one thing to pick out words, but quite another to read fluently. To achieve fluent reading, a much stronger magnifier may be needed. To really relax it may be pleasanter to use ears rather than eyes, and listen to books and newspapers on tape (see chapter 19).

'The kids wanted to get Gran something special for Christmas', explained Mrs. Tompkins. 'They'd been really upset when she told them she'd been to the hospital and nothing could be done. So they clubbed together and got her this lovely big, oblong magnifier — it's a real beauty — and she was ever so pleased. Then I went into her room one day, and found her using a tiny little thing that belonged to great-aunt Ada. "Don't you dare tell the children", she said, "but this little one brings the print up much bigger and it's not so heavy. I don't expect they make magnifiers like that today." '

▶ ... but they do ... and some of them are illuminated (see 3.3.1).

It is not enough, however, just to consider magnification. A hand magnifier should be light and easy to hold if the purchaser intends to read with it, for it will have to be held steady at the correct focus for long periods. If there is a hand tremor, a magnifier on a stand which is pushed along the page would be a better choice. Flat-field magnifiers which look like glass paperweights are often useful as they focus a great deal of light on the text and can easily be pushed along the line. Magnifiers which look like torches, as they have a light incorporated in them, can be obtained in a variety of strengths. Their built-in illumination may solve problems which would normally be resolved only by stronger, and therefore smaller, magnifiers.

3.7 Using magnifiers

The first essential is to sit in a good light. Sitting in the window on a bright day with one's back to the light or at an angle to it is the simplest way of achieving the best conditions, but help in improving artificial lighting will be found in 3.10. After that, best results will be achieved by using the correct technique. This will depend on the strength and design of the magnifier.

3.7.1 Using a low power hand magnifier

Hand magnifiers should be used with distance spectacles, if worn. A low power hand magnifier, around 2x or 3x, should first be placed on the page and then brought closer to the eyes until the print can be read. If the page is held at arm's length, the print will certainly look big but only a few words or letters at a time will be seen. By bringing the page and magnifier closer to the eyes, the size of the print will stay the same but very much more of it will come into view. Holding the magnifier closer to the eye like this also eliminates unwanted reflections from room lights or task lights.

3.7.2 Using a high powered hand magnifier

A hand magnifier of 4x or more (12 dioptres or greater) must be held close to the eye. To find how close this should be, the diameter of the lens (or its longest side if it is rectangular) should be doubled. The magnifier should be held steady somewhere between this measurement and the actual width of the lens. The page is brought closer to the magnifier until the print is clear. The magnifier must not be moved. Read by moving the page to and fro across the line of sight (see illustration in 3.9.1).

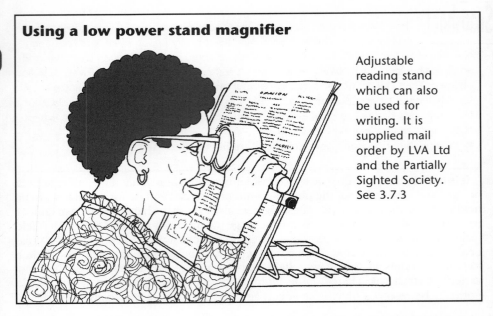

Using a low power stand magnifier

Adjustable reading stand which can also be used for writing. It is supplied mail order by LVA Ltd and the Partially Sighted Society. See 3.7.3

The lenses of some magnifiers have a steeper curve on one side than the other. Experiment to find which side gives the best view. Either way, to get most magnification a hand magnifier should be used with distance spectacles, though reading glasses will probably be sufficient when just checking through the headlines of a newspaper. All this takes practice, but it is easier to hold the text in the right position if it is on a clipboard. When reading a newspaper, it helps to fold it to one column width. That narrow width may then be read without moving the paper.

3.7.3 Using a stand magnifier

A low powered stand magnifier (see illustration in 3.7.2) should be placed on the text and pushed along the line. Generally, stand magnifiers should be used with reading glasses. If it is necessary to lift the stand magnifier off the page to see the text clearly, this generally indicates that the user's reading glasses are not strong enough. A return visit to an optometrist taking both spectacles and magnifier is needed.

A high powered stand magnifier should be held close to the eye in order to see as many words as possible. Because the text must be placed flat against the magnifier stand it is easier to use a clipboard. Read by holding the magnifier steady, and moving the print to and fro across the line of sight (see illustration in 3.8). However, as the focus is fixed by the depth of the stand, it is also possible to read by holding the page steady and moving head and magnifier together to scan the line.

3.8 Reading stands

Reading stands are an answer to the problem of holding the reading material close to the eyes when a clipboard is not appropriate. Using a reading stand avoids some of

Using a high power stand magnifier

the discomfort caused by sitting hunched over a book. At present there does not seem to be a cheap answer to the problem, though some people prop a tea tray on a cushion. The **Eschenbach** wooden reading desk and guide rail (£70.00 plus VAT. *LVA Ltd*) is adjustable and stable enough to be used for writing (see illustration in section 3.7.2). The adjustable magnetic workboard (£42. Partially Sighted Society) described in 8.9 is also suitable for adults. Both can easily be used in conjunction with a fluorescent task lamp. A home-made stand to bring keyboard music closer to the eyes is illustrated in 21.3.1. The *Disabled Living Foundation* and other Disabled Living Centres (see 34) can provide details of most reading stands. See 18.1.5 for details of copyholders.

3.9 Special techniques for special problems

One of the first steps to take when problems arise is to try to discover the reason for them. An eyecare professional is likely to be best placed to advise, but if there is no alternative to self-help, the *Partially Sighted Society* and *RNIB Book Sales* can supply **What You See and What You Do Not See** by Siv Ighe (£10.00) which analyses different types of vision, and contains tests and exercises to help readers identify their areas of useful sight and to find ways of making the best use of it.

3.9.1 Eccentric viewing

A common difficulty when trying to read with a magnifier is that some parts of a word can be seen and not others. With this particular problem, which anyone with central vision loss due to maculopathy may well experience, people often discover that they can see the whole word if they look above it rather than directly at it. This is known as **eccentric fixation**. Therefore, in order to read, it is necessary to hold the eye steady

Using a high power hand magnifier

Hold the magnifier steady, near the eye, and move the text towards it until the print is in focus

To read along the
line, move the text
to and fro whilst
eye and magnifier
are held steady

(**steady eye technique**) with the gaze firmly fixed above the line to be read. Thus it is no longer possible to read in the ordinary way, with the print held steady and the eyes moving quickly along the line, taking in whole words and phrases. Using eccentric fixation, the line of print must be moved, not the eye. Reading by this technique is much slower than by traditional methods, particularly at first as it goes against a lifetime's experience. It can be tiring and frustrating, but at least it does enable reading to take place.

Eccentric viewing methods can also be used for activities other than reading. This is comparatively simple to do when trying to see objects. Most people with maculopathy, for example, soon find that to see the clock on the mantelpiece they need to look at an ornament to the side of it, or to look down towards the fireplace or up towards the ceiling. Relatives and friends can help by making sure, for example, that a cup of tea is placed on the 'good side' rather than immediately ahead.

3.9.2 Scanning

People with a very narrow field of vision, perhaps because they suffer from advanced glaucoma, need to move both their eyes and their head in order to read, for example, a notice pinned up on a wall. Anything printed in columns, such as a newspaper, will be easier to read because the need for scanning will be reduced. When reading longer lines it may be better to move the print across the line of vision in order to read it (see illustration in 3.9).

Keeping to the line and finding the next line can present problems when scanning. A finger on the line, or a ruler underneath it, can help. Many people are helped by using a **typoscope**, a matt black thick card with a window cut out the width of the line. This can be home-made or A4 and A5 size ones can be purchased from the Partially Sighted Society (£1.40 a pair).

When the right hand field is lost, as may happen after a stroke, reading can be extremely difficult as the eye is scanning into nothingness. Loss of the field on the left side is not so incapacitating, though there may be problems in finding the next line. A bright red vertical line drawn down the page margin may help. It would need to be drawn on the side of the visual loss. For someone with a right field loss, the line denotes how far it is necessary to look to complete one line of reading. If the field loss is on the left, it shows the starting point of the line.

Another method is to place a bright bookmark along the left-hand edge of the print, so that the reader can turn his head at the end of each line until the bookmark is seen. **Typoscopes** may also help, by keeping the eye on the line and limiting the number of words that can be seen. This reduces the amount of information the brain has to sort out.

3.9.3 Monocular vision

A large number of people lose the sight of one eye through accident, injury or disease. No one knows exact statistics. The **Artificial Eye Service** has over 1000 new patients every year in England, and of course many people lose full sight in one eye without requiring its removal.

It is important to realise that the remaining eye will have the normal 'blind spot' which will no longer be compensated by sight in the other eye. People who have lost the sight of their right eye will have a blind spot to the left of centre, and vice versa. Looking at the cross and the circle below demonstrates this.

Someone who has lost the sight of their right eye should look at the cross from a distance of about 15 centimetres, and then move the page slowly further way, and then bring it closer. The spot will disappear and then reappear. Someone who has lost sight in the left eye should first turn the page upside down (but still look at the cross) before trying this experiment. People with sight in both eyes can compare what happens if they do this with both eyes open or one eye shut! Anyone with normal vision in the remaining eye is not entitled to be registered as partially sighted, though it may well take them some time to adjust to coping with monocular vision. This is because they lose part of their field of view, and initially at least they will have problems with depth perception.

It is possible to relearn how to see in depth. Nick Rumney, an optometrist who only has vision in one eye, suggests a useful exercise. Pour coloured water into a clear glass, and ask a friend to keep moving the glass so that the distance required to pour into it accurately varies. The safest way to pour is not from a height, but to let the bottle or jug touch the edge of the glass. To learn to judge the distance between objects, move the head from side to side. The objects will appear to 'move' in relation to each other. The distance they appear to move apart can then be used to gauge the actual distance.

Eventually the remaining eye adjusts to its new role, though there is nothing that can be done to compensate optically for the lost field of view. People need to learn to turn their head more, and when driving make more use of their wing mirrors. People

Tips for people with one eye

● When putting a drink down, place the other hand on the table and put the glass down next to it.

● It can be very difficult to judge the last step on a staircase. It may merge into the floor, especially in poor light or when the stair and floor carpets are the same. Move cautiously, feel ahead with your foot, and keep a hand on the banister.

● Wear protective spectacles when gardening or undertaking DIY jobs. Polycarbonate lenses are the safest.

● When going out for a meal with a friend make sure that he or she sits on your seeing side, but remember that the waiter may turn up on the blind side!

● In the early days, stop at a kerb to gauge the depth before crossing the road.

● If you are afraid that you may 'miss' the outstretched hand when a friend greets you, put yours out first!

with one eye can hold an ordinary driving licence, though they must inform the DVLA and their insurance company of their condition. They are not allowed to hold a professional driving licence as needed for public service or heavy goods vehicles.

As with other visual impairments, the best support and advice is likely to come from someone else in the same situation. **A Singular View – the art of seeing with one eye** (Partially Sighted Society. £7.95) was originally written by Frank Brady, an American engineer who lost an eye as a result of a flying accident. The English edition is edited by Ron Hearnden, a Canadian businessman who lost an eye in a skiing accident. Nick Rumney, who lost the sight in one eye as a schoolboy, recalls that the most constructive help he received was from a teacher who only had one eye, and is happy to be contacted at *Marbury House, 38 St. Owens Street, Hereford HR1 2PR* by anyone wanting advice on coping with monocular vision.

3.10 Lighting

A low vision aid is not the only way to help people see better. In fact, it is less than half the story. Most visually impaired people see better if they can work in a good light. Unfortunately, many see less well than they should because their lighting is poor. **The number of patients assessed as 'blind' in a well-lit clinic would be doubled were they to be examined at home[1].**

Eyes need light in order to see. It is not just the size of objects that makes them easy or difficult to see. Contrast is the vital factor. A white elephant in a snowstorm would be difficult for most people to spot! Good lighting enhances contrast, poor lighting reduces it. 'All cats are grey at twilight' is an apt description. Elderly people need more light than young people and this applies even more to older people with poor sight.

Natural daylight is a very strong source of light. Curtains should therefore be pulled well back. Even net curtains can exclude a great deal of light. Furniture should be moved, if necessary, to take advantage of the daylight. Walls painted with a light-coloured matt emulsion paint reflect much more light than a sombre wallpaper and a fresh coat of white emulsion paint to the ceiling can lighten a room to an extent which has to be experienced to be believed.

3.10.1 General lighting

The level of lighting in a visually impaired person's home should be much better than average, and the light levels between rooms and corridors roughly the same. To come out of a brightly lit bathroom onto a stairway or landing lit by one 60-watt bulb can be dangerous. There are many useful light fittings on the market such as spot lights, clip-on lights and concealed lighting, but many people will find their needs are met just by having powerful light bulbs in the conventional pendant ceiling fitting. Unless the ceiling is very high, a pendant light fitted with a simple white shade, wider at the bottom than at the top, with a 100-watt or 150-watt pearl bulb should give sufficient general light in the average sitting room. In the kitchen, fluorescent tubes attached

---

1 Cullinan T. et al. **Visual Disability and Home Lighting**. Lancet, Vol I. pp 642-4

under wall units and hidden by a pelmet are an excellent way of lighting working surfaces. A **visibility indicator** designed by an optometrist to help people check whether their home lighting needs improvement is printed in **Coping Again** (see 2.3.3). Single copies of the indicator, printed on card, can be obtained free from *The British College of Optometrists, 10 Knaresborough Place, London SW5 0TG* ✆ 0171 373 7765. Packs of 100 cost £20.

3.10.2 Task lights

For close work, supplement good general lighting with direct light from an adjustable lamp. The traditional standard lamp is too far away to shine sufficient light on the book being read in the armchair underneath it. An adjustable table lamp placed close to the work in hand is much more effective. Halving the distance between the work and the lamp gives a fourfold increase in light.

The disadvantage is that working so close to the light source can be uncomfortably hot. Fluorescent task lamps, (see illustration in 3.12.1) give an even spread of light, keep cool and reduce glare to a minimum. The Partially Sighted Society stock a range of 11 watt fluorescent task lights, from £41.95, with optional table bases, clamps, or wall brackets. They have cold white fluorescent tubes which give very good contrast.

3.10.3 Torches

A torch is a simple and very effective way of providing more light just where it is needed. Patients suffering from **retinitis pigmentosa** who tend to experience particular difficulty in getting about after dark, have found that a halogen torch is especially helpful. The **Multi Halogen torch** has an adjustable focus, a magnetic base and wrist strap. It costs £13.85 including postage and packing from *FGL Lighting Ltd., Pinewood Studios, Iver Heath, Buckinghamshire SL0 0NH* ✆ 01753 655558.

Some partially sighted people find that a torch which gives a very narrow, intense beam of light is very useful and can easily be carried in handbag or pocket. There are many on the market, and they are often known as **penlights**.

3.11 Advice on lighting

The **Partially Sighted Society** is particularly concerned with lighting and can advise on lighting design and decor. RNIB offers a low-vision enhancement advisory service which includes low-vision awareness and checking lighting levels. A helpful free booklet **Lighting and Low Vision** ● can be obtained from the *Electricity Association.* Help on lighting should also be available through local social services.

3.12 Coping with glare

All lighting, however, needs to be in the right place to help people as much as possible. Otherwise, **instead of seeing better, they may see much less** and complain bitterly, and with justification, that bright lights are positively painful and that they cannot see anything because of the glare. Glare is light in the wrong place; perhaps shining into the eyes or reflecting back into them from shiny surfaces. Everyone experiences this when the evening sun shines straight into your eyes or when walking along a seaside promenade on a sunny day. Although the sun may then be behind you, light reflected from the concrete pavements, whitewashed buildings and sparkling sea makes you reach for your sunglasses. People whose eyesight is affected by cataracts, scarred corneas, or albinism experience this so quickly and acutely that it is known as 'disability glare'. People who have damaged retinas also dislike these conditions, but because they experience them somewhat differently they are often said to suffer from 'discomfort glare'.

3.12.1 Disability glare

Light enters the eye through the eye's own 'window', the transparent cornea. It is then focused on the retina by the eye's transparent lens. When these are not transparent, as happens when the cornea is scarred or the lens is cloudy with cataract, light still enters the eye but much of it is scattered all over the retina. The result is a faded, misty view of the world. The effect is similar to that experienced by motorists. It is perfectly possible to drive safely with a dirty windscreen on a dull day, but the moment the sun comes out and shines through the windscreen, the road cannot be seen clearly. The 'disability glare' has indeed been disabling and the driver is forced to stop and clean the windscreen. Corneas and lenses cannot be cleaned; ways have to be found of avoiding the situations which trigger disability glare.

All who suffer from disability glare need good lighting in order to provide the contrast which enables them to see the task in hand. At the same time they need the least possible amount of direct light to enter their eyes. Daylight therefore needs to be welcomed, but the disabling effect of direct sunlight prevented. **Roller blinds are preferable to curtains as they allow the maximum amount of light to enter the room, but can be adjusted to keep out direct sunlight**. Venetian blinds are not suitable because they cast confusing shadows.

The high level of lighting achieved by a fluorescent ceiling light is still desirable, but the tube must be screened by a diffuser. Louvres, the grid-like shades often fitted to fluorescent lights, are useful as they direct the light downwards. They should be avoided if it is still possible to see the tube. A task lamp which directs the light on the work in hand is excellent, but the surface on which it shines should not be shiny and reflective. Using a typoscope (see 3.9.2) is a cheap and effective solution. The Rolls Royce solution for reading problems is to use closed-circuit television or a television reader. Both offer reversed polarity i.e. white print characters against a black background. Thus two highly desirable situations are achieved simultaneously: high contrast and minimum glare.

Out of doors it is usually the light that comes from above or from the side that is the most troublesome. A simple solution is generally the best, and a hat with a brim or a peaked cap like those worn by baseball players may be all that is needed, and also protects the face. The traditional translucent green eyeshade, or headband sun visor with an opaque shade, may well be other simple solutions. These can be obtained at sports shops and chemists or from the *Partially Sighted Society*, price £2.41.

Sunglasses should not be the first choice as the tinted lenses reduce the much-needed contrast. If simple eye shades are not sufficient, a good compromise is to try clip-on sunglasses which fit on the front of spectacles and flip up, acting as a sun visor. **Dark tinted sunglasses are likely to make things harder to see**.

Adjustable lamps with cold white fluorescent tubes are stocked by the Partially Sighted Society

3.12.2 Discomfort glare

Discomfort glare is the professional description of the uncomfortable feeling which people experience when they go too close to a bright light source or approach a large area of light, like a large window at the end of a corridor. Light that 'gets in the way', perhaps from a badly adjusted spotlight, also causes discomfort glare. Older people in general are more likely to suffer from it and they are also the people who are more likely to suffer from an eye condition, such as **ageing maculopathy**, which affects the retina and reduces their ability to see contrast. 'Newspaper print isn't as black as it used to be' is a very common comment. The best way of increasing contrast is to increase the level of light. But this must be done without causing discomfort glare.

Ways of achieving this are similar to those suggested in 3.12.1. Lights which may 'catch the eye' should be carefully shaded. Indirect lighting in the living room, plus carefully angled spotlights or a task light for close work could well be the answer. For reading, an illuminated magnifier will concentrate the light where it is needed – on the text and not reflecting back into the eye. Light reflecting back from the page can cause discomfort glare. Some *In Touch* listeners have found that using yellow transparent film over the page being read reduces glare and 'sharpens' the print image. **Omnicrom** is stocked by the Partially Sighted Society (80p per A4 sheet). Typoscopes are another option (see 3.9.2).

Out of doors, unlike people who suffer from disability glare, **anyone susceptible to discomfort glare may well find that tinted or dark glasses will be the best option**. The tint chosen should be as pale as is consistent with comfort; the darker the tint, the more the much-needed contrast will be reduced. Close fitting spectacles are desirable and because light bouncing off pavements and buildings can be so troubling, 'wrap-around' designs or spectacles with sideshields are often preferred. It is not easy to make a good choice unaided. An optometrist or dispensing optician is the best person to advise.

In Touch listeners who have tackled discomfort glare in their own way, have opted for industrial protective green anti-glare **eyeshields** and have found them very helpful. **Panorama 9000** series eyeshields (£3.25 plus VAT) with a green anti-glare lens (code 254501) are distributed by *Greenham Trading Ltd., Greenham House, 671 London Road, Isleworth, Middlesex TW7 4EX* ℘ 0181 560 1244. A similar eyeshield that can be worn over spectacles is also stocked: **Spectorama Overspec SP2** (code 254611) £3.84 plus VAT. Other people, especially those who suffer from retinitis pigmentosa, have greater problems. For them, the discomfort is such that it is indeed disabling. The British Retinitis Pigmentosa Society circulates sets of six differently tinted spectacles so that members can try them out at leisure in their own homes. Whether a consensus will emerge as to the 'best' tint is thought doubtful. At present, optometrists suggest that reddish lenses are likely to be a good option.

3.13 Sunglasses

Under extremely bright conditions, most people find sunglasses helpful. For anyone who is visually impaired, they are not easy to select on a do-it-yourself basis. For example, **retinitis pigmentosa** patients have the problem, in common with elderly people, that their eyes take much longer than normal to adapt to changes in light levels. Tinted spectacles may be dismissed as 'useless' when tried on briefly. They may need to be worn for about twenty minutes for the true effect to be felt.

Although the primary job of sunglasses is to reduce the level of light reaching the eyes, not all tinted lenses limit the amount of ultraviolet light. These are the invisible wavelengths of light that cause sunburn. The British Standards Institute standard for sunglasses ensures that lenses marked **BS2724** give protection from ultraviolet light.

Protection from ultraviolet light can be important for visually impaired people. UVA and UVB light is more likely to cause glare problems and should be filtered out. Anyone who has had **cataract surgery** but has not had a lens implant also needs this protection. Normally, in order to protect the retina, the cornea absorbs most of the UVB light. The natural lens of the eye absorbs any remaining UVB light and most of the UVA light, so this protection is lost when the lens is removed. However, lens implants have a protective coating. For general purposes, sunglasses which allow between 20% and 30% transmission of light are generally thought to be preferable. This would include most photochromic lenses which darken according to the brightness of light. Very dark lenses allowing only 10% transmission of light are only needed on the beach or in the snow, or for people who suffer from **aniridia** or **albinism**. Polaroid lenses cut out reflected light so they are very helpful in situations where, for example, highly polished floors look like pools of water. Lenses that are tinted at the top, shading to pale at the bottom, can also be very helpful. Any of the lens tints can be incorporated into prescription lenses. If clinically necessary they attract a small subsidy under the voucher scheme (see 5.13.3). They can also be prescribed through the *Hospital Eye Service*.

3.14 Using visual clues

The onset of severe visual handicap is generally in middle or late life. Visually impaired people will, therefore, be faced with the almost irresistible temptation to compare constantly their present sight with that which they previously enjoyed. This is natural enough in the early days, but it is a fact that continued constant reiteration of what cannot be seen is a certain way of losing friends and alienating people. Difficult though it may be to discern, there is, amidst the haze of blurred vision, one priceless asset: clear visual memories. In other words, the completed jigsaw pattern has already been seen so that now, when some of the pieces are missing or distorted, there is still the potential of reconstructing the whole in the mind's eye. But as many visual 'clues' as possible will be needed; those distinctive jigsaw shapes that, when slotted into the pattern, suddenly make all the hitherto meaningless pieces spring to life.

Unfortunately, there is no list of visual clues that all visually handicapped people find helpful because no two people have the same remaining vision. Therefore only the individual can decide what clues are needed, and under what conditions. Clues are, however, more likely to be identified when lighting is adequate, when they are brightly coloured – orange, yellow, and light green are generally especially helpful – and when their colour and shape contrast with the surroundings. The gross characteristics of objects are more likely to yield clues than the fine ones; the dark mound on the chair which elongates slowly is more likely to be a cat than a cushion – or even a dog! It is often easier to recognise a friend by the outline of their hairstyle than by their features. Visual clues can also be reinforced by data from other senses, so that clues provided by sight, hearing and touch can combine to enable a person to move confidently and act decisively.

If print can no longer be read, it may well be felt that visual clues are of little use, especially when trying to sort out correspondence. Yet the shape and colour of an envelope can often indicate its origin, whilst the heavy black type (for example **On Her Majesty's Service**), even though it appears only as a blur, tells its own story, so the income tax envelope can be distinguished from the junk mail.

3.14.1 Using contrast

Visually impaired people tend to see pastel colours as rather similar shades of grey. Sharp contrasts in colours are much more likely to be noticed although the colours seen may not be the true ones. A brightly coloured plastic holder will enable an otherwise almost invisible glass of water to be seen on the bedside table. The illustrations in the colour section show how contrast can be used around the home to make life easier. But much must be left to each individual's own inventiveness and ingenuity. Each must decide if a red plate shows up the food outlined against it, whether the antimacassar draped over the arm of an easy chair will prevent a collision, whether a contrasting seat to the toilet will make it easier to reach quickly!

3.15 Low vision clinics and centres

In medical and rehabilitation circles, remaining vision is usually referred to as 'low vision'. The limited number of low vision clinics and the scarcity of optometrists with low-vision expertise is a major reason why so many visually impaired people function below their true visual capacity. Twenty years ago it was estimated that only one third of registered blind and partially sighted people had a low-vision assessment and that half of those who 'missed out' would have been likely to benefit if they had been given the chance[1]. There is no reason to think that the situation has changed.

Hospital eye service clinics are still few and far between, and private provision is patchy. Attendance at a low vision clinic is not always as rewarding as patients hope, though if the local clinic does not offer follow up or training with the aids prescribed it may be possible to seek assistance from a rehabilitation officer (see 15.1).

In recent years, however, an increasing emphasis has been put on the importance of looking at all aspects of a person's visual needs. This approach, pioneered in this country by the Partially Sighted Society, consists not only of helping patients achieve their primary goal, which is generally some form of reading, but also identifying other difficulties they experience and showing them how different aids and techniques might help solve those problems. The Society now has seven orthoptists on its staff who are all trained in low vision work. As a result, they provide low vision assessment and training at their Sight Centres in Exeter, London and Salisbury, in about twenty hospitals and through some Ability Development Centres (see 10.4.1).

In Australia, the idea of a multi-disciplinary approach to low vision services was developed in the 1970's. It brought together the skills of the ophthalmologist, optometrist, social worker, mobility officer and occupational therapist. In 1993 Birmingham Royal Institution for the Blind Vision Services opened a purpose-built Low Vision Centre in Birmingham which also brings together medical expertise, low vision assessment and rehabilitation work. Similar services can be found also in Strathclyde, Leicestershire and Bristol.

3.16 Seeing better

The theme of this chapter has been that seeing better is achieved through the joint efforts of patient, professional, friends and relatives: perseverance and ingenuity on the part of the patient, low vision skill and flexibility on the part of the professionals and understanding and co-operation on the part of friends. When someone is making every effort to see as much as possible, it is not encouraging to hear 'He sees what he wants to see'. *In Touch* aims to raise public awareness so that comment is made less often. It is even more dispiriting to be registered as 'blind' when there is every

---

1 **The Provision of Low Vision Aids to the Visually Handicapped** Silver, J.H. et al. Trans. Ophthal. Soc. UK (1974) 94, 310-19.

likelihood that useful vision will be retained. Only government legislation can change the name, and governments, although not blind, are sometimes deaf.

3.17 Further reading

The British Journal of Visual Impairment Low Vision Pack. Contains major articles, comments, letters and book reviews published in the Journal in the last ten years. £10.00.

See 29.7 for details of sight simulating spectacles.

4 Your rights to help 71

B

4 Your rights to help

It is a truth not universally acknowledged that anyone registered blind should also feel permanently grateful. That is not to detract from the glow of appreciation which follows receiving appropriate and perhaps unexpected help. The difference lies deeper. Sighted people using their public library are not expected to call down a blessing on their local authority for providing the service. They may indeed be appreciative, but they accept that, as council tax payers, they have a right to the service. Members of the talking book library are in a different situation. The service they receive, though good, cannot compare with the library service enjoyed by people with sight. Yet the world at large, their friends, and their conscience, tell them that they should be grateful.

This chapter seeks to empower blind or partially sighted people by distinguishing the situations where they have 'rights' because of their very poor sight from those areas of life where they must rely on the goodwill of charitable agencies (see footnote below). The distinction is often blurred. Sighted helpers as well as people with a visual impairment are unclear as to where responsibility lies, what can be done to remedy matters when things go wrong, or who to thank when things go well.

Peter White interviews Margaret Thatcher visiting RNIB Talking Book Service in 1985

Thatcher: I believe that a service like this is better if there is a very large element of voluntary in it. What I have seen today – there is a wonderful spirit here and part of this comes from people knowing it is a voluntary service and I really do not think it would be as good if it were 100% State funded. And you must really never get to an attitude of mind where if something has to be done, it's done by the State. What are people here to do? We are here to choose to do things voluntarily and it's that which makes the way of life in Britain as good as it is, and makes the spirit of Britain so great.

White: You would not think it might be possible to produce even more of the books you obviously admire?

Thatcher: I do not think it could be done as well, and with such loving care and with such effect as it is done here. I do not want a world in which the State does everything and people do nothing.

 This symbol indicates a legal right

4.1 Electoral rights

 Registered blind people are entitled to vote by post or by proxy at all local and parliamentary elections. Application forms **(RPF 7B)** can be obtained from the local Electoral Registration Officer, found at the local Town Hall or Council offices. This form must be completed thirteen working days before the election day itself, so it is wise to register well in advance. Once done, a postal or proxy vote is provided automatically for subsequent elections.

A proxy can only vote on behalf of two people at most, so blind people in a residential home who wish to vote in this way must not all choose the same person.

Partially sighted people who cannot attend the polling station in person can also apply for a postal or proxy vote on the same form, but their application will need to be countersigned by a doctor, nurse or, where appropriate, the head of their residential home or, if they live in sheltered accommodation, the warden.

Alternatively, a blind voter may ask the help of the Presiding Officer at the polling station, or take a close relative, or a companion who has a vote in the same constituency, to help. No companion may act for more than two blind people at any one election.

4.2 Blind people and the law

NEW The Criminal Justice and Public Order Act 1994 has gone some way in removing discrimination against blind jurors by amending section 9 of the Juries Act 1944. There is now a presumption that blind people are 'fully capable' of serving as jurors, though judges retain discrimination rights.

The official view is that blind people cannot serve as Justices of the Peace or as judges because they would not be able to deal with the paperwork, could not observe the demeanour of witnesses and would not enjoy public confidence. The Lord Chancellor received a deputation of blind people on the subject in December 1994, and the matter is still under discussion. **NEW** Research in 1994 by the University of Hertfordshire supports the view of blind people that their judgement is not affected by being unable to observe demeanour. Two specially devised interviews with Robin Day, one where he consistently told the truth and one in which he consistently lied, were shown on television, broadcast on radio and printed in *The Daily Telegraph*. People were asked to decide which interview contained the lies. Radio listeners detected the lies 73.4% of the time, newspaper readers 64.2% and television viewers 51.8%, supporting the view that the presence of visual clues actually reduces people's ability to detect deception.

4.3 The Disability Discrimination Bill

 At the time of writing (May 1995), this Bill has had its third reading in the House of Commons. It covers employment, the right of access to goods and services, transport and the establishment of a **National Disability Council**. This would be an independent body to advise the Government on how existing and new measures to help disabled people are working, and to recommend further ones where necessary. At third reading, the government agreed to amend the Bill:

- to cover access to buses, trains, coaches, trams, taxis and underground systems and to make it illegal for taxis to refuse access to 'service animals' such as guide dogs;

- to review in five years the size of firms specified in the Bill which would be required to 'make reasonable adjustments' for disabled employees and whose disabled staff would have a statutory right to non-discrimination at work. The proposed legislation applies only to firms with over 20 employees. An undertaking was given that this number would not be increased. The Government agreed to include rehabilitation leave (see 10.2.1) as an example of a 'reasonable adjustment';

- to extend the new right of access to goods and services in the Bill to include access to information. The definition of 'information' is not clear, but the Minister for the Disabled, William Hague, said in the House that it would include 'information services and information about services.' It is expected to include things like timetables, but not, for example, manufacturers' instructions on how to use newly purchased equipment.

All organisations of and for people with disabilities are unhappy that the proposed Disability Council will only act in an advisory capacity. In contrast, a **Disability Commission**, similar to the Equal Opportunities Commission, would have 'teeth'. RADAR summarised the situation succinctly, 'There is no point in passing a law if it is not going to be enforced.'

These points will be made in the wide range of amendments which are expected to be brought forward in the House of Lords. There will also be pressure to include the strengthening of special education legislation, including further education, within the Bill. The Bill is expected to receive Royal Assent in July 1995.

4.4 Rights to Community Care Services

 It is **not** necessary to be registered as blind or partially sighted in order to receive help through community care legislation. **If the local authority accepts that there is a need, then help must be provided**. There is a complaints procedure (see 4.4.9) when things go wrong.

Community care legislation is based on the Government White Paper **Caring for People ❶**. This states that anyone who has problems associated with

old age
mental illness
learning disability
physical disability
sensory disability

should be able to obtain care services and support which

enable them to live in their own home

enable them to retain as much independence as possible, whether at home or
in residential care

are tailored to their individual needs.

Both users of services and carers can expect

to be informed about services, support and options

to be involved in decisions that affect them.

Duties placed on local authorities under the **National Health Service and
Community Care Act 1990** include

the duty to assess individual need for the community care services covered
by the Act

a duty to consider the provision of those services to match those individual
needs

the duty to establish a complaints procedure

a duty to publish a community care plan for its area.

The way that local authorities exercise their community care functions is subject to
guidance and directions issued by the Secretary of State.

4.4.1 What are 'community care functions'?

These are the welfare services for people with disabilities provided under
the National Assistance Act 1948 and by implication the services identified
in the Chronically Sick and Disabled Persons Act (1970) **B**. They include
the provision of

practical help and adaptations in the home

radio, television or similar recreational facilities at home

outside recreational and education facilities, and help in making use of them
such as providing means of travel

holidays

meals at home or elsewhere

a telephone and any special equipment needed to use it.

Providing and adapting services to meet individual needs is the essence of
community care. This is achieved through identifying the person's needs
(assessment), and the assembling of services to meet those needs (a care plan).
The person responsible for doing this is a care manager.

Users and carers must be informed about the kind of help that can be offered. This
information should be available on request in braille, or on cassette, or in large print.
RNIB See it Right office can advise on ways to achieve this. A **Directory of
Transcribing Services** **L** **B** **M** **T** **D** (£9.25. 1994. RNIB) includes local services.
For national agencies see 33. See also 4.4.7.

RNIB Social Services Development Unit works collaboratively with staff in social
services departments and other agencies, primarily in consultancy, training and
advisory roles. It can advise across a range of service elements including aspects of
policy, planning, management or practice.

4.4.2 Community care: the duty to assess

 When a person 'appears to be "disabled" under the terms of the Disabled Persons (Services, Consultation and Representation) Act 1986 **B** **T** – a definition which includes blind and partially sighted people – the local authority is required to offer a comprehensive assessment, irrespective of the scale of need that is initially presented.'[1] See also chapter 26.

In theory, this means that visually impaired people who enquire about the availability of talking newspapers should be given that information, but should also be encouraged to discuss any other aspects of life where they are experiencing difficulties. Where the worker dealing with the query is alert – or the visually impaired person persistent – this will happen. However, the person responding to the request may be the receptionist. Or the worker visiting to make the assessment may be much more conversant with services for older people, rather than services for visually impaired people. **It may therefore be prudent to ask in writing for a full assessment including input from a specialist worker such as a rehabilitation officer.**

4.4.3 Community care: what is 'need'?

Much depends on what is considered to be a 'need'. This is not defined in the Act. Department of Health guidance uses 'need' as shorthand for 'the requirements of individuals to enable them to achieve, maintain or restore an acceptable level of social independence or quality of life, as defined by the particular care agency or authority'.[2]

How this can work in practice is illustrated by the vexed question of the provision of telephones. A glance at 4.4.1 might give the impression that all visually impaired people are eligible for help in obtaining a telephone. After all, most visually impaired people feel they need one. In this particular case, the factors that establish 'need' for a telephone have been fairly clearly defined. Generally, people must meet the first and either the second or third of the following criteria:

- they must live alone, or be frequently left alone or live with someone who cannot be relied on to deal with an emergency
- they must be unable to leave the house in normal weather without the help of another person and need a telephone to avoid isolation
- they must be able to show that a telephone is needed for medical reasons and be at risk without a telephone.

 If, after a financial assessment, help with the cost of installation and rental is considered to be needed, there is a duty to provide. On the other hand, some local authorities interpret 'need' more generously than this, and all have complete discretion to adopt any criteria they wish (see also 30).

It is clear, however, that a request for a telephone cannot be dismissed out of hand, perhaps by saying 'we don't provide telephones for partially

1 **Care Management & Assessment. Practitioners' Guide** **T**. HMSO. 1991

2 ibid

Care planning should not be seen as matching needs with services 'off the shelf', but as an opportunity to rethink service provision for a particular individual ... (**Care Management & Assessment. Practitioners' Guide ⓣ**)

Jim is a widower and lives alone. When he lost his sight, his chief concern was his mid-day dinner. A social worker called to see him. Her first idea was meals-on-wheels. Jim didn't think much of that. 'I've always walked up to the pub for my dinner, they make a lovely steak and kidney pudding.' The social worker came back with this plan: Social services would arrange for the pub to deliver a dinner for the next few months. She would arrange for a mobility officer to call and show Jim a safe way of reaching the pub, and then hopefully he would be able to get there under his own steam. How did that strike him? 'If you think I'll be able to manage it, I'll give it a try' replied Jim. 'And it would give me a chance to see my mates.'

sighted people'. An assessment must be made if requested, and details of the criteria must be available.

4.4.4 Assessing need: waiting times

The value of help is doubled if it is given quickly. The Act does not say how quickly the assessment must be made.

In practice, a major concern of visually impaired people is how soon they can reasonably expect an assessment of their needs following their certification as blind or partially sighted by their ophthalmologist (see 4.7.1). It is worth noting that in 1994 the Department of Health recommended

- that ophthalmic units establish and monitor systems to ensure that BD8s are forwarded [to social services departments] within five days of the examination

- that local social services departments calculate, agree and monitor timed targets between (1) the receipt of the BD8 and the dispatch of a letter making initial contact with the visually impaired person and (2) the receipt of the case by the social worker and his or her initial visit.[3]

In other words, it would be reasonable for local voluntary societies or organisations of the blind, who may be in touch with newly visually impaired people, to ask how long it takes BD8 forms to travel between hospital and social services department. And then to enquire what would be the maximum length of delay before the visually impaired person is contacted and visited.

Unreasonably long delay in obtaining an assessment or the provision of a service that has been agreed could be the subject of a complaint (see 4.4.9). Taking this action may well mean that the problem is resolved informally.

---

3 Review of the Effectiveness of Form BD8 Procedures. March 1994. Obtainable from *Health Care Administration 2C, 328 Wellington House, 133-155 Waterloo Road, London SE1 8UG* ℘ 0171 972 4118.

Joanne lost her sight through a stroke when she had her baby. She was very ill, but gradually her health improved and she was ready to return home. But how to manage with a new baby and a toddler? Her sister could give some help, but Joanne's husband was out at work all day. Joanne was still very frail and her short-term memory was poor. Yet both she, her sister and husband were determined to keep the family together. After long discussions with all three, plus their health visitor, district nurse, and occupational therapist, a care plan was finally made. Social Services contracted with a private company for 50 hours care a week for Joanne – the hours to be arranged at the family's wish, so Joanne's husband could 'bank' some hours to give him a week-end or an evening off occasionally. The occupational therapist provided equipment to make Joanne more independent in the bathroom and toilet. A rehabilitation worker visited weekly to help Joanne learn to look after the new baby and cope with the toddler. A social worker was available for counselling when Joanne's husband felt that life was getting too much for him. The local voluntary society for the blind helped by enabling Joanne to join a yoga group and also get out for some leisure activities. One year on, the family is still together, and Joanne is becoming more independent. 'It would never have happened in the old days', commented one of the workers. 'It's still damned hard for them, but they know we're behind them and they have some control over the help they get.'

B

4.4.5 Care management

A full assessment should include a discussion of the special difficulties caused by poor sight, from identifying the controls on the cooker to fears about crossing the road. Unless it is is pointed out by the visually impaired person, it is not always realised that sorting through the contents of the larder, checking sell-by dates, checking if washing or mending needs to be done and making sure everything is clean and hygienic is extremely important and virtually impossible for a severely visually impaired person to achieve unaided. On the other hand, the assessment should not be limited to visual problems; difficulties caused by poor hearing, difficult home circumstances, financial concerns – all aspects of life can be considered if that is desired. **It should also take the needs of the carer into consideration**. See 26.11.

Some people will of course have very complex needs. Parents of multiply disabled visually impaired children or young visually impaired adults needing residential care will need a range of services. A full assessment may take a number of sessions, several different agencies may be involved and the financial implications of possible outcomes will need to be investigated.

Sometimes a service will be needed that the local authority cannot supply. A typical example is mobility training. It is not acceptable for a person who is indisputably at risk when out of doors to be told, 'We're terribly sorry, but we have no-one who can teach mobility'. **If the need for mobility is accepted, the authority has a duty to provide it**. If necessary, they can 'buy in' the appropriate services from a freelance mobility officer or a voluntary agency (see 4.4.6).

4.4.6 Care plans

With the assessment completed, a care plan (or 'who does what and when and who pays for it') can be drawn up.

In the past, most services to visually impaired people were provided by the local authority, with perhaps some social activities supplied by a local voluntary society for the blind. Nowadays, some of the services may be provided by the local authority, but others may be supplied by agencies contracted by the local authority, such as national or local voluntary societies.

Major voluntary societies who are providing direct services – generally rehabilitation and mobility services – include RNIB Community Care Direct Services, Action for Blind People, The Guide Dogs for the Blind Association, Henshaw's Society for the Blind, Projects by the Blind, Wandsworth, and seeAbility. A much larger number of societies provide residential services and a growing number of local voluntary societies are providing rehabilitation services under contract.

The care manager is responsible for bringing the whole range of different services together to meet a person's individual and unique needs.

No plan is perfect, so a good care management programme monitors whether things are going smoothly, and reviews the plan from time to time as people's needs change.

Joanne (see snapshot, 4.4.5) obviously had complex needs, and therefore had a care manager to mastermind the arrangements for her care and be the person whom she or her husband could call upon if anything went wrong. Most visually impaired people will have simpler needs, but they must still know who to contact if things go wrong.

Two rehabilitation workers in Leicester, Usha Bhavsar and Vimbisayi Taruvinga, give these insights:

● It is often considered rude to address older people by their first names. Always start with Mr, Mrs. or Miss.

● An interpreter is a great help in overcoming the language barrier, but interpreters who appreciate the aim of the worker are an even better asset. If interpreters see for themselves how rehabilitation services can change people's lives, their interpretation is likely to carry conviction, but if they feel negative about the services being offered, that feeling also will be conveyed.

● Do not say 'blind'. This word has a stigma within African Caribbean and Asian communities far beyond anything felt by other visually impaired people in this country. It not only means total loss of sight, it also means the end of life. It is synonymous with poverty and beggars. 'Visually impaired' is much more acceptable.

● Family ties are strong, and help offered is most likely to be acceptable and relevant when it is offered in partnership with the carer.

● People from ethnic minorities differ just as much from each other as everyone else!

A video, **Give us guidance**, made with visually impaired Asian people is available in Gujerati, Punjabi, Urdu & English from the *Royal Leicestershire Society for the Blind*, price £10.00

Mrs. Harding is visually impaired and in her 80's. Life has been getting on top of her, and a minor fall has landed her in hospital. Now she is ready to go home, but her flat is in a state, she has no relatives, so how will she manage? The hospital social worker, the local social worker and Mrs. Harding get together and draw up a plan; this is a part of it ...

CARE PLAN Client's name Mrs Harding

Need	Objective	Help	Who by	When	Cost to client
1 daily meals	to provide hot meals	Meals on Wheels	081 937 4077	As from 20.1.95	£7.70 a week
2 clean-up needed	to prevent infection	Home Care Support	Care Options	24.1.95 2 p.m.	£3.00
3 decoration of flat	repairs & to brighten it up	Housing Dept	E. Edwards		
4 shopping & laundry	to keep client at home	Age Concern	Hospital Discharge Team 081 969 8585	As from 24.1.95	NIL

4.4.7 Community care and ethnic minorities

One of the most obvious needs of people whose first language is not English is to receive essential information in the language of their choice and, for visually impaired people, in either large print or on cassette. Some local authorities, such as Waltham Forest, have been producing information in this way for some time; others are following suit. Sheffield Social Services provide their information material in braille, large print, cassette and disk, with Arabic, Bengali, Chinese and Urdu translations on cassette. **Birmingham Royal Institute for the Blind Transcription Services** can translate information from English into eight Asian languages including Hindi, Urdu, Punjabi, Bengali and Gujerati and will produce the translated information in large print, braille and on cassette. Contact *Vision Services (BRIB), Cowley Centre, 23 Gravelly Hill North, Erdington, Birmingham B23 6BT* ✆ 0121 373 1336 for details and prices.

A very effective way of giving information is, of course, by face to face contact, but not all community care workers are used to working with people from other cultures, and may give offence unintentionally. It is only too easy to see this country's customs and culture as normal and others as abnormal. To help effectively, it is important to know something of the culture's values, traditions and standards as they strongly influence the functioning of the family and through it, the individual member.

RNIB's Development Officer for Ethnic Minorities maintains a national database of black and ethnic minority workers and can put enquirers in touch with a worker who can advise on how best to help service users. EMERGE (Ethnic Monitoring, Education and Resource Group for Equality) consists of people working with black and ethnic minority visually impaired people. It issues occasional newsletters. Details from *Kishor Patel, RNIB*.

See 19.4.3 for details of talking magazines and newspapers in ethnic languages.

4.4.8 Charging for community care services

NEW A **Survey of Charges for Social Care 1993-95** (LGMB Publications. £10.00) showed no uniform drift towards charging by social services departments in England and Wales although 13% of authorities made no charge for home care in 1994, compared with 17% in 1993. Generally, the home care charge was related to the user's means. The number of authorities taking capital into account when making income assessments was increasing and some authorities were considering taking the capital value of users' homes into account as well. A third of the authorities were planning to review their charges in the coming year, so the picture is changing all the time.

 The **Health & Social Services and Social Security Adjudication Act 1983 B** indicates that authorities must 'take into account what an individual service user can afford to pay in deciding on the level of charge'. A policy decision not to waive or reduce charges to individual users in any circumstances can therefore be legally challenged. **NEW** In addition, the Department of Health guidance note **Discretionary Charges for Adult Social Services** (January 1994) states that **'Once someone has been assessed as needing a service, that service should not be withdrawn even if he or she refuses to pay the charge required**. The authority should continue provision of the service while pursuing the debt, if necessary, through the Magistrates' Court'. Home care services, for example, must therefore continue to be supplied regardless of the financial dispute.

4.4.9 Complaints procedure

 All social services departments have a formal procedure to deal with complaints under the **National Health Service and Community Care Act**. In the first instance every effort should be made to resolve the matter informally. If the matter cannot be resolved satisfactorily in this way, the local authority must explain the complaints procedure and ask for the complaint to be put in writing and, if necessary, help the complainant to do this. Once this happens, the complaint is 'registered'. If the complainant is dissatisfied with the local authority's response to a registered complaint, a review by a panel can be requested. Review panels consist of three people, at least one of whom will be independent of the local authority. There are strict time limits for each stage of dealing with the complaint, otherwise the local authority must explain the reason for the delay.

Local authorities must publicise their complaints procedure, and information should be available in large print, braille or on tape. Where the complaint is about a service that has been contracted out to another agency, the terms of the contract may have insisted that the agency itself had a complaints procedure.

However, ultimately the duty lies with the local authority, so if the complainant remains unhappy, the local authority complaints procedure should be used.

Other remedies include a complaint to the Monitoring Officer (every local authority has one – often the Chief Executive), or the local government Ombudsman. Citizens Advice Bureaux staff are able to advise, and local voluntary societies for the blind can act as advocates.

NEW **Challenging Community Care Decisions** (£10.00. 1994) from the *Public Law Project, 17 Russell Square, London WC1B 5DR* ✆ 0171 436 0964 is a guide for voluntary organisations advising people dissatisfied with community care decisions or procedures.

Sometimes it is helpful to know the contents of one's personal file when making a complaint. Under the **Access to Personal Files Act (1987)** people have a right of access to information about themselves held by local social services authorities. In England and Wales Circular **LAC/89/2**, and in Scotland Circular **SW 2/89** provide that a person may make a request for access through an agent. There is no legal right of access to information held prior to April 1989, unless it is needed to make current information comprehensible. However, local authorities may make earlier records available on a voluntary basis. A charge may be made for access. Access can be refused where disclosure would be likely to cause serious harm to the physical or mental health of the person concerned, and to prevent the identification of third parties.

RNIB also has an open access policy. Anyone who has been a client of any of the RNIB's services, or who has applied unsuccessfully to become one, can ask RNIB if it still has any files on them. If files exist, the applicant has the right to examine them by appointment. RNIB will make arrangements for the file to be read to the applicant, or the applicant can bring an escort to act as reader if this is preferred.

4.5 Rights of visually impaired children and their parents

The Children Act 1989 **B** **T** was implemented in October 1991, since when local authorities have been required to provide services designed

- to minimise the effect on disabled children of their disabilities and
- to give such children the opportunity to lead lives which are as normal as possible.

The Act lays down a legislative framework so that services should be provided for any child who needs help from a local authority if he is to grow up happily and healthily. This help should be available to all 'children in need'.

A child is considered to be 'in need' if

- 'he is unlikely to achieve or maintain, or to have the opportunity of achieving or maintaining, a reasonable standard of health or development without the provision for him of services by a local authority', or
- 'he is blind, deaf or dumb or suffers from mental disorder of any kind or is substantially and permanently handicapped by illness, injury or congenital deformity', or

- his 'health or development is likely to be significantly impaired, or further impaired, without the provision of services for him'.

The rights of parents of visually impaired children include

- the right to an assessment of their needs. This must take into account the needs and preferences of the child, his parents and his brothers and sisters. This assessment may be combined with assessment under other legislation, such as the 1993 Education Act (see 8.1)
- the right to receive services to meet the needs identified in the assessment
- the right to be consulted and for help to be provided in partnership with them, and to continue to be kept informed and consulted
- the right to obtain published information about services. If necessary, this should be supplied in large print or braille or on cassette
- the right to use a complaints procedure (which should be published and, if necessary, available in large print, or cassette or in braille) and, when needed, to be helped in lodging a complaint
- the right to a decision following a complaint in writing.

In addition, visually impaired children have

- the right to be consulted and, wherever possible, involved in any decision-making.

In order to plan services effectively, local authorities must compile a register of children with disabilities in their area. Parents who do not want their children to be on the register may not be excluded on that account from the use of special services. This register is not the same as the blind and partially sighted registers held by local authorities (see 4.7.2). **It is not necessary to be registered as blind or partially sighted in order to establish 'need' under the Children Act**.

See 8.1 for details of rights under the Education Act 1993.

4.6 Rights to financial help

Registration is necessary to qualify for certain financial benefits. Details will be found in the introduction to chapter 5.

NEW Registration as blind rather than partially sighted is particularly important for people of working age as it can automatically entitle them to incapacity benefit (see 5.2).

4.7 Registration

People who retain some sight can qualify for the blind register, even when their remaining sight is not expected to get worse.

Registration as **blind** means that, according to the National Assistance Act 1948, a person is 'so blind as to be unable to perform any work for which sight is essential'. A patient's sight is considered to have reached this stage if only the top letter on the test chart (called a Snellen Chart) can be seen when the eye specialist holds the chart just in front of him. This is known as 3/60 vision; the patient can see at three metres distance the letter people with normal vision would be able to see when they were 60 metres away from it. Some patients will be registered blind if they can see rather more than this. They may be able to read the top letter on the chart when sitting the usual distance away from it, but only if they can manage to get it directly in their line of vision. In these circumstances, although they have 6/60 vision, they are considerably handicapped because they are liable to bump into objects on either side, or to trip over steps. In other words, their field of vision is severely restricted.

Registration as **partially sighted** means that a patient is 'substantially and permanently handicapped' by defective vision caused through 'congenital defect or illness or injury'. Partially sighted people may be able to distinguish objects no better than a 'blind' person, but their field of vision may not be so limited. Alternatively, they may be able to see more clearly than anyone registered 'blind', but only within a very limited area. When their eyesight is tested on the Snellen chart, they can read the top letter at the usual distance of six metres. If they can read the next three lines down, they will still qualify for registration if their field of vision is limited, perhaps because they suffer, for example, from a disease such as retinitis pigmentosa or glaucoma. People with one eye only will not qualify for the partially sighted register unless the sight in their remaining eye is seriously affected.

Admission to both registers is conditional on a test of distance vision only. Near vision is not taken into account. It is difficult, often impossible, for a layman to differentiate with certainty between people eligible for the blind or partially sighted registers.

4.7.1 How to get registered

A set of forms, known as **BD8** in England and Wales, **BP1** in Scotland and **A655** in Northern Ireland, must be completed by a consultant ophthalmologist. This may be suggested by the specialist when the patient is being examined at a routine hospital appointment, but sometimes it may be left to the patient to raise the matter. People not attending hospital should ask their family doctor to refer them to an ophthalmologist for a certification examination. Examination at home can be arranged for the housebound, and transport to hospital can generally be provided for those unable to use public transport. The examination costs the patient nothing. The District Health Authority pays any fee.

If the patient disagrees with the specialist's recommendation – for example, feeling that blind rather than partially sighted registration would be more appropriate – an **Ophthalmic Referee Service** operates in Scotland and Wales. Contact the *Scottish National Federation for the Welfare of the Blind* or the *Wales Council for the Blind*. Patients in England and Northern Ireland should ask their family doctor to refer them to another ophthalmologist for a second opinion. Under the terms of the Patient's Charter patients have a right to be referred to a consultant of their choice and can also be referred for a second or third opinion if the patient and the family doctor think it desirable.

4.7.2 The registration procedure

The BD8 is a lengthy form. The first sheet has the specialist's certification, and the patient's signed agreement that information concerning the extent of his sight loss may be passed on to his local social services department. **The patient must be**

Understanding the BD8 (see 4.7.2)

The following terms and abbreviations are often used by professionals, both in conversation and on the BD8 form.

acuity	clarity of vision
amblyopia	reduced acuity although the eye is structurally normal, also known as 'lazy eye'
aphakia	without a lens
CF	counts fingers
crystalline lens	the natural lens of the eye
field of vision	the extent to which one can see out of the sides of one's eye when one looks straight ahead
hemianopia	loss of half the field of vision
HM	hand movements
intra-ocular lens	the plastic lens implanted into the eye to take the place of the extracted crystalline lens
iridectomy	surgical removal of part of the iris as in treatment for glaucoma
keratitis	inflammation of the cornea
myopia	short sight
optic neuritis	inflammation of the optic nerve
PL	perception of light
scotoma	a pathological blind spot in the field of vision

given a copy. The second sheet contains the diagnosis. Copies of this are sent to the patient's family doctor and to the Office of Population Censuses and Surveys for research. **The patient only receives a copy at the ophthalmologist's discretion**.

A **register** of blind and partially sighted people living within the area is kept by the social services department of every county council, metropolitan district and London borough, though in some cases, and particularly in Scotland, a voluntary association for the blind may act as their agent.

The same procedure is followed for the **registration of children**. Ophthalmologists are recommended to certify children as blind or partially sighted when they have had their fourth birthday and their sight has been corrected by spectacles or contact lenses. Children younger than this, with inherited eye conditions causing poor sight, will normally be certified as partially sighted unless they are obviously blind.

When the form has been accepted by the local authority, and a social worker has visited, the patient's name is added to the appropriate register if that is the patient's wish. There may be a time lag, but a DSS circular (**LAC 17/74**) asks local authorities to note that **the effective date of registration should be the same as that of certification, that is, the day the ophthalmologist signed the BD8**. This is particularly important for blind people who qualify for income support (see 5.8.2) or who pay income tax (see 5.1).

All these procedures are explained in **Health Notice HN (90)1** and in a Department of Health Local Authority Social Services Letter **LASSL(90)1**. BD8 forms should be ordered by District Health Authorities and Special Health Authorities from *HMSO Manchester, Broad Way, Chadderton, Oldham OL9 9QH* ℘ 0161 681 1191. Minimum quantity 100, price £22.89 plus VAT. BP1 forms are available free of charge from *The Scottish Office Home and Health Department, Room 62, St. Andrew's House, Edinburgh EH1 3DG* ℘ 0131 244 2828. A655 forms are obtained free from *Beechbank House, 11 Derryvolgie Avenue, Belfast BT9 6FL* ℘ 01232 681735.

B

4.8 What's in a name?

When most people on the 'blind' register consider themselves to be partially sighted and many people who are registered 'partially sighted' think of themselves as partially blind, it is not surprising that much thought has been given to finding more appropriate descriptions. *Visually handicapped* used to be the favourite choice. However, the World Health Organisation defines *handicap* as the disadvantage or the restriction of activity imposed by disability which prevents people following their usual everyday life. *Impairment* is chosen to describe the actual physical loss which may (or may not) lead to handicap. Using these definitions, it is correct to call all blind and partially sighted people *visually impaired* and reserve the phrase *visually handicapped* for situations where poor sight limits choice and independence.

These academic distinctions do serve to emphasise that many of the problems faced by people with disabilities are socially determined, and that while it may not be possible to reduce a person's impairment, much can be done to reduce the handicap. They also have the advantage, as an *In Touch* listener pointed out, of instantly making him a VIP!

Other *In Touch* listeners were equally emphatic that they did not regard themselves as 'visually impaired'. They preferred the old names: blind and partially sighted. So in this book, as in life, we use all four descriptions.

A rose by any other name?

Blind, Totally blind, Total, Dim, Registered blind, Braillists, Visually Impaired, Visually handicapped, Visually disabled, Partially sighted, Partially blind, Partially seeing, Vocationally blind, Economically blind, Travelling blind, Functionally blind, Adventitiously blind, Congenitally blind, Medically blind, Educationally blind, Industrially blind, Visually defective, Visually limited, Legally blind, Politically blind, Psychologically blind, Print impaired, Visually challenged, Moderately blind . . .

List of terms noted over several years by Peter Wells, Royal National College for the Blind, and published in the **New Beacon**, January 1993

4.9 Service providers

Services nowadays may be provided by many different agencies: statutory ones such as social services departments (social work departments in Scotland, Health & Social Services Boards in Northern Ireland), or voluntary societies under contract to a social services department.

Depending on the local situation, visually impaired people may meet any one of a number of different workers. These may include a social worker trained to help with a wide range of problems who has not specialised in one particular impairment such as blindness, a mobility officer who has been trained to teach blind people to move confidently and safely both indoors and out, or a technical officer who has been trained to teach communication and daily living skills (reading, writing, cooking, cleaning and simple sewing). Often, technical and mobility skills are combined in one person known as a **rehabilitation worker** (or officer).

NEW There is a severe shortage of such specialist workers. In England in 1994 just under 500 were employed by social services departments to work directly with visually impaired people. This number included 145 specialist social workers, 324 rehabilitation workers and 25 assistants. Voluntary organisations employed a further 155 staff, mainly as rehabilitation workers.[1] These figures indicate an overall ratio of specialist staff to registered blind people of 1:192. However, when registered partially sighted people are included, the ratio rises to 1:355 – double the usual number twenty five years ago. If the estimates of people whose sight is poor enough to qualify for registration, but who are not registered, were to be included, the ratio would rise to 1:1,350[2].

Finding a specialist worker may therefore require persistence. The best advice is to enquire first at a local social services office. **Even if specialist workers are not based there, the staff should know where they can be located**.

4.10 National voluntary service providers

4.10.1 Action for Blind People

With the aim of increasing independence, **Action for Blind People** concentrates predominantly on employment and training, the provision of information and welfare rights advice. A mobile service tours various parts of the country. Other areas of work include accommodation, hotels and cash grants.

4.10.2 The Guide Dogs for the Blind Association

The **Guide Dogs for the Blind Association** breeds and trains guide dogs and trains blind people in their use. Seven regional training centres cater for over 700 students a year (see 12.4). The Association is becoming increasingly involved in offering further services, mainly linked to mobility, to all blind people. A magazine, **Forward, ⓟ Ⓑ Ⓣ** is published quarterly.

---

1 Occupational mapping in the field of visual impairment. National Council for Voluntary Organisations. Final report, 1994.

2 Perspective on training Ⓛ Ⓑ. Visual Handicap Group. RNIB. 1995.

4.10.3 Henshaw's Society

Henshaw's Society became a national charity in July 1993. It provides a wide range of services for visually impaired people including education and rehabilitation services, residential accommodation, community care, support and outreach. Its centres stretch from Newcastle-upon-Tyne in the east to Llandudno in the west.

4.10.4 Jewish Care

B

Jewish Care provides rehabilitation and low vision assessment services in the Greater London area only, but their Sensory Services team can provide information on where to find similar services for people of the Jewish faith in other parts of the country. Nationwide tape services include a weekly edition of the **Jewish Chronicle**, a monthly magazine **Sounds Jewish** and tape recorded books.

4.10.5 National Deafblind League

The **National Deafblind League** exists to enable people with a dual sensory impairment to live full and active lives and to teach and encourage touch-based communications systems. Activities include contributing to individual community care plans, social and rehabilitation activities. They issue a weekly newspaper and a quarterly magazine, **Rainbow** **L** **B** **T** **M** .

4.10.6 Opsis (National Association for the Education, Training and Support of Blind and Partially Sighted People)

Opsis is an association of seven major independent national charities: Action for Blind People, the Royal London Society for the Blind, the Catholic Blind Institute, the Birmingham Royal Institution for the Blind, Henshaw's Society for the Blind, the Royal National College for the Blind and the West of England School for children with little or no sight. Opsis members campaign collectively on behalf of visually impaired people, exchanging experience and best practice between members and mounting joint ventures which might be beyond the resources of just one or two of the charities.

4.10.7 Partially Sighted Society

The **Partially Sighted Society** is a nationwide organisation. Its activities include low vision assessment and training services as well as the provision of equipment and advice on any aspect of living or working with impaired vision. **Oculus** **L** , is issued bi-monthly, annual subscription £4.50, but free to full and corporate members of the Society.

4.10.8 Royal National Institute for the Blind

The **Royal National Institute for the Blind** is one of Britain's largest voluntary organisations and references to its many activities will be found throughout this book. RNIB exists to promote the better education, training, employment and welfare of blind people, to protect their interests and to prevent blindness. A monthly journal, **The New Beacon** **L** **B** **O** (£1.25) carries news of the latest developments. Tape edition from *Cadwell Recording Services for the Blind*, annual subscription £5.00.

4.10.9 St Dunstan's

St Dunstan's was founded to care for men blinded in the First World War. Today the help it gives to individuals is still restricted to men and women from England, Wales and Northern Ireland who are registered blind, or who are eligible for the blind register, and who in addition receive a 50% war disablement pension in respect of an eye injury that has either been attributed to or aggravated by service in the Armed Forces or auxiliary services such as the A.R.P. Once accepted, St Dunstan's offers life long care including the provision of suitable housing, convalescent and residential care and a wide range of leisure pursuits as well as rehabilitation and training.

By May 1995, only 883 ex-servicemen and women qualified for these services, 565 of whom live in this country. 49 St Dunstaners died in 1994/95 and 21 new members were admitted. St Dunstan's also cares for 625 widows in the UK.

St Dunstan's also administers the **Gubbay Trust** which offers limited help to ex-servicemen whose loss of sight is not attributable to their service, and to auxiliary service personnel, such as policemen or firemen blinded on duty (see 9.9).

Visually impaired ex-servicemen and women in Scotland have the option of joining the **Scottish National Institution for the War Blinded**, *50 Gillespie Crescent, Edinburgh, Lothian EH10 4HZ* ✆ 0131 229 1456.

4.10.10 Sense (The National Deafblind and Rubella Association)

Sense works and campaigns with and for people who have a sensory disability. Its priority is people who are deafblind, meaning a severe impairment of both vision and hearing resulting in unique and special needs, but people with a sensory impairment plus other disabilities are included. Advice, support, information and services for individual people, their families, carers and involved professionals are provided. A quarterly magazine **Talking Sense** ❶ ❷ ❸ ❹ is published. Annual subscription £10.00, free to **Sense** families.

4.11 Local voluntary societies

With the coming of community care, the role of many of the larger voluntary societies has changed, as described in 4.4.6. Yet many small societies still exist and continue to give a local service in their own distinctive way. This may amount to little more than an occasional social or outing, a Christmas gift or a party. Or it may take the form of a warm, friendly, informal visiting service, ready to give a helping hand in time of crisis.

Most local societies will give some financial help in cases of hardship, either by augmenting help from state sources or by helping people who are not eligible for state help. It is not unknown for a voluntary society to repair a leaking roof, replace a lost purse, decorate a room, supply an electric blanket or a special toy for a child. The address of the nearest voluntary society can be obtained from the local social services department, or on request from *RNIB's Voluntary Agencies Link Officer* who can supply an up-to-date address list.

The **National Association of Local Societies for the Visually Impaired** (NALSVI) was founded in 1991 as a forum for all local societies, large and small, in the United Kingdom. Its main objectives are the raising of standards of service for visually impaired people and the mutual support and encouragement of its member societies and their staff.

4.12 National self-help groups

'If you want a job done, do it yourself' is a good motto. Organisations run by and for blind people have brought about major improvements in the lives of all visually impaired people.

B

4.12.1 The National League of the Blind and Disabled

The **National League of the Blind and Disabled** is a registered trade union. It is affiliated to the Trades Union Congress and the Labour Party and both the World and European Blind Unions. Membership is open to all blind, partially sighted and sighted disabled people over 16 years of age. The League has 60 branches and 6 Area Councils, with a central office in London. It is involved in all issues regarding the employment of blind and disabled people in the United Kingdom and maintains a watching brief on all legislation affecting disabled people. The League publishes **Horizon**, a braille quarterly, and its inkprint equivalent, **The Blind Advocate**.

4.12.2 The National Federation of the Blind

The **National Federation of the Blind** is open to all blind and partially sighted people over the age of 16. It has 35 branches and a postal branch for those not within easy reach of a local branch. It campaigns for a comprehensive disability income for all blind and other seriously disabled people, better job opportunities and social services, properly resourced integrated education of visually impaired children in mainstream schools, greater public awareness, improvements in the services provided by charitable agencies and greater participation by blind people on their committees. A free information pack for professionals and volunteers gives details and includes campaigning material on safer pavements. A bi-monthly journal, **Viewpoint** ❶ 🅱 ❶ is published.

4.12.3 The Association of Blind Asians

The **Association of Blind Asians** was formed in 1986 to identify the problems and difficulties encountered by blind and partially sighted people of Asian origin and to identify gaps in the welfare services provided. It aims to establish a register of visually impaired Asian people, and to provide an information service for them either in braille or on cassette in the relevant Asian language, as well as social and cultural activities. Full membership is limited to blind and partially sighted people of Asian origin, but anyone can apply for associate membership. The annual subscription for both is £1.00, though life membership for visually impaired people is £11.00, and £15.00 for sighted people. A cassette magazine in Hindi, Urdu and English is sent free to full members. Contact *322 Upper Street, London N1 2XQ* 📞 0171 226 1950.

4.12.4 The Organisation of Blind African Caribbeans

The **Organisation of Blind African Caribbeans** was inaugurated in October 1988. Membership is free. The organisation aims to ensure equal opportunities in education, training, employment and welfare for all blind and partially sighted African Caribbeans. It seeks to improve access to information about employment and social services and can offer information and advice to those who have recently become visually impaired. It is working with other Commonwealth countries to advise members who need help if they wish to return home on retirement. It is also involved in research on how the sight of children with sickle cell anaemia is affected by the disease. Contact *Chigor Chike, 24 Mayward House, Benhill Road, London SE5 7NA* ℘ *0171 703 3688.*

4.13 Where does the buck stop?

A major effect of recent legislation is the progressive separation of assessment from service provision. It means that the person, or agency, who assesses visually impaired people's needs for services will not necessarily be the person or agency that supplies them. For example, a social worker from the local authority may visit, and a need for mobility training may be agreed. In years gone by, both services would have been provided by the local authority – and in many areas this is still the case. In an increasing number of authorities, however, the mobility training will be purchased from a voluntary society for the blind. In other words, the agency paying for the service is not the same as the agency providing the service. This is known as the 'purchaser/provider' split.

So when the rehabilitation worker arrives on the doorstep, he or she may come from a voluntary society which has a contract to provide a rehabilitation service for that particular local authority. Blind people may understandably assume that this help is being financed from charitable funds. In fact, the money comes from their taxes. In other words, it is a community care service for which they have been assessed and to which they 'have a right'. Other services the voluntary society may supply, such as the Christmas party, are likely to be financed from voluntary funds and, in that sense, are truly charitable.

When things go wrong, the first step is to establish who is paying for the service. If this is unclear, as in many cases it may well be, a worker at the Citizens Advice Bureau should be able to sort things out. For example, a guide dog owner, unhappy about the guide-dog he has been allocated, should complain to the GDBA which has its own complaints procedure. On the other hand, someone having mobility lessons which are delivered by the GDBA or another voluntary society under contract to their local authority, should use that local authority's complaints procedure (see 4.4.9). Apart from RNIB, it is rare for a voluntary society to have a published complaints procedure. It is rarer still for it to be given any publicity.

Local authorities are required to monitor their contracts with other agencies, to be sure that everyone is getting 'value for money'. It is very difficult for them to do this effectively unless users of the services (who are nowadays sometimes referred to as 'customers') make both their complaints and their appreciation known to the right people. A useful first step towards achieving this might be for a simple 'rights statement' to be issued in large print or on tape to visually impaired customers, stating the quality of service it is reasonable to expect, who pays for it, and who is ultimately responsible. People have a right to know 'where the buck stops'.

Should you have cause for complaint we want to know about it in order that we can resolve the matter as soon as is practicable. ... If you are unable to discuss your complaint with the person providing you with a service you should contact his or her immediate supervisor who is either the Regional Rehabilitation Services Manager or the Regional Training Manager ... or you can write (or send an audio tape if you prefer) to the Regional Controller. .... During an investigation which will be carried out as soon as possible, you may be invited to the Regional Centre. If this is so, please feel free to bring along a friend who can help to support you. If you still think you have grounds for complaint you should write to the Director General of the Association who will further investigate the matter internally and in addition may arrange for an independent review of your case. This could entail a visit from someone such as a social worker from the Region. ... At all stages you will of course be advised of the outcome usually within three weeks of receipt of your complaint.
Extract from **Client Complaint Procedure** 🄻🄱🅃 *sent to all guide dog owners.*

4.14 Further reading

You and your sight: living with a sight problem 🄻🄱🅃 (HMSO/RNIB. 1994 £4.95) is an attractive, easy-to-read introduction to services for visually impaired people.

Care managers, in particular, will find much useful information in the following publications:

Back from the Wellhouse: Discussion papers on sensory impairment and training in community care (CCETSW Paper 32.1. 1993).

A Wider Vision. The Management and Organisation of Services for People who are Blind or Visually Handicapped 🄿🄱🅃 (Social Services Inspectorate. 1988).

Co-ordinating Services for Visually Handicapped People 🄻🄱🅃 (H.M.S.O 1989).

The **Good Sense Guide** (Department of Health. 1991) offers a structured way of evaluating the services provided by local authorities to people with sensory disabilities.

Perspective on training: Professional support for blind and partially sighted people in the community. Visual Handicap Group 🄻🄱. (RNIB. 1995).

5 Guide to benefits

Everyone tends to be frightened of the benefits maze. This applies just as much to carers, voluntary workers and specialist staff as to the people they are helping. This chapter aims to enable both helpers and visually impaired people to do a simple 'benefits health check' in their own home. Young and old *In Touch* listeners confirm that without such help and information they can and do lose out on benefits. Older visually impaired people in particular find that such help gives them the confidence to make a claim and ring the freephone Benefits Enquiry Line run by the Benefits Agency (see 5.16.1).

Each benefit is therefore introduced in two ways: minimum basic information in a chart to put readers quickly 'in the picture', and key points boxes to allow users to decide whether they need to read further. The aspects emphasised in the main text are always those that are particularly relevant to blindness and partial sight. The descriptions are therefore not comprehensive, nor an authoritative statement of the law.

Worth getting registered?

Although there is no such thing as a 'blind pension', there is a mixture of modest financial help which can be triggered by registration.

Registered blind people are entitled to:

👍 Extra income tax relief (see 5.1)

👍 Exemption from the 'all work' test for incapacity benefit (see 5.2.2) and severe disablement allowance (see 5.3)

👍 Receive slightly more benefit than a sighted person under 80 years of age, in good health and in identical circumstances if entitled to income support (see 5.8), housing benefit or council tax benefit. (see 5.9 and 5.10) Deductions will not be made from these benefits if, for example, a working son or daughter is part of their household (see 5.8.1 and 5.9).

👍 Earn a little more money than sighted people in good health before it affects their income support (see 5.8.4)

👍 A reduction of £1.25 in the cost of a sound and television receiving licence (see 19.8.2)

👍 Car parking concessions (see 13.5) and some travel concessions. Some of the latter apply also to registered partially sighted people (see 13.1)

👍 Registered blind and partially sighted people are eligible for free National Health Service eye examinations

Check also:

👍 5.8.3. A severely disabled person may benefit if their carer is registered blind

👍 5.7 Registration as blind or partially sighted may entitle people to disability working allowance

Registration does not automatically entitle people to **disability living allowance** (see 5.4), **attendance allowance** (see 5.5), or **disability working allowance** (see 5.7), but check these sections to find out more

→ Many visually impaired people make successful claims

→ Many are not aware that they should claim

MAIN BENEFITS AT A GLANCE

BENEFIT	AGE RANGE	Blind registration avoids hassle?	Blind registration affects cash?	Is benefit means tested?	NI Conts needed?	Taxable?	See section for details
Attendance Allowance	65+	Possibly	No	No	No	No	5.5
Disability Living Allowance	0-65	Possibly	No	No	No	No	5.4
Disability Working Allowance	16+	Yes	No	Yes	No	No	5.7
Incapacity benefit	Working age	Yes	No	No (earnings limit only)	Yes	Yes	5.2
Invalid Care Allowance	16-65	No	No	No (earnings limit only)	Yes	No	5.6
Income Support	16+	Yes	Yes	Yes	No	Unlikely	5.8
Income tax relief	N/A	Yes	Yes	Yes	No	N/A	5.1
Severe Disablement Allowance	16-65	Yes	No	No (earnings limit only)	No	No	5.3

B

Brevity is impossible in the sections dealing with attendance and disability living allowances. The quick advice is that all visually impaired people should claim one of these benefits. Whether their claim is successful will depend greatly on how they present their case, which is why these sections are so detailed.

The information in this chapter is correct in May 1995. It cannot cover all situations as the benefits system is so complicated, but the various social security benefits which have particular relevance to visually impaired people are outlined. The agencies and publications in 5.16 can give more detailed information. The Citizens Advice Bureau is an excellent source of local help. Some voluntary societies for the blind are able to advise and some social services departments have welfare rights officers. These are staff who specialise in helping people claim their benefits.

Recent changes in benefit rules and procedures are highlighted with this symbol:
NEW

5.1 Income tax relief

Age range	Means Test	Registration	Time Limit	Rate
All	No	Blind	From date of certification as blind	£1200 increase in personal allowance

B

How to claim

Notify the tax office or put the date of registration and the name of the registering local authority (or equivalent body) in the space provided on the annual tax return form. See also 15.6.3.

More help

IR80 Income Tax and married couples
IR110 A guide for people with savings
Leaflets from Tax Enquiry Centres (listed under Inland Revenue in phone books)

Income tax relief **KEY POINTS**

O The blind person's allowance can be transferred between husband and wife

O **NEW** An extra-statutory concession was announced in October 1994. If a person's BD8 (see 4.7.2) was signed by an ophthalmologist in one tax year but their registration was completed in the following tax year the blind person's allowance for both the current and the previous tax year can be claimed

O Some people will find that the increased personal allowance means that they will no longer be liable for income tax. They will, therefore, be able to register for the gross interest to be paid on their bank and building society savings. To register, complete form R85, available from all banks and building societies

Snapshot Mr Carruthers works in the City. His wife has just been registered blind. His accountant has told him that his wife can transfer her blind person's allowance of £1,200 to him. It's just enough to enable him to get back on to the standard rate of income tax. He gets out a writing frame for her to write the letter, and addresses the envelope himself!

5.2 ⟨NEW⟩ Incapacity benefit

Incapacity benefit replaced sickness and invalidity benefit on 13th April 1995. In general, a lower rate of benefit will be payable under the new rules. For example, there will be no earning-related addition to incapacity benefit. The government expects to save £150 million in 1995/6, rising to £335 million in 1996/7. One way this is being achieved is shown in 5.2.2.

B

Age range	Taxable?	NI contributions?	Earnings limit?	Registration a passport?
Working age: up to **60** (women) up to **65** (men)	Yes, from week 29	Yes	Yes (see * below)	Yes, if blind ('all work' test if partially sighted)

Rate per week?: Weeks 0-28 **£44.40**; Weeks 29-52 **£52.50**; Weeks 53+ **£58.85**

Age addition at onset: Under 35 years **£12.40**; 35-45 years **£6.20** (paid at week 53 onwards)

Dependency increases: Adults: Weeks 0-52 **£27.50**; Weeks 53+ **£35.25**; Children: 1st child **£9.85**; each other child **£11.05**

* Up to £44 per week can be earned without losing any benefit if the claimant's doctor thinks it would assist health and help recovery. The DSS have to approve these 'therapeutic earnings' in advance.

Voluntary work for less than 16 hours a week for a charity or voluntary body or a person outside the immediate family does not affect benefit. Only expenses may be received.

5.2.1 Protection from the new rules

People claiming after April 13th 1995 receive less money than they would have in the past. People who were receiving invalidity benefit at the time of the change-over are protected. Their benefit will not be taxed, and they will be paid under the old invalidity benefit rules though the earnings related addition to their benefit will be frozen. They will receive the usual annual uprates. **But by 1998 their case will be reviewed and they will have to take the 'all work' test unless exempt** (see 5.2.3).

5.2.2 The new incapacity rules

From 13th April 1995, most people who are not fit enough to work will receive statutory sick pay from their employer for the first 28 weeks of their illness. After that, they will be assessed for incapacity benefit.

People not receiving statutory sick pay can claim incapacity benefit as soon as they are not well enough to work. It will be paid at the **short-term lower rate** for the first 28 weeks. They must supply medical certificates. Their doctor will issue these in the

⟨KEY POINTS⟩

Incapacity benefit

○ Replaces sickness and invalidity benefit

○ Registered blind people are exempted from the 'all work' test; registered partially sighted people are not. (see 5.2.3)

More help

IB 201 Incapacity Benefit. Leaflet **B T**
Call Freephone 0800 868868 *for a copy*

Vision

The descriptors relate purely to vision, and not to comprehension or the ability to read and write.

Descriptor	SCORE
Cannot tell light from dark	15
Cannot see the shape of furniture in the room	15
Cannot see well enough to read a large print book	15
Cannot see well enough to recognise a friend across the room	12
Cannot see well enough to recognise a friend across the road	8
No problem with vision	0

'Recognise a friend' means to recognise the facial features. It is not sufficient to be able to discern the outline or clothing, and so recognise a friend even when the face cannot be seen clearly.

Extract from **The medical assessment for incapacity benefit** *Department of Social Security. October 1994.*

usual way if they are not fit enough to do their usual job. This 'own occupation' test applies, broadly speaking, to people who were in regular work before they became ill or their sight failed. People who were not in regular work must take the 'all work' test unless exempt (see 5.2.3).

However, in order to continue to receive incapacity benefit after 28 weeks most claimants will have to pass the 'all work' test. This is a test to assess whether they are able to do any work at all. If assessed as 'incapable of working', they will receive **short-term higher rate** incapacity benefit for weeks 29-52 and **long-term** incapacity benefit from week 53 onwards. They will no longer have to ask their doctor for medical certificates.

An example of government savings

Bill Clarke aged 51 loses his sight in May 1995
Wife not earning, no children

This chart shows what Bill would have received had he lost his sight when the **old** sickness and invalidity benefit rules were in force, and what he will actually receive in 1995/6 under the **new** system.

Period of payment		OLD: Sickness & invalidity benefit	NEW: Incapacity benefit	Reduction
Weekly payments in first 28 weeks of claim	Claimant	£44.40	£44.40	
	Wife	£27.50	nil	
	Total	**£71.90**	**£44.40**	**–£27.50**
Total payments in first 28 weeks of claim		**£2013.20**	**£1243.20**	**–£770.00**
Weekly payments in weeks 29 to 52	Claimant	£58.85	£52.50	
	AP *	£13.40	nil	
	Wife	£35.25	nil	
	Total	**£107.50**	**£52.50**	**–£55.00**
Total payments in weeks 29 to 52		**£2580.00**	**£1260.00**	**–£1320.00**
Total payments in first 52 weeks		**£4593.20**	**£2503.20**	**–£2090.00**
Long term weekly payments after 52 weeks **	Claimant	£58.85	£58.85	
	AP	£13.40	nil	
	Wife	£35.25	nil	
	Total	**£107.50**	**£58.85**	**–£48.65**

After one year there is a total loss of £2090 and a weekly loss of £48.65 thereafter

* Additional Pension (AP) is based on SERPS and varies for each individual; this is an average figure. The invalidity benefit age allowance for a man becoming incapable of work between age 50 and 60 is £3.90 per week; but this amount is offset by the additional pension. No age allowance for people over age 45 is payable with incapacity benefit.

** If the person is terminally ill, or gets the highest rate of disability living allowance care component, the long-term rate of incapacity benefit is paid after 28 weeks instead of 52.

5.2.3 People who do <u>not</u> have to take the 'all work' test

☑ REGISTERED BLIND PEOPLE

☑ PEOPLE OVER 58 years of age on 13th April 1995 and who have been receiving invalidity benefit from 1st December 1993

☑ PEOPLE RECEIVING the highest rate of the care component of disability living allowance

☑ PEOPLE SUFFERING from a terminal illness

☑ PEOPLE WHO HAVE certain specified severe and chronic illnesses

5.2.4 The 'all work' test

The test consists of a questionnaire which will be sent to most claimants for them to complete at week 29. A medical examination by a Benefits Agency doctor may also be required. How the questionnaire is completed is crucial to the claim.

- to read a large print book, held a normal reading distance

This is large print

- to recognise a friend across the r

It is divided into fourteen sections covering activities such as walking, manual dexterity, hearing and vision. Each section consists of a list of statements. Claimants must tick one statement in each section that applies to them. To continue to receive incapacity benefit, claimants must tick statements which either singly or together reach a score of at least 15. The scores for sight loss are shown in 5.2.2.

The crucial question for many partially sighted people is whether they are able to read a large print book. At the time of writing, it is not known how registered partially sighted people will fare. The legislation specifies the size of the print (16 point) which should be used for the reading test and the questionnaire includes a four word sample (see the example). Of course, the ability to read four words is not the same as 'seeing well enough to read a large print book'. Very often, people can read a few words and then 'everything goes misty'.

If in doubt, it is best to tick the box and add more details about remaining vision in the space provided. To help people come to a decision, the whole of this paragraph has been printed in 16 point print.

After completing the questionnaire, most people will be examined by a Benefits Agency doctor who has been advised that 'assessments should not be "snapshots" of

The new procedures at a glance

New claimants, and eventually everybody at present receiving invalidity benefit, will have to take the 'all work' test unless they are in an exempt group (see 5.2.3 and leaflet IB201 for fuller details).

1 Claimant receives and completes the incapacity benefit questionnaire

2 GP completes a medical statement

3 Both documents go to an Adjudication Officer who either decides to award benefit or passes the forms to the Examining Medical Officer (EMO) employed by the Benefits Agency Medical Service

4 Medical arranged. The doctor advises the Adjudication Officer to accept or reject the claim

5 If rejected, claimants should consult their family doctor for medical support **and**

6 Get professional advice (CAB, welfare rights worker, Action for Blind People, RNIB Benefits Rights team). There is a right of appeal to a social security appeal tribunal which must have a medical assessor, selected from a panel maintained by the Independent Tribunal Service, to advise them.

the situation on a particular day but represent whether the function can be carried out regularly and repeatedly.'[1]

In addition, the guidance states that 'Vision should be considered with spectacles or contact lenses if worn and the assessment should include the ability to scan and focus reasonably and the ability to sustain a reasonable speed of reading. Severe tunnel vision may make reading and normal activities difficult, onerous and time consuming. If such limitations exist then the person should not be considered to be able to read 14 point print at 20 cm distance.'[2]. That is, the person scores 15.

This means that 14 point print, somewhat smaller than the print appearing on the questionnaire, will be used for the reading test by the Benefits Agency doctor. To help readers the whole of this paragraph has been printed in 14 point print.

People who have scores lower than 15 in the Seeing section may still qualify for benefit if they have other health problems. They will need to tick the statements that apply to them in other sections, and these may bring their score up to 15.

Anyone helping a visually impaired person to complete the questionnaire must be prepared to spend time and thought upon it, working carefully through all the sections of the form. Much is at stake. If considered 'capable of work' the claimant may well be eligible

---

1 **The Medical Advisers' Guide to Incapacity Benefit** HMSO. April 1995

2 ibid

Joyce Graham is a typist who can still read large print library books but when out, often ignores people she knows because her poor sight stops her from recognising them. She ticks the appropriate box in the **Seeing** section, which gives her a score of 8. But she also has arthritis and cannot turn the controls of her gas cooker so she ticks that box under **Manual dexterity**, This gives her 6 more points. Her arthritis and poor sight together make going upstairs slow and difficult, and she ticks the appropriate box in the **Walking up and down stairs** section and scores 3 more points. She has now scored 17 points, more than the 15 needed so there is good hope that the Benefits Agency doctor will agree that she has passed the test. But to be on the safe side, she uses the boxes on the form to explain exactly what problems her poor sight and arthritis cause her and explains that she needs a support stick, and has gadgets to help her cope with her poor grip. She adds that although she can read a large print book, she finds them too heavy to hold. She points out that at work although she used a word-processor, she had to type from hand-written copy which now was impossible to read. In addition, using the computer keyboard caused the arthritis in her hands and wrists to 'flare up' and she had to wear splints.

Finally, she asks Sheila, her best friend, to check through the questionnaire for her. Sheila reads it and exclaims 'Joan, if I dropped this form on the floor, could you pick it up?' 'Well, I can with my pick-up stick' says Joan. 'That's not the point', says Sheila. We'll tick the box. Better be safe than sorry. And I'll come with you when you have your medical, in case there's anything else you forget to tell the doctor. And I'll make a photocopy of what you've put on the forms, so that we know exactly where we are.' 'You're a brick' says Joan. 'Rubbish' says Sheila, 'What are friends for?'

for unemployment benefit but this is paid for only one year. In 1996 this will be reduced to six months when the Job-seekers allowance is introduced. After that a claimant could be entirely dependent on means-tested income support if still unable to find work.

Key to media of publication   🅟 clear print   🅛 large print   🅑 braille   🆃 tape   🅜 Moon   🅓 disk

Where a full address is not given in the text, see 32 (Useful addresses)

5.3 Severe disablement allowance

An allowance for people who have not paid enough contributions to qualify for incapacity benefit.

More help

NI 252 Severe Disablement Allowance. Leaflet
Freephone 0800 882200

B

Age range	Taxable?	NI contributions?	Means Test?	Rate per week
16-65 years	No	No	No *	£35.55

Additions at age of onset: Under 40 £12.40; 40-49 £7.80; 50-59 £3.90

* *As with incapacity benefit, up to £44 per week can be earned without losing any benefit if the claimant's doctor thinks it would assist health and help recovery. The DSS have to approve these 'therapeutic earnings' in advance.*

Voluntary work for less than 16 hours a week for a charity of voluntary body or a person outside the immediate family does not affect benefit. Only expenses may be received.

5.3.1 The new rules

NEW The new 'all work' test for incapacity benefit applies to severe disablement allowance. Partially sighted people are not exempted unless they receive the highest rate of the care component of disability living allowance, are terminally ill or suffer from certain specified severe and chronic illnesses.

5.3.2 How to claim

Claims are made on form SDA1.

KEY POINTS

Severe disablement allowance

○ Registered blind people are exempted from the 'all work' test (see 5.2.3).

○ Registered partially sighted people who were receiving SDA on April 13th 1995 will not have to take the test.

○ SDA can often be claimed by young blind and partially sighted people still in education. See chapters 8 and 9.

Snapshot

Susan developed macular disease when she was in her 20's. She married, gave up work and brought up her family. Although she found it increasingly difficult to read print and couldn't drive the car, only people close to her realised she had a sight problem. Then one day, she met a friend who had been registered blind, and was full of praise for the help she had received. 'That's strange', thought Susan, 'because I think my sight is, if anything, worse than hers! Next time I go for a check up, I'll ask the eye specialist'. The specialist was amazed. 'I thought you'd been registered years ago – there's no problem. I'll fill in the forms straight away'. A few weeks later, a social worker called and asked her if she had ever applied for severe disablement allowance. 'Never heard of it' said Susan 'and anyway my husband's got a good job so I'm sure I wouldn't get any help.' 'That doesn't matter' said the social worker 'let's fill in the forms'. The result was an allowance of £43.35 a week. 'Bet they'll take it all away again in tax' said her husband. 'No, they won't – it's tax free' retorted Susan. 'Let's go and celebrate!'

5.4 Disability living allowance

More help

DS 704 Disability Living Allowance. Leaflet **B**
Freephone
0800 882200

Disability living allowance is paid to people who need help with getting around (the mobility component) or help with personal care (the care component) or help with both of these. Only one rate of benefit – whichever is the highest – is paid for each of the components. The rate awarded is decided by an adjudication officer at the Benefits Agency.

Visually impaired people are likely to qualify for the lower care and the lower mobility components. **Recent developments (see 5.4.2) mean that many visually impaired people should receive the care component at the middle rate.** The following notes should help claimants give the information the adjudication officer needs in order to make an appropriate award.

Age range	Taxable?	NI contributions?	Means test?	Registration a passport?	Rate	Amount
Care component						
0-65 years	No	No	No	No	Lower	£12.40
					Middle	£31.20
					Highest	£46.70
Mobility component						
5-65 years	No	No	No	No	Lower	£12.40
					Higher	£32.65

5.4.1 The lower rate care component: £12.40 (day-time)

Qualifying conditions:

☑ REQUIRES ATTENTION from another person in connection with bodily functions for a significant portion of the day, during a single period or a number of periods, **or**

☑ AGED 16 or over and would need help to prepare a cooked meal

Most visually impaired people are likely to meet at least one of these conditions. The need for daily help must add up to at least one hour. The 'help to prepare a cooked meal' test merely means that people should ask themselves if, unaided, they could manage all the basic cooking tasks. **Using convenience foods because of the difficulties experienced in preparing fresh vegetables, for example, does not prevent people from qualifying.**

5.4.2 The middle rate care component: £31.20 (day-time)
Qualifying conditions

☑ REQUIRING FREQUENT attention throughout the day in connection with bodily functions, **or**

☑ REQUIRING CONTINUAL supervision throughout the day in order to avoid substantial danger to themselves or others

'Requires' means reasonably required, not medically required.

'Frequently' means needed several times *throughout* the day and on most days of the week.

Until recently, most visually impaired people usually received the lower rate care component. The middle day-time rate was generally only awarded to people with additional disabilities: blind people with no useful hearing (see also 24.2) or with insulin-dependent diabetes qualified. People who suddenly lost their sight tended to be awarded it for two years to allow time for training and readjustment.

Whether most visually impaired people should be regarded as meeting the first of the daytime conditions for the middle rate of DLA has been the subject of much controversy. The argument has raged round the apparently simple question '**Do visually impaired people frequently need help ('attention') because of their sight loss?**'

NEW In April 1994 a House of Lords judgment (the **Mallinson ruling**) endorsed the commonsense view that if a visually impaired person needed to use another person's eyes to enable them to carry out their day-to-day activities, then that should be regarded as needing 'attention'. Guiding out of doors was given as an example.

It was also made clear that the visually impaired person need not be in physical contact with the helper. Contact could be made through speech. Reading correspondence was given as an example.

This ruling seemed to mark a breakthrough for visually impaired people. Its importance lay in the fact that by being able to take 'help with seeing' into

B

account it made it much easier for people to meet the 'frequency' rule – to show that they needed help several times throughout the day.

> *The only attention which can be given to a person 'in connection with' a sight handicap is to provide the assistance to enable that person to do what he could physically do for himself if he had sight.*
>
> *The attention is in connection with the bodily function if it provides a substitute method of providing what the bodily function would provide if it were not totally or partially impaired.* **House of Lords Judgment. April 21 1994. Mallinson v. Secretary of State for Social Security**

A few weeks later, the Central Adjudication Service issued guidance to the adjudication officers who deal with claims, explaining how the Mallinson ruling should be interpreted. Officers should ask themselves:

> *Does the activity fulfil a necessary purpose? Attention for recreational, leisure, cultural or social purposes is unlikely to be reasonably required. Visits to the doctor or dentist, or outdoor exercise on the instructions of a doctor may be reasonably required. Reading correspondence would be reasonably required. Reading novels would not.*
>
> *Has the activity a necessary close connection with the bodily function? Many domestic activities would not have the requisite close connection because they could be carried out without the disabled person being present. There is also case law excluding ordinary domestic duties (reference HEO(AO) 5/94).*

A new dimension was thus added to the Ruling. The new interpretation was much more restrictive. Visually impaired people were likely only to have very limited guiding needs taken into account, and all domestic help such as checking whether food is fresh, coping with spillages or reading cooking instructions was discounted.

As a result many visually impaired people had their claims refused. However, on 14th October, 1994 a Social Security Commissioner, looking at the needs of a profoundly deaf girl, decided that 'attention required to enable the claimant to carry out a reasonable level of social activity should be included as attention that is reasonably required' *(reference CA/780/91).*

Revised guidelines were sent out. Adjudication officers were told that this new decision did not only affect deaf people, but

> *also affects people with disabilities other than loss of hearing who require attention in connection with a bodily function in order to undertake a reasonable level of social activity. The decision should generally be taken to apply to recreation, leisure and cultural activities in the same way as social activities (reference HEO(AO) 13/94).*

The Secretary of State is appealing against this decision. As a result, a number of blind people who had been awarded the middle rate care component have had their payments suspended until the Court of Appeal makes its decision. This was due to be announced just before this book went to press but their decision has been postponed (see yellow pages and **In Touch Gateway**). It is possible to ask for the suspension of payments to be lifted and some blind people have been successful. Details in a free leaflet **Suspension of payments in Mallinson/Halliday cases** 🅛🅑🅣 from *Action for Blind People*.

5.4.3 The middle rate care component: £31.20 (night-time)
Qualifying conditions:

☑ REQUIRES PROLONGED or repeated attention at night in connection with bodily functions, **or**

☑ REQUIRES SOMEONE to be awake during the night for a prolonged period of time or at frequent intervals, in order to avoid substantial danger to themselves or others

Visually impaired people who are in poor health may qualify for the night-time rate. It is important to show that the help needed at night must be prolonged (around 20 minutes) or 'repeated' (at least twice a night). It is not necessary for the help to be needed every night, but it must be a fairly regular feature.

5.4.4 The highest rate care component: £46.70 (day and night)
This is paid when one of the middle rate day-time conditions and one of the night-time conditions is met.

5.4.5 The mobility component: lower rate £12.40
Qualifying conditions:

☑ CAN WALK but needs someone to provide guidance or supervision for most of the time when outdoors in unfamiliar areas.

Even the most competent long cane user or guide dog owner is likely to meet this requirement as help from a companion or from passers-by is always needed when travelling an unknown route.

5.4.6 The mobility component: higher rate £32.65
Qualifying conditions include people who:

☑ CANNOT WALK AT ALL

☑ ARE BOTH DEAF AND BLIND and need someone with them outdoors

People who can hardly walk at all, perhaps because they quickly become breathless or suffer severe discomfort can also qualify. Details of the mobility component and deafblind people will be found in chapter 24.

5.4.7 How to claim disability living allowance

A telephone call to the **Benefits Enquiry Line** (freephone ✆ 0800 882200) will result in the claim pack (DLA1) being posted direct to the caller, date stamped with the day of the telephone call; this is the date from which payment will start if the claim is successful. When the claim pack is received, people have six weeks to complete and return the forms.

5.4.8 Filling in the forms

This is a major undertaking. People have the choice of completing a self-assessment form or asking a Benefits Agency doctor to come and assess them. Self-assessment gives the maximum opportunity to describe how disability affects everyday life. But it is not an easy option for anyone unable to read the 28 page assessment form, the 12 page claim form and, since the Mallinson Ruling, the 10 page additional section, which will not be incorporated into the main form until October 1995.

There are several ways of making the task easier:

- A relative or friend can help
- The claim form completion service (Freephone ✆ 0800 441144) will fill in the form over the telephone. The claimant is then sent the completed form (in large print or braille if requested) for checking and signing
- The **Benefits Enquiry Line** (Freephone ✆ 0800 882200) can arrange for claim packs to be provided on audio cassette.

Probably the greatest danger for visually impaired people is that a quick glance through the papers may persuade their helper that the claim is not worth pursuing. Many pages of the self-assessment have no relevance for the relatively healthy blind person. The important sections are **Part 3** of the '**About Help with Getting Around**' and **Page 15** of the '**About Help with Personal Care**'.

The new 'Additional Section' is also very important for it relates to the **Mallinson ruling**. This section has two blank sheets where people can add their own comments as to the help they need from 'another pair of eyes'. **Although claimants are asked not to give details of the help they need to carry out domestic duties, these should be included.** Below are some of the points to consider. They are taken from a checklist issued by **Action for Blind People** which lists nearly 80 everyday activities with which people with poor sight might reasonably expect to need help. The full list **Seeing as a bodily function** ❶❸❶ is available free.

Do you need help with

- Sorting and identifying clothes?
- Ensuring that clothes are clean?
- Applying toothpaste to a brush?
- Ensuring that you have shaved properly?
- Identifying spillages and breakages?
- Reading use-by dates and checking food is fresh?
- Distinguishing between different tins and packages?
- Cleaning up work surfaces?
- De-boning chicken, fish, chops etc?
- Reading price tags and labels when shopping?

When outdoors do you need someone to help you

- In poor light?
- In bright sunlight or glare?
- Judge when it is safe to cross the road?

At the end of the self-assessment form are two optional sections. If the claimant wishes, the first should be completed by someone who knows the effect of their disability. Comments here such as 'Mrs. Brown manages wonderfully, despite everything' will not be helpful. The 'despite everything' needs to be spelled out and the Action for Blind People list might provide some helpful guidance. The second statement is a medical confirmation of disability by the claimant's doctor. If completed, these sections should allow the claim to be dealt with quickly, as it will probably remove the need for a separate medical opinion.

Good advice at this self-assessment stage can ensure the claim goes through smoothly and relatively quickly. A welfare rights worker, a rehabilitation worker or social worker or the local Citizen's Advice Bureau are good people to ask for this type of help. The specialist telephone helplines listed in 5.16.2 provide further checklists and sample letters in large print, braille and on cassette.

If the claim is unsuccessful, a review should be requested. For details see 5.5.6.

The DLA switchback

Margaret Abbott applied for the care component when DLA was first introduced in April 1992. She was awarded the lowest rate. In 1994, she heard about the **Mallinson Ruling** on **In Touch** and realised that she should be eligible for the midde rate. She asked for her award to be reviewed. A new claim form was sent for her to fill in.

Margaret commented on **In Touch**: 'How absolutely humiliating it is to have to fill in all those forms. To have to go back and relate what you can do now with what you could do with full sight is just heart-rending. And you have to get someone to read the wretched thing and then get someone to fill it in for you. You have to try and understand what the questions are actually trying to get at and you feel as if everything is geared against you having what you understood was your legal entitlement.'

Her claim was turned down. She asked for a second review. This time she kept an audio diary of the help she needed on one typical day.

'First thing, I made Tony sandwiches to take to work and remembered that I hadn't asked my daughter to check whether there was mould on the bread, and I know the cheese has been opened a couple of days, so I'm hoping that's alright ... now I'm in the bathroom and I want to wash my hair, but I really can't remember which is the shampoo and which is conditioner .... now I'm getting dressed, and I have two Tshirts which are identical ... which is the turquoise one? ... it's time to put the washing out ... but first of all I've got to find the line, it's not easy .... my daughter's just come in with the shopping and informed me I was quite right. The vacuum cleaner was not picking up the dog hairs ... I'm not enjoying making this tape one tiny little bit because I have reckoned over the years, having brought up three daughters, we had done pretty well, but having to put it down and analyse it and just realising how often I need sighted help, is not a nice thing to face up to.'

Margaret turned her diary of the whole day's events into a long letter and sent it to the DSS. They sent an itemised rebuttal of all the points she made, saying that the situations she listed did not qualify her for the middle rate. Her claim was again refused. She decided to appeal. She took her tape recorder to the tribunal and reported for **In Touch**:

'After the chairlady had introduced each member she said that the long letter I had written to the DSS on my second review had put things clearly for her and made her really think. I said I was very disappointed as I felt I had been as eloquent as I could be, and it was all wasted. She said 'On the contrary, we have already decided that you're eligible for the middle rate care component. Even the lady from the DSS said on reading through the letter she could not understand why I was not allowed the middle rate. I just couldn't believe it .... And then they said they would backdate it to April 1992! All I can say to anybody else out there who is wondering and feeling disheartened, and feeling rejected, push on through to the tribunal stage.' See 5.5.6.

5.5 Attendance allowance

Age range	Taxable?	NI contributions?	Means Test?	Registration a passport?	Rate	Amount
65 years upwards	No	No	No	No	Lower	£31.20
					Higher	£46.70

B

More help

DS702 Attendance Allowance. Leaflet **B**
Freephone 0800 882200

5.5.1 Lower rate – care needed by day or night: £31.20

Qualifying conditions:

☑ REQUIRES FREQUENT attention throughout the day in connection with bodily functions, **or**

☑ REQUIRES CONTINUAL supervision throughout the day in order to avoid substantial danger to themselves or others, **or**

☑ REQUIRES PROLONGED or repeated attention at night in connection with bodily functions, **or**

☑ REQUIRES SOMEONE to be awake during the night for a prolonged period of time or at frequent intervals, in order to avoid substantial danger to themselves or others

KEY POINTS

Attendance allowance

❍ Attendance allowance can be paid to people who live alone

❍ It is the help that is needed, not the help that is received, that is important.

❍ All older visually impaired people should claim, especially if they have another disability

These conditions are the same as those for the middle rate daytime and night-time care components of disability living allowance. Everything in 5.4.2 therefore applies to this section.

As attendance allowance is claimed by older people, **the Mallinson ruling and the subsequent guidance is even more relevant**. Many elderly visually impaired people may need some help with bathing, cutting up food and perhaps some help in the toilet. The Mallinson ruling enables them to add help with reading correspondence, sorting junk mail and guiding out of doors to this list. When all these things are taken into account, it should not be difficult to show that help is needed 'frequently' and also needed throughout the day, not just night and morning.

The need to help an elderly blind person to the commode more than once during the night, and perhaps help them back to bed could enable them to qualify for the night-time rate.

The Disability Handbook (HMSO 1992), which gives adjudication officers guidance on the likely effects of a range of disabilities, notes that the majority of blind people lose their sight when they are older. 'In some, progressive adjustment actually means progressive restriction of activities which they may be no longer confident or capable of undertaking on their own. Sudden changes in circumstances may mean that any degree of independence already achieved could be reduced. A change of home with unfamiliar surroundings and a new environment may be one of the changed circumstances which poses problems of this kind.'

The Benefit Agency Helplines answer questions like these:

⚫ What's happening to my claim?

⚫ Did you ever receive it?

⚫ When shall I get a decision?

⚫ Where have I got to in the review procedure?

⚫ What do I do next?

⚫ Remind me what components I'm getting

⚫ Send me a copy of my claim form

☏ **0345 123456** for disability living allowance
☏ **01253 856123** for attendance allowance.

The Handbook also looks at people who **have had a gradual loss of sight**. Adaptation is 'individual to each person and many factors can influence the degree of independence ultimately achieved ... such factors may be age, their particular eye condition, any advice they may have had, their motivation, and the existence of any other disabilities'. The Handbook points out that for people who are over 65 who have not achieved independence after two years, and are unlikely to achieve it, the daytime needs are likely to persist for life.

Elderly, frail visually impaired people may also qualify under the '**continual supervision' requirements**. Anyone who has very recently lost a substantial amount of sight is likely to need supervision, especially if they become disorientated at times. Memory loss, 'black-outs', dizziness, unsteadiness are all factors which contribute substantially to the need for 'supervision'.

5.5.2 Care needed by day and by night: higher rate £46.70

This rate is paid when people need the help already described by day and by night.

5.5.3 How to claim attendance allowance

A telephone call to Freephone ☏ 0800 882200 will result in claim pack DS2 being posted direct to the caller. The details given in 5.4.7 also apply to attendance allowance claims.

5.5.4 Filling in the forms
Full details will be found in 5.4.8.

5.5.6 Unhappy with an attendance allowance or DLA decision?
The more fully the claim packs are completed, the less the likelihood of a disappointing result. But **unsuccessful claims are often successful on review. All visually impaired people should consider taking this step**. The only caution to be sounded is when a DLA component is already in payment. A request for a review of one component may mean that the adjudication officer will review the whole of the award. They will only do this when there has been a significant change in the way a person's disability has affected their life since the award was made.

5.5.7 Review procedures
People should ask for a review within three months of receiving the adjudication officer's decision. This is done by sending a letter which should, if possible, include 'further evidence' about the help that is needed. A copy of the completed original claim form can be supplied by the Benefits Agency so that it is easier to identify and plug any gaps in the evidence already provided.

Another adjudication officer will look at the claim forms and will consider new information. Getting advice before sending the letter can help a great deal. RNIB's Benefits Rights Team point out:

Snapshot

Mrs. Botting is a widow who lives alone. She is 78 and for years has been managing on her retirement pension – 'And the Council's very good – they help me with the Council tax – and I've got my little nest egg of £5,000, so I don't have to worry over my funeral.' Recently her sight began to fail and she was registered blind. Mary from the blind society came to see her and persuaded her that a little more cash might make things easier – weren't her heating bills likely to go up now she couldn't move around so fast? Together they filled in an income support application. The result was £2 a week – and the Council tax paid in full. 'Amazing' said Mrs. Botting. 'That's only the start' said Mary. 'Look at the bruises on your legs from bumping into things – and didn't you have a dizzy turn last week when you had that fall – and look what a problem it is to get someone to read your letters. Let's get cracking on these attendance allowance forms.' The result was £31.20 per week.
'I'm speechless' said Mrs. Botting. 'Then I don't know what you'll do when you get the letter I'm expecting the DSS to send you' said Mary.
Next week Mary had a phone call from Mrs. Botting. 'I've got another £35 a week – the letter calls it a severe disability premium. Are you sure it's legal?' 'Absolutely sure', said Mary. 'Well, in that case, I'm going to use some of my funeral money to decorate the kitchen' said Mrs. Botting. 'Good on you' said Mary, thinking it better not to say just then that using her savings would increase Mrs. Botting's income support a little bit more!

'What you are doing in the review is trying to ensure that the adjudication officer gets as accurate a picture as possible of some of the difficulties that you face ... we recommend you complete a diary for a week or two which will give a clearer picture of your needs. This will be the "further evidence" you are providing with your request for a review.' **Disability Living Allowance – Review Procedure ⓛⒷⓉ**.

If the review decision is unsatisfactory, then there is a right of appeal, within three months, to an independent **Disability Appeals Tribunal**. This consists of a legally qualified chairperson, a doctor, and a third member who will either have a disability or will have had practical experience of people with disabilities. It is very helpful at this stage to be represented by someone knowledgeable in welfare rights advice, or at least be accompanied by a friend.

Full details of the review and appeal procedure will be found in **A Guide to Reviews and Appeals** (NI 260) and **How to Appeal** (NI 246 Ⓑ). Freephone ✆ 0800 666555 for copies. A detailed briefing paper on helping

DLA AND ATTENDANCE ALLOWANCE OPENS DOORS

Receiving DLA or attendance allowance can enable people to qualify for the first time, or receive more money, through:

 INCOME SUPPORT

 HOUSING BENEFIT

 COUNCIL TAX BENEFIT

Receiving either DLA lower rate mobility component or lower rate care component is a gateway to apply for:

 DISABILITY WORKING ALLOWANCE (see 5.7)

 THE HOME ENERGY EFFICIENCY SCHEME (see 26.6.3).

visually impaired people take 'Mallinson' cases to tribunal is supplied free in braille, large print and on cassette by Action for Blind People, and on the **In Touch Gateway**.

The Independent Tribunal Service will meet the expenses of a personal reader service for blind people. Contact them at *City Gate House, 39-45 Finsbury Square, London EC2A 1UU.* If still dissatisfied with the decision the only course left open is to apply for leave to appeal to the Social Security Commissioners, but this can only be done on a point of law. This is the route Eric Mallinson took in 1989 – a route which has led to increased benefits for a substantial number of blind people.

5.6 Invalid care allowance

Age range	Taxable?	NI contributions?	Earnings limit?	Rate	Additions	Amount
16-65 years	Yes	No	Yes; £50 per week after allowable expenses	£35.25	Adult dependent	£21.10
					1st child	£9.85
					Each other child	£11.05

More help

DS 700 Invalid Care Allowance. Leaflet **B**
FB31 Caring for someone. Leaflet **B**
Freephone 0800 882200

5.6.1 Is it worth claiming?

ICA is a complicated allowance and there are intricacies which are not discussed here.

Important points to know are:

○ People receiving income support and living alone forfeit their right to the severe disability premium (see 5.8.3) if their carer receives invalid care allowance

○ Carers cannot be paid ICA while they receive the same amount or more from unemployment, maternity, incapacity or widows' benefits or retirement pension

○ Carers receiving income support find that this is reduced by the amount of ICA they receive and that this loss is only partially compensated by the addition of the carer's premium (£12.60). See 5.8.3

○ Carers who have a partner who receives an allowance which includes an addition for an adult dependent find that the partner's income is affected. A blind husband, receiving long-term incapacity benefit who has a sighted wife at home looking after the children is an example. The adult dependent's addition to his benefit (£35.25) will be reduced by the amount of ICA his wife receives

If in doubt, consult the local Citizens Advice Bureau or telephone the ICA Unit on ✆ 01253 856123.

Nevertheless, ICA can still be worth claiming:

○ For each week on ICA, carers receive a National Insurance contribution credit. This could help if retirement or incapacity benefit is claimed in the future

Invalid care allowance **KEY POINTS**

○ Carers must spend at least 35 hours a week caring for someone who receives the middle or highest rate DLA care component (see 5.4.3) or attendance allowance (see 5.5)

○ A carer need not live with, or be related to, the person they are looking after.

113

Mary Smith is 54. 1994 has been a bad year. Her husband died. Her mother, Mrs. Porter, is 82 and registered blind and until this year has lived by herself. But she has had a bad fall and has been in hospital. She is back home now, but is frail, needing help to get dressed in the mornings as well as help in the bathroom. She uses a walking frame but is at risk from falling. Mary decides that the best solution is to give up her council flat and go and live with her mother. She applies for attendance allowance for her mother, and gets it at the lower rate. She applies for invalid care allowance for herself, but she gets a letter saying she satisfies the conditions for ICA but cannot be paid it because she is receiving widow's benefit. Mary's savings stop her from getting income support but she does get council tax benefit. So she takes the letter to the council. They tell her that as she is eligible for the carer premium they can increase the help they give her to meet her council tax bill.

◗ Carers who satisfy the conditions for ICA and are eligible for income support, housing benefit or council tax benefit can benefit as the carer premium (£12.60) can be included in their assessment. (See 5.8.3 and snapshot)

◗ ICA entitles carers to the taxfree £10 Christmas bonus paid with some social security benefits.

5.6.2 How to claim

Claims should be made on the form found in claim pack DS 700 **B** from Freephone ✆ 0800 882200.

5.7 Disability working allowance

Age range	Taxable?	NI contributions?	Means Test?
16 or over (no upper age limit)	No	No	Yes (plus capital limit £16,000

Maximum rates: Single person £46.85; Couple or lone parents £73.40

Child Allowance: Under 11 £11.40; 11-15 £18.90; 16-17 £23.45; 18 £32.80; Disabled child allowance **NEW** £19.80

Fringe benefits: Free prescriptions **NEW**, free dental treatment and other NHS costs (**NEW** capital must be £8,000 or less)

B

More help

Current information on DWA **B L T**, *and a newsheet* **New Start T**
Freephone 0800 444000

KEY POINTS

Disability working allowance

○ Disability Working allowance 'tops up' the income of people on low wages, including self-employed people.

○ Changes introduced in October 1994 and April 1995 make it likely that more people will become eligible. See 5.7.3.

5.7.1 Who can claim?

People aged 16 years of age and over who work 16 hours or more a week on average (either self-employed or employed) and have:

☑ AN ILLNESS OR DISABILITY (such as being **registered blind or registered partially sighted**) which puts them at a disadvantage in getting a job, **and receive either**:

☑ INCAPACITY BENEFIT at either the short-term higher rate or the long-term rate (see 5.2.2), severe disablement allowance, a disability premium or the higher pensioner premium paid with income support, housing benefit or council tax benefit for at least one day during the two months before the claim, or who receive at the time of the claim:

☑ DISABILITY LIVING ALLOWANCE, **or**

☑ ATTENDANCE ALLOWANCE, **or**

☑ AN INDUSTRIAL INJURIES DISABLEMENT BENEFIT which includes a constant attendance allowance, **or**

☑ A WAR DISABLEMENT PENSION which includes a constant attendance or a mobility supplement.

5.7.2 The DWA means test

NEW In order to receive all the money listed in the chart, the earnings of a single person must be not more than £54.75 per week. A couple must not earn more than £73.00 to get full help. These figures are called 'applicable amounts'.

NEW From July 1995 an extra £10 will be included when working out the maximum DWA that can be paid to people working over 30 hours a week.

If people earn more than their 'applicable amount', then their maximum DWA will be reduced by 70p for every £1.00 earned. £1.00 per week will also be deducted for every £250 of savings between £3,000 and £16,000.

5.7.3 Is it worth claiming?

This depends very much on personal circumstances. Until now, DWA has had a very low take-up, though visually impaired people are the second largest group of recipients. In particular, young, perhaps multiply disabled, blind and partially sighted people still living at home may well find it enables them perhaps to get a part-time job and be better off than if they did not work. **However, more people may now be eligible, especially when there are children in the family**.

NEW Earnings of up to £40 per week which go to meet child minding costs are disregarded. The child, or children, must be under 11 and be cared for by a registered child minder.

NEW People receiving DWA do not pay prescription and dental charges if their savings are below £8,000 (see also 5.7.2).

People receiving housing benefit and council tax benefit should get advice before claiming DWA because, as income rises, these benefits will be reduced. Anyone giving up income support, getting a job and transferring to DWA will lose help with mortgage interest payments (see 5.8.4) and may well be worse off.

DSS Benefits Agency offices and Jobcentres have someone whose responsibility it is to help people do 'better off' calculations enabling them to compare their total income in and out of work. Local Citizens Advice Bureaux will also always help.

Snapshot
Kathleen is 19 and single.
She works 25 hours a week and her net income is £65.
She has no savings.
The maximum DWA is £46.85 (see chart). Her 'applicable amount' is £54.75 (see 5.7.2) – but she earns £10.25 more than this. So her maximum DWA is reduced by £7.18 (70% of £10.25).
She gets £39.67 DWA a week on top of her earnings.

5.7.4 How to claim

Telephone the Benefits Enquiry Line freephone ℘ 0800 882200. They can arrange completion of the claim form (DWA1) by telephone. Otherwise, a claim pack can be obtained by ringing the DWA leaflet line Freephone ℘ 0800 444000.

A successful claim lasts for 26 weeks. Towards the end of the award a renewal claim is invited. Blind and partially sighted people are exempted from completing another self-assessment form to establish whether they are still at a disadvantage in getting a job.

For advice on current claims, telephone the DWA Central Enquiry Service ℘ 01772 883300.

B

5.8 Income support

5.8.1 Who can qualify?

 PEOPLE OVER 18[A] who have

 SAVINGS OF UNDER £8,000, and

 DO NOT WORK 16 hours[B] or more a week.

5.8.2 The income support passport

People receiving income support are also entitled to:

 EXEMPTION FROM prescription charges, vouchers for glasses, free NHS dentures and dental treatment

FREE NHS SIGHT TESTS

HELP WITH HOUSING COSTS, which includes full payment of council tax and normally full payment of rent.[C]

HELP WITH MORTGAGE PAYMENTS. People entitled to income support generally get help with their mortgage interest payments or the interest on a loan for certain repairs or improvements (but see 5.8.5).

5.8.3 How income support is worked out – calculating 'needs'

Income support raises low incomes to the level the State considers necessary for everyday living.

The amount thought to be needed depends on age, marital status, family, disability and accommodation. These needs are met by way of a personal allowance and special additions, called premiums.

The income support actually paid is the **difference** between money already coming in and the personal allowance and premiums to which the claimant is entitled. An amount is then included to meet certain housing costs such as mortgage interest payments and ground rent.

The decision charts at the end of this section are a quick way of finding out how this works out in practice

KEY POINTS

Applying for income support

◯ Owning the home one lives in is **not** a disqualification.

◯ Registration as a blind person, or receiving attendance or disability living allowance can enable people to make successful claims for income support, whereas previously they were unsuccessful.

◯ Even an entitlement of 10 pence a week income support is worth claiming. Income support opens the door to other help.

More help
IS 1 Income Support.
Leaflet **B**
Freephone
0800 882200 *or*
0800 666555

Sidenotes

A See chapter 8 for help for 16-17 year olds

B People with disabilities can work more hours than this. But their earnings or their hours of work must not be more than 75% of those of an able-bodied person doing a similar job.

C Registered blind people and people receiving attendance allowance or a care component of disability living allowance have no deduction made from their housing costs if they have non-dependents, such as a working son or daughter, living with them.

Income support is a difficult theory to grasp ... 'Think of Marilyn Monroe and think of her vital statistics. That shouldn't be too difficult. Think particularly of her bra. That's even easier. A lady's bra supports what she's got and if she hasn't got enough it has a bit more built into it to bring her curves up to the level that she likes. Income support does much the same thing. It supports what people already have by adding a bit more to bring income up to the level the government thinks they need.'

▶ Item on **In Touch**. One blind listener commented that he still didn't understand the principle of income support as the thought of Marilyn Monroe had driven everything else out of his head!

B

for most people. Details of the different premiums are given below to help readers understand how the figures in the charts are calculated.

A claimant (or partner) may be entitled to one of the following premiums – normally only the highest is paid

- **The disability premium** of £19.80 (£28.30 for couples): for registered blind people under 60. Partially sighted people under 60 are eligible if they receive attendance allowance, disability living allowance, incapacity benefit or severe disablement allowance.

- The **higher pensioner premium** of £25.15 (£35.95 for couples): for people aged over 80 and **registered blind people over 60**. Partially sighted people over 60 are eligible if they receive one of the 'qualifying disability benefits' described above.

- The **enhanced pensioner premium** of £20.70 (£30.95 for couples): for people aged between 75 and 79

- The **pensioner premium** of £18.60 (£28.05 for couples): for people aged between 60 and 74

- The **lone parent premium** of £5.20.

In addition the following premiums can be paid

- The **disabled child's premium** of £19.80: for a child who is registered blind or receiving disability living allowance

- The **carer's premium** of £12.60: for a carer who is entitled to invalid care allowance

- The **family premium** of £10.25: paid if there are children in the family.

- The **severe disability premium** of £35.05 (£70.10 when both partners qualify, or £35.05 when both partners qualify but one has a carer receiving invalid care allowance). This is the highest premium. To obtain it people must qualify for it in three ways:

They must receive attendance allowance, or the middle or higher care component of disability living allowance, **and**

They must not have a carer who receives invalid care allowance for looking after them, **and**

They must live alone. However, the presence of the following people in the home is ignored:

> anyone under 18
> **anyone registered blind**
> anyone receiving attendance allowance or the middle or higher rate care component of disability living allowance,
> someone who is a co-owner, joint tenant, or landlord (as long as he or she is not a close relative)

5.8.4 How income support is worked out – calculating income and savings

People claiming income support are sent a claim form which asks for details of their income and savings. The Benefits Agency then calculates whether they receive more or less than they are considered to 'need'. Some savings and income are ignored completely. These include:

- The value of the house that the claimant lives in
- The first £3,000 of savings
- The first £15 per week that a blind person (or anyone qualifying for the disability premium) earns
- Up to £20 per week received from boarders plus 50% of any amount received above £20
- Up to £10 per week of any regular charitable or regular voluntary payment. If the payment is intended and used for items other than food, ordinary clothing or footwear, household fuel, accommodation costs or anything else already covered by benefits it is wholly ignored.
- Attendance or disability living allowances.

Capital and income which is **not** ignored includes:

- Savings between £3,000 and £8,000. Above £3,000, every £250 (or part of £250) is assumed to yield an income of £1 per week.
- All national insurance benefits such as retirement pension, severe disability allowance, incapacity benefit
- Any money received from an occupational or a personal pension and any income from an annuity. However, the capital value of the right to receive such income is ignored.

5.8.5 How much will be paid?

First work out how much money is coming in each week, remembering to include any assumed income from capital above £3,000 (see 5.8.4). Consult the **decision charts** to check how much money is 'needed' each week. If less is coming in than is 'needed', then the difference between the two is the amount of income support payable.

5.8.7 Income support and housing costs

Once entitled to income support, other help follows automatically (though there is no help with water charges):

5.8.6 Income support decision charts

Working through all five steps will indicate the amount of money which the government thinks you need to live on each week. If you have less money coming in than this (but check 5.8.3), then the difference will be made up by a weekly income support payment, with extra help for housing costs and council tax (see 5.8.4 for details).

B

STEP ONE
Tick the personal allowance which applies to you

SINGLE PEOPLE

Age	Single parent	Personal allowance	☑
18-24	No	£36.80	
	Yes	£46.50	
25 or over	No	£46.50	

COUPLES

Age of eldest adult	Personal allowance	☑
18 or over	£73.00	

STEP TWO
Complete these boxes if you have children (include 'disabled children')

Number of children aged under 11		Multiply this by	£15.95	= £
Number of children aged 11–15		multiply this by	£23.40	= £
Number of children aged 16–17		multiply this by	£28.00	= £
Number of children aged 18		multiply this by	£36.80	= £
			Add up the boxes	= £

121

STEP THREE Select your age band, family and disability situations, then tick the premium total which applies

SINGLE PEOPLE

Age	One or more children in the family?	Adult who is Disabled?	Premium Total †	☑
Under 60	No	No	–	
	Yes	No	£15.45	
	Yes	Yes	£30.05	
	No	Yes	£19.80	
60 – 74	No	No	£18.60	
	Yes	No	£28.85	
	Yes	Yes	£35.40	
	No	Yes	£25.15	
75 – 79	No	No	£20.70	
	Yes	No	£30.95	
	Yes	Yes	£35.40	
	No	Yes	£25.15	
80 or over	No	*	£25.15	
	Yes	*	£35.40	

* At 80 or over, disability does not affect your amount

† This amount includes, where appropriate, age-related premiums, disability premium, lone parents premium, and family premium

COUPLES

Age of eldest adult	One or more children in the family?	One or more adult disabled?	Premium Total †	☑
Under 60	No	No	–	
	Yes	No	£10.25	
	Yes	Yes	£38.55	
	No	Yes	£28.30	

If one of a couple is under 60 and the other 60+,
they should ask for advice from a welfare rights worker or CAB

Age of eldest adult	One or more children in the family?	One or more adult disabled?	Premium Total †	☑
60 – 74	No	No	£28.05	
	Yes	No	£38.30	
	Yes	Yes	£46.20	
	No	Yes	£35.95	
75 – 79	No	No	£30.95	
	Yes	No	£41.20	
	Yes	Yes	£46.20	
	No	Yes	£35.95	
80 or over	No	*	£35.95	
	Yes	*	£46.20	

* At 80 or over, disability does not affect your amount

† This amount includes, where appropriate, age-related premiums, disability premium, lone parents premium, and family premium

Number of 'Carers'		multiply this by	£12.60	= £
Number of adults who are 'Severely Disabled'		multiply this by	£35.05	= £
Number of 'Disabled Children'		multiply this by	£19.80	= £
			Add up the boxes	= £

Definitions

▷ Carer

A 'Carer' is someone who has successfully claimed invalid care allowance (see 5.6) – whether or not the cash is actually received (see Mary Smith's Snapshot in 5.6.1).

▷ Disabled adult

If you are registered blind you are automatically classed as 'disabled'. If you are registered as partially sighted, or not registered at all, then to qualify as a 'disabled adult' you must either get incapacity benefit or severe disablement allowance or any of the components of disability living allowance or attendance allowance, or be under 60 and able to prove that you have been incapable of work for 28 weeks.

▷ Disabled child

A child who is registered blind or gets any of the components of disability living allowance.

▷ Severely disabled person

Anyone who receives attendance allowance or middle or highest care component of disability living allowance. You must also live **alone unless your carer/partner is a registered blind person**. Double check 5.8.3 for further details.

STEP FIVE
Put the figures from Steps 1: 4 in the boxes below

Step 1: Personal allowance	= £
Total from Step 2: Children	= £
Step 3: Premium total	= £
Total from Step 4	= £
Finally, add them together	= £

This is the money the government says you need to live on each week
See 5.8.7 for help with housing and council tax costs

Look out

○ If you are under 80 and registered blind your income support should be increased from the date of your certification (see 4.7), the day your eye specialist signed the BD8. There is no way the Benefits Agency is going to know this **unless someone tells them**

○ If you are a householder who is registered blind or receiving attendance or disability living allowance you should check that no deduction has been made from your income support or housing benefits because you have non-dependents living with you (see 5.8.1)

○ Check your premiums! Especially the severe disability premium! (see 5.8.3)

○ Check your tariff income! This is another name for the 'assumed income' from savings. The Benefits Agency cannot constantly check your capital so will be unaware that you may have reduced it by buying an essential item for your home. Spending only a small amount may increase your weekly benefit. For example, if savings of £4,050.00 come down to £4,000, income support and housing benefits are reduced by only £4 per week instead of £5, whilst capital of £3,250 brings the reduction down to £1 per week (see 5.8.4)

○ People receiving income support should ask for form A124 which will give all the details of how their benefit has been worked out

 FERRET Income support charts have been devised with the help of Ferret Information Systems Ltd, and Mike Joseph of Pia

People who qualify for income support do not pay council tax and normally their rent is paid for them in full. There is also help with mortgage interest payments, though not with capital repayments.

50% of mortgage interest payments is met for the first 16 weeks of a claim made by someone under 60. After that, the interest is generally met in full. Claimants over 60 get full help from the date of their claim.

NEW From October 1995 the government proposes that people under 60 taking out a mortgage will not be able to receive interest payments until after the first 9 months. For existing mortgage holders under 60, instead of 50% of mortgage interest being met for the first 16 weeks of a claim, there will be no payment at all for the first two months; and for the next four months, payment of 50% of mortgage interest will be paid direct to the lender. Thereafter interest will be paid in full.

5.8.8 How to claim

Complete the coupon on leaflet **IS 1** found at main Post Offices. A full postal claim form for pensioners **(SP 1)** can be obtained from Benefits Agency branch offices whilst **B1**, a similar postal claim form for unemployed people, can be found at Unemployment Benefit offices or Jobcentres.

Snapshot | **Too old to be blind?**

The Government thinks people who live at home and receive income support need more money to live on if they lose their sight, but only if they are under 80 years of age.

Single people under 60: £19.80 per week extra
Single people between 60 and 75: £ 6.55 per week extra
Single people between 75 and 80: £ 4.45 per week extra
Single people over 80: nothing extra

Most blind people are over 80

5.9 Housing benefit and council tax benefit

These social security benefits are paid by local councils to people who need help to pay their rent or their council tax.

5.9.1 Who can qualify?

☑ PEOPLE WITH SAVINGS of no more than £16,000 **and**

☑ PEOPLE WHO HAVE A LOW INCOME (even though they may be in full-time employment)

5.9.2 How housing and council tax benefit is calculated

Both are worked out in much the same way as income support.

The main differences are:

◗ When calculating 'needs' (5.8.3) the lone parent premium is increased to £11.50

◗ When calculating existing income and savings (5.8.4) the following are also ignored:
  £25 of a single parent's earnings
  £10 of a couple's earnings

NEW Child care costs of up to £40 per week can be offset against earnings. The child, or children, must be under 11 and be cared for by a registered child minder or in a day nursery.

More help

RR 1 Housing Benefit – help with your rent. Leaflet **B**

Freephone 0800 666555

B

5.9.3. How much will be paid?

1 Consult the **decision charts** (see 5.8.6) to check how much money is 'needed' each week, but single parents not receiving the disability premium should, however, increase their 'premium total' on the chart from £15.45 to £22.30.

2 Work out how much money is coming in each week, remembering to include any assumed income from capital above £3,000. (See 5.8.4)

Subtract **1** from **2**.

For housing benefit: take 65% of the answer and deduct that from the weekly rent (the amount paid for accommodation – inclusive heating costs and water charges do not count as part of rent). The answer is the money that will be given to help meet the rent (a rent allowance paid to private tenants) or the amount by which the rent will be reduced (a rent rebate paid to council tenants).

For council tax benefit: take 20% of the answer and deduct that from the council tax bill. The answer is the amount of help that will be received to meet the council tax bill.

5.9.4 How to claim

Housing benefit and council tax benefit claim forms can be obtained from local council offices and claim forms NHB 1 (HB) and NHB1 (CTB) can also be found inside income support forms (see 5.8.5).

5.10 Other ways of reducing council tax

5.10.1 Second Adult Rebate

There is an automatic 25% discount when a householder or tenant lives alone. But there is another type of help available through council tax benefit which applies when there is someone else (a second adult) in the household who cannot afford to contribute to the council tax bill.

Snapshot Mrs. Worthington is a widow. Her mother, Mrs. Huggett, came to live with her. When Mrs. Worthington received her council tax bill, she found she had not been given a 25% discount as she was no longer living alone. 'It doesn't bother me' said Mrs. Worthington. 'My Jim left me well provided for'. 'Well, it bothers me', retorted her mother. 'Why should you lose money just because you've been good enough to look after me? It can't be right. Never mind you being well off. You ask the council.' Mrs. Worthington went off to the council for the sake of peace and quiet. She told them her mother's income was only £100 per week, and to her amazement her council tax bill was reduced by 15%. 'There you are' said Mrs. Huggett to her friends at the blind club. 'If you don't ask you don't get – but some people do need pushing.'

5.10.2 Who qualifies?

Householders or tenants who are liable for council tax and who share their home, on a non-commercial basis, with another adult (or adults) on a low income.

5.10.3 Who is a second adult?

In order to be classed as a second adult, the person must NOT be:

 SOMEONE WHO IS LIABLE FOR COUNCIL TAX

 A SPOUSE OR PARTNER

☒ A JOINT OWNER OR TENANT

☒ A COMMERCIAL BOARDER OR A SUB-TENANT

A maximum 25% rebate on the council bill will be awarded if the second adult, or all second adults, are on income support.

If the other person living with the householder does not receive income support but has an income of £111 gross per week or less, the householder will receive a 15% rebate. A 7.5% rebate will be given when the other person's income is between £111 and £144.99 gross per week.

Claims for these discounts can be complex. Some adults, such as students and some carers, are classed as 'invisible'. Their presence does not affect the householder's 25% discount. Local council offices, Citizens Advice Bureaux and the specialist services listed in 5.16 can always advise. The **Council Tax Handbook** (Ward, M. Child Poverty Action Group. 1993. £7.95) is especially helpful on discounts, disability reductions and appeal procedures.

5.10.4 How to apply

Complete a council tax benefit claim form (see 5.9.4). An application for council tax benefit is also an application for second adult rebate. If entitled to both council tax benefit and the second adult rebate, the local authority will award whichever is the greater.

5.10.5 Council tax Reduction for Disabilities Scheme

This scheme takes the property down one valuation band if it has certain features which are essential or very important for people 'who are substantially and permanently disabled' – a phrase which includes registered blind and partially sighted people and anyone eligible for those registers. Obviously, the tax reduction can only apply to dwellings in Band B and above.

Miss Williams, a lady in her 70's, heard a discussion on **In Touch** about the council tax reduction scheme. She contacted her council and said there were four reasons why she needed a room set aside for her personal use: She did not want to disturb other people by listening to talking books when they were watching television; she needed space for her talking computer; she needed space for her exercise bike (essential for her health) and she needed enough floor space to practice yoga. The council agreed to a rate reduction without demur.

B

5.10.6 What features qualify?

☑ A ROOM, but not a bathroom, kitchen or lavatory, which is predominantly used (whether for providing therapy or otherwise) by the disabled person; **or**

☑ AN ADDITIONAL BATHROOM or kitchen within the dwelling, **or**

☑ SUFFICIENT FLOOR SPACE to permit the use of a wheelchair.

Guidance from the Department of the Environment explicitly advises local authorities that a room set aside for equipment used by blind people can qualify. 'Blind people will qualify for a reduction if they meet the above criteria. This could be the case for example, if a blind person requires a room to house equipment such as a brailler, word processor or tape recorder. The room would have to be predominantly used by, and required for meeting the needs of the blind person; and it must also be essential or of major importance to his well-being on account of the nature of his disability'[1].

Some blind people have claimed successfully under this scheme. The essential point is to demonstrate that the room is of 'essential or of major importance to well-being'. Others have had their application rejected by their local authority. If this happens, the first step is to write to them giving reasons why their decision is thought to be wrong. The authority has two months in which to reply. If it refuses to alter its decision an appeal can be made to a valuation tribunal (a valuation appeal committee in Scotland). A local Citizen's Advice Bureau or the specialist agencies listed in 5.16 will be able to advise.

5.10.7 Who obtains the reduction?

The person who is liable to pay the council tax on the dwelling. This may, or may not, be the disabled person.

5.10.8 How to claim

A written application must be made each financial year. Most local council offices have a standard application form for this purpose.

---

1 **Council Tax Practice Note 2 Liability, Discounts and Exemptions**. DoE/WO. 27 July 1993

5.11 The social fund

Help in times of emergency may be made through this Fund to people who receive income support or similar means-tested benefits. Fuller details are in **How the Social Fund Can Help You** (SFL2 **B**). Some help is discretionary. Other help is available 'by right'.

5.11.1 Help 'by right'

This includes **maternity grants**, **funeral grants** when a partner or relative has died and **cold weather payments**.

Payments of £7 are made automatically when the average temperature is at freezing point or below for seven consecutive days. Registered blind people of any age who receive income support, and people whose income support includes a pensioner or disability premium (see 5.8.3) or who have a child under 5 receive this help.

5.11.2 Discretionary help

This section of the Fund is cash-limited. It depends not only on the discretion of the officers administering it, but also on whether there is money in the Fund. Money can be loaned in certain circumstances, but most relevant to the needs of visually impaired people are **community care grants**.

5.11.3 Who qualifies?

☑ PEOPLE RECEIVING INCOME SUPPORT or

☑ PEOPLE IN RESIDENTIAL CARE who will receive income support within six weeks of moving out into the community, **and**

☑ WHO CAN SHOW that if they were to purchase the item needed that would reduce their capital to less than £500 (£1,000 for people over 60).

5.11.4 What costs do community care grants meet?

- The cost of an essential item in the home. A gas fire or a microwave cooker could make all the difference between a blind person managing and not managing to cope
- Minor structural repairs
- The cost of moving into more suitable accommodation, or nearer to helpful friends or relatives
- The costs of moving out of residential care and setting up home.

Grants will not be paid to meet telephone costs, fuel costs, housing costs or medical costs. See 30 for grant making charities.

B

John and Alison are both blind. They met at residential college and fell in love. Their aim to set up home together seemed impossible: no job, no money, no accommodation. But where there's a will there's a way. They found a semi-furnished flat and moved in. Whilst John tried to get a job, Alison tried to manage on income support. 'I never realised how much it cost to set up home – even buying a saucepan wrecked our budget.' Their welfare rights worker helped them complete an application for a community care grant from the Social Fund. Alison made a shopping list: pots and pans, some bedding, a microwave oven, a deep fat fryer, a washing machine/tumble dryer as there was no outside drying space, a vacuum cleaner to cope with the guide dog hairs and some storage units. 'It sounds a lot but these things weren't luxuries as I'm totally blind and John's not much better' said Alison. A grant of £1,500 was made. Their welfare rights officer said 'I must admit I was a bit surprised as well as delighted, but I did make sure they explained on the form why their blindness made it important that they should have these items.'

5.11.5 How to claim

Claims should be made on form **SF300**, available from the Benefits Agency. A leaflet **Community Care Grants for Visually Impaired People** can be obtained free from *Action for Blind People* **B L T** and through the **In Touch Gateway**, and is well worth reading before making an application.

5.12 War pensions
5.12.1 Who qualifies?

Any ex-service man or woman **who considers that their loss of vision is due to or was made worse by Service**, may apply for a 'war pension' to the *War Pensions Agency, Norcross, Blackpool FY5 3TA* ✆ 01253 856123. Anyone already entitled to a war pension for loss of vision may ask the Agency to review the assessment of their disablement at any time, and also if they feel that their vision has worsened since last examined. This is known as a deterioration claim.

If there has been a deterioration in vision, the Department's own doctors will use the Hambresin scale to determine the severity of the additional disability. This is a slightly different way of assessing vision from that used at a BD8 examination (see 4.7). A person certified as partially sighted could be considered as 80% disabled on the Hambresin scale.

If the war injury damaged one eye only and a pension has been paid for it, it is recognised that **a fresh visual impairment, even though it is not caused by service, but perhaps by one of the common causes of visual impairment in the elderly, such as macular disease (see 2.3.3) imposes a greater disability when sight is already poor**. In these circumstances, a deterioration claim should be made. A review will often lead to an increase in assessment and an increased award.

5.12.2 How to claim

The **War Pensions Helpline** ✆ 01253 858858 answers callers' questions and puts them in touch with the sections of the War Pensions Agency that can deal with their special problem. The operators are willing to accept claims and help complete claim forms over the telephone.

War pensions KEY POINTS

◗ Anyone receiving a War Pension for loss of vision should ask for a review of their disablement assessment if their sight worsens.

◗ War pensioners who receive a pension because of an injury to one eye should ask for a review if the sight in the other eye deteriorates.

B

More help
MPL 158 War Pensions and other support. Leaflet
WPA1 Notes about War Pensions and allowances.
From War Pensions Helpline
01253 858858

133

5.13 Help with NHS costs
5.13.1 Free prescriptions

Who qualifies?

☑ ALL PENSIONERS (women aged 60, men 65 and over)

☑ PEOPLE AND THEIR PARTNERS receiving income support or family credit

☑ ALL CHILDREN UNDER 16 and under 19 if in full-time education

☑ EXPECTANT MOTHERS and women who have had a baby in the last year

☑ **(NEW)** PEOPLE OR THEIR PARTNERS receiving disability working allowance if their savings are £8,000 or below

☑ PEOPLE ON A LOW INCOME (see 5.14)

☑ PEOPLE OF WORKING AGE who suffer from a 'specified condition'. These include diabetes (unless treatment is by diet alone) and epilepsy

☑ PEOPLE WHO HAVE A 'CONTINUING PHYSICAL DISABILITY which prevents them leaving home without the help of another person'.

| **More help**
| **Details of help with prescription charges will be found in**
| **AB11** Help with NHS costs
| **G11** NHS sight tests and vouchers for glasses
| **P11** NHS Prescriptions: how to get them free
| *Freephone* 0800 882200

How to claim

Pensioners and people who receive income support or family credit need only tick the box on the back of the prescription form.

People who are claiming because they have a low income should follow the directions in 5.14.

People who suffer from a 'specified condition' or a 'continuing physical disability' will find a claim form in **NHS Prescriptions: How to get them free** (P11). In recent years, some blind people have been exempted from prescription charges because their doctor has agreed that they 'suffer from a continuing physical disability' and need an escort when out of doors. Both **Action for Blind People** and **RNIB** can supply letters giving background information. These are intended to be given to doctors when they are being asked to complete the medical section of the claim form.

5.13.2 Free sight tests

Who qualifies?

☑ CHILDREN UNDER 16, or young people under 19 if in full time education

☑ PEOPLE OR THEIR PARTNERS receiving income support or family credit

☑ **NEW** PEOPLE OR THEIR PARTNERS receiving disability working allowance who have £8,000 or less in savings

☑ REGISTERED BLIND and PARTIALLY SIGHTED PEOPLE

☑ PEOPLE ENTITLED TO VOUCHERS for complex lenses (see 5.13.3)

☑ PEOPLE SUFFERING FROM DIABETES

☑ PEOPLE SUFFERING FROM *DIAGNOSED* GLAUCOMA

☑ PEOPLE OVER 40 YEARS OF AGE who are close relatives of diagnosed glaucoma sufferers. A close relative is defined as a parent, brother, sister or child. The diagnosed sufferer need not still be alive

☑ WAR DISABLEMENT PENSIONERS who require the sight test because of their war disability

☑ PEOPLE ON A LOW INCOME (see 5.14)

☑ HOSPITAL EYE SERVICE PATIENTS. If the sight test for glasses is needed as part of treatment and the hospital does not have its own facilities, the patient will be given Form **HES1** for a free NHS sight test from a high street optometrist.

Patients who are eligible for a free NHS sight test but are unable to attend at an optometrist's practice can have an examination in their own home without having to pay for the optometrist's visit.

How to claim

The optometrist can provide and complete the necessary form unless the patient is claiming on grounds of a low income. If so, it is best to apply for this help as described in 5.14 before the sight test.

5.13.3 Vouchers for spectacles and contact lenses

Who qualifies?

☑ CHILDREN UNDER 16, or young people under 19 if in full time education

☑ PEOPLE OR THEIR PARTNERS receiving income support or family credit

☑ **NEW** PEOPLE OR THEIR PARTNERS receiving disability working allowance who have £8,000 or less in savings

☑ PEOPLE ON A LOW INCOME (see 5.14)

☑ PATIENTS WHO NEED VERY POWERFUL OR COMPLEX LENSES

☑ HOSPITAL EYE SERVICE PATIENTS who need frequent changes of glasses or contact lenses (see 5.13.4)

What help is given?

When introduced in 1986 the voucher scheme aimed 'to provide a basic pair of spectacles to meet a person's clinical needs.' This has not happened. In 1992 a survey by the Department of Health showed that in 50% of optometrists' practices current voucher values did not meet the cost of all spectacle prescriptions. Unless able to 'shop around' it is quite likely that the voucher issued by the optometrist will only help meet the cost of spectacles. Sometimes, in cases of special need, the local society for the blind may be able to meet the remainder of the cost.

Spectacle voucher rates

SINGLE VISION GLASSES		BI-FOCAL GLASSES	
Voucher type	**Maximum value**	**Voucher type**	**Maximum value**
A	£26.40	E	£45.50
B	£40.10	F	£57.90
C	£54.70	G	£69.80
D	£107.30	H	£118.00
Prism (per lens)	£5.10	Prism (per lens)	£6.30
Tint (per lens)	£2.60	Tint (per lens)	£3.10
Small frame supplement £43.50			

The value of the voucher varies according to the type of lens needed; see the **Spectacle voucher rates chart** in this section. In addition, people who need very powerful or complex lenses are entitled to either a £4.30 voucher for single vision glasses or a £23.40 voucher for bi-focal spectacles, plus the extra amounts listed in the table for any prisms or tints that are clinically necessary. The voucher should be supplied automatically by the optometrist.

5.13.4 Special help through the Hospital Eye Service

The maximum charge for spectacles that can be made to patients (irrespective of their means) is £47.30 for single vision lenses and £76.90 for other types. The maximum charge for clinically necessary contact lenses is £38.60 per lens.

Patients who qualify for a voucher may be entitled to type **I**, worth a maximum of £118.00 for multi-focal or vari-focal lenses, or voucher **J**, value £38.60 per contact lens when these are clinically necessary. A voucher for £43.50 can be issued when specially made frames are needed.

The supply of contact lens solution is regarded as an integral part of treatment. It can be issued through the HES and charged in the same way as any other NHS prescription.

Patients who frequently need new spectacles because their eye condition is changing are only required to meet the cost of one pair. If eligible, they will also receive a voucher. This arrangement, called 'technical non-tolerance', can only be authorised by their consultant and its duration is a matter of clinical judgement.

5.14 What is a low income?

If low income is the basis of a claim for help with any NHS costs, these notes are relevant. A low income is almost impossible to define. Whether a person's income is considered to be low depends greatly on what help is required. If sight is so poor that the patient qualifies for one of the high value spectacle vouchers, for example, his income in regard to that voucher may well fall into the 'low' category. But it might not be considered low enough for him to get help with prescription charges. Examples of how the scheme works will be found in **AB11 Help with NHS Costs**. You can apply if you have capital of £8000 or less.

How to claim

Complete form **AG1**, which can be obtained from DSS Benefits Agency offices or an optometrist. Return it to the *Health Benefits Division, Prescription Pricing Authority, Sandyford House, Newcastle-upon-Tyne NE2 1DB* who will either issue certificate **AG2** for full help or certificate **AG3** for partial help.

The certificates last for six months. **It is best to obtain a certificate before buying spectacles or having a sight test as refunds are difficult** and, for glasses, are only possible when the spectacles have been obtained through the Hospital Eye Service.

5.15 Refunds of charges

5.15.1 Sight Tests

Refunds can only be made to people who have a low income. Form AG1 must be completed and returned to the Health Benefits Division within 14 days of the sight test. People eligible for full help, receive certificate AG2. People eligible for partial help receive certificate AG3.

To receive the refund, certificate AG2 must be sent, with the optician's receipt, to the local Family Health Services Authority within three months of having the test. The FHSA will then reimburse either the full cost of the NHS sight test or the private sight test fee, whichever is the lower amount.

People with certificate AG3 will only get help if this certificate shows they are able to contribute less than £13.15 to the cost of the test. The refund must be claimed by sending the AG3 plus the optometrist's receipt to the FHSA within three months of their sight test.

Optometrists can give the address of the FHSA and advise on the procedure.

Refunds cannot be made to any of the other exempt groups (see 5.13.2).

5.15.2 Spectacles

Refunds are only given to patients receiving income support, disability working allowance (but see 5.13.3), or family credit, or who have a low income, and whose spectacles were supplied through the Hospital Eye Service.

5.15.3 How to claim

Complete form AG5 entitled **Claiming money back** plus, if applying for help on grounds of low income, form AG1. Return the form (or forms), with the prescription and receipt, to the Health Benefits Division (see 5.14) within one month from the date the spectacles were supplied.

5.16 Getting information

5.16.1 By freephone

- The **Benefits Enquiry Line** (BEL) is an advice service for people with disabilities provided by the Benefits Agency on Freephone ✆ 0800 882200 (✆ 0800 220674 in Northern Ireland and ✆ 0800 243355 Minicom) between 8.30 a.m. and 6.30 p.m. Monday to Friday and between 9.00 a.m. and 1.00 p.m. on Saturdays. BEL operators can give advice about disability benefits and how to claim them. They can also complete claim forms over the telephone or send a letter, and sometimes a claim form, in braille or large print.

- These **Freeline Social Security** numbers can give general advice and information about benefits and National Insurance contributions:

English	0800 666555
Cantonese	0800 252451
Punjabi	0800 521360
Urdu	0800 289188
Welsh	0800 289011
Northern Ireland	0800 616757

- **Senior Line** gives general benefits advice for senior citizens. Freephone ✆ 0800 289404 (Britain) and Freephone ✆ 0800 616757 (Northern Ireland).

5.16.2 Specialist telephone helplines

- **Action for Blind People** ✆ 0171 732 8771 and **RNIB Benefit Rights Team** ✆ 0171 388 1266. The advisers are always willing to ring callers back.
- The **Rights Advice Line** (Disability Alliance, London) ✆ 0171 247 8763. Three sessions a week for urgent or complex welfare rights matters. An answerphone message gives details of the next session.

5.16.3 Specialist advisory services

RNIB Benefits Rights Team and Action for Blind People provide individual and confidential advice to visually impaired people on their benefit entitlement. They can advise welfare rights workers helping visually impaired people and can assist in preparing cases for appeal.

A welfare rights officer is based at the **Wales Council for the Blind** and can offer information, advice and training on welfare rights for people with a visual disability.

5.16.4 Specialist publications

Publications on welfare rights written especially for visually impaired people include:

- **Social Security Benefits: A Guide for Blind and Partially Sighted People** (FB 19). Free. ⬤⬤⬤. It can be obtained from local Benefits Agency offices or by ringing the Benefits Enquiry Line.
- **Your Benefit: A Guide to Weekly Social Security Benefits for Visually Handicapped People** ⬤⬤⬤⬤⬤. Published annually in April by RNIB and available in Gujerati, Urdu, Hindi, Bengali, Cantonese, Greek, Turkish and Welsh. Price £1.00 (£3.00 organisations). This is supplemented by a series of

factsheets (**L B T**) including **Council Tax – An Introduction**, **Free Prescriptions and Blind and Partially Sighted People**, **Incapacity Benefit** and all aspects of the Mallinson case.

- Action for Blind People produce a series of fact sheets including **A Guide to the ABP Welfare Rights Service**, **Income Support for Pensioners**, **Disability Living Allowance**, **Attendance Allowance**, **Disabiliity Working Allowance** and **Severe Disablement Allowance**, and on all aspects of the Mallinson case.

5.17 Further reading

The Disability Alliance Educational and Research Association publishes the **Disability Rights Handbook** (£8.95 or £5.00 if receiving a means tested benefit) in May every year. It is updated in the summer, autumn and winter by three bulletins, the complete package costing £14.00 p.a. It is essential reading for anyone wishing to help a visually handicapped person with their welfare rights. Available in print, on disk and, on request, extracts can be supplied in braille. Also available in print from *In Touch Publishing.*

NEW **From Claim to Appeal** (Disability Alliance. £4.00). A guide to Disability Appeal Tribunals for disabled people and their advisors.

See 22.8 for financial help towards the cost of holidays.

See 6.14 and chapter 9 for financial help for children and young people.

See chapter 24 for help for deafblind people.

6 Parents and children

143

7 Extra help for extra problems

158

8 Education

6 Parents and children

5,696 children and young people aged seventeen years and under were registered as blind or partially sighted in England in March 1994[1]. In Northern Ireland, 168 young people aged fifteen and under were registered in March 1993, and in Scotland in March 1994, the figures were 175. The figures for Wales are not known. It is generally agreed that these registers are far from complete. **Blind and Partially Sighted Children in Britain: the RNIB Survey** (1992) estimated that not only were there at least 10,000 children in Great Britain with visual impairments severe enough to pose problems at school, but more than half of those children aged between three years and nineteen years of age had one or more additional disabilities such as impaired hearing or speech, physical handicaps or learning difficulties. A welcome development in recent years has been the increased attention paid to the needs of visually impaired children with multiple disabilities. Details will be found in chapter 7. However, because the number of visually impaired children in proportion to the entire child population is small, it is almost inevitable that the first professionals parents turn to when they are seriously worried about their child's sight will have had little, if any, experience of severe visual loss. This chapter aims to point parents and professionals in the right direction to find the help they need, and to reassure parents that they do not have to be 'experts' to care tenderly, imaginatively and positively for their child.

Touch me, kiss me, fondle me ... I will begin to know you love me. When you leave me by myself and talk to me without touching me, it doesn't mean the same thing. I need to hear you, feel you, and smell you in order to begin to know you're really there – and that you love me. Keep in touch.[2]

6.1 Help for children in hospital

A family support worker is based in the Children's Unit at **Moorfields Eye Hospital**, London. She is there to help children who have just been diagnosed as having a serious eye problem that is likely to lead to educational problems or developmental delay. Parents have an opportunity to discuss their anxieties on the spot, when they have just seen the consultant. She acts as a link between the consultant, parents, children, education advisors, schools and local social services. A similar service is offered by **Henshaw's** at Manchester Eye Hospital. For further details, contact *Jackie Howe, Children's Unit, Moorfields Eye Hospital* ℘ 0171 608 3677 (direct line) or *Maggie Harrison, Manchester Royal Eye Hospital* ℘ 0161 276 5515.

1 **Registered and Blind and Partially Sighted People at March 31 1994, England.** Government Statistical Service. Department Of Health Personal Social Services. 1994

2 The quotations in this chapter are taken from **Get a wiggle on** by Sherry Raynor and Richard Drouillard, an American Alliance for Health, Physical Education and Recreation (AAHPER) publication. Copies can be borrowed from **Vision Aid library**

6.2 Eye conditions causing significant sight loss

Most parents want to know details of their child's eye condition. The child's eye specialist and family doctor are the first people to ask, but it is not always easy to remember what has been said. Sometimes it is not even easy to remember the strange name of the eye condition. No-one should feel foolish asking the doctor to write it down. It is a failure of communication on the doctor's part if it is not offered. If genetic counselling is not suggested, parents should double check that it has not been overlooked, because genetic disorders are frequently responsible for the vision loss. Some Eye Departments in hospitals provide factsheets which give basic information and it is always worth asking if these are available. The information in the following sections is a quick starting point. More information about specific eye conditions is offered by the support groups listed in 31.1.

6.2.1 Albinism

This is a term given to a group of inherited conditions in which there is a congenital lack of melanin in the body. This is the brown pigment which is normally found in hair, eyes and skin. Eyesight is poor because the eyes keep moving involuntarily (nystagmus) and stable images are not received by the retina. In addition, abnormally high amounts of light enter the eye because the iris has a reduced pigment layer. The structure of the retina is also slightly different so that fine vision is impaired, with the most acute problems arising on sunny days and in brightly lit environments. Tinted spectacles or tinted contact lenses are often helpful.

6.2.2 Congenital cataract

Congenital cataract is a major cause of blindness and partial sight in children. The condition is generally inherited, but there is a substantial proportion of babies for whom no cause can be identified. Rubella infection in early pregnancy still causes multiple disabilities, often including cataracts. **Early diagnosis is vital**, especially if a new born baby has dense cataracts. If visual messages are not sent to the brain from birth, the brain loses its ability to receive and interpret them. This implies surgery before the age of four months for children with a cataract in one eye and even earlier, before the baby is three months of age, if there are dense cataracts in both eyes. In the latter case, both eyes are operated on within a short time and contact lens wear starts soon after surgery. As yet, lens implants are only considered appropriate for older children whose eyes have stopped growing. Less dense cataracts need to be monitored carefully, and the good eye is often 'patched' to encourage use of the weaker eye.

6.2.3 Congenital glaucoma

This is a rare condition in children and is caused by abnormal development of the eye. The first thing a parent may notice is that the baby cries a lot, feeds poorly and the eye is red and watering. The baby is particularly upset by bright lights and may try to bury its head in the pillow. The colour of the eye may seem to change and the eyes are enlarged so that visitors will comment on the child's 'lovely big eyes'. **Early diagnosis, generally followed by surgery, is essential** if sight is to be preserved.

6.2.4 Bardet-Biedl Syndrome

This syndrome, also known as the Laurence-Moon-Bardet-Biedl Syndrome, is a rare inherited disorder. Symptoms include poor sight due to retinitis pigmentosa, (see 2.3.4) and can also include other problems which vary in severity, such as extra toes or fingers, obesity, kidney problems, developmental delay and learning difficulties.

6.2.5 Microphthalmos and Anophthalmos

Either of these conditions can occur when a baby's eye or eyes do not develop normally in the womb. As a result, in **microphthalmos** the baby is born with a small malformed eye or eyes. In **anophthalmos** one or both eyes fail to develop at all. The eye socket or sockets in this condition also fail to develop properly.

6.2.6 Nystagmus

Children (and adults) who suffer from nystagmus find it impossible to hold their eyes steady. Both eyes keep moving, generally horizontally, though both the extent of the uncontrolled eye movement and its effects vary widely between individuals.

The condition can result in extreme short-sight as well as poor depth perception and balance. It can lead to registration as partially sighted or blind. Vision varies due to fatigue and stress. By holding the head sideways, and looking to one side, it is often possible to find a position at which eye movement is reduced and the best vision possible achieved. Nystagmus cannot be corrected by spectacles or contact lenses, though these should be worn to correct any other eye problem.

6.2.7 Retinoblastoma

This is a rare malignant tumour affecting between 40 and 50 children in the U.K. each year. It develops in the cells of the retina, mainly in the under-fives, though some children are born with it. It may be inherited and in one third of the children affected, both eyes are involved. If untreated, the tumour can spread to the brain with fatal consequences, **so early diagnosis is essential**. Often the first indication is when the baby's mother notices a white reflection when the pupil catches the light, or it is identified during treatment for a persistent squint. Pain is uncommon.

The first aim of treatment must be to prevent the tumour spreading, and secondly to preserve vision. There are a number of options, including freezing therapy (cryotherapy), radiotherapy, chemotherapy or removal of the eye (enucleation). Considerable advances in the treatment have been made over recent years and nine out of ten children are now cured. The majority retain useful vision. The Retinoblastoma clinic at St. Bartholomew's Hospital, London has pioneered these advances and is the only such clinic in the U.K.

6.2.8 Retinopathy of prematurity

The development of the retinas of premature babies may be abnormal if they have a birthweight of less than 1500g or are born at less than 32 weeks. The abnormality can be minor and self-correcting or, at its most severe, cause advanced retinal

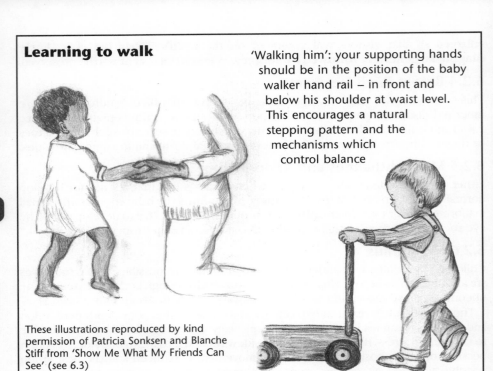

Learning to walk

'Walking him': your supporting hands should be in the position of the baby walker hand rail – in front and below his shoulder at waist level. This encourages a natural stepping pattern and the mechanisms which control balance

These illustrations reproduced by kind permission of Patricia Sonksen and Blanche Stiff from 'Show Me What My Friends Can See' (see 6.3)

detachment. Treatment, usually involving surgery, depends on the degree of sight loss and the best expected outcome. Unfortunately, even successful surgery may only produce minimal sight in high risk babies, and it can take up to a year after reattachment of the retina before results can be assessed. **Very early diagnosis is essential** if some sight is to be saved.

6.2.9 Stickler Syndrome

This is a progressive genetic condition. Symptoms may include myopia, retinal damage and detachment, cataract, and glaucoma. Skeletal anomalies, facial irregularities, hearing problems and learning difficulties are among other possible abnormalities.

6.2.10 Usher Syndrome

Usher syndrome is a genetic condition which affects hearing and sight. The sight loss often begins in late childhood and is caused by retinitis pigmentosa (see 2.3.4 and 24.1.8).

6.3 Detecting visual impairment

Poor sight in babies and small children is not always obvious. Some parents even find it difficult to convince professionals that their child has poor sight. It is hard to believe that the toddler who happily sprawls on the garden path and follows the movements of an ant with her finger tip has a sight problem, yet when her mother is with several adults she may run to the 'wrong' one. A baby with very little sight may be such a 'very good' baby, lying contentedly in the pram, gazing upward with nothing obviously wrong and being no trouble to anyone. Simple tests that anyone can carry out at home include checking if the baby's eyes turn towards the ray of light from a torch (though it is vital to make sure no click is made as it is switched on, or the child may turn to that), or spinning a coin on the table in front of the child. Watch what happens when the coin is silent. Does a hand go straight out to grasp it? A few Smarties scattered on a light background soon shows whether the child spots them quickly or has to peer or look sideways to find them. "Hundreds and thousands" can be used in the same way for a more difficult test.

Early diagnosis is essential if the child is to be helped to make the best use of any residual vision and parents should press for developmental tests at the earliest opportunity if they are seriously worried. Professional help will be available if their family doctor refers them to a children's development unit (a paediatric assessment centre). Here a team of people, led by a paediatrician and including an educational psychologist, a physiotherapist, an occupational therapist and a social worker, will monitor the child's development. The assessment process should provide the basic information on which a programme of education and treatment can be based, and also refer the parents to appropriate sources of help outside the unit.

The **Developmental Vision Clinic** at the Wolfson Centre, London aims to identify aspects of general development which may be affected by visual impairment, and to devise individual programmes to help the families overcome these gaps. The way the baby uses near and distance vision is assessed and methods of encouraging the best possible visual development suggested. Early referral is desirable, as both parents and babies derive most benefit during the early months. The Wolfson Centre now has the only UK low vision aid clinic for pre-school children. Based on their work at the clinic, Patricia Sonksen and Blanche Stiff have written an attractive, easily read book **Show Me What My Friends Can See** for parents and their professional advisors. Separate sections cover various aspects of development, such as language and speech, hand skills, mobility and early concept formation. The book can be purchased direct from the *Wolfson Centre, Mecklenburgh Square, London WC1N 2AP* quoting ISBN 0 951 7526 OX. Cheques (£6 including postage) should be made payable to the *Institute of Child Health*. See also 6.11.

6.4 Early days

Keep me with you ... Tell me what you're doing and what the sounds and your movement mean.
Babies who don't see well can't know what makes sounds or what the sounds mean without help. They need to touch the objects and to have someone tell them

what it all means. Babies who don't get this help 'tune out' and stop paying attention to sounds around them.

Keep me tuned in.

All babies are special, but it is a rare parent who does not feel that a visually impaired baby is 'extra special'. And indeed they are, but it is important to remember that first and foremost they are babies. Because they cannot see, or see only a little, more and different kinds of help are needed than for other babies, but their basic needs are just the same. In the first year, touch is the most important form of communication. Sighted children follow their mother's movements around the room with their eyes, but the blind baby will need her touch as the reassurance of her presence.

At first her distinctive way of holding the baby, her special tickle or caress, are all important. Even so, if the baby has very little sight, there may seem to be no response. His face may seem distressingly blank if there is no eye-to-eye contact. Yet, although the baby's face does not light up, his movements in her arms will be quite different from those made when held by anyone else. When she speaks, the baby may tend to be still in order to listen more attentively. At first she may have to guide the baby's fingers to her face, but soon those fingers will explore her features as if charting well-loved territory.

Before the baby is ready to reach out to the intriguing noise made by a toy she holds, his fingers will start moving, sending the message "I am interested" even if his face does not show it. Or he may lie very still, appearing to be unresponsive, but in fact refraining from moving because he is listening intently. The response is there, and by watching closely, the mother can learn the language and reinforce the bond between them. As the child grows, so also must the parents' ingenuity as they try to show, in meaningful ways, all the hundred and one everyday things sighted children absorb through their eyes. **Tempting as it is to provide background music for much of the day, it is a temptation that should be resisted. It blocks out all the other vital sounds that the child needs to hear and learn to interpret**.

6.5 Coping with feelings

In the early days parents have to cope with more than physical strain and practical problems. Severe visual impairment can have a shattering impact on the whole family. Parents have to come to terms with blindness itself, with feelings of anger sometimes against themselves, their partner or the medical profession, and with times of overwhelming grief and sadness. It is often hard to acknowledge these feelings openly. Sometimes contact with a local social worker or health visitor will give the opportunity for parents to unburden themselves. Sometimes the most helpful support will come from another parent who has lived through a similar experience (see 31).

Heart to Heart – Parents of Blind and Partially Sighted Children Talk about Their Feelings (see 6.15) is a booklet which no new parent of a blind child could pick up without finding within its pages something that speaks to their condition. The authors say, 'We wanted **Heart to Heart** to be a description, not a prescription, of many feelings which parents have experienced. You may have felt one of the

148

feelings, or some of the feelings on any given day. But all parents say that "time does heal" and life does return to normal. There will come a time when you will not be constantly preoccupied with unanswered questions and doubts, when you will think about your child as a child first, and as a blind child second.'

6.6 Getting moving

Walls help me get around … Now that I'm walking, encourage me to follow the walls before I take off into the wide open spaces on my own. I had one map of the house when I was crawling about, now I need to learn about it in this new way. If you lead me around by holding my hand, I'll never be sure enough of myself to try it alone. If I'm a wall follower, I won't be a wallflower.

Moving around in the cot and being held in their parents' arms is the start of a long journey for visually impaired babies. The destination is the achievement of 'mobility' or 'orientation' skills – which sounds even more awe-inspiring. **NEW** **Reaching, Crawling, Walking, Let's Get Moving** (see 6.15) is a booklet which brings things down to earth and shows parents, through photographs and text, how they can guide their child's steps most effectively:

'Sighted guide techniques for young children are important. Adults commonly take a guide's arm, just above the elbow, in order to judge better where the person's body is moving. For small children, either holding an adult's two fingers or wrist, offers similar information. **Adults tend to take a small child's hand to guide them. To children who are visually impaired this practice can feel like they are being pulled around. It is important for the child to choose to hold onto the adult.** Wearing a ring on your finger or bracelet on your wrist can help the child remember where to hold.'

Professional help should be available through health visitors, physiotherapists and mobility or rehabilitation officers. The LEA Visual Impairment team (see 8.6.1) should also be able to devise programmes to help parents develop their child's body and spatial awareness and to teach pre-cane skills. **Clap your hands, stamp your feet** (RNIB. £15.00) is an enjoyable video full of good ideas of ways to make it fun to 'get moving'.

6.7 Choosing toys

Children learn through play, and well-designed attractive toys chosen to encourage certain skills have special value for visually impaired children who may receive little stimulus through their eyes. At first, they may play quite differently from sighted children. A toy car is likely to be much more fun if held upside-down, with wheels that can be spun to make an intriguing noise. Pushed along the floor it merely disappears.

New toys and experiences may frighten me … When you give me something new, I may be afraid of it at first. Go slow. Remember it really is all new to me. I've had no previous experience with it and although you may think I'll enjoy it, I have to find out in my own way what it is, whether it makes an interesting sound, that it

won't hurt me, and that it feels nice. Keep trying; encourage me to play with it. Be persistent with new things, but be understanding, too.
Don't give me too much of a surprise!

Rough and ready rules for selecting toys are to choose ones that are shiny, or in bright colours which the child is known to distinguish. The child should, by manipulating it, get an immediate reward, and thus a sense of achievement. The **Activity Centre** (Fisher-Price), the **Pop-Up-Cone Tree** (Pedigree) and **Active Baby** (Ambi-Toys) are all good examples. If the child has very little sight, the shape and texture of the toy are obviously important. Soft furry toys are often disliked by young blind children, though they may be more acceptable if they have a music box mechanism inside them. **Models should be used with caution; it is far better to learn from life**. One of RNIB's education advisors makes the point vividly: 'A duck to your baby is the sour smell of the pond, the gurgling sound of water and the familiar quack, nothing at all like a small plastic model'.

Help with choosing toys for children up to about five years of age can be found in **Toys with a Purpose ❶❷❸** (RNIB Education Information Service. 70p, single copies free to parents). **Play Helps** by Roma Lear (Butterworth-Heinemann. 3rd ed. 1993. £14.95) is a treasure house of ideas for cheap, easy, home-made toys that stimulate the five senses. The section on **Making the Most of Touch** has ideas for ways of helping babies and toddlers to feel, such as making a 'feely corner', a feely caterpillar and feely bingo. A home-made 'open sesame' board enables children to become familiar with different door catches. Other sections include ways of making a clanky pull-along and a noisy busy-board, as well as how to go on a 'listening loiter'.

6.7.1 Toy shop toys

One Hundred Popular Toys and Games for Blind and Partially Sighted Children is a catalogue of toys, suitable for all ages, which can be bought in high street shops. Published annually by the British Toy & Hobby Association and RNIB it is available free from *RNIB Education Information Service*. All the toys meet special criteria including good colour, tonal contrast and tactile variety. They are chosen by a panel of parents and teachers of visually impaired children.

6.7.2 Toy libraries

Toy libraries for children with disabilities will be found in many parts of the country. **The National Association of Toy and Leisure Libraries (Play Matters)** will put parents and carers in touch with their nearest toy library, and will use the expertise of its advisory members to answer enquiries. Publications on play in relation to child development include **Look and Touch** (£1.80 members, £2.80 others), a booklet on toys and play for visually impaired children published jointly with RNIB. Contact *Play Matters, 68 Church Way, London NW1 1LT* ✆ 0171 387 9592.

6.7.3 Specialist toy libraries

RNIB schools at Northwood, Middlesex, Southport, Merseyside, Rushton Hall, Northamptonshire and Condover Hall, Shropshire have toy libraries for visually impaired children in the neighbourhood. All RNIB Education Centres have toys which may be borrowed including those listed in **One Hundred Popular Toys and Games** (see 6.7.1), as does a toy library in Edinburgh run by LOOK Scotland.

The **Research Centre for the Education of the Visually Handicapped**, Birmingham University, has a library stock of over 300 toys. A full list is available on request. Henshaw's, Dorton House and Linden Lodge schools can all offer toy library services to children who do not attend their schools. **Vision Aid** (see 6.13.4) has a postal toy library service and a range of fibre optics and other visual stimulation equipment. Some of the LOOK groups listed in 31.2 have toys for members to borrow.

6.7.4 Specially designed toys

The RNIB has a number of very attractive board games, including **Ludo** (£14.00) and **Snakes and Ladders** (£13.91) in tactile formats so that blind and partially sighted children can play with sighted children. **Monopoly** (£15.70) has been adapted, with braille and large print bank notes and **Scrabble** is available in braille (£24.15) or in large print (£16.22). **Easy to See dice** which are also tactile cost 53p a pair. A range of **audible balls** is also stocked, including a football approved by the English Schools Football Association. It contains lead shot which rolls around inside making it possible to track it. Details in **RNIB Product Guide, Games and Puzzles** 🅛🅑🅣 (see 29.1).

Some manufacturers specialise in toys for children with special needs. **Fun and Achievement** mail order catalogue from Toys For the Handicapped includes a range of fibre optic light effects for visual stimulation, as well as adhesive-backed diffraction paper which is useful for catching a child's attention when stuck on an otherwise uninviting object. **The Raven Collection: Toys to encourage child development** is a mail-order catalogue produced in response to parents' requests for easier access to toys widely used by professionals to help encourage all aspects of child development. Details from: *Raven Educational Supplies, 13a Victoria Road, Wellingborough, Northants NN8 1HN* ✆ 01933 279108.

Unfortunately, one thing all the items in this section have in common is expense, presumably because the market for these 'specials' is so limited. It is here that a good toy library can often help. If the toy needed is not in stock, the library may well be prepared to purchase it and lend it (see 6.7.2). Failing that, the local voluntary society for the blind may be able to help with a cash grant (see also 4.11).

My home is my first playground ... When I start to crawl about, leave some of the doors of the kitchen cupboards open. I'd like to find out what's kept there! Let me pull things out that can't harm me. I'll bang on them, chew on them a little, even roll on them! I'll explore and learn about them using all my senses! I may even crawl right into the empty cupboard. If I don't get into one, and can't see into it well, will I really know what a cupboard is? Will I know they exist and what interesting things they hold? Open the door and keep some cupboard space for me. But first remove anything that can be dangerous to me.

6.8 Reading

Good, clear, boldly contrasting print is not too difficult to find when hunting through the children's section in a bookshop. Books where the print is superimposed on a colourwash design or picture should be avoided, though that is not so easy.

NEW Books with sound effects help children discover the joys of reading. **Golden Books** (Western Publishing Co.) are widely available and include board books with four 'Touch 'n Listen' pads for very young children and Golden Sound stories and Golden Talking Tales for older children. Golden Sound Story **Little Stevie Wonder in Places Under the Sun** (£10.99) not only talks, plays music, and creates sounds but also has a braille overlay. ClearVision books (see 8.8) are a pleasant early introduction to braille, as the parent can read the story and the toddler pretend to read at the same time. **NEW** Feel Happy, children's books with braille overlays and tactile pictures, together with a cassette recording, are now beginning to be produced. Details from *The Living Paintings Trust*.

Children's tapes are widely available, and often can be borrowed from local public libraries. Attractive, basic tape recorders with easy to use controls include **My First Sony** and Fisher-Price's tape recorder with microphone (see also 8.8.2).

6.9 Playgroups

Most parents will want their child to join a playgroup, but sometimes playgroup leaders, although wanting to help, feel at a loss to know how to do so effectively. The booklet **What shall we do to help?** (RNIB £1.50) is a stimulating and positive guide for nursery and playgroup leaders with a visually impaired child in their group. Social services departments register all playgroups in their area and so are often well placed to advise parents and may help to meet the fees (see also 6.12).

The **Pre-school Learning Alliance** (previously known as the Pre-school Playgroups Association) encourages its member groups to cater for all children and has an advisor on special needs. The Association's **Opportunity Groups** often accept children with disabilities from birth, and have a high ratio of helpers to children. It publishes a range of information sheets, including one on **Helping the visually impaired child**. More details from the *National Pre-School Learning Alliance, 69 Kings Cross Road, London WC1X 9LL* ✆ 0171 833 0991.

Specialist playgroups are generally linked to a RNIB Sunshine House (see 7.6) or special school. The **Nottinghamshire Royal Society for the Blind** is unique in having a special **NEW** Early Start unit, open throughout the year for babies and children below school age. It includes a multi-sensory room, a soft play room, ball pool, baby room and outdoor play area. Contact *Doreen Hill, NRSB, Ortzen Street, Radford, Nottingham NG7 4BN* ✆ 0115 927 1021. The **Research Centre for the Education of the Visually Handicapped** has a pre-school playgroup at the School of Education, Birmingham University, with a 'dark room', microcomputers and colourful lighting displays for visual stimulation. Contact *Mrs. Pat Evans* ✆ 0121 414 6732.

6.10 Help from the statutory sector

When a District Health Authority knows that a child has, or is likely to have, special educational needs, it must inform the LEA. If the child is visually impaired, the authority must also tell the parents about appropriate voluntary services such as those offered by RNIB and LOOK (see 31.2). The 1993 Education Act places a duty on District Health Authorities and Social Services Departments to work together with LEAs.

6.11 Local Education Authorities

The 1993 Education Act **Code of Practice** **P** **B** **T** stresses the need for early identification and support of the under-fives. The majority of local education authorities (LEAs) provide services for visually impaired children and it is not necessary to wait until the child is of school age before enlisting their help. Specially qualified teachers can work with parents and families in their homes using programmes such as the **Oregon Project**. The Code of Practice recommends that 'For very young children LEAs should consider home-based programmes such as Portage or peripatetic services for children with hearing or visual impairment'. **Portage** is a carefully planned pre-school education scheme tailored to meet an individual child's special needs when there is developmental delay (see 7.5.1).

Oregon is a similar programme to Portage, but is designed for use at home or in school with blind or partially sighted children from birth to six years. It can be used by parents as well as by teachers, nurses, and psychologists. It includes teaching activities and a manual. Further details from *JAG Enterprises, Brookfield, High Road, Swilland, Ipswich IP6 9LP* ✆ 01473 785452.

Parents should contact their LEA direct and ask for the Special Needs Advisor or the Sensory Impairment Team for their help. Parents have a right to ask for a statutory assessment of their child's needs even when the child is under two years of age. This assessment, which roughly follows the procedure described in 8.2.2 can open the door to home-based teaching or a developmental play programme. The LEA does not have a duty to provide these services until the child is two years old even if the assessment shows they are needed. However, they often provide them informally. If this does not happen, parents should contact their social services department for this help to be provided under the Children Act (see 4.5).

When the child is two years of age, the LEA does have a duty both to assess the child's needs and to meet the agreed needs. This can open the door to payment of fees at, say, a Sunshine House or other nursery school, an ancillary helper at playgroup, or help with playgroup fees as well as continuing support from a qualified teacher of visual impairment. How best to meet a visually impaired child's needs depends to a great extent on how well they use any remaining vision. A clinical assessment is not difficult to obtain. The child's eye specialist or optometrist is able to report on how much the child can see in the consulting room. This needs to be supplemented by an assessment of **functional vision** if the most appropriate ways of helping the child are to be provided. This is not always easy to obtain, but is essential if the most effective help is to be offered. The child's ophthalmologist or the family doctor are obvious people to consult, and may be able to make a referral to a clinic which can assess functional vision. Other good sources of advice include the agencies, listed in 7.1.1, 7.1.2 and 8.4.1, the Partially Sighted Society, who can give information about the nearest low vision clinic, the LEA Visual Impairment team, rehabilitation workers, and RNIB Advocacy Service.

6.12 Local social services departments

Help from social services departments is provided, in the main, under the Children Act 1993. The organisation of the service varies. Some departments have a team comprised of occupational therapists, others have children's teams, some have disability teams which deal only with children, others have sensory impairment teams. Sometimes the only specialist help available is from a rehabilitation worker who may, or may not, have experience in working with young children. But social work staff, experienced or inexperienced, are excellent allies and parents have a right to enlist their support. A mutual discussion of the child's needs can result in the provision of an imaginative package of services to meet their particular situation.

The Children Act (see 4.5) lays a general duty on local authorities to provide help with holidays and day-care, including after-school and holiday activities for children in need. This could include financial help in order to run a holiday playscheme for blind children, or help with meeting the fees. Other services could include specialist help from a rehabilitation worker or teacher, parent counselling and meetings with other parents for mutual support. Practical help might include the provision of equipment, support by a family aide or a home carer, a baby-sitting service or respite care (see 7.7 and 7.8). For details of the Children Act see 4.5.1.

6.13 Help from voluntary agencies

6.13.1 RNIB Family Support Services

RNIB family support services are based in their Education Centres (see 8.6.2). **RNIB Education Information Service** provides information, including a wide range of booklets, on bringing up a baby or child with impaired sight. Where families need one-to-one support RNIB family liaison officers can make a home visit.

RNIB's Family Weekends bring together eight to ten families including the blind or partially sighted child and siblings of a similar age. Parents can share experiences and discuss areas of concern and get expert advice from RNIB professional staff whilst all the children are fully entertained with games, trips and outings. Details of the current programme from *RNIB Education Centre, London.*

RNIB Sunshine House Schools in *Northwood, Middlesex; Southport, Merseyside;* and *East Grinstead, West Sussex* offer part-time, day or weekly facilities and respite care. They generally accept children from the age of two, who usually stay until the age of eight. All RNIB Sunshine House Schools admit multiply disabled children.

6.13.2 RLSB Family Support Services

The Royal London Society for the Blind offers its support to any family with a visually impaired child, irrespective of the child's age, home area or school placement and has a **Family Centre** at Dorton House, Sevenoaks, Kent. The regular programme of activities includes information days and grandparent weekends. A nursery and pre-school facilities are integrated with a local day nursery. A family flat is available for those who live at a distance from the Centre and who wish to stay overnight.

6.13.3 Henshaw's Society for the Blind

Although based in the North West, Henshaw's can offer its family services nationwide. It can provide support through counselling, family weekends, holiday playschemes, mobility assessments, parental training days as well as leisure activities for children in mainstream schools and holidays. It has a toy library and resource centre. Henshaw's rehabilitation workers work with pre-school and school age children. An advice line for parents is provided on ℘ 0161 872 1234.

6.13.4 Vision Aid

NEW 1995 has seen an expansion in Vision Aid's services from its beginnings as a self-help group. The premises have been extended to include an expanded toy library, a visual stimulation area, and a demonstration bedroom showing how a safe, but stimulating and attractive environment can be provided with maximum ingenuity and minimum cost. Other services include counselling, family support, a home visiting service, a family to family contact line and a range of publications. There are weekly 'drop-in' sessions and parents' evenings. A 24 hour telephone helpline is provided on ℘ 01204 31882.

6.14 Financial help for parents and children

6.14.1 The Family Fund Trust

This is an independent organisation funded by the Government. It helps families caring for a very severely disabled child under the age of 16 years. A child with a severe visual impairment would be likely to be eligible, especially if there were also physical or learning difficulties. The eligibility of children with visual impairment alone depends on the extent to which they are able to use the vision they have, or to manage without sight. The purpose of the Family Fund Trust is to complement the help available from other sources. It cannot help with goods or services that are the responsibility of statutory organisations, nor can it provide regular continuing payments. The Trust will not normally be able to help those families with an income above £17,000 p.a. It justifies each grant in the light of the family's financial circumstances overall.

Parents are asked what help they need. Requests are often for washing machines when more than normal laundry has to be done each day or when more than usual time has to be spent communicating with the child. Help may also be given towards family holidays or outings which can help to stimulate communication as well as relieve family stress. New applicants are visited by one of the Trust's workers. Further details from *The Family Fund Trust, PO Box 50, York YO1 2ZX* ✆ 01904 621115.

6.14.2 Disability living allowance: care component

For full details of this allowance, see 5.4 and **Disability Living Allowance for Visually Impaired Children ❸❼**, a free leaflet from **Action For Blind People**.

There are special rules for children under 16 who claim this allowance. They are likely to be awarded the middle rate care component (£31.20) if it is shown that they need 'attention or supervision substantially in excess of that normally required by a child of the same age and sex'. Parents should consider whether their child needs more stimulation than a sighted child needs in order to learn and develop, whether they have to 'describe the world' to their child, whether their child needs more attention and supervision than a sighted child of the same age. If so, they should clearly state this on the claim form.

The guidelines used by adjudication officers indicate that such 'attention or supervision' is normally required up to puberty. By this age, it is felt that the blind child can be expected to be a competent touch reader and may have learned to cope with traffic and to move around in familiar surroundings without danger. If the award is for a limited period, a self-assessment form will be sent shortly before it ends. It is very important to state then exactly what the child's needs are. If the component is then withdrawn although the need for care remains, it is always worth asking for a review, in order to explain again exactly how much attention the visually impaired youngster needs, compared to other children of his age.

How to claim

There is no special claim form for children. Parents should call the Benefits Enquiry Line Freefone 0800 882200 for a claim pack which will include the claim form (DLA 1). The care component can be paid from the age of 3 months.

6.14.3 Disability living allowance: mobility component

For details see 5.4.5.

Most blind and partially sighted children are likely to qualify for the lower mobility component (£12.40). Adjudication officers are recommended to recognise that a blind child's mobility needs out of doors in unfamiliar surroundings will persist up to and after puberty, and it is accepted that 'the very great majority of blind children will require guidance or supervision from another person for most of the time' (Disability Handbook. HMSO. 1992). It is therefore likely that they will continue to be eligible for the lower mobility component.

How to claim

The procedure is the same as for the care component. The mobility component can be paid from the child's fifth birthday, but claims can be made three months earlier.

6.14.4 Other financial help

Parents should check chapter 5, especially the sections on invalid care allowance, income support and housing benefit. If their child is registered blind or receiving disability living allowance this could make them entitled to any of the above allowances, or to receive more help.

6.15 Further reading

A series of attractively produced and simply written booklets are distributed free throughout the world by the *Blind Children's Center, 4120 Marathon Street, Los Angeles, California 90029* ℘ 00 1 213 664 2153. Titles include **Heart to Heart**; **Talk To Me – A Language Guide for Parents of Blind Children; Talk to Me II – Common Concerns**; **Move with Me; Dancing Cheek to Cheek**; **NEW** **Let's Eat – Feeding a child with a visual impairment** and **Reaching, Crawling, Walking ... Let's Get Moving**'. Copies of the Blind Children's Center booklets can be obtained in this country from *Vision Aid.*

Help Starts Here: a guide for parents of children with special needs. 1995. Single copies free to parents from *Council for Disabled Children, 8 Wakely Street, London EC1V 7QE* ℘ 0171 278 9441.

RNIB **Early Start** series includes **Helping your visually impaired child: an introduction to key services ℗ ⑬ ⑪** (£1.50); **Getting Started**, (70p) a guide to children's eye conditions and the people who can help and **One Step at a time ...** (50p) ways to help and encourage a visually impaired baby or young child. Single copies free to parents. Contact: *RNIB Education Information Service.*

A Benefits Guide for Children and Young People with Disabilities (Disability Alliance. 1992. £4.00).

6.16 Videos

The World In Our Hands is a series of five videos with supporting booklets. It was produced in response to the needs of parents, particularly those who had recently been told that their baby was blind. Each unit focuses on a different aspect of a child's development. Individual titles **My baby is blind, Moving on, Sounds important, Clap your hands, stamp your feet,** and **It's me!** cost £15, (complete set £70) from *RNIB Book Sales* and can also be borrowed from Vision Aid.

7 Extra help for extra problems

'Take her home and love her'. This was the advice that a mother and father were given when they were told that their baby was visually impaired and also had other severe disabilities. Their response was, 'Of course we'll do that. We want to do more'. This chapter aims to point the way for the many parents who find themselves in a similar situation.

Professionals would probably have described that particular baby as 'multiply disabled visually impaired'. The initials MDVI probably figured prominently in the clinical notes. In this chapter they will only appear when absolutely necessary. References to babies and children will assume that they do indeed have 'extra problems'. Children without those 'extra problems' will be referred to as 'sighted children' or as 'visually impaired' children.

The 'extra problems' children and babies may experience are not trivial. The difficulties can include physical, sensory, intellectual and emotional disabilities, each severe enough in itself or in combination with very poor sight, to interfere with normal development or education. **In an average sized health district there are likely to be about 50 children who are visually impaired, and just over half will have other disabilities.**[1]

Often the other difficulties are so severe that it is easy to overlook or underestimate the baby's visual problems. Yet poor sight compounds the other problems; it is not an 'add-on'. A child may have physical limitations which make movement very difficult indeed. But what is the point of moving if there is nothing 'out there' to make it worth the effort, or if it only means painful bumps and bruises? Better to stay still and be safe, but also become even more immobile. Anything that can be done to increase a child's visual ability is likely to enhance the whole of the child's life.

7.1 Helping children see better

The first essential is a visual assessment. The Royal College of Ophthalmologists and the British Paediatric Association recommend special screening for retinopathy of prematurity (see 6.2.8) in premature babies or babies whose birth weight is less than 1500 grams, and for uveitis (an inflammatory eye condition) in children with juvenile chronic arthritis. Children with juvenile diabetes should be examined for retinopathy from puberty. Other children with additional disabilities who have a high risk of sight problems include children with Down's syndrome, cerebral palsy, severe learning disability, severe hearing disability and some neurological conditions.

The first tests can be done very early, when the baby is about six weeks old. A clinical examination of a child's vision is normally carried out by a consultant ophthalmologist. This examination is vital because it will enable any treatable conditions such as cataract, glaucoma, uveitis or retinopathy of prematurity to be identified and any congenital infections such as toxoplasmosis and CMV to be treated.

---

1 **Ophthalmic Services for Children**. Royal College of Ophthalmologists and the British Paediatric Association. December 1994

Parents may feel that further tests are pointless because the child's other disabilities would make meaningful results impossible. But by itself a clinical examination is unlikely to provide all the information needed. Functional vision tests are needed to complete the picture. Parents need to know the 'quality' and extent of their child's remaining vision – how much can be seen in day-to-day life. Nowadays, new ways of measuring vision include identifying the way a child's eye movement or eye position changes in response to a target. This enables the angle at which the child sees best to be established. This helps parents, for example, to place the toy where it is most likely to encourage the child to reach out for it.

eye OPENER

'Five month old Alison and her mother are playing with a shiny, crinkly pom-pom. When Alison first touches it, she starts to cry because she cannot figure out what it is. The strange shape and texture bother her. When a light shines on the silver streamers, Alison who has some developing vision, becomes fascinated by the gleaming strands and wants to poke at them for long periods of time'

This type of assessment is very different from an adult's experience of an eye examination by the high street optometrist. Ideally it is done in a familiar situation by familiar people, with the parents' contribution given as much weight as that of the 'experts'. A good visual assessment will identify how the child responds to light and movement, how the child's eyes move, which colours are preferred, and if a child's eyes follow a moving object. Once a parent has that information they have some of the tools which will enable them to 'do more'.

As the child grows, visual assessments should continue. The child has to be about six months old before a check can be made to make sure both eyes are working together. The visual skills of sighted children continue to develop until they are eight or twelve years old and this time span is likely to be much longer for other children.

It can happen that children who have been diagnosed as clinically blind gradually develop some useful sight. Some children's eyes appear perfect but because of damage in the visual pathways between the retina and the brain, or in the brain itself, they cannot see. This is known as cortical visual impairment. They generally retain a little sight and sometimes, very slowly, some residual vision develops. The same is true for other children who have been diagnosed as clinically blind, but whose parents have had a gut feeling that some sight remains. But sight will not develop unless it is used. So all children with very poor sight – perhaps no more than being able to see the difference between light and dark – need plenty of visual stimulation. The little boy pictured in the colour section is enthralled by the coloured, moving bubbles in the tube. There are simpler, cheaper ways of achieving the same result. Brightly coloured mittens can encourage babies to 'find' their hands, but the mittens must be loose enough for them to be able to pull their hands out of them very easily.

A Parents' Guide for Baby's Discovering His Hands, a leaflet giving more ideas, can be obtained from *Vision Aid*. A little later, brightly coloured socks or bootees may enable them to watch their feet moving. Flashing Christmas tree lights all the year round, bold black and white stripes stuck on objects to attract the child's attention, these are simple ways to help stimulate vision. A range of black and white toys is available from *Playring* including a baby mirror which has eye-catching black and white graphics on the reverse side. The information obtained from the visual assessment will provide many other ideas and will demonstrate more ways of stimulating vision.

7.1.1 Visual Assessment Teams

The following centres are staffed to give multi-disciplinary assessments for visually impaired children with multiple disabilities. In areas where no centre is listed contact the special needs team in the local education authority (see 8.6.1). In Scotland information on local centres can be obtained from the *Scottish Sensory Centre, Moray House, Institute of Education, Heriot-Watt University, Holyrood Road, Edinburgh EH8 8AD* ✆ 0131 558 6501.

Bedford
Sensory Impairments and Communication Difficulties Team, Hill Rise, Kempston, Beds. MK42 7EB ✆ 01234 857575

Birmingham
Maas Road Child Development Centre, Maas Road, Birmingham B21 ✆ 0121 476 6969

Child Development Centre, Birmingham Children's Hospital, Ladywood Middleway, Edgbaston, Birmingham B16 8ET ✆ 0121 454 4851

Both Birmingham centres assess multiple disability, but do not include visual assessment specifically as they have access to eye units and liaise closely with Sense family centre, Birmingham.

Blackburn
Holly House Child Development Centre, 5 Blackburn Road, Rishton, Blackburn BB1 4B5 ✆ 01254 888503

Bristol
Tyndalls Park Children's Centre, 31 Tyndall Park Road, Bristol B58 1PH ✆ 0117 923 8083 or 0117 923 7998. Under 5s only

Cambridge
Visual Assessment Team, Child Development Centre, Addenbrookes Hospital, Hills Road, Cambridge CB2 2QQ ✆ 01223 245151

Dartford
Child Development Centre, Livingston Hospital, East Hill, Dartford, Kent DA1 1SA ✆ 01322 292233

Exeter
Honeylands Children's Centre, Pinhoe Road, Exeter EX4 8AD ✆ 01392 467171

West of England School for Children with little or no sight, Topsham Road, Countess Wear, Exeter EX2 6HH ✆ 01392 454200

Hereford
Child Development Centre, Ross Road, Hereford HR2 7RL ✆ 01432 356438.
Pre-school children only

Hull
Child Development Centre, Hull Royal Infirmary, Anlaby Road, Hull ✆ 01482 675080
(address from September 1995: *The Children's Centre, Walker Street, Anlaby
Road, Hull*)

Liverpool
*Child Development Centre, Royal Liverpool Children's Hospital, Eaton Road, Liverpool
L12 2AP* ✆ 0151 228 4811

London
Wolfson Centre, Mecklenburgh Square, London WC1N 2AP ✆ 0171 837 7618.
Only pre-school low vision clinic
Donald Winnicott Centre, Queen Elizabeth Hospital, Hackney Road, London E2 9AG
✆ 0171 729 2333
Priory Manor Child Development Centre, 1 Blagdon Road, Lewisham, London SE13
✆ 0181 690 3838
*Newcomen Child Development Clinic, Guy's Hospital, St Thomas's Street,
London SE1 9RT* ✆ 0171 955 5000

Manchester
Rodney House School, 388 Slade Lane, Burnage, Manchester M19 2HT
✆ 0161 224 2774. This is not a school but an assessment unit for under 5s
serving the Greater Manchester area

Oxford
*Hugh Ellis Paediatric Assessment Centre, Churchill Hospital, Headington,
Oxford OX3 7LJ* ✆ 01865 225330

Plymouth
Child Development Centre, Scott Hospital, Beacon Park Road, Plymouth PL2 2PQ
✆ 01752 550741 ext 3226

Sheffield
Reigate Children's Centre, Tapton Crescent Road, Sheffield S10 5DD
✆ 0114 267 0237

Walsall
Walsall Child Assessment Unit, Coalheath Lane, Shelfield, Walsall WS4 1PL
✆ 01922 691133
*Warrington Child Development Centre, Guardian House, Guardian Street, Warrington
WA5 1TP* ✆ 01925 405700. They are developing a team and have an
orthoptist, so they are working towards the ideal

Northern Ireland
Sense, Knockbracken Health Care Park, Saintfield Road, Belfast BT8 8BR
✆ 01232 705858

Scotland
*Department of Ophthalmology, Royal Hospital for Sick Children, York Hill, Glasgow
G3 8SJ* ✆ 0141 201 0000

Wales

Special Assessment Clinic, Department of Optometry and Vision Science, University of Wales in Cardiff, Redwood Building, Edward VII Avenue, Cardiff CF1 3XF
℘ 01222 874357

7.1.2 Other assessment centres

RNIB Sunshine House School
2 Oxford Road, Southport, Merseyside PR8 2JT ℘ 01704 567174. Offers assessment services, including a functional vision assessment, of children under 10 years of age. Overnight accommodation provided on request.

RNIB Condover Hall School
Condover, Shrewsbury SY5 7AH ℘ 01743 872320. Offers a low vision service which includes comprehensive assessment of visual skills, based on how individual children use their sight in functional situations. Brochure, factsheets and a video available on request. Contact *Catherine Southwell*.

RNIB Forest House Assessment Centre
Rushton, Near Kettering, Northants NN14 1RR ℘ 01536 710506 or 710002. Offers a range of assessments from just a few hours on a single day for a very specific request to a full assessment over five days. Staff include a qualified teacher of visually impaired children, a paediatric physiotherapist, a speech therapist and an educational psychologist with other specialist workers called in where necessary.

Sense, National Deafblind & Rubella Association
11-13 Clifton Terrace, Finsbury Park, London N4 3SR ℘0171 272 7774. Offers assessment for children from babyhood up to seven years at Sense Family Centres in London and Birmingham.

7.1.3 Video and computer programs for visual stimulation

'Hello' (£9.50 RNIB Book Sales Service) is a video produced by the Oxford Visual Impairment Service designed to encourage children to use their eyes more actively. There is no story line; it consists mainly of abstract images, strong colour contrasts, clearly defined shapes and unusual sounds which catch children's attention and draw their eyes to the screen. There are lots of opportunities to follow the movement of brightly coloured objects across the screen and so begin to learn the complex skill of tracking a moving object.

A range of computer programmes designed to stimulate vision and encourage scanning, hand/eye coordination and visual discrimination have been developed in recent years, many of them often written for pre-school, infant and primary age children (see also 8.15). Details from *Research Centre for the Education of the Visually Handicapped*, and *Northwest SEMERC, 1 Broadbent Road, Watersheddings, Oldham OL1 4HU* ℘ 0161 627 4469. **Condover Hall School** (see above) provides an Information Technology Service supplying advice, support and training to outside agencies, including parents, based on their long experience of multiple disability and visual impairment.

162

Emma came into the school's nursery when she was three years old, after having received home tuition through the local Portage scheme. She could not walk or feed herself and early assessment indicated that she had severe visual and learning difficulties.

When she was six, she came into my class. She could now walk for short distances unaided. My early observations led me to believe that her visual skills had improved since her initial assessment, so I asked Humberside Visual Handicap Service to re-assess her. To everyone's delight, they were able to recommend ideas to further stimulate Emma's vision. These recommendations were then incorporated into a mobility and education programme specifically designed for her. It was very detailed so that all staff who came into contact with Emma could adopt the same approach. Emma's mum had a copy, and so did the Respite Care Unit that Emma attends. After two terms, Emma could

- open the classroom door with minimal prompts
- walk to the hall unaided at hometime, carrying her bag, and find the right place to wait for the minibus
- find her own way into the cloakroom
- visually track objects previously out of her visual field.

Her progress has delighted us all. It has come about through the co-operation and support of all the agencies involved and, most importantly, her mum who carries on the work at home.

▶ Alison Harland. St. Luke's School, Scunthorpe writing in *Eye Contact*.

7.2 Learning to move

Moving about depends a great deal on vision, and not just for the obvious reasons. Watching other people is an important part of learning how to move which is denied to visually impaired children. Vision co-ordinates our physical actions and enables us to build up a picture of our surroundings. Lis Grundy, a physiotherapist whose own child has substantial 'extra problems', maintains: 'It is so important for our children who have motor disabilities to be in an upright position, for more important reasons than the hope that they will learn to walk. A child has the right to be upright.' Benefits include not just physical improvements. It puts the child on the same level as other children and it allows them to interpret the world in a normal way. If the world is seen or felt only from a prone position, the child inevitably has a distorted impression.

Lis feels it is unfortunate that children are so often placed in a standing frame rather than encouraged to use a walking frame, because a child cannot move of its own volition in a standing frame. Voluntary movement 'enables a child to recognise itself as a "being" capable of independent movement – if you never experience purposeful movement then you never have a reason to repeat it; neither do you know what is it that you wish to repeat!'

The MOVE programme, developed in America for children with severe disabilities, particularly children with Down's Syndrome, is now being used in this country with multiply disabled visually impaired children with encouraging results. Details from

Mike Lambert, Move International (Europe), Centre for Educational Development, University of Wolverhampton, Gorway Road, Walsall WS1 3BD
℘ 01902 323066.

7.2.1 Sources of help

The family doctor should be able to refer for physiotherapy, which is often also available through a hospital clinic, or a children's special centre or school.

Occupational therapists, either in hospital or based in a local social services department, can advise and often supply equipment on loan and are knowledgeable about walking aids and wheelchairs for children. The LEA Visual Impairment Service or a local authority mobility or rehabilitation worker may be able to advise on appropriate sources of local help, though workers in the community with mobility expertise with very young children are in short supply. Parents should also not hesitate to contact any of the special schools for blind children (see 7.6) as they often have special groups for pre-school children and mobility staff with experience of working with very young children who have additional disabilities.

7.3 Learning to communicate

For some children speech may not be a realistic goal, but learning to communicate is a crucial skill to achieve, regardless of ability. It enables children to exercise choice, to play an active role, to accept or reject. Successful communication is an antidote to frustration. Children may have very subtle ways of indicating their wishes. It may be a hand or head movement or a distinctive noise, which parents understand but which they need to interpret for professionals. From these beginnings, communication can be built up.

One way of building on this foundation, taken from work in Holland with deafblind children, is the use of 'objects of reference'. A mug is always handed to the child before a drink is offered. At this stage, the mug means 'a drink is coming next'. Eventually, the mug represents a drink and the child picks up a mug to indicate that a drink is wanted. This is a huge leap forward, for it also means that the child has realised that there is someone 'out there' ready to respond. Depending on visual ability, some children will use pictures or photographs instead of objects. Using 'objects of reference' can enable quite complicated messages to be conveyed. A time-table can be composed with each activity being represented by the appropriate object of reference. **Objects of Reference**, by Adam Ockelford (RNIB. £3.50) gives more details (see also 24.1.4).

Musical sounds can also be used as a medium of symbolic representation. Different activities, places, people and times can have a different sound or piece of music associated with them. These ideas are currently being investigated by RNIB as part of the project **Music Moves**. More details from *Adam Ockelford, RNIB Education Centre, London.*

Other children will build on the use of gesture and, with expert help, will be able to begin to communicate by signing.

7.3.1 Sources of help

Speech and language therapists are skilled in helping children's speech to develop. A health visitor would be able to give details of local speech therapy services. The LEA Visual Impairment Team should be able to advise and help.

Sense has an advisory service for children and young people with communication problems and is one of the main sources of expertise for all methods of communication by signing. Peripatetic teachers cover the east and south west regions of England.

7.4 Learning through play

It is hard to know where to start when a baby shows little response, or recoils from the new toy which was so kindly meant. The child needs lots and lots of time to accept something new. If our only experience of the world is that it is full of strange and often hard, painful objects, why should this new one be any different? Talking, describing, offering up the toy to the fingers and demonstrating are good ways of helping the child discover the pleasure to be found. So is being quiet. Sometimes children do better when they are allowed quietly and slowly to explore the new object for themselves in their own way.

Toys which are likely to appeal are brightly coloured, or sparkle, or have bold patterns. Often the expensive toys in the shops and those sold by the specialist toy suppliers have limited value for visually impaired children.

I have a sneaking suspicion that a hardware store is a more inspiring source of play materials. Ragged chamois leather, sponges with a rasping edge for scouring pans, wooden spoons, hinges, whisks, squeaky toys for pets, baking trays, a bottle brush – all these items supply a great variety of textures, tastes, forms, responsiveness, size, weight and temperature. And call in at the chemist's for an electric toothbrush – the vibrations are very popular. RNIB advisor, Robert Orr

In recent years much thought has been given to ways of providing friendly, yet stimulating environments for children which will encourage them to 'reach out' into the world and discover what interesting things there are to find or see, and also enable them to experience the pleasure of moving freely in a totally safe setting.

The **Little Room** in the photograph in the colour section was the result of three years' research by Lilli Nielsen, a Swedish psychologist and pre-school teacher. Her findings have inspired many of the recent developments in work with children. The Little Room, with its wooden walls, provides a safe, compact space for the child. It has good acoustics, yet is small enough for him to feel he is 'in charge'. It is safe to explore and once the interesting objects which have been suspended from the roof, or attached to the walls, have been found, they will stay in the same place. At first, the child encounters them accidentally, but then discovers that by making the same movement he finds them again. So unintentional movements become intentional. The child is finding that he can reach out to a world outside himself – he is beginning to make the difficult connection between reaching out and the idea of space.

Little Rooms are naturally small, so they can be used at home. They can be imported from Sweden (see 7.4.1), but some parents have utilised the kneehole space of a desk.

'Class 2 set off on a trip to SPACE (Soft Play Area Controlled Environment) which turned out to be a very large room with white walls and ceiling and a soft white floor. When we entered it was dimly lit with a pink light. The atmosphere was very tranquil and relaxing. Joel was struck by the change and stopped wriggling to think about it for a long time.

Joel and Amanda spent some time in a pool of white plastic balls which shone with different colours projected into them from a revolving disc. Joel loved watching the moving lights and Amanda enjoyed feeling and playing with the balls. We climbed up into the twilight near the ceiling, slid down a big soft slide and landed on the soft floor. Lucy was first into a hammock cleverly suspended so that it could be swung or rotated. Joel and I crept into a box which was pitch black with tiny beads of light like stars in the night sky.

Too soon, our hour's session was over. I left inspired to make Joel a 'different' environment he could go into at home.'

▶ Natalie Abbott describes in *Information Exchange* a visit to SPACE, Pedders Lane, Ashton, Preston PR2 2TH ✆ 01772 760403 which is designed for children and adults with special needs by the Friends of the Willows Ltd, a registered charity. Visits by appointment.

This works best if the desk is on a wooden floor, not carpet, so that some resonance is obtained. **Space and self**, Lilli Nielsen, (RNIB Book Sales Service. £14.20) gives more details of the Little Room.

Multi-sensory rooms are much bigger, extremely expensive and generally found in schools and centres for visually impaired children, including the **Early Start** unit at Nottingham (6.9) and Henshaw's Greater Manchester Regional Resource Centre. **All white rooms** are designed generally for relaxation, though visual stimulation is often provided by the play of coloured lights and fibre optic displays. **Dark rooms** are primarily for visual stimulation. **Soft play rooms** are attractive, brightly coloured, padded environments where it is possible to roll, jump and slide without any possibility of bumps and bruises. Parents may find it is well worth visiting these rooms, because some of the ideas can be adapted for use at home.

Playring is a soft play system which has been designed to offer babies and children a cosy and safe play environment. It provides a secure area which stops them toppling over, and also incorporates interesting play activities for them to explore. It therefore combines some of the advantages of the Little Room and a soft play room – though it is not a substitute for either. Details from *Playring Ltd.*

7.4.1 Sources of help

Toy libraries often can provide some of the more expensive equipment, such as Playring, for parents to borrow before deciding to purchase. See 6.7.2 and 6.7.3. Local voluntary societies for the blind may also be happy to help meet the cost of necessary, but expensive, play equipment.

Advice on toys and toy libraries is offered by **Connect**, a regional advisory service of **Sense** which can be contacted through their London headquarters. **Sense**

Woodside Family Centre, *Woodside Road, Kingswood, Bristol BS15 2DG* ✆ 0117 967 0008, has a toy library and is a day centre for visually and sensory impaired children, primarily in the Avon area.

Advice on purchasing some of the very expensive sensory equipment, such as soft play environments or sprays of fibre optics which constantly change colour along their length, is not easy to find. It may be worth investigating the coloured lighting displays on sale in the high street for discos as well as the specialist manufacturers' catalogues. **Sense** Family Centres are a good source of advice. **Planet** is a national information resource on play, leisure and recreation for children, young people and adults with disabilities. It is not especially for visually impaired children but many of the children it helps have a visual disability. It is able to give impartial advice. Details from *Judy Denziloe, Planet, Cambridge House, Cambridge Grove, London W6 0LE* ✆ 0181 741 4054.

An English catalogue of products designed by Lilli Nielsen is available from *LH-verkstan, Verkstadsgatan 29, S-776 35 Hedemora, Sweden.*

Also worth reading is **More Play Helps: Play ideas for children with special needs**. Roma Lear. New ed. 1992. Butterworth/Heinemann. £13.99.

7.5 Growing up

Middle-aged adults tend to say sorrowfully about sighted children that 'they grow up too quickly nowadays'. In contrast, children with extra problems develop very slowly and need a great deal of extra time. Sometimes it is very difficult to identify progress. Parents are torn between doing too little, too much or the wrong thing.

Many children develop mannerisms, and it is not unusual to see a visually impaired child rocking to and fro. Sometimes these mannerisms can become very pronounced and lead to self-damage. The reason may be boredom; the child is trying hard to obtain some stimulation. 'We try not to be reactive about the mannerism', explained a teacher at Dorton House School. 'Instead of telling the child not to eye poke or flap, we put something (a toy or a card) into their hands.' But it should be remembered that the child may be getting feedback from the movement – confirming that it still exists, or simply comforting itself. It is not reasonable to try to eliminate mannerisms entirely.

> ## *eye*OPENER
>
> 'We all need something of a safe haven in our daily routine. We need to listen to "The Archers", do the crossword, poke our eyes, or rock a little. Even odd behaviours should be respected as an expression of self before there are plans to modify them'
> *Roger Wilson-Hinds writing in* **Focus**, *the RNIB newsletter for staff working with people with visual and learning disabilities*

167

7.5.1 Sources of help

Portage and **Oregon** (see 6.11) programmes, for children from birth to rising five, aim to give parents the confidence to help their child effectively. The programmes are based on weekly home visits by a trained home visitor, with weekly written teaching activities designed for each individual child and parents. The service is free. A health visitor or social worker can refer parents, or parents can apply to join a local Portage scheme themselves. Public libraries will have details.

The community team for people with learning disabilities (sometimes still known as the community mental handicap team) is a good source of local support. The team includes educational psychologists and has access to a range of health staff including physiotherapists, speech therapists and psychiatric nurses. Contact them through the health visitor or family doctor.

7.6 School days

When school days arrive, assessment of special educational needs follows the pattern described in chapter 8. A local school for children with special educational needs may be the most appropriate placement but some children make significant progress only if an integrated team of carers reinforces behaviour consistently over twenty four hours. This can only be achieved in a residential special school.

RNIB Sunshine House Schools at East Grinstead, Sussex, Northwood, Middlesex and Southport, Merseyside provide this type of care for children from two to eight years. **RNIB Rushton Hall, Kettering** is for children aged from 5–12 years. Dryden House, based at the school, can offer care up to 52 weeks for children and young people between 5 and 19 years. Their **Rainbow Scheme** welcomes children and their families on Tuesday and Thursday mornings to use the facilities offered by the school and to meet specialist staff and relax with other families whilst the children enjoy themselves in the Rainbow Room. **RNIB Condover Hall**, near Shrewsbury, is a school for children aged 5–19 years with multiple disabilities. It also offers the **Pathways** deafblind programme. **Royal School for the Blind, Liverpool**, takes children from 3 years of age for 5 days a week. **St. David's, Exeter** (part of the West of England School for Children with Little or No Sight), offers similar provision and will take younger children if their parents are with them. **Barrie House, Royal Blind School, Edinburgh**, takes children from 3 years of age on a daily basis four days a week, and has an informal weekly morning playgroup for children under 3. Details of all special schools from *RNIB Education Information Service*.

Henshaw's College is a college of further education for young people and adults from 16 plus. It can offer special help for young people with multiple disabilities, including some learning difficulties. There are special units for young people who are deafblind or have Battens' Syndrome.

7.7 Help through the Children Act

A broad outline of the help available is described in 8.1. Parents have a right, under the Children Act, to ask their social services department for an **assessment** of their child's needs (see 4.5). Parents may be wary about approaching social services, but are likely to be pleasantly surprised. Social workers want to help, and although shortage of money may prevent them doing as much as they would wish, they can be powerful allies is helping parents 'find their way round the system'. They may open doors to hitherto unknown sources of support and help.

It is only fair to add, however, that not all parents have been impressed by the service they have received – or have failed to receive. In **Services to Disabled Children and their Families** (1994. HMSO), the Social Services Inspectorate of the Department of Health recommended that following assessment a **written plan** should be drawn up which includes 'the services to be provided to the child and family by each agency, taking account of each agency's statutory duties and reflecting good inter-disciplinary practice. The plan [should] record the child's and parents' view of the plan, including any disagreement.' **It would be perfectly appropriate for parents, therefore, to ask for their child's plan in writing.**

7.8 Respite care

Respite care can be provided through the Children Act, and the need to give parents a break should certainly be considered when a 'written plan' is being compiled.

Respite care should be an enriching experience both for the hard-pressed family and the child. Some of the alternatives which may be provided through social services include 'family foster schemes' where two families are paired together. The families get to know each other and the child spends an afternoon with the foster family. Then, as the relationship develops, the two families will work out a pattern of respite care between them. Respite care might also take the form of a stay at a special centre for severely handicapped children, or a holiday scheme linked to a school. RNIB run several respite care schemes in August. Details from *Lisa Moreau, RNIB Education Information Service*. **Sense** offers a variety of residential holidays for deafblind children and young people, ranging from outdoor activity centres to cottages, farms and caravans. Contact *Lucinda Dowson, Holidays Officer, Sense Headquarters*. **Sense Scotland** can also offer respite care.

7.9 Help from voluntary agencies

RNIB regional education centres (see 8.6.2) can offer advice, support and assessment services on all aspects of caring for visually impaired children with additional disabilities, including advocacy and respite care schemes. A special advisor for deafblind children, Jonathan Griffiths, is based at *RNIB Condover Hall School, Condover, Shrewsbury, Shropshire SY5 7AH* ✆ 01743 872320.

Sense Family Centres offer individual family weekends planned according to each family's unique needs. During the weekend the child's developmental progress will be assessed together with his or her mobility, visual, auditory, motor, communication and self-help skills. The next goals to be set in the child's development are jointly identified, and ways of achieving them planned. Home visits are offered by a team of peripatetic teachers, as well as weekend courses and workshops for parents. The service is regionally based at **Sense Family Centres**, but contact in the first instance can be made through the London office.

7.10 Coping with feelings

Something which colours the whole of life should not, perhaps, be left to the end of a chapter. But thinking about it here does emphasise that grief and sorrow – and anger and frustration too – are not just part of 'the early days' but continue through the child's life. Counselling support is not easy to find, though an RNIB regional education centre (see 8.6.2) may be able to help. Sense Family Advisory Service offers counselling, guidance, support and advice to families who have a child or young person who has hearing loss as well as poor sight.

Most people develop their own support networks: friends or relations to whom they can talk freely when feeling at their worst. Often joining one of the self-help groups (see 31) is a great source of strength. Support from someone who has had similar problems, and found a way round them, can be a comfort. **LOOK plus** is a new group which is in the process of being formed with the aim of supporting families and carers responsible for children and young people who have a visual impairment and other sensory, physical or learning difficulties. Contact *Kate Scott and Peter Catley, 11 Haslemere Road, Windsor, Berkshire SL4 5ET* ℘ 01753 866854.

7.11 The professional and the parent should be friends

One theme has been dominant whilst researching this chapter – the bitter cry of parents. Time and again their accounts of dealing with 'them' – health staff, social work staff, teachers, officials in general – has been in terms of a battle: 'We have to fight to get anything.'

The feelings are so strong that it is difficult to ascribe them all to lack of resources – although that certainly plays a part. A parent who had worked as a professional in the Health Service before becoming the parent of a profoundly disabled child gave a new perspective. 'Over the first few years of our new and very different life it began to seem that the professionals had a higher regard for information gleaned from science and technology than that from the mere intuition of a mother or father. There seemed to be an easy acceptance of our trauma – as if this was how professionals dealt with our pain – "this is all in the past, it's better to forget it, we're now looking (without too much expectation) to the future." But the past had formed the present and would go on, inextricably, to create the future – it was difficult to erase.'

Many parents would echo those comments. Even more would endorse the next stage: 'We became acutely aware of our lack of knowledge in our new role as disabled parents and information seemed difficult to come by.' The final stage sets the boundaries of the battlefield: 'Was this because professionals felt that we didn't need to know, or because they felt that we wouldn't be able to understand, or were they simply trying to disempower us?' Communication becomes blocked by suspicion and misunderstanding.

Is peace negotiable? Of course it is. The strength of the knowledge of professionals is its width, the strength of a parent's knowledge is its depth. When parents and professionals meet on that basis, not only do they become friends but each says of the other, 'Every time we meet, I learn something new.'

7.12 Further reading

Information Exchange (£9.60 p.a. UK, £10.50 p.a. Europe) describes itself as being a magazine which delights 'in new found discoveries: sensory trinkets, soothing aromas, new concepts, issues, rag-bag ideas. We strive to help our daughters and sons, students and friends to access the quality of life they so richly deserve. It is also for all of us: parents, carers, teachers, therapists, who need to gain confidence from each other by challenging and discussing, and thereby learning and growing.' Contact *Ken Woods, 53 The Circuit, Cheadle Hulme, Cheshire SK8 7LF* ✆ 0161 486 6514.

Eye contact (RNIB £6.00 p.a.) is a magazine for parents and professionals involved in the education of visually impaired children who have additional learning difficulties. It carries news of latest developments as well as contributions by parents.

Both magazines are issued three times a year.

Vital Information (£5. RNIB). This is a pack for people working with visually impaired children who have additional special needs. It is compiled by the RNIB/ VIEW Curriculum group for multiply disabled visually impaired children.

A Practical Guide to Multisensory Rooms (Richard Hirstwood and Mark Grey. £13.95. Hirstwood Publications. 1995). Available from *Toys for the Handicapped* or *Hirstwood Training, 7 Ellesmere Road, Morecambe, Lancs. LA4 4LF* ✆ 01524 426395.

7.13 Videos

One of the Family (RNIB. £110) is a series of four educational videos and booklets which aim to help specialists working with blind children who have a number of other disabilities. Parents have also found it helpful. It covers the main themes of this chapter in greater depth through compelling film.

8 Education

At their best, education services for visually impaired children offer individual, imaginative and comprehensive support embracing the needs of the whole family. At their worst, they are elusive, and, when found, seem to try to make the family fit the service, so that parents bitterly talk of their experience in terms of battles lost and won. This chapter aims to empower parents and the people who help them by describing the wide range of services that can be provided in school and at home by Local Education Authorities (LEAs) and voluntary organisations. Wherever possible, it indicates routes parents might follow when they come up against problems and describes the services they can obtain and organise for themselves.

8.1 The 1993 Education Act

NEW The section of this Act which deals with children's special educational needs in England and Wales came into force in September 1994. In Scotland and Northern Ireland a broadly similar system operates. The hope is that it will be easier and quicker for children to get the special help they need. The assessment procedure, through which a child's needs are identified and the way to meet them is planned, now has a time limit. The new Act strengthens the role of parents. They must be consulted throughout the assessment process and they have new rights of appeal if they are not happy with the decisions made. The major changes that happened in September 1994 are flagged **NEW**.

The best features of the old legislation remain. The needs of the visually impaired child, rather than the cause of the impairment, should be the first concern of everyone involved in identifying an appropriate school place. Children with special educational needs should normally be educated in mainstream schools (but see 8.3). Special educational needs continue to be defined as covering learning difficulties which range from minor and transient to severe and complex.

NEW **Special educational needs: a guide for parents** **P B T**, a free booklet issued by the Department of Education, is an excellent introduction to the changes. It describes what schools and LEAs can do for children with special needs and how parents can become fully involved and properly advised throughout the child's school life. Contact *Department for Education* ℘ 0171 510 0150 for a free copy. In Scotland, the information is contained in **A Parents' Guide to Special Educational Needs**. Copies are free from *The Scottish Office Education Dept., Room 4/20, New St. Andrew's House, Edinburgh EH1 3SY* ℘ 0131 244 5144.

NEW **Making your voice heard: helping parents to secure educational support for their visually impaired child (England and Wales)** **P B T** (£4.85. RNIB Book Sales Service) is a companion to the Department of Education booklet. It looks at the particular needs of visually impaired children and the education they require. The corresponding publication for Scotland is **Making your voice heard: a guide for parents to the Record of Needs** **P B T** (£3.00. RNIB Education Centre, Scotland).

172

POINTS FOR PARENTS

How to get help – a quick guide

- Visit the school and ask to talk to the teacher who is 'the special educational needs co-ordinator'. But as that teacher is unlikely to be familiar with visual impairment, also contact the LEA Sensory Impairment Service (or Visual Impairment Service) for advice

- The Co-ordinator will work out what can be done to help your child and his class teachers within the school's budget for special educational needs. In an LEA school this budget is funded by the LEA. In a grant-maintained school this money comes through the Funding Agency for Schools, a new Authority set up under the 1993 Education Act

- If you feel your child needs more help than this, you have the right to ask for a formal assessment and a 'statement of special educational needs'

- If your child has a 'statement of special educational needs', the money to meet those needs will 'follow the child'. The LEA can, however, specify that some provision should come from the school's budget

- Funding will come from the local authority's central special needs budget whether the child is attending an LEA school or a grant-maintained school. Services will be delivered through the LEA visual impairment service, or through another independent agency, at the discretion of the school

- If the LEA provides a free peripatetic visually impaired service to its own schools it must also provide it free to grant-maintained schools

- In some areas, the local authority visual impairment services are having to become private businesses, selling their services to LEA and grant-maintained schools

- In an independent school the responsibility is upon the individual school to 'buy in' appropriate services. The LEA has no obligation to provide support or funding

Dissatisfied at any stage?

- Talk things through with the school Special Education Needs Co-ordinator
- Consult the LEA Visual Impairment Service
- Take your concerns to the school governors
- Talk to the RNIB Advocacy service

See 8.2.4 for formal appeal procedures

Key to media of publication ❶ clear print ❶ large print ❶ braille ❶ tape ❶ Moon ❶ disk
Where a full address is not given in the text, see 32 (Useful addresses)

8.2 Assessing 'special educational needs'

Local education authorities (LEAs) must identify all children aged two years and over (including young people up to 19 years of age if they are still at school) who are likely to need special educational provision. They must then arrange for those needs to be assessed and, if appropriate, make a formal **Statement** describing how those needs are to be met. LEAs have a duty to follow a similar procedure with children under two years of age if the parents request it.

8.2.1 The school-based assessment

Until now, many partially sighted children attending mainstream schools have 'got by' without ever being formally assessed and a statement drawn up. Yet a statement could have been the key to the services they needed if they were to work to the best of their ability with the least strain. But the length and complexity and possible implications of the statementing process daunted parents and deterred professionals.

NEW There is now a new five stage procedure recommended for assessment. Stages 1 to 3 should particularly help this group of children. The new **Code of Practice on the Identification and Assessment of Special Educational Needs** **P B T** gives details. For a free copy contact *Dept. for Education* ℘ 0171 510 0150.

Stage 1:

Class or subject teachers talk with parents and child about the difficulties and consult the school's Special Educational Needs Co-ordinator (SENCO).

Parents should ask for the Visual Impairment Service (see 8.6.1) to be involved. Simple specialist equipment such as a work board or improved lighting may resolve the difficulty at this stage and there will be no need to move on to Stage 2, though the situation must be kept under review.

Stage 2:

The Co-ordinator consults parents, teachers and becomes responsible for collecting information and co-ordinating special educational provision.

This should result in an **Individual Education plan** with a programme, targets, monitoring and review arrangements.

If more intensive help is needed, then the child moves on to Stage 3.

Stage 3:

Teachers and the Co-ordinator get specialist help and advice.

If not already involved, a qualified teacher of visually impaired children must now be consulted. A new **Individual Education Plan** must be drawn up, with review arrangements made.

Together, Stages 1, 2 and 3 should mean that straightforward equipment such as the items described in RNIB's **Product Guide Learning** (see 29.1), simple low vision aids or special lighting, should be provided out of the school's special education budget. The LEA Visual Impairment Advisory Service is likely to be involved and there may be several hours a week special help from a non-teaching assistant. Parents will have a right to know who to contact at the school if they are worried.

8.2.2 Statutory assessment

Where children have needs that cannot be met through stages 1–3, the headteacher will have to decide whether to ask the LEA to make a statutory assessment, and so move on to stages 4 and 5. These stages are crucial for children with a severe visual loss or children who have poor sight and other handicaps. Stages 4 and 5 are designed to identify and meet complex needs. It should mean that more sophisticated equipment such as closed-circuit television, braille writers and computers, or services expensive in man-hours such as enlarging **all** paperwork, providing a full braille transcription service, a class-room assistant and specialist teaching help, will all be provided and the cost met from the LEA's central special needs budget. Alternatively, it could mean that the LEA takes financial responsibility for the child to attend a special school.

Parents may well need outside advice at this point, and the LEA must identify someone who is independent (known as the **Named Person**) such as a representative from **LOOK** (see 31.2), or one of the voluntary societies for the blind listed in 7.9 who could help them. Alternatively, parents might prefer to have a friend, relative or a professional who knows them well, as their 'Named Person', who can accompany them to meetings and help them record their views. Parents can ask directly for a Statutory Assessment (Stage 4) and the LEA must agree or refuse this request within six weeks. The LEA also can leapfrog the school-based procedure if parents, school and specialist advisors agree.

Stage 4:

The LEA considers and consults as to whether or not a statutory assessment is needed and tells parents what it is doing. When a child is visually impaired, the Code suggests that when deciding whether to go ahead with a statutory assessment, the LEA should consider:

- 'clear recorded evidence of the child's visual difficulty, in the form of assessments of the level of the child's functional vision'
- 'clear recorded evidence that the visual impairment significantly impairs mobility, emotional or social development, access to the curriculum, ability to take part in particular classroom activities or ... school life
- 'clear substantiated evidence, based on specific examples, that the child's visual difficulty places the child under stress, with associated withdrawn or frustrated behaviour'.

If the result of Stage 4 is agreement to the need for a statutory assessment the LEA must complete it within ten weeks unless the parents need more time, perhaps to obtain an independent assessment report (see 8.4.1), or the summer holidays intervene. The LEA must seek medical, educational, psychological and social services advice or any other advice that those consulted think desirable. Parents must be asked to contribute their views. Nor must how the child feels about the situation be forgotten. At this stage, parents might ask for a 'second opinion' assessment (see 8.4.1) or a report from a mobility officer qualified to teach children.

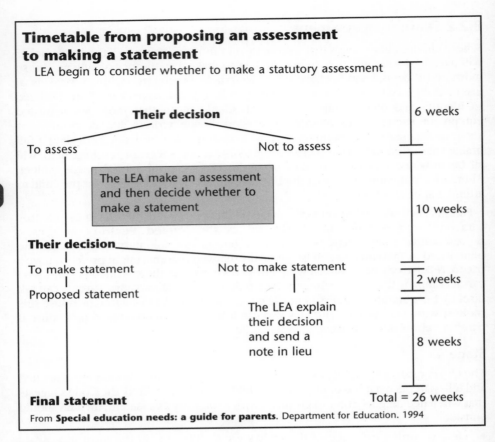

Timetable from proposing an assessment to making a statement

LEA begin to consider whether to make a statutory assessment

Their decision

To assess   Not to assess   6 weeks

The LEA make an assessment and then decide whether to make a statement   10 weeks

Their decision

To make statement   Not to make statement   2 weeks

Proposed statement   The LEA explain their decision and send a note in lieu   8 weeks

Final statement   Total = 26 weeks

From **Special education needs: a guide for parents.** Department for Education. 1994

Stage 5:

The LEA considers the need for a statement (known in Scotland as a Record of Needs)

The Code of Practice recommends that LEAs should implement Stage 5 when the assessment indicates that:

'the balance of the evidence ... suggests the child's learning difficulties and/or disabilities:

- are significant and/or complex
- have not been met by relevant and purposeful measures taken by the school and external specialists
- may call for special education provision which cannot reasonably be provided within the resources normally available to mainstream schools in the area.'

8.2.3 The statement of special educational needs

A formal six part statement is drafted, based on the Stage 4 reports. Parents have the right to examine the draft statement and must tell the LEA within fifteen days (which

POINTS FOR PARENTS
Check your child's draft statement of special educational needs!

- Read the professionals' reports. Do you agree? Have they missed anything out?
- Does Part 2 describe **all** your child's special needs?
- Does Part 3 list **in detail** how the LEA will meet those needs? What extra help will your child have? Who will give it? A qualified teacher of visually impaired children, an aide (non-teaching assistant), the class teacher? Have mobility lessons been included? If physio or speech therapy are essential for educational progress are they specified here?
- Does Part 3 identify clearly and specifically medium and long term objectives for your child?
- Is the equipment needed listed? A brailler, portable wordprocessor, low vision aids, etc.? Part 3 must state what is required to meet the child's needs. The question of resources or money should not influence this.
- Do not accept that 'it is better to be vague, because provision can be changed more easily'. **Everyone working with your child needs to know clearly what is involved and why. Unless it is specified the LEA is not required to provide it**.

Neil Anderson, RNIB Advocacy Service

can be extended if they need more time to get advice) if they are unhappy with it so that their concerns can be discussed before a final statement is issued. LEAs must review a child's statement every year, and again parents have a right to be involved and must receive written reports in advance. The review following the child's fourteenth birthday must prepare a **Transition Plan** looking to life after school.

8.2.4 The appeal procedure

NEW If parents are dissatisfied with the provision proposed when the final statement is made, they can appeal to an independent Special Educational Needs Tribunal whose decisions will be binding on the LEA. Subjects for appeal include an LEA's refusal to assess or reassess a child, their identification of the child's special educational needs in the statement, and their choice of the school named in the statement. RNIB Advocacy Service will advise, support and represent parents. A **Notice of Appeal** form is included in the free booklet **Special Educational Needs Tribunal. How to Appeal ⓑⓣ** from *Dept. for Education* ✆ 0171 510 0150.

8.3 Choosing a school

The Statement of special educational needs asks parents to say which school they would like their child to attend. As in the past, there is a let-out clause in the new legislation. The LEA **must** name the same school **unless** it considers it unsuitable because of the child's age, ability or special educational needs, or if attendance there would be incompatible with the efficient use of resources. If the parents opt for a grant-maintained school and the LEA also names that school, then the child must be allowed to go there and the school must provide the services listed in the Statement.

NEW From September 1995 all LEA and grant-maintained schools will be required to publish details of their schools' policies for all pupils with special educational needs and issue an annual report on how provision has been made. These reports should prove useful to parents looking around for a suitable school.

8.4 Help and advice for parents

RNIB Advocacy Service for Parents offers help, support and advice to parents. RNIB staff can be contacted by telephone through the RNIB Education Centres (see 8.6.2) or a message can be left on the Advocacy Co-ordinator's answerphone ✆ 01676 541429. Staff can help parents prepare their contribution to their child's statement, or accompany parents to meetings. They can support parents at Tribunal appeals. More details in **Making your voice heard** (see 8.1).

ACE adviceline ✆ 0171 354 8321 (2-5 p.m. weekdays) is a service provided by the **Advisory Centre for Education**. It advises parents of children with special educational needs on the legal aspects of special education.

8.4.1 Independent assessment providers

Parents who need a 'second opinion' regarding their child's formal assessment of special educational needs may wish to approach one of the following agencies. A charge may be made. Help with the cost may be available from the local authority or a charity, the agencies will advise.

Birmingham University, *School of Education, Research Centre for the Education of the Visually Handicapped, Edgbaston, Birmingham B15 2TT* ✆ 0121 414 6733. Research staff can provide an objective and impartial assessment of needs and abilities which can be used as a basis for discussion as to the child's best placement.

Dorton House Assessment Team, *Dorton House School, Seal, Sevenoaks, Kent TN15 0ED* ✆ 01732 764123. Free service to parents and LEAs. Clinical and functional visual assessment. Educational assessment. Mobility and daily living skills assessment if requested by local authority.

West of England School for Children with Little or No Sight, *Topsham Road, Countess Wear, Exeter, Devon EX2 6HA* ✆ 01392 454200. One to three day assessment for pre-school and school age children by paediatrician, speech therapist, physiotherapist, educational psychologist, mobility worker, ophthalmologist and teacher of visually impaired children.

Wolfson Centre, *Great Ormond Street Hospital for Sick Children NHS Trust, Mecklenburgh Square, London WC1N 2AP* ✆ 0171 837 7618.
Free functional visual and development assessment, plus low vision clinic for pre-school children (see 7.1.2). Referral through ophthalmologist, paediatrician or GP.

RNIB Education Support Services

A wide range of assessments is offered. Costs range between £200 and £300 depending on the nature and location of the assessment. Mobility assessments are charged at a standard rate of £150.

Visual functioning in an educational context – aims to identify the functional rather than the clinical aspects of vision and relate them to educational implications. Contact *Suzanne Mehta. RNIB Education Centre, North* ℘ 0113 274 8855.

Mobility and orientation – aims to establish how a child functions in school and/or home environment and to identify the elements of a programme required to give them a level of independence appropriate to their age and circumstances. This service is available in London and the South-East. Contact *Roger Willis. RNIB Education Centre, London* ℘ 0181 968 8600.

Music assessments for visually impaired and multi-disabled visually impaired children – for children pursuing musical ambitions beyond the norm or for children for whom music is essential for wider development, for example, in communication. Contact *Sally Zimmermann. RNIB Education Centre, London* ℘ 0181 968 8600.

Technology and study methods – aims to establish how a child functions using visual, auditory and/or tactile media, and to identify technological aids and study methods which could increase independence and efficiency in approaches to learning. Contact *Max Hampson. RNIB Education Centre, London* ℘ 0181 968 8600 (see also 8.20.3).

8.5 School days

An increasing number of visually impaired children now attend mainstream schools. Sometimes a special unit for visually impaired children is attached to a mainstream school. As a result, in recent years the role of specialist schools has changed. For example, although RNIB continues to be the largest provider of specialist schools, the schools also act as resource centres for mainstream schools. Specialist schools for visually impaired children can provide services and fire the imagination of staff in mainstream schools, with visually impaired pupils but little expertise in visual handicap. Older pupils often attend classes at local mainstream schools, supported by the resources of their own 'special' school. In this way the choice between 'special' and 'mainstream' school is becoming blurred. Children can and do move between the two, and choosing one does not necessarily mean a complete cut-off from the other. Special schools are likely to be residential, though day pupils are accepted and weekly boarding is common and encouraged. They are run by local authorities or by voluntary organisations. RNIB Education Information Service can supply a list. **Choices for Children** ⊕⊕ (50p, free to parents. RNIB Education Information Service) is an attractive booklet which describes the educational options.

8.6 School support services in mainstream schools

8.6.1 LEA Services

The majority of LEA Special Education Departments have teachers who specialise in working with visually impaired pupils. Some LEAs have a 'sensory impairment service' which brings together the staff dealing with hearing and visual impairments. Others have a visual impairment service which may consist of a group of teachers or one individual. Sometimes that teacher will be supporting individual children in several schools within the authority's area. In other areas, the specialist teacher will be found in a unit or will be a resource teacher in an ordinary school.

Specialist teachers, often familiarly known as 'peris' (short for peripatetic), support children from pre-school days until college. Since September 1994 LEAs have continued to provide these services in their own schools and in grant-maintained schools within their area and beyond. However, both LEA schools and grant-maintained schools are free to 'buy in' specialist services, such as braille tuition or mobility, from alternative suppliers.

8.6.2 RNIB Services

RNIB education centres offer a range of services including integration and curriculum support, assessment services, family support, family weekends, an advocacy service for parents, vacation schemes, technology assessment and training and equipment hire schemes. A music education advisory service and a mobility service are based in London.

London, *Garrow House, 190 Kensal Rd, London W10 5BT* ✆ 0181 968 8600
Scotland, *10 Magdala Crescent, Edinburgh EH12 5BE* ✆ 0131 313 1876
Wales, *4th Floor, 33-35 Cathedral Road, Cardiff CF1 2HB* ✆ 01222 668606
Midlands, *c/o RNIB New College Worcester, Whittington Road,*
Worcester WR5 2JU ✆ 01905 357635
North, *Grosvenor House, Grosvenor Road, Headingley, Leeds LS6 2DZ*
✆ 0113 274 8855
South West, *Level 5, Northernhay House West, Northernhay Place,*
Exeter, Devon EX4 3RL ✆ 01392 493643

RNIB plans to establish other regional centres nationwide.

8.6.3 RNIB Integration Support Service

NEW This service encourages and helps visually impaired children to study in mainstream schools. Its illustrated guide **Including Visually Impaired Children** ❶❷❸ is designed to help schools respond to the new legislation, but parents would find it an interesting, easy-to-read introduction to ways in which a visually impaired child's needs can be met in primary and secondary schools. Copies from *RNIB Education Centre, North*. An **Integration Support Scheme** helps RNIB and LEAs to work together when a child who needs non-sighted means of communication enters an LEA school. RNIB will contribute up to £3000 per pupil, on a pound for pound basis, towards the cost of special equipment on condition that it is allowed to provide in-service training for staff development

'For six months prior to my blind pupil starting school, I would go to her playgroup, introducing braille to her almost immediately. I would tell her stories, teach her to use the Perkins brailler to write her name and encourage her to read some of the early braille letters.... In the reception class I arranged specific braille lessons every day and at first withdrew her from the class because she needed to concentrate well and was still developing her listening skills. Apart from this, she was fully integrated in every other lesson .... All class worksheets are put into braille and this has become a major part of the special support assistant's working day ... To compensate for difficulties she has in participating fully in games periods, I have organised horse riding lessons. ... She joins in with the school recorder and handbell clubs, and also has flute lessons. After nearly five years, we are all, parents, teachers, governors and children of this small primary school, still working together well as a team and she is happy and confident.'

▶ Brenda Derby. Support teacher for visually impaired children, Hereford & Worcester, writing in **VISability**, Spring 1995.

and monitor progress for three years. More details from *Judy Bunting, IRNIB Education Centre, North* (see also 8.16).

8.7 The National Curriculum

8.7.1 RNIB Curriculum Support Service

This Service provides advice and information to those working with visually impaired children in secondary schools. It is particularly concerned with making the national curriculum accessible. An information pack is available on GCSE arrangements for visually impaired candidates. Details from *Rory Cobb, RNIB Education Centre, Midlands*.

8.7.2 Visual Impairment National Curriculum Groups

A major concern is that hard-pressed staff in mainstream schools may too readily consider the 'disapplication' of some of the National Curriculum for their visually impaired pupils because particular subjects are thought to cause too many difficulties. Parents and teachers should be aware that many of the practical problems can and have been overcome, and should contact the groups listed below for information.

Details of Curriculum Groups in Scotland can be obtained from *RNIB Education Centre, Scotland*.

Art, Craft and Design: Joyce Ogden, Smestow School, Windmill Crescent, Wolverhampton WV3 8HU ℘ 01902 764141

Business Studies & Information Technology: Peter Richardson, RNIB Redhill College, Philanthropic Road, Redhill, Surrey RH1 4DZ ℘ 01737 768935

Craft, Design & Technology: Jan Kear, RNIB New College, Whittington Road, Worcester WR5 2JX ℘ 01905 763933

English: Julie Elson, St. Vincent's School, Yew Tree Lane, West Derby, Liverpool L12 9HN ℘ 0151 228 9968

Further Education: Paul Lynch, Loxley College, Myers Grove Lane, Stannington, Sheffield S6 5JL ℘ 0114 260 2242

Geography: Jenni Rolls, RNIB New College, Whittington Road, Worcester, WR5 2JX ℘ 01905 763933

History & Social Studies: (including Economics, R.E., Politics and Sociology): Will Gale, RNIB New College, Whittington Road, Worcester WR5 2JX 01905 763933

Mathematics: Sue Clamp, St. Vincents School, Yew Tree Lane, West Derby, Liverpool, L12 9HN ℘ 0151 228 9968

Mobility: Sue Jones, RNIB Redhill College, Philanthropic Road, Redhill, Surrey RH1 4DZ ℘ 01737 768935

Modern Languages: Richard Roberts, RNIB New College, Whittington Road, Worcester WR5 2JX ℘ 01905 763933

Multi-disabled (VITAL): Jonathan Griffiths, RNIB Condover Hall School, Condover, Shrewsbury, Shropshire SY5 7AH℘ 01743 872320

Music: Jill Smith, Dorton House School, Seal, Sevenoaks, Kent TN15 0ED ℘ 01732 761477

Physical Education: Angela Beach, St. Vincent's School, Yew Tree Lane, West Derby, Liverpool L12 9HN ℘ 0151 228 9968

Primary: Kevin Barrett, Visiting Teacher Service, Vauxhall Gardens, Barrack Street, Birmingham B7 4HA ℘ 0121 359 0883

Science: Gerry Corfield, Royal National College, College Road, Hereford HR1 1EB ℘ 01432 265725 ext 2226

Under 5s: Annette Hope, Co-ordinator of Service, Saltwells Educational Development Service, Bowling Green Road, Netherton, Dudley DY2 9LY 01384 634155 ext 390

ADVISE is an advisory panel for the needs of visually impaired students in Art and Design, CDT and Design Crafts (see 21.1).

8.8 Reading

A series of free leaflets **P B** from RNIB Education Service gives details of tape, braille and large print resources for children.

The **National Library for the Handicapped Child** *Wellington House, Wellington Road, Wokingham, Berkshire RG11 2AG* ℘ 01734 891101 is a resource centre for children who have problems affecting reading and communication. Stock includes a wide range of Big Books (see 8.8.3) audio cassettes and samples of braille and ClearVision books. Visits by appointment. Information packs according to enquirer's needs are available on request.

8.8.1 Braille

Newcomers can be forgiven for thinking that the use of tape recorders, recorded books, scanners and computers have made braille redundant. In fact, braille reigns supreme as the only medium which gives true independence not only in reading, writing and academic work but also in everyday activities (see chapter 17). **Information on learning braille for children and teenagers ❶ Ⓑ**, a free leaflet from RNIB Education Information Service, gives basic information on starting braille. The **RNIB NEC Braille Certificate** is designed for parents and teachers and can be gained through a correspondence course. Details from *RNIB Education Centre, London* ✆ 0181 968 8600.

Reading courses supplied by RNIB include:

- **Braille for Infants** (5 to 7 year olds) £29.95. Teacher's handbook £5.00
- **NEW** Takeoff (primary school children) £40.00. A range of **Ladybird** books are available to accompany this course
- **Braille in Easy Steps** (10 to 13 year olds) £15.00
- **Spot the Dot** (13 to 18 year olds) £15.00
- **NEW** Dechrau Darllen Braille Cymraeg (Learning to read Welsh Braille) consists of 40 graded books to help young children to learn the new Welsh braille code launched in November 1994 (£40 complete, or £12 for 10 titles from RNIB Education Centre Wales ✆ 01222 668606)
- **NEW** Reading in braille Ⓑ (£4.60. RNIB Customer Services) is a reference manual for teachers in mainstream or special schools.

A **Young People's Reading and Resources Committee** meets once a term, usually in London to promote the provision of braille for all young people, particularly for leisure reading. Parents or professionals should contact *Kathleen Gaster, Linden Lodge School, 61 Princes Way, Wimbledon Park, London, SW19 6JB* ✆ 0181 788 0107.

Details of braille publications will be found in 18.2.

Braille magazines for children include:

- **Roundabout** (RNIB. Monthly. £1.80 p.a) for children between around 7 to 11 years with stories, competitions and activities for younger children
- **Fizz** (RNIB. Weekly. £10.40 p.a) for 16 to 19 year olds with fashion news, pop gossip, the charts and a horoscope
- **Tempo** (Scottish Braille Press. Monthly. £6 p.a.). 17 to 25 year olds covering the music scene, the environment, relationships and health
- **Spark** (Torch Trust. Monthly. Free) is a Christian magazine for children between 7 and 12 years. **Searchlight** (Torch Trust. Quarterly. Free) is for young people from 13 upwards.

8.8.2 Audio cassette

Many children's story tapes are stocked by record shops, and can often be borrowed through public libraries. **Chivers** and **Cover to Cover Cassettes Ltd** both issue children's titles in unabridged versions. **RNIB Talking Book Library** and **Calibre Cassette Library** have children's sections (see 19.1.1, 19.1.3, 19.2).

Audio magazines for children and young people are issued on free loan by **Cue and Review** a national youth tape service for the visually impaired. It aims to provide a comparable range of magazines to that available in print for sighted young people. Titles include **Just Seventeen**, **Sound Explosion** (pop), **Sliding Tackle** (football), **Fashion & Beauty**, **Channel V.T.V** (weekly TV listings plus film and video releases), **Rock Solid** (Heavy Metal), **Timescan** (general interest) and **Cue & Review** (current affairs). Details from *Cue & Review Recording Services, 18 Crowhill Road, Bishopbriggs, Glasgow G64 1QY* ✆ 0141 762 1299.

Live Wire is a free monthly magazine, composed mainly of original material, for 11 to 16 year olds. Details from *Susan Crow, Cathedral Centre, Captain Street, Bradford BD1 4AH* ✆ 01274 308707. **Spark** and **Searchlight** (see 8.8.1) are both issued on cassette, and Spark is also produced in large print.

8.8.3 Large print

Cartwheels, Gazelle, Piccadilly Press, Viking Read Alones and Young Puffin books offer reasonable print for newly fluent readers. Two large print books for children are published each month by **Chivers** under the imprint Galaxy. These should be available in public libraries together with their Lythway series for children between 8 and 13 years. Local libraries can also borrow Austin large print classics from the **National Library for the Blind** (see 18.1.1). Otherwise, large print for teenagers is virtually non-existent.

Large Format Books, often known as Big Books, are around 24 inches high and 15 inches wide and may help some children. Text and pictures are giant sized. Titles include the **Giant World Atlas** (Hamlyn. £10.99) and a range of fiction, mainly Australian. Big Books are stocked by public libraries and can be purchased from *Peters Library Service Ltd., 120 Bromsgrove Street, Birmingham B5 6RL* ✆ 0121 666 6646. A large print children's booklist **Books at Large**. (£1.20 cash with order) can be obtained from *Kyle & Carrick District Libraries, Carnegie Library, 12 Main Street, Ayr KA8 8ED* ✆ 01292 285385.

NEW A leaflet on information books in large print will be available from **ClearVision** during 1995 (see also 18.1).

8.8.4 Viewbooks

These books are similar to conventional books but are published on disk and have a text search facility. Titles include the **Oxford Children's Dictionary** (£40.00) available in a special edition for use by visually impaired children. Details from **Information Education,** *Unit 35, Enterprise Centre, Bedford Street, Stoke-on-Trent ST1 4PZ* ✆ 01782 281643.

8.8.5 CD-ROM

CD-ROM has opened up new possibilities for visually impaired children and adults. References can be swiftly found, and read immediately through the braille, speech, or large character display output of a computer. Students can do their own research or browse at will. **Opening up the library for visually impaired learners** ❶❸❼❹ gives details. Free copies from *RNIB Education Centre, London* (see also 20.10).

8.9 Writing

Heavily lined stationery is stocked in a range of formats, including **music staved packs** and school-size exercise books. Free catalogue from the *Partially Sighted Society* (see also 18.1.6).

An adjustable **workboard** (£42. *Partially Sighted Society*) can be used for writing. Notepaper is anchored by magnets, and a magnetic ledge is deep enough to take most large print books. The stand, though portable, is heavy, as it is designed to survive the roughest school life. Spare magnets and ledges can be supplied.

Father Christmas has mastered braille! And is good at tape recording! Write to him c/o *PO Box 16, Peterborough PE2 6WS* **in braille, large print or on tape and he will send a reply in the same medium. Post early for Christmas. Ring Lo-call 0345 023153 for the latest date.**

(NEW) Touch Typing Tutor (£24) is a computer program designed for IBM and Archimedes computers which has been specially developed to teach touch typing skills to young visually impaired children. The exercise text can be read through a speech output and can be shown in different colours, sizes and fonts on the screen. The program has been used with older children and adults. Details from the *Research Centre for the Education of the Visually Handicapped* (see also 18.1.6).

Write Away, a pen pal club for children with special needs, matches up suitable partners who can then correspond using whatever means they wish: braille, audio cassette, or letters. Club membership £2.00. Braille paper and cassette tapes can be provided. More details from *Write Away, 29 Crawford Street, London W1H 1PL* ✆ 0171 724 0878.

(NEW) Chatter-Post is an audio cassette pen pal scheme. New 'chatter-friends' receive a blank audio-cassette and wallet, record their letter and send it to a 'chatter co-ordinator' who forwards it onto another 'chatter-friend'. Details from *Chatter-Post, c/o Merton Talking News, The Guardian Centre, 67 Clarendon Road, London SW10 2DX* ✆ 0181 540 5446.

8.10 Mathematics

A factsheet **Teaching mathematics to visually impaired pupils** ⓛ (£1.00) is available from RNIB Education Information Service. A range of specially designed mathematical equipment, including large square graph paper, is listed in RNIB's Education Product Guide ⓛⓑⓣ .

(NEW) Tactile rulers and protractors which also have clear markings, plus a compass kit, have been developed to meet the National Curriculum Key Stage 1 through to Key Stage 4. Details from *RNIB, Customer Services*.

A computer program which offers mathematics output in braille and large print, as well as large character on-screen editing is supplied by *Pia*. **Braille Maker Professional** (£495) was developed in consultation with the Royal National College for the Blind and Dorton House School.

'At university level, students in courses as diverse as economics, electrical engineering and environmental science have used Nomad extensively. At the other end of the scale, a five year old blind child was given a tactile picture of a teddy bear. Using Nomad, the bear spoke his own name and identified the parts of his body and his clothing'.

▶ Ron Hinton, Research Fellow, University of Loughborough

8.11 Making tactile diagrams and maps

Making meaningful tactile diagrams is not simple. Often it is best to convey the information by text. Diagrams which do need to be represented in tactile form should be as simple as possible, with all inessential elements removed.

NEW A **spur wheel** (from £3.85) used on plastic embossing film (£2.50 per 100 sheets), both stocked by RNIB, is a basic method. A new alternative is the **Thermos Pen** (£125.00). This is a heat pen which, when used on paper that swells when heated, gives an instant tactile line. Both the Thermos Pen and the heat-senstitive paper can be obtained from *Queen Alexandra College, Birmingham*.

Black line drawings can be converted into a tactile format through RNIB's **Raised Diagram Copying Service** within seven days. The explanatory manual and service subscription costs £3.50. Details from *RNIB, Customer Services*.

A much more sophisticated result can be achieved by making a tactile master diagram, similar to a collage, using a **Map and diagram making kit** (RNIB £19). This is then reproduced on heat sensitive paper using a fuser. The **Hotspot** desktop fuser (£895 plus VAT) is available from *Visualeyes, Stable Cottage, 4 Home Farm, Blakeney Road, Letheringsett, Holt, Norfolk NR25 7JL ✆ 01263 711179*.

New Ways with Diagrams by R. Hinton (£8.95 RNIB Customer Services) demonstrates how complex scientific information can be conveyed in diagrammatic form. The American publication **Tactile Graphics** (Polly Edman. £55.40 RNIB Book Sales Service) is an encyclopaedic handbook on translating visual information into a three-dimensional form that blind and visually impaired people can understand.

NEW The **Tactile Diagrams Research Unit** can give expert educational advice nationally on the use of tactile diagrams in Higher Education, as well as supplying specially commissioned diagrams for specific individual needs. Details from *Dr. R. Hinton, Loughborough University of Technology, Ashby Road, Loughborough, Leicestershire LE11 3TU ✆ 01509 263171*.

8.11.1 Talking diagrams and maps

Nomad (£850.00) is a computer peripheral consisting of a touch sensitive pad which gives spoken information for tactile diagrams. Touching the diagram triggers the voice response. Nomad works with MS-DOS and most Apple computers. It is distributed by *Queen Alexandra College, Birmingham*.

8.12 Mobility

A local authority mobility officer or rehabilitation worker should be able to provide mobility training in the home surroundings and, if necessary, in school or college. Such training is also needed for PE and to make sure children can safely cope with, for example, bunsen burners in science lessons or tools in Craft, Design and Technology classes. In some areas this training will be provided through the LEA visual impairment team which may have a member who is a teacher specially trained to teach mobility to children. Training may be as simple as making sure that a partially sighted youngster knows how to travel safely to school, or it may be the much more intensive help described in chapter 12.

(NEW) **Working with Visually Impaired Children: Guidelines for Mobility Specialists** (£2.00) is an illustrated booklet compiled by the **Mobility Specialists in Education Group**. Copies and updates can be obtained from: *Richard Ellis, Mobility Department, West of England School, Countess Wear, Exeter, Devon EX2 6HA* ✆ 01392 454200.

Contact with mobility or rehabilitation staff makes it likely that the child or young person will have the chance to be included in various outdoor activities locally, or join in the **Have a Go** days which British Blind Sport organises in various parts of the country. These provide an opportunity to try out a variety of sports including archery, athletics, judo, bowls, goalball, tandem cycling, table tennis, aerobics, swimming, canoeing, sub-aqua diving and football.

RNIB **Mobility Assessment & Training Service** can provide individual training if the local authority has no mobility service. Details from *Roger Willis, RNIB Education Centre, London*. **Henshaws** offer mobility assessment and training as 'one-offs' to parents and children and on a contractual basis to LEAs.

8.13 Music

RNIB Music Education Advisory Service (see 8.6.2) helps professionals and parents with pre-school and school-age children and students studying music in further and higher education. It can advise on equipment, examination papers, and the teaching of music generally. **Music and Visually Impaired Children**. A. Ockelford. (£1.50 RNIB Book Sales Service) discusses braille and large print music and the needs of children with multiple disabilities (see also 21.3).

8.14 Physical education

Looking into PE: Curriculum Guide **L B T** (£6.00. RNIB Customer Services) is designed for all PE teachers who have visually impaired children in their classes. It provides ideas and guidance for each Key Stage of the National Curriculum and is endorsed by the School Curriculum and Assessment Authority. An earlier short companion guide for youth leaders and sports coaches, also called **Looking into PE** is available free while stocks last.

8.15 Computers in school

A wide range of educational technology is on permanent exhibition at RNIB Education Centre, London. Visits can be made by appointment by professionals, parents and children to examine equipment and to consult the technology advisors. **Access technology: a guide to educational technology resources for visually impaired users** (£7.00. RNIB Customer Services) is issued annually. It gives comprehensive information about specific systems and uses the minimum of jargon.

Other centres where specialist technology equipment can be inspected, preferably by appointment, include the Technology Centre (Royal London Society for the Blind); Henshaw's College, Harrogate; Dorton House Information Technology Centre, Sevenoaks; RNIB Resource Centres in London, Stirling and Belfast and their Education Centres outside London, as well as at some local resource centres.

Over fifty **Centre Software** programs for BBC, IBM, Nimbus 186 and Archimedes computers have been developed for visually impaired children by the Research Centre for the Education of the Visually Handicapped. Some are designed for pre-school children with multiple disabilities and aim to stimulate vision. They can be used with joysticks, switches and the concept keyboard. A **mathematical program** (£48) is based on the ILEA SMILE scheme. **Talking Grass** (£14) adds speech to the educational database **NEW** 'Grass'. A new version of **Soundbook** (£25) was released in 1994. This links particular areas of a concept keyboard with sound or speech and enables teachers to devise their own projects. For example, braille text placed on the board can be both felt and heard.

Training and demonstration days are held at the Research Centre every Thursday (10 a.m.–12 noon and 2 p.m.–4 p.m.). Parents and children are welcome, but if tuition and hands-on experience is needed, it is important to make an appointment. More details, free catalogue and termly Newsletter from the *Research Centre for the Education of the Visually Handicapped* (see also 20.9).

8.16 Holidays and leisure

Holidays can be a problem when children are away at residential school during term-time and so have few friends at home. Some social services departments and local voluntary societies for the blind run special holiday activity groups for visually handicapped children. Most of the parent support groups (see 31.3) have outings and activity days. A number of holiday activity schemes are arranged for children in the London area. Contact *Paul Holmes, Projects by the Blind.*

NEW Let's Go! is a termly pull-out calendar of leisure activities and events included in **VISability** (see 8.26). It covers all aspects of leisure nationwide including sport, arts and crafts, exhibitions and museums, music, playschemes, holidays, activity days and audio-described plays and pantomimes.

RNIB vacations schemes offer a week of educational and leisure activities for visually impaired children and young people aged between 8 and 19 who attend mainstream schools and colleges. Educational activities may include opportunities to improve independence, mobility or develop braille and technology skills. Leisure activities can include anything from a trip to a local theme park to rock climbing, water sports, dry slope skiing, swimming or horse riding. Contact *Judy Bunting, RNIB Education Centre, North* (see also 8.6.3).

Blind in Business, a charity which has financed a number of computer projects at schools for visually impaired children, sponsors occasional holiday computer training courses especially for visually impaired young people in mainstream schools. Using all the latest access technology, the courses provide a unique opportunity for intensive hands-on experience. Details from *Carole Wilkinson, Blind in Business, Rolls House, 7 Rolls Building, Fetter Lane, London EC4A 1NH* ✆ 0171 931 2198.

The **Scout Association** aims to include all young people in normal Scouting activities. A national network of Assistant Commissioners (Special Needs) and Advisors are a good first point of contact for parents or children who are unsure of approaching a local group directly. Contact *Libby Morgan, National Commissioner (Special Needs), The Scout Association, Gilwell Park, Chingford, London E4 7QW* ✆ 0181 524 5246. The **Guide Association** welcomes young people whose disabilities may 'limit their activities but not their hopes and achievements'. It has County Advisers for Members with Disabilities. The Brownie and Guide Handbook are both produced in large print and braille. Contact *Jennie Lamb, Guiding Activities, The Guide Association, 17-19 Buckingham Palace Road, London SW1W 0PT* ✆ 0171 834 6242 ext. 260.

8.17 Open learning

VIOLA (Visual Impairment and Open Learning Adaptation) is a network of organisations able to modify open learning material to meet the needs of visually impaired learners. All have appropriate equipment, and can undertake large print, audio tape or braille transcription on either a commercial or charitable basis. Details and a **Directory of Centres** from *Mark Braithwaite, RNIB Vocational College*.

8.18 Further education

Details of Colleges of Further Education will be found in chapter 9.

8.19 Higher education

All universities accept applications from suitably qualified visually impaired students. In 1994 there were 671 such students in campus-based higher education.

NEW St. John's College, Oxford has funds available specifically for visually impaired undergraduates and wishes to encourage applications. The application procedure is the standard route via UCAS and the Oxford Colleges Admission Office. Details from *Tutor for Admissions, St. John's College, Oxford.*

The **Open University** has some 500 visually impaired students – roughly 10% of the OU's total disabled student population. The OU has a sophisticated and wide range of services for visually impaired students including audiocassette versions of printed course texts and books, the free loan of talking calculators and other study-related equipment, helpers at residential schools and home-based examinations. There is also a local counselling service through which students can get help on any aspect of OU study. At the beginning of each OU academic year (normally in early March) there is a **Study Skills** weekend residential course for new OU students and their tutors. The course has three aims: to build confidence, to help students develop some basic study techniques and to provide information about the various OU facilities available to visually impaired students. Most OU courses and study packs are available on tape, as are the brochures and prospectuses for the main OU study programmes. The OU's campus-based recording centre is part of RNIB's national network of recording centres and tapes of OU course set books are available through RNIB cassette library (see 19.1.2). An *Office for Students with Disabilities* ℘ 01908 653273 coordinates service provision, and an *Adviser on the Education of Disabled Students* can be consulted on academic and policy matters.

Research is undertaken at the OU's Institute of Educational Technology into the application of information technology for visually impaired learners. Recent projects include an investigation into how **NEW** CD-ROM technology can be used to provide print-based course units in alternative media such as digital text and digital audio. Further information on this research can be obtained from *Dr. A. T. Vincent, Institute of Educational Technology, The Open University, Milton Keynes MK7 6AA* ℘ 01908 652907.

8.20 Support services for higher education

8.20.1 RNIB Student Support Service

RNIB Student Support Service offers advice and support to visually impaired students. A team of eight student advisors can help with career planning, advise on study skills, loan equipment and act as advocates. Details in a **Student Information Pack** ❶❸❼ is supplied by *RNIB Student Support Service, PO Box 49, Loughborough, Leicester LE11 3DG* ℘ 01509 211995.

The **Partners in Access** scheme described in 9.6.1 applies also to higher education. The following Universities are all Partners in Access:

Anglia Polytechnic University (Chelmsford), Bolton Institute of Higher Education, Glasgow Caledonian University, Glasgow University, University of Hertfordshire, Universities of Lancaster, Leicester, Liverpool, UMIST, Manchester Metropolitan University, St. Martin's College (Lancaster), Nene College (Northampton), Nottingham Trent University, University of Sunderland, University of Ulster, University College of North Wales (Bangor) and University of the West of England (Bristol).

8.20.2 Skill: the National Bureau for Students with Disabilities

Skill provides an information service for individual students and professionals. The information service is available for telephone enquiries on ℘ 0171 978 9890 on weekdays 1.30 – 4.30 p.m. Skill publications are available on tape on request and their range of information sheets are all offered in braille and large print. Up to 10 information sheets are free to students/trainees on receipt of a stamped addressed envelope.

8.20.3 National Federation of Access Centres

This is a national network of specialist centres, including RNIB Vocational College and the Royal National College. It aims to increase opportunities in further and higher education, training and employment for students over the age of 14 who have physical disabilities, a sensory impairment or learning difficulties. Each Centre provides assessment, initial training and ongoing support for students with special needs in higher and further education, as well as training in the use of new technology for teachers, trainers, employers and students.

A service is offered to LEAs to undertake assessments and make reports for students eligible for equipment under the Disabled Students Allowance. Further details from the *National Access Centre, Hereward College of Further Education, Bramston Crescent, Tile Hill Lane, Coventry CV4 9SW* ℘ 01203 461231.

8.21 Student organisations

The Association of Blind and Partially Sighted Teachers and Students (ABAPSTAS) is a self-help organisation which holds an annual conference, exhibitions of special equipment, and runs study skills and confidence-building courses. It is a forum where visually impaired people with an interest in education and training can meet with a view to influencing local and national education policy. Members receive regular circulars and bulletins **❶❸❼**, *BM 6727, London WC1N 3XX*, contact *Nick Clarke* ℘ 01484 517954.

Student Vision Scotland (SVS) is a self-help and advocacy group run by visually impaired students studying in Scottish post-16 education. It organises termly meetings with invited speakers and provides a forum for students to discuss issues and concerns of common interest. Contact *Dr. Archie Roy, RNIB Student Support Service, Level 5, Graham Hills Building (East), University of Strathclyde, 40 George Street, Glasgow G1 1QE* ℘ 0141 552 2626.

8.22 Financial help in higher education

8.22.1 The Disabled Student's Allowance

Students who gain a LEA mandatory award are also able to claim a **Disabled Student's Allowance**. Mandatory awards are means-tested and are only available to students who are following a full-time designated course of higher education (degree or degree-level). The Disabled Student's Allowance is in three parts: a general annual payment of £1,215 maximum, a grant of up to £4,850 p.a. for non-medical personal help and payments of up to £3,650 for the purchase of specialist equipment (September 1995/6 figures). In Scotland broadly the same rules apply, but awards are administered by the *Scottish Office Education Department* ℘ 0131 244 5832. In Northern Ireland the Education and Library Boards have responsibility for issuing student grants.

All the elements in the Disabled Student's Allowance are means-tested and only students who qualify for a mandatory award will be automatically eligible. The actual amount of the allowances paid is at the discretion of the LEA. This means that students must be able to explain their needs and the ways, and the cost, of meeting them. Students starting courses are especially likely to find it helpful to contact any of the support services described in 8.20 for advice and help in their negotiations. Unsuccessful applicants can apply to RNIB Student Support Service for a grant up to a maximum of £450 (£900 over a five year period). Postgraduate students in receipt of awards from most of the Central Government funding bodies can apply for the Disabled Student's Allowance.

An information sheet **Funding for Students with disabilities in higher education** ❶❸❼ (1995) is free from *Skill*. It also explains the special repayment help for students with disabilities who have taken out a loan under the Student Loans Act.

8.22.2 Finances during the holidays

Most students have lost their entitlement to social security benefits but registered blind students or partially sighted students receiving incapacity benefit, disability living allowance or severe disablement allowance continue to receive these allowances. If they are eligible on financial grounds, they are also entitled to continue to receive housing benefit and income support during term-time and during the vacations. A Skill information sheet **Income support and housing benefit in full-time education** ❶❸❼ (1995) gives details.

8.22.3 Open University students

Open University students who have financial difficulties may qualify for a RNIB grant of up to £450 or the loan of essential equipment. Details from *RNIB Student Support Services.*

8.23 Help from charities

The **Cambrian Educational Trust Fund** offers financial assistance to blind and partially sighted young people under 21 years of age who need help in their education, perhaps by the provision of items such as braille writers or typewriters, which cannot be provided by statutory funds. Enquiries to the *Secretary, Mrs. P. Fish, 20A Crescentdale, Longford, Gloucester GL2 9EP.*

Electronic Aids for the Blind may be able to help provide equipment such as braille notetakers, laptop PCs and closed-circuit televisions for use at home by children in mainstream or special education. Applications should be channelled through the school.

The **Kate Mann Memorial Fund** can provide financial assistance to young people between 11 and 25 years of age who have a serious interest in musical performance or appreciation. Help has been given, for example, towards summer music school costs, and the purchase of electronic composing equipment and private tuition in various instruments. The trustees' tastes are catholic, ranging from tuba to tambourine, from rhapsody to rock! Details from *David Mann, 63 Hillside Crescent, Harrow, Middlesex HA2 0QU* ✆ 0181 864 2156.

RNIB Leisure Service may be able to offer financial support towards the costs of activity/adventure holidays. The scheme is aimed at groups formed by schools/ colleges, clubs and voluntary associations. 50% of the members of the group must be visually impaired. Other sources of help, though not specifically for visually impaired young people, include **The Prince's Trust** and **The Royal Jubilee Trusts** who consider making cash grants to young people aged 14 to 25 to enable them to develop their talents. The Trusts operate through a network of local committees to which applicants should apply direct. Further details from the *Director, The Prince's Trust and The Royal Jubilee Trusts, 8 Bedford Row, London WC1R 4BA* Freephone ✆ 0800 842842. A factsheet **Grant awarding charities** gives details of charities who have provided financial assistance to visually impaired students in the past. Contact: *RNIB Student Support Service*. See also 30.

8.24 Adult education

Many visually impaired people join in the evening and day classes arranged by adult education departments, and the **Workers' Educational Association**. The local library will be able to give details of local classes. Sometimes special classes for visually impaired people are held, when it is felt that more personal tuition is required than could be given in a large class of sighted students. Visually impaired adults who are interested in joining any group but are hesitant about their ability to keep up with the class, should discuss the matter with the adult education officer responsible – the name and address will be known at the local library.

The **University of the Third Age** welcomes visually impaired people who are not in full-time paid work. No qualifications are needed. Local groups pool their talents and organise their own activities. Further details from *University of the Third Age (U3A), 1 Stockwell Green, London SW9 9JF* ✆ 0171 737 2541.

The **NEW** **Dark Horse Venture** encourages people over 55 to find new challenges. A number of visually impaired people have developed new interests by selecting an activity which they had not tried seriously before and becoming involved in it for twelve months under the guidance of an advisor of their choice. Contact *The Administrator, The Dark Horse Venture, Kelton, Woodlands Road, Liverpool L17 0AN* ✆ 0151 729 0092.

Prospective physiotherapy students are advised to contact the manager of the **RNIB Physiotherapy Support Service** who can help with applications and the selection of an appropriate course in a mainstream college. The Service provides teaching support in theoretical, practical and clinical sessions, and extra tutorial support. A resource centre based at the University of East London offers a wide range of specialised equipment and services to all visually impaired physiotherapy students throughout the UK.

A consultancy service is offered to visually impaired students who wish to follow other health-related careers, such as **occupational therapy** or **speech therapy**.

The Social Work Division, Staffordshire University welcomes applications from visually disabled people who wish to train as social workers. It has installed services and equipment aimed at making the **Diploma in Social Work** more accessible.

A second year 'sight impairment option' is also available within the Diploma. This means that sighted social work students have the opportunity to acquire some specialist expertise within their social work qualification.

Further information from *Alison Read, Admissions Tutor, School of Social Sciences, Staffordshire University, College Road, Stoke-on-Trent ST4 2DE* ℘ 01782 744531 ext. 3461.

8.25 Adult literacy

RNIB Basic Education and Skills Service (BESS) can advise and help visually impaired people who wish to join a basic education class in their home area. It can also advise Adult Basic Education (ABE) tutors who for the first time have a visually impaired student. Workshops and training weekends are occasionally held to raise awareness and encourage those teaching visually impaired students.

Publications include a comprehensive resource pack (£1.50). Basic education material is available **L B T M**. A tutor's handbook, **In Perspective**, offers advice and information to tutors.

When Paths Meet (£6.95) **L B T M** is a collection of delightfully and vividly expressed reflections on life in this country. Written for people learning English as a second language it would be equally suitable for adult basic education classes.

All publications should be ordered from *BESS, RNIB Vocational College.*

8.26 Further reading

VISability is a termly magazine for parents and professionals concerned with the education of children with impaired vision. It focuses primarily on children and young people who are integrated into their local school or college and covers all major issues in a very user-friendly and comprehensive manner. Annual subscription £6.00 from *RNIB Education Information Service.*

NEW **ACE Special Education Handbook** (Sixth edition, 1994). Written for parents and gives up to date information on the Education Act 1993 and the Code of Practice. £7.50. Advisory Centre for Education. 1994.

RNIB Book Sales Service can supply over 100 titles of educational books and videos which are normally difficult to obtain. American Foundation for the Blind, Royal Victorian Institute for the Blind (Australia), Sikon (Denmark) and RNIB publications are all stocked. Free catalogue from *RNIB Education Centre, London.*

11 Blind parents 218

D

9 Further education and training

The days have long gone by when the 'university of life' was the substitute for any further educational opportunities. Nowadays there is a wide range of opportunities not only for school leavers, but for people at all stages in their lives. This is reflected in the increased opportunities for visually impaired people to be found in colleges of further education, all of which have a responsibility for people with special needs, regardless of age.

This chapter aims to bring together the further education and training opportunities for school leavers transferring to a college of further education, for unemployed adults and young people, and for retired people. A number of the mainstream colleges listed in this chapter mentioned that visually impaired people in their 80's had joined some of their courses. Details are also given of the growing number of specialist training centres as well as specialist colleges.

Identifying who is likely to be responsible for paying the fees for a particular course is more complicated. Sitting side by side in a word-processing class at a FE college could be a student whose admission was arranged by the Local Education Authority, a young person on a Youth Training scheme, an unemployed adult on a Training for Work programme and a retired person paying either the full or a specially reduced fee. This chapter tries to untangle the different strands.

D

9.1 Colleges of further education

Local colleges of further education must provide academic, vocational, independent living and communications skills courses. As long as these courses lead directly to a qualification or prepare the student for such a course they can be funded through the **Further Education Funding Council**. The courses are officially known as **Schedule 2 courses** because they are included in Schedule 2 of the **Further and Higher Education Act 1992**.

Local Education Authorities (LEAs) have a responsibility for full time students with disabilities up to 19 years of age and therefore will often arrange for visually impaired young people to follow a 'Schedule 2' course in a local FE college alongside their sighted friends. They also have the power to make discretionary awards for courses not covered by Schedule 2. They may provide transport for students with disabilities.

Students with special needs in a college of further education are supported either by their LEA visual impairment advisory service, or by a resource centre in the college itself, or one which is shared with other colleges in the vicinity. If their needs cannot be met at a local FE college the Further Education Funding Council can meet the fees of a specialist residential college (see 9.7). This funding can be available to the student's 25th birthday.

NEW **Further Education for young people with learning difficulties and/ or disabilities** ⊕ (free) is published annually by the FEFC. It is written for young people who are about to leave school and are thinking of going on to futher education. It contains a great deal of useful information about obtaining special help and funding at mainstream and specialist colleges.

9.1.2 How to apply

Students should contact their LEAs Careers Service. The Further Education Funding Council is guided in its funding decisions by assessments carried out by the prospective student's LEA.

9.2 Allowances for young people in education

9.2.1 Severe disablement allowance (SDA)

Young people who are registered blind and attend classes or have supervised study for less than 21 hours a week may qualify for **severe disablement allowance** from their 16th birthday. Partially sighted young people may qualify if they also pass the 'all work' test. See 5.2.4 and 5.3.

When calculating the time spent at classes or in supervised study, it is important to remember that time spent in the following ways does not count:

- in breaks and mealtimes
- in unsupervised study and free periods
- in classes that would not be considered suitable for 'persons of the same age and sex who do not suffer from a physical or mental disability'.

Classes are not 'considered suitable' when special methods of teaching, such as specially enlarged or braille texts, are used.

9.2.2 Income support

Most 16 and 17 year olds are not entitled to apply for **income support**, but exceptions include young people who are registered blind or 'incapable of work by reason of physical or mental condition or disability'. Even if they are in full-time education, they can still qualify for income support if their disability makes it unlikely that they would find work within 12 months of leaving school. Income support can 'top up' the SDA of a qualifying blind 16 or 17 year old.

See chapter 5 for how to apply for SDA and/or income support. Further details will be found in a factsheet **L B T** free on request from *Action for Blind People*.

9.3 Youth training

Visually impaired young people under 18 who are not in full-time education or employment are guaranteed the offer of a place on the Government's **Youth Training scheme**. Visually impaired young people up to the age of 24 can also join if they have not started Youth Training earlier or had to leave as a result of their disability. Youth Training is provided through local Training and Enterprise Councils (TECs) or, in Scotland, Local Enterprise Councils (LECs).

Youth Training aims to give all young people who are considered capable of eventually taking up open employment the chance of gaining qualifications which are at or equivalent to a National Vocational Qualification (NVQ), level 2. Wherever possible young people with a visual impairment train locally, often in a college of further education, alongside other trainees. Special help and/or equipment is available through **Access to Work** (see 10.7.4).

Those for whom training aimed at NVQ level 2 is not considered a realistic option are offered an individual training plan based on their needs. This is designed to give them the support and help they require to progress as far as they can towards general and vocational competencies. On the other hand, some visually impaired young people need a period of preparatory training before they are ready to join a vocational training course (see 9.7).

Where a specialist residential or day placement is required, funding comes through the Training Enterprise and Educational Directorate (TEED) Residential Training College Unit at Newcastle. This is arranged by the Disability Employment Advisor (see 10.4.1). The length of a trainee's programme will depend on individual needs and the likely training outcome.

9.3.1 Allowances during Youth Training

Non-employed trainees under the age of 17 receive a training allowance of at least £29.50 per week. At 17 this rises to at least £35 per week. There may be help with travel and other support costs. Although income support cannot usually be paid to young people under 18, blind and partially sighted young people between 16 and 17 can claim, and so top-up their training allowance.

9.3.2 How to apply

Contact the LEA Careers Office or the DEA (see 10.4.1) through the local Jobcentre.

9.4 Training for Work

Training for Work aims to help unemployed people, including those with visual impairments, aged between 18 and 63 years of age, to get jobs by providing them with training, work preparation, work experience, or a mixture of these activities. The training can range from a short work preparation course (a pre-work course), to job specific courses or training customised for individual needs. People with disabilities can join Training for Work without having to fulfil a waiting period.

The scheme is the responsibility of the Department of Employment, but is run by local TECs/LECs. The first step towards a training course is assessment. Following assessment, the participant is referred to a training provider. Together they agree on the programme to be followed (the activity plan) and this is incorporated into a **participation agreement**.

The training provider may well be a college of further education so that a visually impaired person can attend a local course alongside sighted trainees, using adapted equipment or special aids where necessary. Specialist agencies, such as **Action for Blind People**, **RNIB** or the **Royal London Society for the Blind** are also training providers, and offer a wide range of courses (see the tables in 9.6.3).

A training course may last only a few weeks or take up to 12 months. TECs/LECs can provide longer periods of training where this is necessary to complete the agreed training package. Residential training can be arranged for people who would benefit from the additional resources found in a residential training setting.

> Tom learned a little German when he was at work, and always intended to study it properly when he retired. Then, for many years he nursed his wife. He finally enrolled at the Loxley Centre, in Sheffield College of Further Education, and gained a B grade at GCSE level in 1994. This year, he is studying for 'A' level.
>
> 'I can't read very well as I've got cataract and glaucoma and one eye is blind. So I shut that eye and manage slowly with the other one. I can't see the blackboard, but the College provides a young lady who sits besides me and tells me what's on the board. And they've fitted up a loop system so that I can hear what the tutor says. My brain doesn't retain things like it used to do, but I'm managing. I read as well as I can and study as much as I can. And with all the help the college gives me, it would be folly to give up'.
>
> Tom celebrated his 90th birthday in May 1995.

9.4.1 Allowances during Training for Work

An allowance is paid equivalent to any State benefits already received (including sickness benefit, incapacity benefit and severe disablement allowance), plus a premium of £10.00 per week. Trainees continue to be entitled to any other benefits they may already receive linked to their social security benefits, such as free prescriptions, spectacle vouchers, etc. TECs/LECs may also provide help towards travel and other costs incurred.

9.4.2 How to apply

Contact the DEA (see 10.4.1) through the local Jobcentre.

9.5 Other sources of financial help for further education

Reduced course fees for further education classes are often available to retired people or anyone whose income consists of disability benefits. Sometimes local voluntary societies for the blind can help, or provide help with transport. If a course were considered necessary to enable an individual to live a fuller life in the community, funding might be available through a community care plan drawn up by social services. In special circumstances, help may be available through one of the charities listed in 30.

RNIB may make grants towards the cost of specialist equipment and/or services up to a maximum of £450 (up to a total value of £900) over a five year period to visually impaired students in mainstream further, higher and continuing education. Consideration will not normally be given to students who are eligible for funding from statutory sources (see 8.22.1). Contact *Student Support Services.*

9.6 Further education support services

9.6.1 Partners in Access

RNIB Student Support Service provides advice and training to enable colleges and universities to develop their own support facilities. When a suitable standard is reached, usually over a number of years, and where there is planned commitment to continued development, RNIB recognises the institution as a **Partner in Access**.

Such a college will normally have a development programme which gives staff an insight into the needs of blind students. Their resource development programme is likely to include work stations with CCTVs, computers with large print and speech output, a scanner and a braille printer.

Participating colleges are: Ealing Tertiary College; East Devon College, Tiverton; Falkirk College; Farnborough College; Furness College; Glenrothes College; James Watt College of Further and Higher Education, Greenock; Lancaster and Morecambe College; Llandrillo College, Colwyn Bay; Monkwearmouth College, Sunderland; New College, Durham; Northallerton College; North Derbyshire Tertiary College, Chesterfield; North West Institute for Higher Education, Londonderry, Northern Ireland; Northampton College; Plymouth College of Further Education.

9.6.2 RNIB Outreach Service

RNIB Vocational College supports students and their tutors at South Fields College, Leicester; Newark & Sherwood College, Nottinghamshire; Grantham College, Lincolnshire; South Nottingham College, Nottingham; North Lincolnshire College, Lincolnshire; Melton Mowbray Corporation, Leicestershire; JHP Training, Nottingham; Jobs for Coventry Ltd., Warwickshire; and Nottinghamshire Chamber of Commerce, Mansfield.

Outreach services include curriculum support and teacher training to facilitate the inclusion of visually impaired students, on-site training for visually impaired people in employment, a mobile training service, and the opportunity to purchase specially developed resources.

9.6.3 Support facilities at other colleges and training centres

A number of mainstream colleges listed in the table in 9.11 have well-established support facilities and offer some discrete (specialist) courses in subjects particularly relevant to visual impairment. The table also lists the agencies offering further education and Training for Work courses known to *In Touch*.

9.7 Specialist colleges of further education

All the specialist colleges for visually impaired students offer **foundation courses** for people who have the potential to follow vocational courses but who lack basic or essential learning or communication skills. Suitable entrants are often new braille users and those whose basic literacy and numeracy has suffered through absences from school, or from deteriorating vision. The training offered is tailored to the needs of the individual following a full assessment.

The resources of all six colleges include teaching mobility, orientation and daily living skills, as well as offering vocational guidance, literacy, numeracy, computer keyboard and job-searching skills.

The following colleges cater primarily for people with physical disabilities and offer day or residential courses. Whenever possible, they admit students who are

'In June 1992 I completed a BTEC National Diploma in Computer Studies at Loughborough College as an "integration student". It was a very technical course and my ability to access and complete it depended on the specialist equipment and services available to me through the Vocational College. I feel that working with fully sighted students on a mainstream course provided me with an insight into the problems I would face in the workplace, both in terms of using conventional and specialist equipment, and in terms of the response which I might encounter from colleagues unsure of my potential output and quality of work.

'The experience and knowledge gave me a tremendous sense of confidence. I'm now employed as an Information Officer by a Local Authority.'

▶ Colin Herridge, aged 36, quoted in *Life in the Mainstream, VisAbility*. Spring 1994.

visually impaired, and generally some specialist equipment is available. For a prospectus, contact individual colleges.

Finchale Training College, *Durham DH1 5RX* ℘ 0191 386 2634

Hereward College, *Branston Crescent, Tile Hill Lane, Coventry CV4 9SW* ℘ 01203 461231

Portland College, *Nottingham Road, Mansfield, Notts NG18 4TJ* ℘ 01623 792141

Queen Elizabeth's Training College, *Leatherhead Court, Leatherhead, Surrey KT22 0BN* ℘ 01372 842204

St Loyes College, *Fairfield House, Topsham Road, Exeter, Devon EX2 6EP* ℘ 01392 55428.

9.8 Professional training

Visually impaired people have careers in many professions following the same undergraduate and graduate courses as sighted people. See 8.19, 8.20 and 29.

9.8.1 PICKUP

PICKUP (Professional, Industrial and Commercial Updating) services are available to employed and self-employed visually impaired people to enable them to update their skills and knowledge. Training programmes are individually tailored to requirements. A short course programme is also available for both visually impaired people and professionals who work with them. A **Services to Employment** folder for PACTs, TECs/LECs and employers of visually impaired people, gives details of assessment services, work experience, independence skills and careers counselling. Further details from *Karen Ball, Development Officer, Royal National College for the Blind.*

9.9 The Gubbay Trust

The **Gubbay Trust**, set up by St Dunstan's, offers training to ex-servicemen and women whose blindness is not attributable to war service. Candidates should be under the age of 60 and otherwise fit for employment. Members of uniformed organisations, such as the police and firemen, who have lost their sight on duty, are eligible for similar help. Full details are available from St Dunstan's (see 4.10.9).

9.10 Further reading

The Visually Impaired: Curricular Access and Entitlement in Further Education. ed. David T. Etheridge and Heather L. Mason (David Fulton. 1994).

9.11 Further education and Training for Work courses

A number of mainstream colleges listed in the following table have well-established support facilities and offer some discrete (specialist) courses in subjects particularly relevant to visual impairment.

The table also lists the agencies offering further education and Training for Work courses known to *In Touch*. Specialist colleges of further education for visually impaired people are listed in white lettering. They cater for students ranging in age from 16 to 50 plus and support them on mainstream courses at nearby colleges as well as providing specialist courses. For full details, contact individual colleges for a prospectus. Most specialist colleges can also loan a video showing their facilities.

🅑🅑🅣 denotes that a braille, large print and audio transcription service is provided.

D

Key to course codes

a	administration	h	health & social care, health & safety	r	retailing
ac	accounts			sh	shorthand
ah	amenity horticulture	ht	horticulture	st	specialist technology
art	art and design	ir	iron work	t	typing
ass	assembly quality	it	information technology	tl	telephony
b	basic education			tn	training the trainers
br	Braille	j	job hunting	tr	travel & tourism
bs	business studies, business administration	l	leisure administration: sport & recreation	wd	woodworking
				wp	wordprocessing
		lg	foreign languages	🅑🅑🅣	
c	commerce	m	microcomputer studies		braille, large print & audio transcription service
ck	cookery, catering				
CLAIT	computer literacy and information technology	mc	machine operation		
		med	human sciences	$	course held at an associated college
		mp	manufacturing practice		
cr	crafts				
cs	core skills	ms	mainstream courses		
cus	customer care	mt	music technology		
cy	cycle maintenance	of	office skills		
e	engineering	pa	performing arts		
EFL	English as a foreign language	pm	piano maintenance		
		prep	preparation for higher education		
Eng	English				
glass	glass engraving	pt	peripatetic support		

NVQ Lev. 1	NVQ Lev. 2	RSA	Other courses	Remarks	Contact
Action for Blind People, 23-25 Castle Street, Carlisle CA3 8SY ✆ 01228 595121					
bs it	bs it		bs cus tn		Cath Clarke
Action for Blind People, 25 Lime Street, Liverpool L1 1JG ✆ 0151-708 9008					
bs it	bs it	CLAIT	literacy and numeracy	Information and guidance centre	David Bamber
Action for Blind People, 24-32 Murdock St, London SE15 1LW ✆ 0171 635 7483					
a cs it	a (and Level 3); it	CLAIT	mainstream courses supported	specialist staff and equipment; employment counselling; computer access technology	Laura Alexander
Action for Blind People, Miller House, Lancaster Road, Preston ✆ PR1 2RY 01772 563944					
bs it	bs it		EFL m		Cheryl Woodman
Birmingham Royal Institute for the Blind, Queen Alexandra College, 48 Court Oak Road, Harborne, Birmingham B17 9TG ✆ 0121 428 5050 L B T					
ass art bs e h l r tr	bs e of r		b br ck cr cy glass j m mc mp prep wd; mainstream courses at local colleges supported	business centre	Audrey Banner
Bolton College, Room 309, Manchester Road, Bolton BL2 1ER ✆ 01204 531411 L B T					
a	a		b br bs it wp; support unit for all mainstream courses		Linda Owens
Bourneville College of F.E., Bristol Road South, Birmingham B31 2AJ ✆ 0121 411 1414 ext 261 L B T					
a bs ck h it l of	bs ck it; all courses levels 1-3	bs t wp	b EFL h it lg ms wp; all mainstream courses supported	b m of tr; specialist staff, specialist equipment	Carrie McHattie
Hull College, Queens Gardens, Hull HU1 3DG ✆ 01482 329943					
		wp	b br it prep; mainstream courses supported	resource centre	Barry Wheatley

NVQ Lev. 1	NVQ Lev. 2	RSA	Other courses	Remarks	Contact
Jewel & Esk Valley College, 24 Milton Road East, Edinburgh EH15 2PP ℡ 0131 657 7303 ❶ⒷⓉ					
			b st; all mainstream courses supported	peripatetic support service; guidance; 2 resource centres, specialist staff	Mary Dallas
London Guildhall University, Department of Communications & Music Technology, 41 Commercial Road, London E1 1LA ℡ 0171 320 1845					
			piano tuning BTEC ND HND B.Sc(hons) Music Technology	some specialist support	Terry Pamplin
Park Lane College, Park Lane, Leeds LS3 1AA ℡ 0113 244 3011 ⓁⒷⓉ					
full range available		lg m	b it; mainstream courses supported	resource centre; computer access technology	Brenda Sargison
City of Liverpool Community College, Barkfield Centre, Barkfield Road, Liverpool L13 0BQ ℡ 0151 252 3824 ❶ⒷⓉ					
ac bs	wp		b br Eng it of m maths; advanced bs; advanced l & tr; all mainstream courses supported	specialist staff resource centre	Brian German & Dorothy Chance
Motherwell College, Dalzell Drive, Motherwell ML1 2DD ℡ 01698 232305 ⓁⒷⓉ					
			mainstream courses supported	access centre specialist equipment available	Jeanette Gillies
Oldham College, Rochdale Road, Oldham OL9 6AA ℡ 0161 624 5214 ext 1815 ⓁⒷⓉ					
bs levels 1-3 and HND	art & l levels 2 & 3; ck e		ac b bs cr e h it lg med of pa prep r wd wp; all mainstream courses supported	access centre; specialist staff & equipment available	Liz Hampshire
Royal Blind School, Craigmillar Park, Edinburgh EH16 5NA ℡ 0131 667 1100 ⓁⒷⓉ					
wp	of wp	wp	tl	flexible hours	Rob Jones
Royal London Society for the Blind, Dorton College of F.E., Seal, Sevenoaks, Kent TN15 0ED ℡ 01732 764123 ⓁⒷⓉ					
a	a bs it	wp	b br j	students supported at local colleges including horticultural courses at Hadlow College	Brian J. Cooney

D

NVQ Lev. 1	NVQ Lev. 2	RSA	Other courses	Remarks	Contact
Royal London Society for the Blind, Kilburn Centre, 105 Salusbury Road, London NW6 6RH ✆ 0171 624 8844 🅛🅑🅣					
bs of c	bs of c	cr	cr	training office centre	
Royal National College for the Blind, College Road, Hereford HR1 1EB ✆ 01432-265725 🅛🅑🅣					
art a bs it; l advanced	bs it l; a (& level 3)	sh t wp	b EFL j m mt of; pa (BTEC); remedial therapy (mature students 23+); GCSE/A levels; Access to Higher Education; piano tuning (AEWVH); City and Guilds Applications Programming Certificate (4250) or Preliminary Applications (4240)	access centre; assessment for training & equipment; short courses (1 day-12 wks)	Dr Colin Housby-Smith, Principal, or Marion Edwards, Registrar
Sheffield College, the Loxley Centre, Myers Grove Lane, Stannington, Sheffield S6 5JL ✆ 0114 260 2242 🅛🅑🅣					
full range available	full range available		b br ck; all mainstream courses supported	peripatetic support service	Paul Lynch
Royal National Institute for the Blind, Alwyn House, Ceres, Fife KY15 5LX ✆ 01334 828289					
ah cr wd	ah		br e mc of; bs (Scot. Nat. Cert.)	work placements near the centre or in trainee's home area	Craig Stockton
Royal National Institute for the Blind, Manor House, Middle Lincombe Rd, Torquay, Devon TQ1 2NG ✆ 01803 214523					
cr wd mc	br bs ck cy ht it j of				Brian Hewitt
Royal National Institute for the Blind, Redhill College, Philanthropic Rd, Redhill, Surrey RH1 4DZ ✆ 01737 768935 🅛🅑🅣					
ac bs h ht it	ac bs ht it	cr ir	cy mp; of (modular – RSA/Pitman)	students on courses at East Surrey College of F.E. also supported	Dr M Rowe
Royal National Institute for the Blind, Vocational College, Radmoor Road, Loughborough, Leics. LE11 3BS ✆ 01509 611077 🅛🅑🅣					
a br bs it j of tl wp	br bs it j of wp	t wp	bs$ ck$ EFL$ es$ h$ it it$ l$ lg$ m$ tr$	residential and day courses offered in conjunction with Loughborough College of F.E. (on same campus)	Kevin Connell

10 Finding a job

Finding a job is difficult for everyone today. Visual impairment makes job-seeking even more difficult. But it does not make it impossible; there is help along the way. Work may not be easy to find, but determination and a refusal to take 'no' for an answer, are qualities that every blind job-seeker has to develop. This chapter gives details of both the formal and informal help that can be provided.

10.1 Support groups of visually impaired people in employment

Sometimes advice from someone who has had to cope with similar difficulties is the best way of rekindling hope and finding the courage to launch into the unknown. Where a number of visually impaired people are employed in a profession or occupation, mutual support groups have generally emerged. They meet together, circulate newsletters and generally keep members up-to-date with the latest developments in their field. The contacts listed below can give 'grass roots' information to the newcomer.

D

Association of Blind Chartered Physiotherapists Mrs. Mary Fairbrother, 22 Ermine Way, Stamford, Lincs. PE9 2XN ✆ 01780 54931.

Association of Blind Piano Tuners Mr. A. F. Spencer Bolland, 24 Fairlawn Grove, London W4 5EH ✆ 0181 995 0295

Association of Visually Handicapped Telephonists Martyn Wilson, 34A The Broadway, Woodford Green, Essex TG8 0HQ ✆ 0171 240 7151 (work), 0181 506 0955 (home)

Association of Visually Handicapped Office Workers (AVHOW) The secretary, BM AVHOW, London WC1N 3XX ✆ 0181 995 0050

Blind Business Association Ltd (for the self-employed) June Bretherton, 98 Aldborough Road, Upminster, Essex RM14 2RS ✆ 01708 458475

British Computer Association of the Blind Steve Plumpton, BCM Box 950, London WC1N 3XX ✆ 01203 563111

Clerics Group Rev. R. M. Hetherington, 3 Colinbar Circle, Barrhead, Glasgow G78 2BE ✆ 0141 880 6654

Society of Blind Lawyers John Wall, 20 Cleveland Road, Worcester Park, Surrey KT4 7JH ✆ 0181 330 1290

Visually Impaired Musicians Association Julie Smethurst, 79 Duncan Road, Crookes, Sheffield S10 1SN ✆ 0114 268 5405.

10.2 Job retention and redeployment

For people whose sight begins to fail whilst they are still in employment, the place to start is their own place of work. The question to ask is, 'Am I utterly certain there is no way I can continue to hold down a job here?'

There does come a time when it is no longer possible to disguise the fact that failing sight is making it increasingly impossible to continue working in the same way. This

---

Key to media of publication ❶ clear print ❶ large print ❸ braille ❶ tape ❶ Moon ❶ disk

> Helen had been working for 3 years as a peripatetic teacher serving about 20 schools for the Hampshire Music Service which is part of Hampshire County Council. When her sight deteriorated to such an extent that she was no longer able to drive, she thought that she would have to resign from her job. Her employers suggested that instead of the car allowance she had previously received they would meet the cost of public transport and taxis whenever necessary, so that she could still reach all the schools in which she taught. Although she is now registered as partially sighted, Helen has continued to do her job and the LEA meets her travelling expenses, which total about 15% more than the car allowance she would otherwise receive.

is, perhaps, the moment of greatest danger. It is fatally easy for both employer and employee mutually to decide that it is time to part.

Good decisions are rarely made on a base of ignorance. No-one would argue that a lorry driver whose sight has failed should continue driving, but is there any other work in his organisation that he could do? Could his encyclopaedic knowledge of routes and the quirks of customers be put to good use in other sections of the company? The answer may be 'yes', given some extra training, equipment or, perhaps, a little extra 'help on the job'. Help to both employee and employer is offered by the Employment Department and by voluntary agencies. Together, they can provide a comprehensive and individual service which, at its best, offers counselling, assessment, rehabilitation, training, equipment and practical help on the job.

10.2.1 Disability leave

Often the first thing that is needed is time; time to allow employees, employers and the helping agencies to assess the problems, explore alternatives, and co-ordinate services; time for employees to come to terms with their sight loss and concentrate on learning the skills needed to continue in employment, secure in the knowledge that their job is safe. RNIB has pioneered the concept of **disability leave** which would give this opportunity.

Disability Leave – A Guide for Employers L B T (Free. RNIB) outlines a pilot scheme and includes a sample personnel policy statement and a cost benefit analysis.

10.3 Finances when unemployed

Few people can concentrate on job-seeking when desperately worried about their financial situation. Anyone with a significant visual loss, whether registered or not, should consider applying for Disability Living Allowance (see 5.4).

Registered blind people should check their eligibility for **incapacity benefit** (see 5.2) and if necessary get advice from any of the agencies listed in 5.16.

Unemployment benefit is paid to people who are unemployed and have made sufficient appropriate Class I National Insurance contributions. It is a taxable benefit paid for up to one year. It can be 'topped up' by income support, but cannot be paid in conjunction with other national insurance benefits such as incapacity benefit.

NEW From October 1996, unemployment benefit will be replaced by the Job-seekers Allowance (JSA). It is anticipated that this allowance will be paid in two ways. **Contributory JSA** will be paid for a maximum of six months to claimants who satisfy the present National Insurance contribution test. There will be no additions for dependants or partners. It will not be means tested, but if the claimant has a personal or occupational pension this will affect the amount paid. Earnings of the claimant's partner will be disregarded.

Income-related JSA will be means-tested and will be similar to income support. Partners will be able to work up to 24 hours a week, with an earnings disregard of £10.00 a week. The government has estimated that these changes will save it £140 million in 1996–7 and £270 million in 1997–8.

Registered blind people, in particular, should also bear in mind the help offered through **Disability Working Allowance** when a job is found. (See 5.7).

10.4 Sources of advice when job-hunting

10.4.1 The Employment Service

The local **Jobcentre** is the doorway to a range of help offered by the Department of Employment for people with disabilities, including anyone with a visual impairment.

People with poor sight who are trying to find a job can use either Jobcentre self-service facilities or get advice from Jobcentre **Client Advisers**. If, as is likely, they need extra help, they should ask at the Jobcentre for an appointment to see the **Disability Employment Adviser (DEA)**.

Disability Employment Advisers (DEAs) are based at local Jobcentres. DEAs offer professional advice and support to help improve the job prospects of people with disabilities. They can arrange for assessment services (including residential assessment when needed) to help secure appropriate work or training. This can include a low vision assessment to identify whether special workplace aids or equipment are needed. DEAs can also arrange for visually impaired people to attend residential and non-residential employment rehabilitation courses.

DEA's can also offer help through the Disabled Persons Register (see 10.9), the Department's special schemes for people with disabilities (see 10.7), supported employment (see 10.11) and the training schemes described in chapter 9 under **Training for work**. DEAs are members of **Placing, Assessment and Counselling Teams (PACTs)**. PACTs are supported by nine regional **Ability Development Centres (ADCs)** in West London, Bristol, Birmingham, Nottingham, Leeds, Manchester, Newcastle, Cardiff and Glasgow. Many ADCs have technical consultants who advise PACTs and employers on appropriate equipment to enable a disabled person to do a particular job and some have a wide range of employment aids and equipment which disabled people can try out.

10.4.2 RNIB Employment Network

RNIB offers counselling, vocational assessment and advice on equipment to visually impaired job-seekers as well as a consultancy service on job retention and redeployment. Mobile teams including specialist employment consultants, occupational psychologists, business development specialists, are based at *10 Magdala Crescent, Edinburgh EH12 5BE* ℘ 0131 313 1877 (Scotland and Ireland); *5 Skinnergate, Darlington, Co. Durham DL5 7NE* ℘ 01325 364913 (North East); *10-12 James Street, Liverpool L2 7PQ* ℘ 0151 255 0562 (North West); *7 The Square, 111 Broad Street, Birmingham B15 1AS* ℘ 0121 631 3372 (Central England and Wales); *224 Great Portland Street, London W1N 6AA* ℘ 0171 388 1266 (London and the South East); **NEW** *Bristol Royal Society for the Blind, Stillhouse Lane, Bedminster, Bristol BS3 4EB* ℘ 0117 953 7750 (South West).

10.4.3 Action for Blind People

Action for Blind People's Employment and Training Division can help and advise people wishing to train or enter employment. Employment and development officers are based at *26-32 Murdock Street, London SE16 3DZ* ℘ 0171 635 7483; *Miller House, Lancaster Road, Preston PR1 2RY* ℘ 01772 563944; *25-35 Castle Street, Carlisle, Cumbria CA3 8SY* ℘ 01228 595121 and *25 Lime Street, Liverpool L1 1JG* ℘ 0151 708 9008.

10.4.4 Opportunities for People with Disabilities

Opportunities aims to help people with disabilities find worthwhile employment matched to their talents and aspirations. It has regional offices in Birmingham, Brentwood, Bristol, Cardiff, Crawley, Leicester, London, Manchester, Mersey and Deeside, Newcastle, Sheffield and South Hampshire. Contact *Opportunities for People with Disabilities, 1 Bank Buildings, Princes Street, London EC2R 8EU* ℘ 0171 726 4961. See also 10.11.2.

10.5 Vocational assessment and rehabilitation

When spirits are low, it may seem hopeless even to try to identify a possible job. An informal discussion with one of the voluntary agencies listed above is a good place to start, but the DEA and the PACT team are the formal doorway to assessment and rehabilitation courses. Job-seekers therefore need to discuss their work experience, abilities and work preferences with their DEA. Out of this discussion, an 'action plan' may emerge, an agreement on the way to find suitable work or training. Alternatively, both DEA and job-seeker may feel that it would be best first to have a period of assessment to find out more about the options available.

Assessment and employment rehabilitation courses are provided by a number of agencies, including the specialist agencies listed below. A good assessment teases out what is possible for the individual and how it can be achieved, raises expectations and indicates how they can be fulfilled. It provides opportunities to discuss expectations with an occupational psychologist and a social worker as well as people who are experts in the resources available to visually impaired people. It should lead to an 'action plan' that is relevant and realistic and challenges job-seekers, rather than channelling them into undemanding jobs.

10.5.1 Action for Blind People Centres

Action for Blind People's centres in London, Preston, Carlisle and Liverpool offer an advisory and assessment service. The London centre offers a part-time 13 week course which includes confidence building, identifying personal skills, and job searching techniques. Pre-work programmes are provided through host colleges in London and the Home Counties.

10.5.2 RNIB Centres

RNIB Skill Development centres at Manor House, Torquay and Alwyn House, Ceres, Fife offer a five day residential **assessment programme** including a full low vision assessment.

Pre-work courses are offered in office and commercial skills including keyboard skills, word processing, office technology and braille, and in manual and allied skills such as assembly, machine operating, stores management, vocational crafts and horticulture. Each student follows an individual programme, so course lengths vary from two to nine weeks.

10.5.3 Royal London Society for the Blind

The Kilburn Training Centre offers a programme of initial assessment which includes vision assessment, drawing up an agreed training plan, support towards a pre-vocational qualification and daily living skills.

Dorton College of Further Education, Sevenoaks, Kent offers a three day residential assessment programme which involves visual and foundation skills assessment and a careers interview. Pre-work programmes include communications skills, keyboarding and word processing skills, Job seeking skills and exploration of specialist aids and adaptations. Rehabilitation programmes can last for up to 13 weeks depending on the needs of the individual.

See 9.4 for details of vocational training programmes under **Training for work** schemes.

10.6 Allowances at residential assessment or pre-vocational courses

Students have no special allowance for an assessment programme but retain their existing benefit, whether it be income support, unemployment benefit, incapacity benefit or any other national insurance or income maintenance benefit already being paid, or combination of any two.

Students taking a pre-vocational rehabilitation course may receive a tax-free employment rehabilitation allowance of £38 per week (or £62.70 when students have a wife or husband who does not earn more than £36 per week take-home pay). This can be 'topped up' by income support if the allowance does not meet students' full income support requirements (see 5.8). In these circumstances they should consult their local DSS office.

Students receiving severe disablement allowance or incapacity benefit have the option of retaining their benefits instead of receiving the rehabilitation allowance.

However, if they choose the latter, they must reapply for severe disablement benefit or incapacity benefit within eight weeks of finishing their rehabilitation course.

Free travel warrants are issued for travel to and from the centres as well as for monthly 'home visits' if the course is residential and lasts more than seven weeks.

Unfortunately, it is not unusual for blind and partially sighted people to arrive at a residential rehabilitation centre and find that the first few weeks are spent unravelling their eligibility to benefit. **A great deal of anxiety can be avoided if the prospective students discuss their finances beforehand in detail with their DEA, their social worker, or the Citizens Advice Bureau**.

A minority of students who receive income support when living at home find they will not be eligible to receive it at the rehabilitation centre. They would be well advised to make sure that expenses such as dental treatment and travel to hospital appointments, from which income support has hitherto exempted them, are not incurred during their course and that any new spectacles needed are supplied before they start.

10.7 Help provided by the Employment Service

10.7.1 Jobclubs

Jobclubs enable unemployed people to work together at finding a job and to develop a professional approach to jobhunting. The **Jobclub members' workbook** 🅱🅣 complements training sessions on job search techniques and CV completion. Office facilities are provided to help members in their job search and extra help such as improved lighting, low vision aids and a personal reader service can be provided.

There are a few Jobclubs especially for visually impaired people, run by voluntary societies such as **Action for Blind People** and **Royal London Society for the Blind**. Usually visually impaired people are included in standard Jobclubs where they can also often benefit from the voluntary help given by fellow Jobclub members.

The **Travel to Interview** scheme provides cash help to hunt for jobs beyond the normal travelling distance from home.

10.7.2 Job Introduction Scheme

This scheme allows a disabled person to try out a job for an introductory period. The employer receives £45 per week towards the employee's salary for the first six weeks. This can be extended up to 13 weeks if the disabled person, employer and DEA think it necessary. The employer pays the normal rate for the job during the trial period. The job can be full or part-time but must be expected to last for at least six months after the trial period ends.

10.7.3 The Job Interview Guarantee Scheme and Work Trials

The **Job Interview Guarantee** Scheme matches unemployed people who have the right skills and qualifications against the vacancies notified to the Jobcentre by employers and guarantees an interview. A **Job Preparation Course** and **Customised Training** in co-operation with the prospective employer can be provided to prepare the jobseeker for the interview. A **Work Trial**, lasting up to three weeks, can be arranged with a potential employer who is wanting to fill a vacancy. Jobclub membership, the Guaranteed Interview Scheme and Work Trials are open to people with disabilities without having to fulfil a waiting period.

10.7.4 Access to Work

This is a range of practical help tailored to the needs of the individual. It aims to enable employed or self-employed people to overcome the obstacles they face at work and is also open to people who have a firm offer of employment. DEAs can give full details.

Access to Work can, for example, pay for:

- a part time reader or assistance at work
- an interpreter for a deafblind person
- a support worker if someone needs practical help either at work or getting to work
- equipment (or adaptations to existing equipment) to suit individual needs
- adaptations to a car, or taxi fares or other transport costs if someone cannot use public transport to go to work or while at work
- alterations to premises or at a working environment so that an employee with a disability can work there.

Equipment supplied under Access to Work must be needed either to enable the worker to do the job efficiently, or to increase the person's capacity for work. Access technology such as speech output, enlarged displays and braille input for computers (see chapter 20) or items such as tactile micrometers, pocket memo tape recorders, braille machines, talking calculators and industrial magnifiers can be supplied. Low vision aids, including closed-circuit television, can be provided after a full assessment at a low vision clinic. Up to £21,000 is available to individuals over every five year period, though this is not a fixed ceiling. When pressed by *In Touch* interviewer Gary O'Donaghue in February 1994, the then Employment Secretary, David Hunt, said that this limit could be exceeded. It was recognised that some blind workers needed extremely expensive equipment.

A Government proposal to require employers to meet 50% of the cost of special equipment for disabled workers has been postponed at least until June 1995, when it is likely that the Access to Work scheme will be reviewed. The **Disability Discrimination Bill**, if enacted, may also affect the provision of equipment through Access to Work. The **In Touch Gateway** will have the latest news.

There is no formal appeal procedure for situations when users feel that help given through Access to Work is inadequate, inappropriate or unreasonably slow. If the matter cannot be settled by mutual discussion, a letter should be sent to the manager of the PACT team asking for a review. If still dissatisfied, the Regional Disability Services Manager (address in telephone directory under Employment Service, Regional Office) should be contacted, giving as much information as possible to support the complaint. In the experience of a number of **In Touch** listeners, it is at this stage that the matter is likely to be satisfactorily resolved. Others, undaunted, have pursued their case to **The Employment Service**, *Disability Services Branch, Skills House, 3-7 Holy Green, Sheffield S1 4JA* ℘ 0114 259 6135 and 'that is where

Access to Work in practice: a tale of two PACTs (1)

'I can't believe how good they've been.' John is a self-employed computer programmer whose ancient CCTV would not work with his computer. He asked his PACT team for a replacement under **Access to Work**. PACT asked RNIB to assess his needs. A Kurzweil reading machine plus a very sophisticated CCTV and software was recommended. His PACT agreed to provide both, and without delay about £11,000 of equipment arrived. 'The Kurzweil is incredible, I use it an enormous amount; but the CCTV – the software would not work with my programmes and the suppliers could not sort it out.' His PACT called in another advisor, a specialist in computer technology. He recommended another type of CCTV and software. The equipment was changed over without any fuss. 'It's almost embarrassing, the help I've received. My PACT seems to try to find how much they can do, not how little.'

Access to Work in practice: a tale of two PACTs (2)

In Bill's department, all his fellow computer programmers changed over to Windows programs in 1993. As a braille user, he asked his PACT for similar equipment. They asked RNIB to assess his needs. RNIB recommended an electronic braille display, appropriate software and a PC that would work with both. Then the delays started. 'PACT had to get three quotes for the PC, even though there was only one on the market which worked with the software I needed. By April 1994 they were saying it was my employer's responsibility anyway to provide the PC. But my employers said as this particular PC was not on their list they could not support it. 15 months later I'm still having to use a PC which I have to disconnect from all the other systems in order to braille anything. I can't fully use the £1,700 of software that PACT did supply. My employers recorded on my end-of-year appraisal that I should use more initiative in sorting things out. But every time I try to contact my PACT either they've moved, the officer has changed or my case is being dealt with somewhere else. Face to face, I've always got on well with my DEA but trying to get them to sort out my problems is like putting your hand into a rabbit hutch – wherever you feel, the rabbit is somewhere else.'

most of my members get matters put right' reports the secretary of a self-help group of blind people.

RNIB Employment Development and Technology Unit works closely with Access to Work. The Unit consists of a team of computer professionals who provide technical support to people either in or seeking employment. The Unit advises employers about the needs of visually impaired staff and provides a regularly updated **Technical Information Service**. Visually impaired people who need advice regarding technology in the workplace can contact the Unit direct (see also 20.12.3).

10.8 Setting up in business

The Business Start-up Scheme which officially came to an end in April 1995 has helped many unemployed people, including visually impaired people, to start their own businesses. However, some Schemes may continue to be run by local TECs or LECs. A taxable allowance, which may be anything between £20 and £90 per week, may be paid for at least 26 weeks and can continue up to 66 weeks whilst the business gets established. Contact the local TEC/LEC or enquire at the local Jobcentre for details of the current situation.

RNIB **Small Business Unit** is a specialist service which helps people who wish to run their own business. It offers business advice and support, including advice and support on training and funding, a business information network, reference library, information factsheet service and a newsletter **An Eye for Business**.

The Prince's Youth Business Trust helps 18–30 year olds who have a disability and who are unable to raise all or some of the money, to set up in business for themselves. Applicants must have a viable business idea, show that they can make a success of it, and have tried and failed to raise all the necessary money elsewhere. The PYBT works closely with **RNIB Small Business Unit**. Contact the PYBT at *5 Cleveland Place, London SW1Y 6JJ* ✆ 0171 321 6500.

10.9 The Disabled Persons Register

PACTs administer the **Disabled Persons (Employment) Acts 1944 and 1958** which established a range of employment provision for people with disabilities, including the **Disabled Persons Register** and the **Quota Scheme**.

People who wish to register are assessed by a DEA and issued with a 'green card' if they meet the eligibility conditions for registration. People who are registered blind or partially sighted should not find this a problem. People who choose to register and whose disability is severe can get help through the Supported Employment programme (see 10.11).

10.10 The Quota Scheme

Being registered should, in theory, make it easier to get a job. Under the **Quota Scheme** employers with 20 or more employees have a duty to employ a 3% quota of registered disabled people. It is not an offence to be below quota, though employers in this situation should allocate job vacancies to suitable registered disabled people. The advantages of the quota scheme are, in the experience of many people with disabilities, more apparent than real. Employers are, however, regularly monitored, which means that DEAs are well placed to know the local job situation.

The future of the Disabled Persons Register and the Quota Scheme is unclear at the time of writing (May 1995). The **Disability Discrimination Bill** currently being debated in Parliament would, if enacted, abolish the quota scheme. Instead, employers would be required to make 'reasonable adjustments'. These would be more clearly defined in a Code of Practice which would apply only to employers with 20 or more employees.

10.11 Supported employment

The Employment Services **Supported Employment Programme** is open to people with severe disabilities who:

- are registered under the Disabled Persons (Employment) Act 1944
- whose disability is so severe that they are unlikely to be able to obtain or retain work in open employment
- can achieve and maintain an output of between 30% and 80% of that of a non-disabled person doing the same or similar work.

Supported employment includes homeworker schemes, workshops and supported placements (SPS). Admission to supported employment is a matter of agreement between a voluntary association or local authority and the Employment Service. Before being accepted for supported employment, the worker must be sponsored by his local authority or a voluntary agency. The **National League of the Blind and Disabled** and the **Blind Business Association** are always ready to advise applicants and, where necessary, act as their advocate.

10.11.1 Workshops

Workshops are special factories run by local authorities, voluntary agencies and Remploy Ltd. They receive funding from the Employment Service. Workshops are engaged in light engineering, injection moulding, PVC welding, window manufacture, furniture making, packing and assembly work. Some workshops have hostel accommodation. Workshops are run on business lines and workers must be able to meet minimum productivity levels. Conditions of employment in many of the workshops (but not Remploy) are determined by the **National Joint Council for Workshops for the Blind**, a body on which both employers and workers are represented. The wage rate, determined by the NJC, is linked to the Local Authorities Manual Workers Rate, between grades 2 and 3.

10.11.2 Supported Placements

Supported Placements (SPS) enable people with severe disabilities, including people who are blind or partially sighted, to work alongside non-disabled staff in an industrial or commercial setting. The employee receives the rate for the job, the 'host' firm pays for the work actually done and the Employment Service pays a grant to the sponsor. SPS is operated by the Employment Service and involves either a local authority or a voluntary body sponsoring the visually impaired worker.

Placements are sponsored by the **Royal London Society for the Blind**, **Opportunities for People with Disabilities** (see 10.4.4) and **Shaw Trust**. RLSB offer additional specialist services such as ophthalmic assessment, mobility training and social rehabilitation appropriate to individual needs as well as suitable training programmes either with the host employer or through RLSB's own training courses. Shaw Trust has 2000 SPS placements, about 10% of which are held by visually impaired people. It has officers in most regions of Great Britain who find appropriate work and support employers and employees subsequently. Contact *Shaw Trust, Hawker House, Greenways Business Park, Malmesbury Road, Chippenham, Wiltshire SN15 1BN* ✆ 01249 443770. Further information about all forms of supported employment can be obtained through Jobcentres or RNIB.

10.11.3 Homeworker schemes

Homeworker schemes, as the name suggests, are home based and still include the traditional crafts of chair caning, piano tuning, carpentry and knitting. Nowadays they have been joined by more modern professions like computer programmers, photographers, therapists and bicycle repairers.

Homeworker schemes are run by local authorities or by voluntary agencies such as **Action for Blind People**, **Royal London Society for the Blind**, **Henshaw's**, and **Bristol Royal Society for the Blind**, who receive assistance from the Employment Service. They help visually impaired and severely disabled people, particularly those who live in isolated parts of the country. Once accepted, help may be given with any necessary training and items of capital expenditure, such as tools and a workshop. Homeworkers must be able to reach the minimum earnings rate for the relevant trade. Earnings are then augmented on a sliding scale by the local authority. As the earnings of the worker increase, so the augmentation decreases, and ceases altogether when earnings approximately reach the basic wage which would be earned in a workshop. Homeworkers are self-employed, but receive supervision and support from the local authority or voluntary body administering the scheme. This may include the purchase of materials, marketing of produce, or technical, business and marketing training.

The future of homeworker schemes is very unclear. The guidelines for the augmentation of earnings issued in the past to social services departments have been discontinued and it is now left to the discretion of individual local authorities as to whether and how the scheme should be run.

10.12 Personal strategies

Good advice, training, and the speedy provision of appropriate equipment are all important elements in whether a job-search will be successful, but it would be wrong to end this chapter giving the impression that these alone are sufficient. The determination, drive and self-confidence of the blind person count for far more. **Take Charge: A Strategic Guide for Blind Job Seekers** **P B** (£11.95. RNIB Customer Services) by Rami Rabby, a blind consultant on employment for disabled people, and Diane Croft, discusses techniques and strategies for managing a successful interview, but starts at the heart of the matter with a chapter on 'Assessing who you are and what you can be'. Although the book includes a great deal of information about American organisations, the advice it gives, based on the experience of successfully employed blind people, is very relevant to British jobseekers.

10.13 Further reading

Unemployment and Training Rights Handbook. (£10.00 Dan Finn. Unemployment Unit. 1995).

Guide to Training and Benefits for Young People (£7.00. Youthaid. 1995). Both books are available from the *Unemployment Unit, 322 St John Street, London EC1* ✆ 0171 833 1222 and from *In Touch Publishing.*

11 Blind parents

Nobody knows exactly how many blind parents there are in Britain; but there seems a general impression that there are now more blind women who are having babies – often supported by sighted husbands and partners – than in the past. As more youngsters with visual impairments attend the same schools as everyone else in their neighbourhood, it is easier for them to be part of the local social life and more common for friendships between blind and sighted youngsters to develop into lasting relationships. There are no supportive statistics but the impression is that it is nowadays far more common for a visually impaired woman to marry a sighted man than it was ten or twenty years ago – though blind men never seemed to have many problems in finding sighted wives!

*eye*OPENER

'There is a lot of prejudice about the abilities of blind parents; it is important to understand that blind people can and do take responsibility effectively in their own familiar environment where things are under their control.'
Mary Stevens, blind mother of a partially sighted child

This chapter is intended to give some guidelines to parents with visual impairments based on the experiences of those who have already brought up their families despite poor sight or none at all. Obviously the practical problems for a couple where both parents are blind are likely to be different from those where one parent is sighted, even if child-care is frequently the responsibility of the blind parent. The suggestions contained in this chapter are aimed to be of help to a blind parent coping unaided for at least part of the time. **Without exception blind parents who have contacted the In Touch programme over the years have emphasised that the best help they received was from other blind parents**. This chapter is at best a starting point – with suggestions based on the experience of blind mothers and fathers – and can best be augmented by contacting one of the parent support groups described in this chapter, which are an ongoing source of information and advice.

11.1 Genetic counselling

As many of the blinding conditions affecting younger people are congenitally determined, it is possible to get advice about the likelihood of any children inheriting visual impairments from a **genetic clinic**. There are about a dozen such clinics in Britain, all based in large teaching hospitals, and those with a serious sight problem who would like advice before starting a family can ask their GP to refer them to the nearest centre. While it is preferable to be referred by a doctor, it is not essential. People can refer themselves. The recently established **Genetic Interest Group**, which represents nearly a hundred voluntary groups concerned with genetic disorders, has a Helpline which can give callers details of the nearest genetic information centre and any other relevant support groups. The GIG

Helpline is available Monday to Friday between 10 and 12.30 in the morning, and 2 to 4.30 in the afternoon ✆ 0171 430 0090.

It is important to understand that the role of the geneticist is not to tell blind parents whether or not they should have a child, or proceed with a pregnancy. Their task is to give information about the likelihood of any child inheriting the parent's visual problems, but it is for the parents to decide whether or not to go ahead. Geneticists usually work in association with **genetic counsellors** who on the basis of the diagnosis given will spend time with the patients and talk through the possible outcomes and options, so that they can make well informed decisions for themselves about their future families. Dr. Gareth Evans, a consultant geneticist from St. Mary's Hospital, Manchester, said on an *In Touch* programme that the blind people he had advised varied enormously in their attitude to the prospect of having blind children: some felt that they would not wish to subject a child to the problems they had themselves experienced while others were horrified at the thought of contemplating the termination of a pregnancy because the baby would be blind. This seemed to them to be tantamount to saying that the blind parents themselves should not be allowed to exist. In some conditions such as certain forms of Retinitis Pigmentosa, or Lebers Optic Neuropathy, children of blind parents do not show any symptoms but the defective gene is transmitted in either the male or the female (but not both) to the next generation. So parents who would like to have a family which is not affected by visual impairment can get advice from a geneticist. This is one of the issues discussed in a helpful booklet **Genetics and RP** available from the British Retinitis Pigmentosa Society, who also have a Helpline every weekday evening from 6.00 to 10.00 ✆ 01280 860363.

11.2 Preparing for childbirth

11.2.1 Getting help from the professionals

Unfortunately many visually impaired women have encountered rather unhelpful attitudes from the staff at ante-natal clinics and even in the maternity wards. This means that even though all pregnant mothers are in need of help and support from doctors and nurses, a visually impaired mother-to-be will often find that she needs to convince her medical helpers that she will be able to cope with the care of a baby. It is not always easy for a blind person to demonstrate independence and mobility when they are in unfamiliar territory in a hospital clinic or ward. However a number of initiatives have been undertaken in recent years, by nurses and midwives who have looked after blind women during pregnancy and childbirth, to help colleagues who are looking after a visually impaired patient for the first time. **ParentAbility**, which is a National Childbirth Trust network supporting pregnancy and parenthood for people with disabilities, has a **Professionals Link** which will try to put any professional caring for a blind mother in touch with others who have had relevant experience. In Leicestershire in 1991 the local voluntary association for the blind in collaboration with local maternity services ran a special course for three sets of blind parents who were all expecting their first babies at about the same time. These parentcraft classes proved extremely successful in preparing for childbirth, and subsequently the same team ran a short course on coping with small babies, raising issues such as first aid and safety and ways of weaning babies onto solid food. The health visitor and midwife involved would be happy to advise any other professional, as would Usha Bhavsar, the rehabilitation officer who co-ordinated the course. They can be contacted via the *Royal Leicestershire Society for the Blind* ℘ 0116 249 0909.

In general it is unlikely that there will be more than one blind parent attending an ante-natal clinic at any one time. There is absolutely no reason why blind parents should not attend the same ante-natal classes as everyone else, though it might be sensible to have a word in advance with the teacher and explain problems, if any, with written material. Many teachers with advance warning can

arrange to have any handouts produced in braille, large print or even taped. It is also standard practice in almost all maternity hospitals to organise a tour of the labour wards; this is where, if at all possible, a visually impaired mother would benefit from a special guided tour, which enables her to touch and examine the equipment which she may be using in labour. It would also be helpful to have an advance visit to the ward where she will be after delivery so that she gets an idea of the layout, and is enabled to be more confident moving around once her baby is born.

11.2.2 Help from other parents

However there is no doubt that any first time blind parent would get a lot of support from more experienced blind parents. There are several ways in which they can make contact. ParentAbility has a **National Contact Register**, so blind parents can be linked with others who have recently had a baby. In addition, the **Disability Network** has now established a regular teleconference call for blind parents and those expecting children, so that there is an opportunity for the exchange of information on a whole range of issues relating to baby and child-care. For details contact *Brian Hartgen, Disability Network* ℘ 01744 451215. It may also be possible to find other visually impaired parents in the locality either through the local voluntary society, some of whom in response to demand have set up a support group for blind parents, or through the local **Look** groups – detailed in 31. These Look groups are primarily set up to support families with visually impaired children but in almost every group there are likely to be some visually impaired parents who could be a very helpful source of local information and advice.

Sound album

David and Janet are both blind. When their first child was born nearly 20 years ago they decided that as photographs meant nothing to them they would keep a tape record of their son's progress. They recorded him, and later his little sister, as regularly as sighted friends took photographs of their own children. The tape collection is now a source of delight to them (and some embarrassment to their teenage children) and several of their sighted friends have said that they regretted not having done the same, because the recordings were so evocative, particularly those made when the children first started to talk!

11.2.3 Accessible information

A catalogue **Pregnancy and Child Care** published by the RNIB in April 1994 lists the publications available in braille or on tape. This is available on request from *RNIB Customer Services* who can also give details of more recent publications likely to be of interest to parents. However, almost all the publications listed were originally written for sighted parents and therefore do not take into account any of the special needs or concerns of parents with little or no sight. To try to address their needs, the RNIB in 1994 launched a new braille magazine **You and Your Child** which contains articles from a selection of print magazine as well as material from blind parents about their experiences.

Disability Network (details in 11.2.2) distributes a monthly tape magazine **Parent** produced by and for visually impaired parents, and the quarterly magazine produced by **Disability Pregnancy and Parenthood International** is also available on tape. Details from *Mukti Jain Campion, 1 Chiswick Staithe, Hartington Road, London W4 3TP* ✆ *0181 994 0896.*

The National Childbirth Trust has produced a tape on **Relaxation and Childbirth**, available from *NCT Sales, Burnfield Avenue, Glasgow G46 7TL* ✆ *0141 633 5552.* A **Mother and Baby** birth tape is available from an experienced ante-natal teacher. Contact *Caroline Flint, PO Box 136 Peterborough PE2 0XW* price £1.95.

Thanks to an initiative from a blind parent, it is now possible to get taped versions of both the Mothercare and the Boots **Mother and Child** catalogues, which include descriptions of the products illustrated in the print version so that a blind parent can 'browse' unaided. The catalogues are recorded onto five 90 minute cassettes which are tone-indexed to make it easier to find a particular section (see 19.1.2 for explanation of tone-indexing). The catalogues are available (free) on request from Disability Network, which also has taped versions of the **Bounty** advice guides on pregnancy and childbirth which are distributed to all new mothers in hospitals.

11.3 Coping with babies and toddlers

11.3.1 Breast feeding

Mothers who want to breast feed their babies can get help and support from **La Leche League**. Groups meet regularly and breast feeding counsellors offer telephone help all over the United Kingdom. The League has a tape library on breast feeding and related subjects which is free for blind mothers. The tapes can be obtained by telephoning ℘ 0171 242 1278 at any time, or by writing to *La Leche League, BM 3424, London WC1N 3XX*. Information on breast feeding as well as mother to mother support on a variety of issues related to mothers and babies can also be obtained from the *National Childbirth Trust, Alexandra House, Oldham Terrace, London W3 6NH* ℘ 0181 992 8637. Their quarterly magazine **New Generation** is available in large print and on tape.

11.3.2 Bottle feeding

Blind parents who bottle feed their babies have found that the task of making up feeds and sterilising bottles can be relatively simple if care is taken with the selection of bottles and sterilisers. A former nurse who has lost her sight and is now caring for her baby grandson found that it was easier to use wide necked feeding bottles, and measure out the feeds using measuring cups sold by RNIB. Several of the baby milk manufacturers do produce ready made feeds which need only to be heated up; while this avoids the problems of measuring and mixing feeds it is a much more expensive way of feeding the baby. Local maternity units may be able to arrange for a supply to be made available to a blind parent, or the manufacturer may be willing to make arrangements directly with the family. Contact *Cow and Gate, Newmarket Avenue, White Horse Business Park, Trowbridge, Wiltshire BA14 0XQ* ℘ 01225 768381; *Milupa, Milupa House, 1390 Uxbridge Road, Hillingdon, Middlesex UB10 0NE* ℘ 0181 573 9966.

One totally blind father who was determined to feed his baby heated the feed up in the microwave. Although quite a few parents are using the microwave to heat up feeds, this is not recommended by professionals as food or liquid is not always equally heated in a microwave oven. A bottle of milk feed may feel warm to the touch but some parts may be scaldingly hot, and of course food heated in a microwave goes on cooking after it comes out of the oven. It is actually no quicker to heat bottles in the microwave than in the time honoured fashion of placing them in a jug of hot water and this avoids the risk of scalding the baby's mouth, which has been known to happen with feeds heated in a microwave.

Blind parents probably would find it easier to clean and sterilise teats and feeding bottles by immersing them in a sterilising solution than by using a steam steriliser. Mothercare sells a sterilising tank which includes a grid that floats on top of the water and ensures that all the bottles are properly submerged. It is possible to get a steam steriliser which can be used in a microwave, but without such equipment bottles should not be sterilised in a microwave as cold spots may occur and some parts of the bottle may be left unsterilised.

11.3.3 Hints from blind and partially sighted parents on coping with babies and toddlers

* I found it easiest to change the baby on a changing mat on the floor; that way I could be sure he could not roll off and hurt himself.
* I kept everything needed for nappy changing in a holdall which was always left next to the changing mat, so that I never had to leave the baby while I went off to find something.
* The new terry nappies with Velcro fastenings are a godsend to partially sighted parents who previously had to wrestle with nappy pins.
* When the baby was small I took my computer off its workstation and put the baby's changing mat on top instead. The various drawers were perfect for keeping everything I needed for cleaning and changing the baby.
* Choose a high chair that has a rimmed tray and is easy to clean.
* Spread large sheets of newspapers underneath the baby's high chair before feeding; it makes the job of clearing up afterwards much simpler.
* The best bib was a plastic one with sleeves which meant that the baby's clothes did not get covered with food, and on top of that I put the plastic pelican bib which had a little pouch to catch any food I dropped or the baby spat out.
* If the baby dropped any food on the floor our guide dog was better than a hoover at picking it all up!
* When first feeding solids to a baby, hold the spoon with the food with the thumb and last three fingers and use the forefinger to touch the baby's cheek and so persuade it to turn its mouth towards the food.
* Give the child lots of finger food when it first starts to feed itself; leave more tricky food like meat with gravy, or peas, for meals when sighted help is available.
* Always have a clean, damp cloth handy for wiping hands and face after your child has eaten and before it escapes to put sticky fingermarks everywhere!
* I got a brightly coloured baby bath and put this in our big bath. I found this was the safest way to bath the baby.
* To keep track of our baby once she started to crawl I bought her a tiny charm bracelet which tinkled gently as she moved, and as her wrist grew we added new links.
* A cat-bell fastened with a nappy pin onto the back of a child's garment works well as an indicator of their movements.

11.3.4 Safety in the home

Once children are able to move independently this can present new challenges for a blind parent. Perhaps even more than other parents they need to minimise the dangers that lurk for inquisitive toddlers in every home. Among precautions worth considering are:

* Safety covers on electric sockets
* Childproof locks on cupboards containing substances such as medicine or cleaning materials, that could be dangerous for a child to open or taste

Jenny Vyse had worked for seven years as an infant teacher before leaving to start her own family. By the time the youngest of her three children was born her sight, which had always been poor, had deteriorated to such an extent that she was registered as partially sighted. She lived in a fairly isolated rural community which had absolutely no pre-school provision and so she started a mother and toddlers group which met daily in the local village hall. This proved such a success that she decided to start a playgroup which now operates as a private venture in a spare classroom at the local primary school. Jenny employs three trained nursery nurses, and has recently opened a second private nursery in a neighbouring village. She says that visually impaired parents should feel confident of their abilities to relate to children. 'If you can't read a book, you can always tell them a story, and even if you are no good at story-telling you don't need sight to sit down with a child who is playing and talk with them about what they are doing, or to give them a cuddle or comfort when they need it.'

D

- Catches on doors well above a child's reach so that it cannot easily wander out of a room when the parent is momentarily distracted.

11.4 Going out with a baby

11.4.1 Prams and pushchairs

Probably the single most agonising problem is how a blind parent can move about safely out of doors with a baby. If the baby can be carried either in a sling or in a backpack, of which there is an ever increasing selection, this leaves the blind parents free to use their normal mobility aid, whether it is a cane or a guide dog. However, there will inevitably come a time when the baby is too heavy to be carried by the blind parent and requires some kind of baby buggy or push chair. It is obviously safer for these to be pulled behind the blind parent rather than pushed ahead of them, but unfortunately even though it might well be of benefit to all parents particularly when crossing roads, manufacturers persist in producing only models that can be pushed. Numerous attempts have been made to find ways of adapting baby buggies so that they can be pulled but no one universally satisfactory solution has yet been found. But it is much easier to pull push-chairs or buggies that have a single bar rather than the umbrella stick handles.

One possible solution has come from a project initiated by the Guide Dogs for the Blind Association after a number of parents who were guide dog owners pointed out the problems that they were having. In association with a London manufacturer, who distribute a Greek made pushchair called **Martino**, the GDBA has designed an adapted 'arm' which can be clipped onto this pushchair and held under the blind parent's arm to enable the pushchair to be pulled safely and easily. The pushchair has had various modifications to its basic design which make it suitable for this type of use. The brakes have been moved to the front wheels, so that they are on the wheels nearest to the person pulling the pushchair; the suspension has been improved to sustain extra bumping up and down kerbs and the pushchair has a 5 point harness which meets EC regulations. The pushchair costs between £140 and £160 in the shops, but guide dog owners can obtain it at a special price of £110. The adapted arm is currently only available to guide dog owners and can be loaned free of charge, but it is hoped a manufacturer will be found who can produce it commercially (see picture in the colour section).

Over the years blind parents have made various attempts to adapt pushchairs, often in association with their local branch of **REMAP** which provides technical expertise free to solve practical problems faced by people with disabilities. One adaptation which has proved successful in the past has consisted of some kind of harness which fastens to the parent's waist so that the pram or buggy can be safely pulled along. Contact *REMAP* for details of the nearest local group.

11.4.2 Ideas on safety in the park or playground

- When the children were small I always insisted that they were on reins, not only with me but with anyone else who took them out. I later had very strict rules about where they have to hold hands and where they can run free.
- If you are not actually needing to hold their hand in a park keep talking to them and insist on a reply so that you are constantly aware of their presence.
- If the children are in a playground there is usually only one entrance. Make it a rule to stay by that gate so there is no chance of their leaving without passing you.
- If you have any residual vision, and can see bright colours, dress your child in a distinctive colour so that you can easily spot them in any group.

11.5 Pre-school education and parenting

Parents with young children may well experience feelings of isolation if they find themselves away from daily contact with people at work, or if they have moved to a new home since starting a family. The usual contacts through Mother and Toddler groups or Pre-school Playgroups may be more difficult to achieve for a blind parent who cannot drive and may be reluctant to undertake a lengthy walk in unfamiliar territory, or in bad weather. However, it is so valuable to have this contact with other parents that it is well worth trying to get help with this. The situation and provision varies around the country, but it is something that the health visitor at the local clinic should be able to advise on. Again, it is often the experience of blind parents coming for the first time to a group of parents who probably have never met a blind person before that any initiatives have to come from them, and this may not always be easy.

11.5.1 Playgroups

The **Pre-School Learning Alliance** (previously known as the Pre-School Playgroups Association) recommends that its playgroups give priority for admission to children whose parents have a disability, and that the parents be asked how they would like to be involved within the group. But policy statements depend on individuals to put them into practice and blind parents report mixed reactions from playgroups to which they have taken their children. At best when parents are themselves confident and able to relate easily to people in a new group, they have been integrated without too much difficulty. Visually impaired parents who are less assertive can find themselves a little isolated. Peg Anney, a partially sighted mother who has successfully completed the PPA's basic training course, suggests that visually impaired parents offer to supervise an activity where children are sitting round a table and engaged in play with which the parents are familiar. She also points out that many of the games designed for very young children are made with bright colours as well as large letters and numerals which many partially sighted people could distinguish. It might also be helpful to go with another sighted parent on initial visits to the playgroup, so that the onus of familiarisation is not placed solely on the playgroup staff.

11.5.2 Choosing toys and books

For blind parents with sighted children the selection of toys would be easier if more toy manufacturers made their catalogues available on tape or in braille. The **Early Learning Catalogue** has been put onto tape, (available free on request from the Disability Network) and Boots now regularly produce their Christmas catalogue, which has a range of children's toys and games, in braille and on tape. Linda Oliver, a blind mother who teaches in a prison transcription unit (details in 11.5.4), has produced the Early Learning catalogue and the RNIB's **100 Popular Toys** in braille. The braille text includes a code number for each illustration, which is also marked in braille, so that a sighted child can point at a picture and the parent can read the appropriate description.

Apart from the pre-Xmas rush, toy shops would usually be prepared to give some time to show their range of goods to a visually impaired parent. It might also be possible to contact a local secondary school where sixth formers undertake community service and see if one of the students might be available to do a guided tour of the local toyshop with explanation from their more recent experience of what the toys are like. All too often parents – blind or sighted – are unaware of the range of toys and games that have appeared on the market since their own childhood. This is possibly also a way in which a well-informed volunteer from the local society for the blind might be able to help, but it does need someone knowledgeable about toys and their uses.

11.5.3 Ideas on toys from visually impaired parents

* If a parent is blind then it is worth avoiding toys which have lots of easily lost small parts until the child is old enough to find them for himself.

* Be strict about where toys can be left. I did not allow our children to bring toys into the kitchen so that there was no risk of my tripping over something our children had abandoned on the floor when I was carrying something hot or breakable.

* Training children not to leave toys lying around is even more important for blind parents, who might accidentally step on the toys and break them.

* The large colourful plastic storage boxes made in a variety of sizes are useful and a reasonably cheap way to keep children's toys.
* In the corner of our living room I keep a supply of robust toys which are suitable for children of any age. High on a shelf I keep the fragile toys and puzzles which are brought to the table by me, one at a time, on request.

11.5.4 Reading

A very great deal of thought and effort has been put in mainly by blind parents to find ways in which they could read to their children in their pre-school years. For parents who can read braille the **Clear Vision Project** provides a nationwide lending library of standard children's picture books, where the print is interleaved with braille embossed on clear plastic sheets. This enables blind parents to read the text while their sighted children look at the pictures. The collection consists of over 100 fiction and non-fiction titles suitable for pre-school and primary school aged children. The stock of board books, lift the flap books, non fiction books and books for juniors with a lower reading age is currently being increased. A national loan scheme supplies individual readers (subscription £10.00 per year – waived in cases of hardship). Details from *ClearVision Project, Linden Lodge School, 61 Princes Way, London SW19 6JB* ✆ 0181 780 2712. The National Library for the Blind has the **Two way** series of picture books which show the original print, pictures and braille on the same page but they also import other titles with interleaved clear plastic sheets to carry the braille.

There are also other individual initiatives to produce material for blind parents to read to their children. Linda Oliver, a blind mother with four children, has been working with prisoners to produce material for blind parents – or grandparents. She can arrange on request to have any book brailled and has specialised in making picture books accessible by describing the pictures, which are also identified by a brailled code. Linda can also arrange for instructions for toys and games to be brailled. For details of this free service contact *Linda Oliver* evenings after 6 p.m. ✆ 01642 582331.

The **Living Paintings Trust** has adapted a number of children's picture books which not only have the text in braille but include a number of tactile representations of the main characters in the book and a tape describing the pictures. Available on free loan from *Feel Happy Project, Living Paintings Trust.*

Some blind parents have been delighted with a service offered by **Create a Book**, a company that produces children's books which will incorporate some personal details about the child who is to receive it. For blind parents the books can also be interleaved with the text in braille. Details from *Create a Book, 4 Highfield Road, Biggin Hill, Kent TN16 3UT* ✆ 01959 575501.

For parents who cannot read print and do not know braille there is the option of getting books on tape. An increasing number of commercial companies do now produce unabridged versions of a wide range of children's books (see chapter 19 for details of companies).

The **National Library for the Handicapped Child**, though primarily set up to meet the needs of children, is also prepared to advise blind parents in relation to the reading needs of their children. The librarian has, for example, helped a partially sighted parent to draw up a suitable reading list for her young daughter. The Library is at *Wellington House, Wellington Road, Wokingham, Berkshire RG40 2AG* ✆ 01734 891101.

11.6 School-age children

Once children go to school blind parents will need to be alert to ways of overcoming problems caused by practical difficulties when so much communication between school and home is in print. There is also the very real difficulty for a blind parent anxious that her child should not miss out on socialising that not all parents will be happy to let their child play under her supervision. Blind parents cannot take a turn in the inevitable driving to dancing classes, music sessions or swimming pools – and while some blind parents can and do walk miles each day to ensure that their child does not miss out, not everyone is able to do this, especially with more than one child. It is a situation which calls for careful communication and sensitivity as to how the real needs of the blind parent can be addressed. In schools which have a good parent teacher association, and a willing band of parent volunteers it should be possible to find the appropriate solution, but it would be misleading to assert that this is easily done.

11.7 Special needs

11.7.1 Adoption and fostering

A number of blind people have been accepted as foster or adoptive parents. Anyone who is considering making an application should bear in mind that the main consideration in any agency would be the needs of any particular child and who is available to meet them. While in principle this should not rule out people with disabilities it may well do so in a situation where there are usually not enough babies available for adoption. However, there are some agencies which specialise in placing children with disabilities and they may welcome applicants who can identify with, or have experience of, a similar condition. For further information about such children contact either *Parents for Children, 41 Southgate Road, London N1 3JP* or the *Thomas Coram Foundation, 40 Brunswick Square, London WC1N 1AZ*. Another source of useful information is the adoptive parents organisation **Parent to Parent Information on Adoption Services (PPIAS)** which might be able to link inquirers

228

> John's mother, who could not see well enough to read any print, made an arrangement with the parent who was the rep. for John's class that she would ring any time the children brought a note home from the teacher. In return she undertook to be the baker of endless batches of fairy cakes and biscuits for class parties and outings.

with other visually impaired adoptive or foster parents. Write to *PPIAS, Lower Boddington, Daventry, Northamptonshire NN11 6YB* ℘ 01327 260295.

11.7.2 Twins

Blind parents with twins might be able to get practical advice from the helpline run by **TAMBA** (the Twins and Multiple Birth Association) ℘ 01732 868000, available from 7p.m. to 11p.m. on weekdays, and from 10a.m. to 11p.m. at weekends.

11.8 What about the children?

A blind mother's viewpoint
Judy Watson

Head of English at a large comprehensive school, Judy Watson has a teenage daughter, Hazel, and a baby son. She is totally blind. She won the Frink Award for outstanding achievement by a blind woman in 1992. When asked by *In Touch* for her comments on the advantages for children who have a blind mother, she wrote the following:

I think my daughter's life has been enriched by my disability in so many ways and I am convinced that she has never viewed having a blind mother as being a disadvantage. Firstly she has always been proud of, and celebrated, my difference. When she was small her friends were fascinated when they first met me but quickly viewed me as any other mother. This has the effect of helping children to be more open minded about other people who are

A daughter's perspective
Carol Mitchinson

Both my parents are blind, one totally and the other seems to be more partially sighted these days. If you are ever stuck for conversation it's great, though I never liked to mention it much as a child. I have now been around for 23 years and it doesn't seem to have done me much damage.
At school my friends could not comprehend how the responsible position of mum or dad could be filled by somebody who couldn't see. Their image was of a poor old fumbling person trailing around behind a 'blind dog', with the dog knowing where the cooker is and where the toilet is, and probably doing all the cleaning anyway as my parents wouldn't possibly be able to find the hoover. How many times did I have to make the point that cooking, washing, cleaning, grass-cutting and gardening are all just the same as in any other household. Yes, dyeing white things pink or a greying shade of green does happen perhaps slightly more often, and a pound note was once thrown away during a bedroom purge. But one of the lovely things about having blind parents was not having to have the light on when the bed-time story was being read.
Other kids would love to see my dad's

'different' in our society. Hazel, my daughter, is accepting of people who often experience prejudice and she does not make assumptions easily. Indeed she is very challenging of others when they express opinions she considers to be unacceptable.

Hazel is somebody who displays self confidence. I think this is because she has had to deal with both people and situations which other children have not. This is not necessarily about being a child in an adult world, more about being a link between two different worlds. It is this increased level of responsible contact with adults which has helped to develop this aspect of Hazel's personality.

Her verbal confidence is another advantage which has directly arisen from living with a blind person who relies so completely on verbal communication. She was always advanced in terms of language development and was able to describe surroundings and convey information most articulately. Now that I have a son it will be interesting to see whether his language development is as advanced, when it has been well documented that boys develop rather more slowly.

plastic eyes. He had a spare set so while he was wearing the brown ones, my sister and I could take the blue eyes to school for the delight and sometimes horror of our friends. One thing I did not suffer as a result of my mum being blind was being dictated to about my physical appearance; I was never dressed up like a doll! I feel I was more able to develop my own ideas and 'design' my own appearance. From a very early age I was aware of wanting to have long hair; 'When you can wash it and look after it yourself', I was told, so practicality rules O.K.

'You must be a great help to your mum and dad!' Oh yes, my halo shines. What do I remember? 'Mind the bush! Step up. Step down. Duck!' From an early age I had a lot of responsibility for such things as crossing roads. Normally it is the adult who decides when to cross, but in my case the tables were turned and I willingly volunteered the information that it was clear to cross. This responsibility was never forced upon me but was taken as a natural course of events. But I can remember feeling viciously angry that other people found it necessary to stare; my responding looks were deadly. Of course, when the cussed teenage times came along I resented such thing as 'having' to walk with dad or read the post. I certainly wasn't always a 'great help'. I was just as thoughtless as any child in many ways, such as leaving toys all over the place and leaving doors ajar for head bashing etc.

As a child, your parents are the universe in which you orbit and children are very good at adapting to life. My parents could not see, so I therefore learnt very early to vocalise, as words and not visual display were the main means of communication. I even went a bit overboard and undertook to do the talking for both myself and my younger sister. It is an early lesson in life to speak before you get trampled underfoot.

I think Hazel's listening skills were enhanced because she was brought up by me. She would notice things which other children had not, and this in turn helped her in debate and discussion, particularly at school. I point things out to Patrick, my baby, which sighted adults around us ignore totally – the sound of a seagull, a car engine in the distance, the sound of horses' hooves as they troop up the hill. The other adults in his life point things out to him constantly and he is visually stimulated all the while. It never occurs to them to concentrate on sound. I do feel that children of blind parents become much more aware of the world in which they live; there is an added dimension.

Finally and probably most importantly, I know that Hazel has been made aware of the importance of problem solving and determination. She values challenges and has the drive to strive for what she wants. This is not about ambition but about dealing with the mundane, the difficult and the frustrating.

I have been a role model, and I hope that Patrick will achieve in his life because he has the personal skills to do so. I hope that my disability will be a contributory factor.

Just like the guide dogs in our house, you had to be used to the idea of moving out of the way very quickly. Of course there were also occasions when it was prudent to be very quiet; when raiding the sweet tin for instance!

During my formative years there were always two guide dogs in the house, and often more when other blind friends were visiting. Many of my happiest memories as a child are associated with great expeditions of one kind or another involving dogs, pushchairs, ruck-sacks, papoose carriers etc. These memories are sometimes laced with stress, as when we loaded ourselves into the first class compartment of a train and waited for the inevitable visit from the ticket inspector. Some would take in the situation at a glance and just clip our tickets but the occasional one would ask, 'Do you know this is a first class compartment, sir?' Dad's response was usually to the effect that, 'You are welcome to help us move if you can find suitable second class accommodation!'

For many years Christmas was spent with another family whose father was blind. There was much eating, drinking and merry-making which allowed five children to have their own fun, which usually involved staying up all night to witness the spectacle of two blind and drunk Santas attempting to deposit the right sacks at the bottom of the right beds! Yes, being brought up by blind parents is different but, like everything else in life, there are advantages and disadvantages. My mum and dad are the most capable people I know, and I think that is what really counts. I feel that life has treated me fine, but perhaps in reality I am still floating off the beach at Ryde in the Isle of Wight wearing orange armbands and having the end of a dog leash clipped to my swimming costume!

Daily living skills   E

E

E

12 Getting about safely

White canes and guide dogs have given many visually impaired people of all ages the freedom of being able to get out and about without the constant need for a sighted guide, but training by professional instructors is necessary. In a perfect world, the loss of sight or the point at which someone is registered as blind or partially sighted would be the start of a process of what is known as 'mobility' training with a **rehabilitation worker**. This is a specialist teacher who helps people cope with the practical problems posed by loss of sight. Teaching people with impaired vision how to move about by themselves safely, indoors and out, is one of the main roles of rehabilitation workers. In the real world, a newly blind person may be handed a white stick with no indication of how to use it, and left to find out by trial and error how best to move around.

12.1 Mobility in the home

Even without specialist training, there are many ways in which blind people can help themselves. Most people know the way round their own homes and can usually remember the layout of furniture in any of the rooms. Some

> **'Only 5% of blind people receive any significant mobility training. Blind people are less likely to be able to go out independently than other disabled people.'**
>
> *RNIB Needs Survey 1991*
>
> Blind and partially sighted people who have not been offered mobility instruction or advice should contact their local **social services department** and ask for a full assessment of their needs. If the local authority itself does not provide mobility advice and training, social services can be asked to buy in the services of an instructor. Some voluntary associations employ mobility instructors, as do some specialist schools. In the case of children attending other schools, RNIB can be approached for help (see 8.12).

newly blind people instinctively learn to get information from their other senses. The ticking of a clock, for example, or the sound of a radio can help them find their way around. A **sound beacon** (£22.92 from RNIB) serves the same purpose. When switched on, it gives a continuous signal varying from a loud whistle to low intermittent bleeps, so it can be used to mark the position of objects in a large room or out in the garden. **Textures** underfoot can also give valuable clues. Providing it is firmly fixed, a strip of carpet that leads from a favourite chair to the door of the sitting room may help. A large doormat in the hall gives advance warning of the approach to the front door. Breakable objects can be moved into

---

Key to media of publication 🅿 clear print 🅛 large print 🅑 braille 🆃 tape 🅜 Moon 🅓 disk

Where a full address is not given in the text, see 32 (Useful addresses)

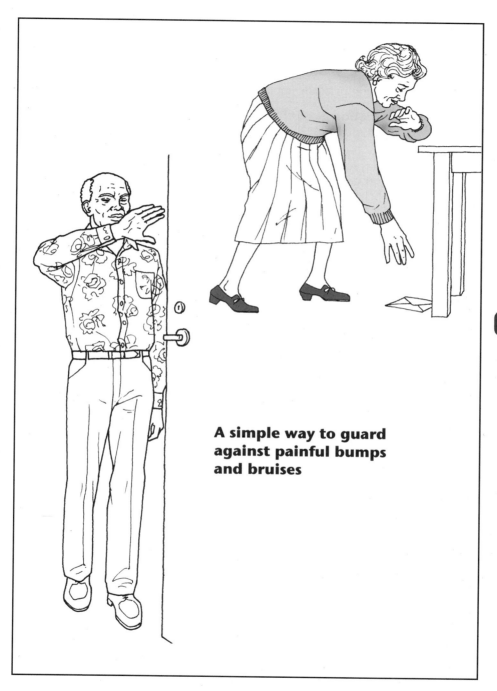

A simple way to guard against painful bumps and bruises

places where an inadvertent movement will not send them flying. Clocks, telephones and other frequently used objects can be anchored with non-slip mats or material available from RNIB. Advice on making the most of residual vision and on appropriate lighting is given in chapter 3. With careful thought and suitable equipment, even the kitchen can be safe for a visually impaired person to use. See chapter 16.

12.1.1 Self-protection techniques

People who cannot see where they are going instinctively hold an arm out straight ahead to feel the way. It is more effective to run the back of one hand along a wall or other guideline, keeping the fingers lightly curled to avoid jamming them in openings. When there is a likelihood of coming into contact with head height obstacles such as shelving or a half open door, the face and the upper part of the body can be protected by raising the other arm to shoulder level, with the elbow bent and the hand held, palm facing outwards and fingers straight, six to eight inches in front of the forehead (see illustration in 12.1). There will be no injury to the hand if the elbow is relaxed so that the hand gives way if it comes in contact with an obstacle. A totally blind person can check if his hand is in the right position by blowing upwards to find out if the breath can be felt on the back of the hand.

A similar technique should be used when bending down to protect the face from the edges of chairs or other hard objects. It is much safer to squat, if possible, with the back straight and the knees bent, than to bend down from the waist. When reaching into a low cupboard, place a hand on the top edge where the risk of bumping the head is greatest.

12.2 Getting about safely outdoors

Many people with deteriorating vision still venture out alone without a mobility aid. They need to bear in mind the kind of safety precautions taught by rehabilitation workers. Some of the equipment mentioned below could be as useful to them as to those who have been trained to use a white cane or guide dog.

12.2.1 Crossing roads

Visually impaired people are advised never to cross a busy road without sighted help. Even on a quiet road, it is vital for anyone with less than normal sight to have good hearing. If only nearby traffic can be heard, it would be dangerous to cross any road alone. Anyone dependent to any degree on hearing to judge whether it is safe to cross a road should remove scarf, ear-muffs, or anything else which might muffle sounds. All pedestrians should be aware that loud noises – aeroplanes, lawn mowers, etc. – can mask the sound of approaching traffic, and in particular that the sound of one vehicle can mask that of another following close behind. Crossing points should be chosen, away from the brow of a hill or a bend in the road or parked vehicles, so that the pedestrian is in full view of other road users, including cyclists. Side streets are best negotiated a short distance away from the main road. At a zebra crossing, pedestrians should be sure that traffic from both directions has come to a halt.

Waiting to cross the road.

A white stick or cane does not give a pedestrian the right of way when crossing the road. A cane should be held diagonally, across the lower half of the body, pointing down and slightly outwards. On no account should any stick or cane be held straight out or waved about as this can be hazardous, especially to passing cyclists. If a driver does stop, or toot his horn, it is safer to wave him on (see chapter 28).

12.2.2 Clothing hints

A light-coloured top-coat makes a pedestrian more visible to drivers. Dark colours do not show up at night, or on a grey, rainy day. Fluorescent yellow reflective **arm bands** are easy to see in poor light and reflect the headlights of approaching cars so that the pedestrian can be seen from a safe distance. A pair of arm bands costs £2.25 from *Colan Ltd., Unit 6, Hurlbutt Road, Heathcote Industrial Estate, Warwick CV34 6TD* ℘ 01926 831584. Bright yellow waterproof coats, Sam Browne belts, stickers, etc. are also supplied by Colan.

To prevent slipping in icy weather, **shoe chains** can be worn over ordinary walking shoes, though they are not suitable for leather soles. They cost £12 a pair (to visually impaired customers) from *RUD Chains Ltd, John Wilson Business Park, Units 10-12 Thanet Way, Whitstable, Kent CT5 3QT* ℘ 01227 276611. State shoe size when ordering. There is a very slight risk that the chains, which lie across the flat of the foot, may catch on an obstacle if the wearer shuffles rather than walks normally. Some people may prefer **Continental Schuh Spikes**, which pull over shoes and fasten with a button. They have spikes embedded in the sole, but they are not so easy to put on and have been found not to grip as effectively as the chains when the surface of the ice is slushy. Continental Schuh Spikes cost £10 from *Davies & Co. (Kettering) Ltd, Beatrice Road, Kettering, Northants NN16 9QS* ℘ 01536 513456.

Glove Snuggler Muffs keep the hand warm while allowing the fingers to be in direct contact with a white cane. The muffs are warmly lined waterproof tubes with cuffs at each end. They are supplied by *Plumbs Sewing Services, 3 Redbourne Drive, Davyhulme, Manchester M31 2NU* ℘ 0161 747 9795, at £3.00 each or £24 for 12.

Some people whose eye defect is not obvious find that a badge is a useful way of indicating visual impairment to members of the public, particularly in shops, restaurants, trains or buses. **Lapel badges** with a symbol denoting visual impairment (see illustration) on a white or a yellow background are 77p each from the *Partially Sighted Society*. A **limited vision symbol**, a white plastic oval badge which can be clipped to a cane, is supplied by RNIB for £1.50. It carries the words 'limited vision' printed in black.

LIMITED

VISION

12.3 White sticks and canes

A blind person with a white stick is a familiar sight to most people, but the distinction between **white sticks** and **white canes** is not generally appreciated. A stick may be painted white, but its essential function is to support the user. White canes are designed to be used as a mobility aid and are not meant to take any weight at all.

Unless otherwise indicated, white sticks, white canes and accessories described below are supplied by RNIB and listed in their **Mobility** product guide (see 29.1).

12.3.1 White sticks

To be both useful and comfortable, a walking or support stick must be the correct height. It should reach the user's wrist if he stands with his arm hanging loosely by his side. RNIB recommends that any support stick should be used only with the advice of a physiotherapist, orthopaedic surgeon or occupational therapist, who can set it to the correct length. Using a support stick without professional advice could cause posture problems or damage to the back. White sticks listed below all have crook handles, and all are fitted with a rubber ferrule, an essential safety feature.

- **Wooden or aluminium walking sticks**, from £2.50, 85 or 90 cm (33.5" or 35.5")
- **Adjustable aluminium walking stick**, £5.25, extends from 71 to 96 cm (approx. 28" to 38")
- **Ambutech Support Cane**, £14.16, length adjusts from 72.5 to 92.5 cm (approx 28.5" to 38") in one version, from 82.5 to 92.5 cm (approx 32.5" to 36.5") in the other. Black handle designed to keep hand in correct position
- **Folding support cane**, **NEW** £10.57 from *Cobolt Systems*: 31", 33" or 36".

12.3.2 White canes

Symbol cane

The **Symbol cane** is primarily intended as a signal to others that its user is visually impaired. It is very light, folding into four to fit handbag or pocket, and has limited use warning of obstacles ahead. It costs £2.32 (£5.72 with crook handle), choice of lengths from 70 to 105 cm (27.5" to 41.25").

Guide cane

The **Guide cane**, a longer and sturdier version of the symbol cane, can be used to check the depth and width of steps and stairs and give some protection indoors. It may be adequate for people with some useful vision. £9.58, choice of lengths from 85 to 115 cm (33.5" to 45.25").

When I was first registered blind, I was reluctant to use a white stick, thinking that it created a false impression of a very severe disability. Now I think it's a great idea. It alerts people to my needs before I ask for help at pedestrian crossings, cafeterias, bus stops and railway stations. Acquaintances maybe started up in this way too.

▶ Mary (from Finchley) in *Sideview*, April 1994.

Symbol and guide canes may be used without special training, but it is wise to consult a rehabilitation worker before setting out alone with either.

Long cane

Long canes are the safest canes for anyone uncertain of being able to see obstacles and hazards in time to avoid them, or unsure of detecting kerbs, steps or stairs. Training with a qualified rehabilitation worker is essential. This may take some months of regular tuition, depending on individual requirements, and is usually done from a person's own home. The cane is held in front of the body at an angle of about 30 degrees to the ground. As the user walks, he moves the cane from side to side, the tip just above the ground, in an arc extending an inch or two beyond the width of his body, swinging the cane to the left as he steps out with the right foot, and vice versa (see illustration in 12.3.3). With practice, this becomes automatic and the user can walk quickly and confidently. Long canes are made of lightweight aluminium, rigid or folding into two or four sections, with or without a crook handle and in a range of lengths. When held upright, the cane should normally reach mid-chest. Prices range from £7.98 to £11.12.

Extending cane

The **Extending cane**, £10.50, a light weight alternative to other canes, is in two metal sections, one screwed into the other. It can be set to any length from about 80 to 149 cm (31.5″ to 58.5″).

12.3.3 Replacement parts

Guide canes and long canes are fitted with **replaceable tips**, made of aluminium, rubber, metal or nylon. Each type of tip has its own merits, so users could experiment to see which suits them best. RNIB recommend approaching the local voluntary society or social services department for fitting replacement tips.

All long canes have a reflective finish, a feature particularly useful in unlit country districts where motorists rely on headlights. RNIB will fit **white reflective tape** to symbol and guide canes. A white stick or cane banded with **red reflective tape** indicates that the user has a hearing impairment as well as sight loss. With the exception of the extending cane, where tape would interfere with the extension mechanism, any cane or stick can be supplied to special order at no extra cost banded with red reflective tape. Rolls of white and red reflective tape are available from RNIB so that canes and sticks can be adapted by the voluntary society or social services.

Cane techniques

▲ Using a guide cane with a rolling tip

▲ Using a symbol cane to judge the depth of steps

▼ Using a long cane

E

12.3.4 Roller tips

Long canes with a **roller tip** are used with a technique similar to that for other long canes, but the tip remains in contact with the ground instead of being held just above it. In an evaluation by the Guide Dogs for the Blind Association of a Canadian-made cane with a roller tip, 48 of the 50 users who took part found that their mobility was improved and have continued to use the cane. The roller tip is particularly effective on grassy or other rough and uneven surfaces, and, because the ground takes the weight of the cane, there is less strain on the wrist.

NEW An Ambutech four piece long cane, also made in Canada, with a screw-fitting roller tip is stocked by *Cobolt Systems* at £24.95, replacement tips £8.95.

The Hoople

NEW RNIB will be providing specially designed **roller tips** to screw into their own long canes, having taken into consideration the experience of people who have used Canadian canes or RNIB canes fitted with one of the screw-in roller tips already available (Heathfield Roller, £8.75 from *Heathfield Roller, PO Box 33, Daventry NN11 4XF* ✆ 01327 71051; Innotec Rotatip, £8.95 from *Cobolt Systems*). The RNIB roller tip is to be a modification of the Heathfield Roller, with a replaceable helmet, the part subject to most wear. To increase durability, the helmet will be slightly larger and thicker than other models. RNIB roller tips should be ready for distribution by the autumn of 1995. Customers who have had no experience of roller tips will be advised to consult a rehabilitation worker. All but one of about 30 people who had used a Heathfield Roller told RNIB that they found it easy to convert to the roller tip. About a third of them, mainly less experienced long cane users, thought that some further training would be useful.

12.3.5 The Hoople

The **Hoople** (see illustration) is a simple, low cost alternative to the long cane devised by two mobility lecturers at the Royal National College for the Blind. Evolved from a hula-hoop modified to form a loop about the width of the body, it has proved easy to use and effective on rough ground unsuitable for a long cane. Its disadvantage is that, at the present stage of its development, there is no way a Hoople can be folded up when not in use. Further information from *Clive Ellis* or *Tony Larkin* at the RNC.

12.4 Guide dogs

Any visually impaired person aged 16 or over who is normally resident in the UK can apply to **The Guide Dogs for the Blind Association**. It may be possible to train a person who has other disabilities, but all applicants must be fit enough to use and care for the dog. Learning to use a guide dog safely and effectively usually takes place at one of the Association's residential training centres. Regional centres are based at Exeter, Wokingham, Redbridge (NE London), Leamington Spa, Bolton, Middlesbrough and Forfar, small centres at Belfast, Cardiff, Liverpool, Maidstone, Nottingham, Larkhall (near Glasgow) and Southampton, with several others planned for the future. Training lasts for up to four weeks. In a few cases all or part of the training may be carried out from the applicant's home.

Rehabilitation training can also be provided. It includes orientation and mobility (the use of white canes and other techniques for getting around independently), daily living (coping with kitchen and other household tasks) and communication (typing, braille, Moon, and the use of equipment such as low vision aids or a personal computer). Orientation and mobility training can help blind people to train successfully with a guide dog, and, for a newly blind person seriously considering an application to the Association, it can be the first stage towards that training. Rehabilitation services are also available to past and present guide dog owners. For example, alternative mobility training may be offered to a guide dog owner who is still fit enough to get out and about, but who is unable to continue using a guide dog.

Application can be made direct to the Association, either by the blind person or by a relative, friend, or social worker on his or her behalf. A doctor's medical report on general fitness will be required. The applicant will then be interviewed at home by a representative of the Association to assess his or her suitability for training, to decide what kind of dog would be appropriate, and to check that the home conditions are suitable for a guide dog. The Association would want to be assured that the applicant is aware of the responsibility involved in dog ownership. If necessary, arrangements can be made for the applicant to stay at a training centre for a few days' further assessment before a final decision is made about taking full training. Once an application for a guide dog is accepted, there is a waiting period until a suitable dog is available to match the particular applicant's needs. This is usually about six months, but may be a year or more where an individual has special requirements.

After successfully completing training, the blind person is asked to pay a nominal sum of 50p for the guide dog. Routine 'aftercare' visits are made only once a year, but the Association states that it will always respond quickly if a guide dog owner requests a home visit from a trainer to give help or advice. The cost of keeping a guide dog should not pose a problem. The Association pays a feeding allowance of 60p a day to all guide dog owners. Some manufacturers will deliver dog food in bulk at reduced prices. All guide dogs are registered with a vet, and the Association will pay all veterinary bills. In fact, many vets do not charge for their services to guide dogs. The Association can provide portable kennels/runs for use at the owner's workplace if the dog cannot stay with him or her, and may be able to help with any necessary fencing of gardens or free run areas. A free 30 minute audio cassette describing what it is like to be a guide dog owner can be obtained from the Association (dial 100 and ask for Freephone Guide Dogs).

12.5 Electronic mobility aids

The extent to which a long cane or guide dog can interpret the environment around the user has inevitable limitations. No warning can be given, for example, of head height obstacles such as overhanging branches. In an attempt to remedy this deficiency, a number of electronic devices have been developed which use reflected ultra-sound or infrared light to detect the presence of nearby objects and translate it into an auditory or tactile signal.

The **Laser Cane** combines the function of a long cane with a built-in ability to give tactile and audible warning of objects at head height and in the travel path. An evaluation by the Guide Dogs for the Blind Association found it to be a useful mobility aid, but it costs $2,500, has to be serviced in the United States and few instructors in the UK are able to provide the essential training.

Other devices are appropriate only as a supplement to a guide dog or long cane. They cannot give warning of steps up or down, for example, or of hazards which do not reflect their beam, either because they absorb it or because they are outside its range. They too are expensive, have to be serviced by the makers, and training in their use is not readily available in this country. The Australian made **Sonic Pathfinder**, for example, would cost about £1,150. It is mounted on a head-band and its signals are selective, giving priority to objects in the user's path. The New Zealand made **Mowat Sensor** is a hand-held ultrasonic torch with a vibrating or audible display. Its main use is to help locate such things as doorways, gaps between parked vehicles or post boxes. It can be imported through *Sensory Systems* for about £495.

The **WalkMate**, £155 from *Cobolt Systems*, is a much less sophisticated device which is not selective in its display of information, and may not be of much use in a cluttered environment such as a city street. It is similar in appearance to a 'Walkman' stereo, and is either hand held or worn with a neck strap and waist band to hold it just below the chest. It responds with bleeps and has a plug-in **vibration unit**.

Few electronic mobility aids are in regular use in this country. Anyone considering the purchase of even a relatively inexpensive device would be well advised to discuss the idea first with a mobility instructor. RNIB and the GDBA collaborate in the evaluation of electronic mobility aids and try to keep abreast of developments. Details ❶❷❸ of suppliers, prices, training facilities and servicing can be supplied by *RNIB Technical Research Department*.

12.6 Maps

The kind of information that helps blind people making their way around on their own is not necessarily the same as that which helps a sighted person. A **verbal map** can be recorded on a pocket tape recorder and played back bit by bit as each stage of the journey is completed. It can take into account features like the smell of a fish shop, the gradient of a hill, hazards such as a protruding hedge, the sounds associated with a particular location – all difficult to represent on an ordinary map.

The value of **tactile maps and diagrams** is in giving a general idea of the shape of an area, whether it is a whole continent or the lay-out of a flat, and of the relationship between its features. RNIB publishes a series of large tactile plastic maps, produced with strong colours and names in large print. As well as atlas-style maps, the series includes a number of city centre maps. Details are given in RNIB's **Learning product guide** (see 29.1). See also 8.11. Tactile maps and diagrams can be produced by some transcription services.

To avoid duplication of time and effort in producing tactile maps, a **National Register of Maps for the Visually Handicapped** is kept by *Dr. A.F. Tatham, c/o Royal Geographical Society, 1 Kensington Gore, London SW7 2AR*. All tactile map-makers are asked to register their maps on special forms available from him. A regular newsletter about tactile maps and diagrams is available from Dr. Tatham.

A battery operated Robotron **talking compass**, £59.95 from *Techno-Vision Systems*, is designed for everyday use in familiar as well as unfamiliar areas.

12.7 The outdoor environment

Pressure from campaigning groups has helped to ensure that some progress is being made towards making access to the outdoor environment easier and safer for people with a visual impairment. Organisations of and for blind people are represented on the **Joint Committee on Mobility of Blind and Partially Sighted People**. In consultation with public authorities, JCMB is concerned to ensure that visually impaired pedestrians can move about safely and freely. Any problems which blind people encounter which hinder their mobility should be drawn to the attention of the JCMB Secretary c/o RNIB.

The JCMB encourages membership of local **Access Groups** so that visually impaired people as well as people with other disabilities can have more say in consultations with local authorities on issues such as tactile paving, pedestrian precinct planning, pavement obstacles and the accessibility of public transport. Further information from the *National Access Committees* ✆ 0171 250 0008 (England), ✆ 01222 887325 (Wales), ✆ 0131 229 8632 (Scotland) and ✆ 01232 491011 (Northern Ireland).

With the backing of organisations such as Age Concern and the Pedestrians Association, the **National Federation of the Blind** carries on with its long-standing 'Give us Back our Pavements' campaign against the increasing encroachment of impediments such as bicycles, shop displays and parked cars on pavements. Full details from the Federation's national office.

The **Joint Mobility Unit**, formed as a partnership between RNIB and the Guide Dogs for the Blind Association, aims to bring about improvements in streets, transport systems and public buildings so that blind, deafblind and partially sighted people can move about with greater freedom, independence and safety.

A number of features to help blind pedestrians have been developed by the Department of Transport in consultation with blind and partially sighted people. Reactions, comments or questions from visually impaired people on these or on any

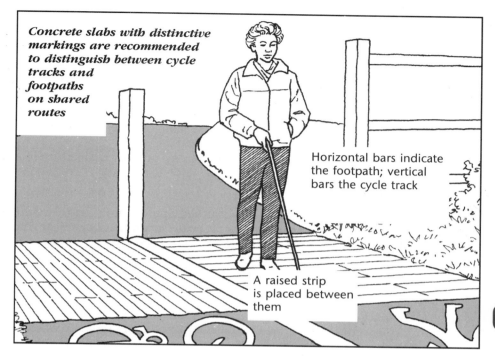

Concrete slabs with distinctive markings are recommended to distinguish between cycle tracks and footpaths on shared routes

Horizontal bars indicate the footpath; vertical bars the cycle track

A raised strip is placed between them

E

other issues concerning mobility should be directed to the *Department of Transport, Mobility Unit.*

12.7.1 Tactile surfaces

A surface with **small raised domes** is recommended by the Department of Transport where the kerb has been dropped flush with the road surface. At **pedestrian crossings** and at traffic lights with a pedestrian phase, the surface is laid so as to enable visually impaired people to find the crossing, locate the pedestrian push-button box and align themselves in the correct direction to cross. At other crossing points where kerbs have been lowered, the same tactile surface is recommended, but in a different colour and layout. It is also recommended that wherever possible dropped kerbs at uncontrolled crossings over side streets should be sited a short distance down the side street.

On **cycle tracks** which are shared between pedestrians and cyclists, the Department of Transport recommends that local authorities install a raised, contrasting strip between the two sides, and provide tactile surfaces at each end of the shared track, so that visually impaired pedestrians can tell which side is which. Slabs with parallel channels indicate the start of the cyclists' side, slabs with a ladder pattern the start of the pedestrian side. See illustration above.

Also authorised by the Department of Transport is **corduroy paving**, which has a pattern of half rod shaped bars, to warn of hazards such as steps, and a surface with

lozenge shapes to mark the edge of platforms at stations serving the new rapid transit systems like those in Manchester and Sheffield.

Detailed information and advice on all tactile paving surfaces is available from RNIB/GDBA Joint Mobility Unit.

12.7.2 Pelican and Puffin crossings

At **Pelican crossings**, crossings with light signals and a push-button control for the pedestrian, someone whose vision is too poor to see the green man may still be able to see the WAIT sign beside the push button. This should light up when the button is pressed, and go out at the start of the short period during which the traffic is halted and it is safe to cross.

Many Pelican crossings are fitted with an **audible signal** which bleeps while the steady green man is showing. This is the period during which traffic has been signalled to halt and it is safe to start crossing. The use of **tactile signals** is authorised on Pelican crossings, either in addition to a sound signal, or as an alternative where it is not possible to install audible signals. The tactile signal consists of a small knob fitted at the base of the push-button box, and it rotates when the steady green man is showing. A **localised audible signal** (the 'bleep and sweep') which adjusts to the ambient noise level was developed by the Department of Transport for use at dual carriageways where Pelican crossings are staggered. The standard audible signal cannot be used at such a location because a blind pedestrian might confuse the signal for one half of the crossing with that belonging to the other, and step into the road while the traffic is still moving. In Scotland, which does not come under Department of Transport jurisdiction in this respect, voiced signals are in use in some places, with male and female voices to distinguish the different sections of the crossing.

Some pedestrians, particularly those who are elderly or disabled, are worried that insufficient time is allowed for them to cross at a Pelican crossing. At the new **Puffin** (Pedestrian User-Friendly Intelligent) crossing, with the green man signal mounted above its push-button box, traffic is not signalled to move on again until the crossing is clear of pedestrians. Traffic lights are controlled by an infra-red detector which senses the presence of pedestrians on the crossing. A pedestrian wanting to use the crossing presses the button in the same way as for a Pelican, but should stand near the push-button box (on the detector mat, if there is one) to be within the range of the detector. The lights will not change unless the detector senses the presence of someone waiting to cross. Puffins have been installed on a trial basis at a number of sites throughout the country. When the trials have been successfully completed, it is envisaged that Puffins will gradually replace Pelican crossings and pedestrian facilities at junctions.

12.7.3 Railway crossings

Blind pedestrians need to take greater care at level crossings now that few of them still have the traditional gates. When the road is open, there may be no gates or barriers between pedestrians and the railway, and the only guide across the tracks is a white line marking the footway. At automatic level crossings, the barriers come down over the left hand side of the road only, or there are no barriers at all. In most cases, when the red light signals are flashing to halt traffic, a warbling noise now sounds continuously until the train has passed. An increased rate of warbling indicates the approach of a second train. But at a number of the older half-barrier automatic crossings, mainly south of London, the audible warnings still stop as soon as the barriers have come down – *before* the train has passed. These crossings will eventually be modernised, but in the meantime it may be better to avoid them and use an alternative route.

At all types of automatic crossings where pedestrian use is particularly great or where vulnerable groups of pedestrians in large numbers use the crossings, **guard rails** should be provided to segregate pedestrians from other traffic on the approaches to the crossings, and there should be flashing signals consisting of a black figure on a red illuminated background to warn pedestrians not to cross.

Blind people who need to use level crossings would be wise to seek the advice of a rehabilitation worker.

12.7.4 Street works

All street works must be adequately signed and lit at all times and must be enclosed by a rigid colour contrasting barrier displaying the name and telephone number of the contractor alongside (see illustration in 12.8.1). On completion of the works the street must be reinstated so as not to represent a hazard to disabled people, and facilities such as dropped kerbs and tactile surfaces should be restored. The local highway authority should be notified of any failure to comply with these provisions.

12.8 Making access easier

12.8.1 Public buildings

Regulations in force throughout the UK make it compulsory to take into account the needs of people with impaired sight in the design and construction of **new** public buildings. All steps on at least one set of internal or external stairs must have contrasting edgings, and handrails must extend at least 300mm beyond the top and bottom nosings of steps. Corduroy paving (see 12.7.1) is required on top landings of external stairs to give advance warning of the change of level, and may be provided on internal stairs. Passenger lifts should have tactile indicators on or adjacent to lift buttons on the landing and within the lift.

For anybody with impaired sight, good design also means buildings that are visually stimulating, very well lit and glare-free. Only then is it possible to use remaining vision to the full. Ideally, at the same time, the building should appeal to the other senses. Outstanding examples of good design include the resource centre at the Royal Leicestershire Society for the Blind, the swimming pool at The Guide Dogs for the

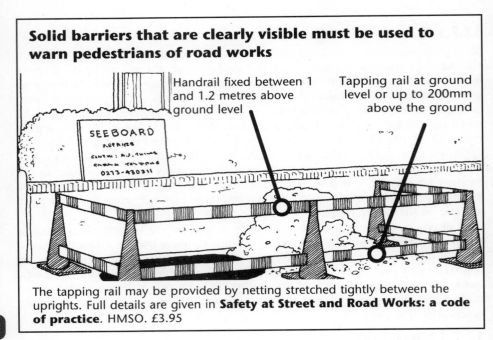

Solid barriers that are clearly visible must be used to warn pedestrians of road works

Handrail fixed between 1 and 1.2 metres above ground level

Tapping rail at ground level or up to 200mm above the ground

SEEBOARD

The tapping rail may be provided by netting stretched tightly between the uprights. Full details are given in **Safety at Street and Road Works: a code of practice**. HMSO. £3.95

E

Blind holiday hotel in Teignmouth, and RNIB's Vocational College, Loughborough which won a Civic Trust award in 1990. It was praised for the use made of texture, acoustics, solidity and resilience as well as for good lighting and colour schemes.

NEW Details of manufacturers and suppliers of products designed to meet building regulations can be obtained from *RNIB/GDBA Joint Mobility Unit*, together with advice on all aspects of the design and construction of any public buildings in relation to visually impaired users. Design features appropriate to visually impaired people will be described in **Building Sight**, to be published by the Unit in July 1995. The JCMB (c/o RNIB) is also prepared to assist. RNIB Housing Service can provide advice specifically for local authorities, housing associations and other organisations providing residential accommodation.

Advice for shops, banks, offices and public transport systems on ways of helping visually impaired people to find their way around independently is given in an **Access Guide** available free from the *Partially Sighted Society* in return for a large (A4) stamped, addressed envelope. Advice on making provision for the needs of visually impaired people is included in **Designing for Accessibility – an introductory guide**. 1993. £7. *Centre for Accessible Environments, Nutmeg House, 60 Gainsford Street, London SE1 2NY* ✆ 0171 357 8182. In consultation with architects, ergonomic experts and quantity surveyors, the **Construction Industry Research and Information Association** has compiled definitive design guidelines for improving access to existing as well as new buildings for people with sensory or physical disabilities. The results are to be published in summer 1995 by *CIRIA, 6 Storey's Gate, London SW1P 3AU* ℘ 0171 222 8891.

12.8.2 Visual and tactile signs

Better use of colour and tactile features as well as braille could ensure that signs indicating public toilets, exits, lifts etc. are clear and easily understood by people with visual impairments as well as by other members of the public. In conjunction with the **Sign Design Society** and the **British Sign Association**, RNIB/GDBA Joint Mobility Unit is conducting an assessment of sample designs for use in public areas with a view to drawing up a guide to good signage practice. It is hoped that this will be ready for publication by the end of 1995.

12.8.3 Talking signs

Systems are being developed which use a voiced message to help locate facilities such as a telephone kiosk, a ticket machine or the entrance to a shop. A small electronic card carried by the visually impaired person either triggers a voice message from a beacon installed at the location, or gives the voice message itself. Some examples have been tried out in locations such as Great Portland Street underground station in London and a shopping centre in Bury, Lancashire, but insufficient interest has yet been shown in these systems to make them commercially viable. Unless blind people themselves are more aware of their potential value and express a wish to have them installed in public places, the situation is unlikely to change. Besides continuing its involvement in research and development, RNIB is trying to stimulate the interest in talking signs which would create a demand for their installation. Further information from *RNIB Technical Research Department.*

E

12.8.4 Access for guide dogs

Guide dog owners who sometimes may be refused admission to food shops because of hygiene regulations should be aware that in 1976 a circular was sent by the Department of Health to all local authorities recommending that notices prohibiting dogs from food premises should specifically exempt guide dogs. Guide dog owners can obtain from **The Guide Dogs for the Blind Association** cards which indicate, with the authority of the Institution of Environmental Health Officers (or the Royal Environmental Health Institute of Scotland), that guide dogs are allowed entry to restaurants, food shops and other food premises. The Association also supplies information sheets about guide dogs in Gujerati, Urdu and Chinese. **Stick-on notices** suitable for display in shop windows can be obtained free from the GDBA.

12.9 Further reading

A **Mobility pack** can be obtained for £10 from the *British Journal of Visual Impairment.* It contains a selection of articles published in the Journal between 1983 and 1993.

13 Transport and travel

Little by little, features are being introduced, such as handrails in contrasting colours and improved lighting, which make public transport more easily accessible to visually impaired people. They, as well as people with other disabilities, will benefit if buses of the future can lower their steps at bus stops as do the low floor buses on trial in London, Liverpool, Whitley Bay and Tayside.

Also of interest are the screens on trial at a number of bus stops in London and Southampton. They indicate the order, destination and expected time of arrival of buses. **NEW** Units giving the information in **digital speech** have been installed at route 18 stops in Great Portland Street near RNIB headquarters and 'Ha'penny Steps' on the Harrow Road. **NEW** A Train, Bus and Coach **timetable information service** on 0891 910 910 (calls charged at 49p per minute peak times, 39p at other times) covers all Britain's train, rural bus and most long distance coach services.

Help and advice on planning journeys and on any aspect of travel is offered by **NEW** **Tripscope**, a charity which provides a nationwide service to older and disabled people. Contact Tripscope's Information Officers at *The Courtyard, Evelyn Road, London W4 5JL* ℘ 0181 994 9294 (Minicom) for UK or international enquiries, or at *Pamwell House, 160 Pennywell Road, Bristol BS5 0TX* ℘ 0117 941 4094 for South West England and South Wales. Callers can be rung back if they are worried about the cost of their call. Responses to postal enquiries can be put on tape.

Finding an escort is often a problem for a blind person who is unused to travelling, or needs to make a journey on an unfamiliar route. If contacted in good time, the **British Red Cross** and the **WRVS** can usually find a volunteer to take someone to hospital, or to a rehabilitation centre, or escort a child to residential school, and might also consider 'social' journeys such as a visit to relatives if there is no more urgent call on their helpers' time. Applications should be made to the nearest branch; the address should be listed in the phone book.

Blind and partially sighted people are among those entitled to **concessionary fares** on some public transport. In Northern Ireland all registered blind people, regardless of age, can travel free on all buses and trains. In other parts of the United Kingdom a variety of concessions apply to both local and long-distance travel. However, guide dogs travel free on all forms of public transport.

Snapshot

We have had low floor buses in the Uxbridge and Hounslow area since spring 1994 and for many people they have made it possible, or easier, to use a bus. I am a guide dog owner but I also have some difficulty in walking and have to use an elbow crutch in my right hand when working my dog. It does not take much imagination to appreciate the difficulty I would have in using a conventional bus.

▶ Sarah Arnull writing in *British Journal of Visual Impairment*, Dec 1994.

13.1 Local services

All local authorities have discretion to operate a concessionary fares scheme for blind people, defined as 'persons so blind as to be unable to perform any work for which sight is essential'. In areas where such schemes are in operation, it usually means that the bus company or the local authority issues a special bus pass, but the extent of the concession varies from one area to another. Examples of schemes operated in major urban areas include:

Greater Manchester: registered blind and partially sighted people are eligible for a concessionary pass which entitles them to travel free at any time on all local buses, trams and trains.

Merseyside: registered blind and partially sighted people travel free on all local bus, rail and ferry services.

Tyne and Wear: registered blind or partially sighted people are eligible for a concessionary fare of 15p per journey at all times if they are in full time employment, otherwise at off peak times only.

West Midlands: visually impaired people travel free on all public transport at the discretion of the district council for the area in which they live.

West Yorkshire: registered blind people travel free at any time on all buses and trains; registered partially sighted people are entitled to the same concession as old age pensioners.

Strathclyde: registered blind people can travel free at any time on all local transport, including the underground; registered partially sighted people, and people who have been refused a driving licence on grounds of sight impairment, are entitled to the same concessions as other handicapped people, i.e. reduced fares for journeys made after 9 a.m. If the cardholder is in receipt of Attendance Allowance or Disability Living Allowance (Care Component), a Companion Travel Card allows a companion to travel with the cardholder at the concessionary fare.

London: registered blind people under pensionable age can, on production of a pass issued by the local social services department, travel free on London Underground and LT bus services at any time. Blind people who continue to work after retirement age are restricted to the off-peak concessions available to all elderly people.

NEW Some blind people have found that their eligibility for a free travel pass has been disputed when they were awarded a mobility component of the disability living allowance. The Solicitor General has ruled that this contravenes section 73(14) of the Social Security Contributions and Benefits Act 1992, which prevents the DLA mobility component from being taken into account in assessing a person's entitlement to services such as concessionary travel. Contact *RNIB Benefits Rights Team* for further details.

Blind people living in **rural areas** are increasingly dependent on the goodwill of friends and relatives with cars, but it is worth checking with the local social services department or voluntary association about community bus services or car rotas to meet local needs. Apart from helping individuals, community transport groups are often able to provide mini-bus transport for a party of blind or disabled people wishing to undertake some activity or just go on an outing.

Information about this type of scheme, and about other services such as the door to door mini-bus and discount taxi services operating in some (mainly urban) areas, is included in **Door to Door**, a guide to transport for people with disabilities compiled by the *Department of Transport Mobility Unit* and also available on cassette from them free of charge. An updated edition was due for publication in July 1995.

13.2 Long distance travel

Rail

Given the uncertainty about the future of British railways, it is worth noting that guidelines for rail operators were set out in **Meeting the needs of disabled passengers – A code of practice** published by the Office of the Rail Regulator. This is available free in print or on tape from *Sue MacSwan, ORR Library, 1 Waterhouse Square, Holborn Bars, 138-142 Holborn, London EC1N 2SU* ✆ 0171 282 2001. One of the conditions of granting a licence to a rail operator is that full account should be taken of these guidelines. They include specific reference to visual impairment in matters such as making printed material available where possible in alternative formats, training staff to understand the needs of visually impaired passengers, the use of good lighting, colour contrast and textured surfaces in the design of stations and rolling stock, and the clarity of both visual and tactile signs.

Full details of provision for blind and other disabled people travelling by rail are given in **British Rail and the Disabled Traveller**, a leaflet available from main rail stations and travel centres. It includes an application form for a **Disabled Persons Railcard**, currently £14 a year, for which visually impaired people are eligible. It entitles the holder travelling alone, or both the holder and an adult companion, to reductions of up to 34% off most rail fares. The original application should be accompanied by a copy of a letter from social services confirming registration as blind or partially sighted. All railway operators must accept the Disabled Persons Railcard under the 1993 Railways Act.

Registered blind and partially sighted people who do not hold a Disabled Persons Railcard, but who are **travelling with a companion** are also entitled to certain fare concessions, regardless of the purpose of the journey. Both are entitled to one third off Standard Single tickets and First Class/Standard Open Returns, and to half price First Class/Standard Day Returns. One adult Season ticket can be issued to allow both to travel for the price of one. A different companion may travel on different days. Proof of registration is required to obtain these concessions. They do not extend to Cheap Day returns, or to Network Awaybreaks and Saver, Super Saver, Apex and Advanced Apex tickets. This range of tickets may offer better value than a Standard return less the concession. Blind travellers with guide dogs are accommodated in first-class sleeper compartments, but only charged the second-class fare. Guide dogs are allowed to accompany their owners into restaurant and buffet cars.

There are some fare concessions on rail travel to the continent. **NEW** On **Eurostar** trains to Calais Frethun, Lille, Brussels or Paris, European Passenger Services (EPS) allows a reduction on first or standard class fares to one companion travelling throughout by the same train and in the same class with a blind passenger.

Blind people travelling with a companion by rail/sea to Austria, Belgium, the Czech and Slovak republics, Denmark, Eire, France, Germany, Greece, Hungary, Italy, Luxembourg, the Netherlands, Northern Ireland, Poland, Portugal, Spain and Switzerland can travel two for the price of one on **through international return tickets**, first or second class, and on some economy return fares. The sea crossing must be by **Sealink-Stena Line** or **Ostend Line** ferry services, and be part of the through rail/sea/rail journey to the final continental destination. Proof must be shown that the traveller is registered blind. The Disabled Persons Railcard does not in itself provide entitlement to this concession. Full details from stations which are Continental ticketing points. A traveller who has difficulty in obtaining any of the concessions should ask to be referred to the person in the local Railway manager's office who is in charge of travel arrangements for disabled people.

Arrangements can be made at a staffed departure station to meet a blind person travelling alone, and escort him or her safely on to the train. Similar arrangements can be made at the destination station or at any intermediate changing point, provided these stations are staffed. Advance warning (a couple of days' notice is ideal) should be given to an office listed in the leaflet **British Rail and the Disabled Traveller**.

Any problems encountered by visually impaired travellers that cannot be resolved at railway enquiry offices should be referred to the Railway Director responsible for the line in question, whose name, address and telephone number will be displayed at the station. If the response is unsatisfactory, contact the Secretary of the local **Rail Users Consultative Committee** (**London Regional Passengers Committee** in the London area) whose addresses are shown at stations.

One of the conditions of granting a licence to a rail operator is that full account should be taken of guidelines set out in **Meeting the needs of disabled passengers – A code of practice** published by the Office of the Rail Regulator. This is available free in print or on tape from *Sue MacSwan, ORR Library, 1 Waterhouse Square, Holborn Bars, 138-142 Holborn, London EC1N 2SU* ✆ 0171 282 2001. The guidelines include specific reference to visual impairment.

Coach

Some of the 60 or so companies operating long-distance routes offer fare concessions to blind passengers, so it is worth checking with local operators.

Air

Within the United Kingdom, a blind person accompanied by a guide can travel on **domestic airlines** for one fully flexible adult fare when the journey is for business, education, training, medical or rehabilitation purposes. The blind traveller or the local authority should apply to the airline for a certificate, which has to be signed by a blind welfare authority and presented when buying the air ticket. The concession does not apply to discounted fares. No fare concessions are given at present by any airlines for travel outside the United Kingdom, with the exception of **Saudi Arabian**

E

Airlines who offer a 50% discount on economy class and excursion fares to passengers flying with them who can provide documentary evidence of blindness. The concession also applies to a blind passenger's sighted companion.

Airlines try to help disabled travellers in other ways. Given advance warning, most will provide a member of staff to help a blind person travelling alone through the terminal and onto the aircraft once he or she has checked in. An updated version of **Plane Easy** ●, produced free by RNIB in cooperation with British Airways, will be available by the summer of 1995. It advises on all aspects of air travel, from making the reservation to arrival at the destination airport. Enquiries about **travel concessions in other countries** should be made to the appropriate organisation for the blind in that country. Addresses can be obtained from *RNIB Reference Library*.

13.3 Getting around London

Information available from London Transport *Unit for Disabled Passengers, 55 Broadway, London SW1H 0BD* ℘ 0171 222 5600, includes a range of free maps in accessible formats:

Harnessing London Transport: A Guide Dog Owner's Guide ● ● ●
London Underground map ● ●
Underground stations in alphabetical order with details of stairs, lifts and escalators ●
Central London bus routes ●
Central London Underground (tactile – also available from *RNIB*)
Stationlink, guide to wheelchair accessible bus service between London main line stations ●

The **RNIB London Underground Guide** gives lists in braille of the stations on each line as well as other useful information.

Given at least a week's notice, the **Metropolitan Society for the Blind**, *Duke House, 4th floor, 6-12 Tabard Street, London SE1 4JT* ℘ 0171 403 6184, may be able to arrange for an escort to help blind travellers cross London safely.

13.4 Stopping a bus or taxi

To help visually impaired people wanting to stop a bus RNIB supplies a free white plastic **bus card** with the word 'BUS' printed on both sides in bold black letters. A notch at the top edge indicates which way up it should be held. Another bus card, £1.85 from *RNIB*, is designed to show the number of the bus required when waiting at stops serving several different routes. It is a ferrous metal plate welded into a black plastic wallet and is supplied with a choice of white magnetised numbers three inches high. A **taxi card**, with the word **TAXI** printed boldly on both sides on a reflective background, is available free from *RNIB*. Blind people who have used these cards report that taxi drivers like them, as they are easy to see.

13.5 Cars and the Orange Badge scheme

Registered blind people are eligible for a **Disabled Person's Badge**, known as the Orange Badge. The badge entitles the holder or his or her driver to certain **parking**

concessions: to park without charge or time limit at meter bays, to park for any length of time in streets where waiting is otherwise limited, and, in England, Wales and Northern Ireland, to park for up to three hours on single or double yellow lines (except in a bus lane, or where there are double white lines in the centre of the road, or when a ban on loading and unloading is in force). In Northern Ireland the badge does not entitle the holder to leave a vehicle unattended in any control zone area.

Badges carry the holder's name and photograph and should be displayed on the dashboard or fascia panel of any vehicle in which the holder travels, with the front of the badge facing forward so that the relevant details are legible from outside the vehicle. An **Institution Badge** is available for larger passenger vehicles, such as mini-buses, used by institutions to carry groups of disabled people entitled to the concessions. When parking on yellow lines, a special parking disc must also be displayed which should be set to show the time of arrival. In Scotland, where there is no limit for parking on yellow lines, parking discs are not required.

Applications for a badge should be made to the local social services department (England and Wales), the Regional or Island Council (Scotland) or the nearest Road Service Division of the Department of the Environment (Northern Ireland). A vehicle registration number is required by law for local authority records. Some issuing authorities charge a fee to cover administrative expenses.

Badges are valid for three years and must be renewed after that period. If a badge is no longer required by its holder it must be surrendered to the issuing authority, and not transferred to another person. It is an offence for ineligible drivers to use the parking concessions bestowed by the badge if they are not transporting a badge-holder at the time. Badge-holders may risk forfeiting their badges if they allow them to be misused in this way. Badges must therefore be removed from display whenever the parking concessions are not being used. The use of any window badges which might be confused with the Disabled Person's Badge is discouraged.

The Orange Badge scheme applies throughout the United Kingdom with the exception of Central London (the City of London, City of Westminster, the Royal Borough of Kensington and Chelsea and part of the London Borough of Camden). These boroughs issue Disabled Person's Badges for use outside Central London, but disabled people who are resident or working **within Central London** are offered limited concessions (consisting primarily of spaces reserved for badge holders and some form of concessionary parking at meters).

Holders of Disabled Person's Badges are allowed parking concessions in a number of **European countries**. An explanatory leaflet can be obtained from the *Department of Transport, Orange Badge Unit.*

13.5.1 Road tax

Blind people who have other very severe disabilities may be exempt from road tax. Details of eligibility are given in the application form **V188** from the *DVLA, Swansea SA99 1AN* ✆ 01792 772134.

14 Health

This chapter looks at ways in which people with little or no sight can get help with problems likely to be of special concern to them, and also has information for people with visual impairments on general health issues.

14.1 Eye care

People who are registered as blind or partially sighted are entitled to a free NHS sight test, as are people with glaucoma or their close relatives over the age of 40 (for full details see 5.13.2). The **Patients Charter** states that a NHS eye test should include a thorough eye examination to check for any disease or abnormality as well as checking sight, and where appropriate prescribing spectacles. The booklet **The Patients Charter and You ⓛⒷⓉ** which details the government's requirements for all parts of the NHS is available free from the *Patients Charter, Freepost London SE99 7XU*, or ring Freephone ℘ 0800 555777.

14.1.1 Optical Complaints Service

Anyone who feels that they have a grievance about the way they have been treated by an optician or an optometrist which they have been unable to settle with the professional concerned can take the matter up with the **Optical Consumer Complaints Service**, an independent body funded by the main professional associations to act as an Ombudsman for the optical profession. Contact the OCCS at *PO Box 4685, London SE1 8YH* ℘ 0171 580 8249.

14.2 Artificial eyes

Nowadays artificial eyes are usually made of plastic, not glass (though occasionally someone with a medical allergy to plastic material might be fitted with a glass eye). Every artificial eye is made to a patient's individual needs, and without charge to NHS patients or War Pensioners. Details of the 18 Artificial Eye Centres in England are available on request from the *National Artificial Eye Service, 221 Bristol Avenue, Blackpool FY 20BF* ℘ 01253 306469 which also has very helpful leaflets on the use and care of artificial eyes, including **My Pretend Eye**, designed for children. For information about artificial eye centres in Scotland, contact the *Glasgow Eye Infirmary, 3 Sandyford Place, Glasgow G3 7NB*. The AES in Wales can be contacted at the *Artificial Limbs and Appliance Centre* in the *Rookwood Hospital, Llandaff, Cardiff CF5 2YN*, and in Northern Ireland services are based at the *Contact Lens Unit* in the *Royal Victoria Hospital, Grosvenor Road, Belfast BT12 6BA*.

One new development not yet available on the NHS is a porous hydroxyapatite (synthetic coral) implant which replaces the globe of the eye. The eye muscles fuse into the porous material and the false eye has a locating peg so that almost full movement is restored. For details write to *John Weiss and Son, 89 Alston Drive, Bradwell Abbey, Milton Keynes MK13 9HF* ℘ 01908 318017.

Although many people find it quite satisfactory to clean their artificial eye just with soapy water, Nick Rumney, an optometrist who himself has an artificial eye, advises the use of a **Hard Contact Lens Cleaner**, ideally daily or at least once a week. The Cleaner should be rubbed over the eye in the palm of the hand, and then rinsed thoroughly under cold running water. Nick Rumney also advises that the artificial eye should be inserted using a Hard Contact Lens wetting solution.

14.3 Coping with sight loss

The loss of vision whether from one eye or both will require a period of emotional as well as practical readjustment. Almost everyone who loses their sight experiences a period of grief, anxiety, bewilderment and depression. Some people come to terms with their situation unaided after a period of time. Others may welcome the opportunity to talk through their problems and express feelings that could be painful or threatening to friends or relations. A few local voluntary societies are acknowledging the need for help with the emotional distress of sight loss, and run groups to give blind people, particularly those who have recently lost their sight, the opportunity to discuss their feelings and through mutual support come to terms with their situation. **Projects by the Blind (Wandsworth)** runs such groups on a regular basis, and these are open to people in the London area. For details contact *Paul Holmes*, ℘ 0181 675 3900, who would also be happy to advise people wishing to set up such groups in other parts of the country.

14.3.1 Counselling help

Anyone who feels that they would like more individual support should contact one of the counselling agencies. Counselling is not the same as psycho-therapy. Many people rightly resist the implication that they are in need of psychological treatment because of their sight loss. A counsellor is trained to listen attentively while someone talks through their problems. They are not there to give advice, but to help someone to gain insight into their problems and support them in finding an appropriate way to cope with their difficulties. A list of local counsellors (in large print on request) can be obtained in return for a stamped addressed envelope from the *British Association*

Love is Blind?

'I don't think that my ex-husband ever adjusted to my loss of sight. He was always just hoping that tomorrow I'd wake up and my eyes would be all right, but of course that never happened. I was trying to make my sight all right and make everything else all right, and it became a great strain.'

'I was the manager of a supermarket but had to give up the job which I loved when I lost my sight. I felt that having failed in my career I could not cope with failing in the sex side of marriage. So I used to wait until my wife had fallen asleep before going to bed. I thought that by denying it the subject of sex would never crop up, so therefore I was not failing!'

▶ *In Touch* listeners describing how blindness affected their marriages.

---

for Counselling, 1 Regent Place, Rugby, Warwickshire CV21 2PJ ✆ 01788 578328 (recorded information) or 550899 (queries). The Association has a sub-committee devoted to disabled issues.

As sight loss is often compared to bereavement, a counsellor who has been trained to help people to cope with loss in general might also be appropriate. Contact *National Association of Bereavement Services, 20 Norton Folgate, London E1 6DB* ✆ 0171 247 1080.

Loss of sight often affects not only the individual concerned but also his or her partner and closest relations. It may be appropriate to seek advice from **Relate** – formerly the National Marriage Guidance Council. The local branch should be listed in the telephone directory. In case of any difficulty contact the head office at *Herbert Gray College, Little Church Street, Rugby CV21 3AP* ✆ 01788 573241.

Even if counselling is not offered in name by the local social services department as part of their rehabilitation programme, the basic training in daily living skills which is usually offered provides newly blind people not only with practical skills but introduces them to other local people experiencing sight loss, and the mutual exchange of experiences can be very therapeutic. However, some people may benefit from a longer and more intense course at a residential centre (see 15.1.1).

14.3.2 Assertion training

This is an increasingly popular way of learning how best to present oneself in a variety of everyday situations. It can be particularly valuable for someone who has, together with their sight, lost their self confidence for dealing with other people, particularly those who persist in seeing only the blindness and not the person involved. These courses are often to be found at local adult education classes and there is no reason why a blind person should not participate in these; it might well be the first step to re-integration in ordinary life. Anna Tylor who is herself partially sighted organises assertion courses of varying lengths, and when she cannot help, she might be able to put enquirers in touch with other trainers. Contact *Total Communication, 80 Harborough Road, London SW16 2XW* ✆ 0181 769 8673.

14.3.3 Relaxation methods

It is generally agreed that people with poor sight are more likely to make the most of their remaining vision if their general state of health is good, and quite a number report that they have found relaxation techniques helpful. Classes and groups may well be run at the local voluntary society or at a local adult education centre. It is also possible to get a range of music for relaxation tapes, frequently sold in health shops, which some people find helpful when trying to relax and reduce stress.

14.3.4 Therapeutic beauty care

One very practical form of help for women who have lost their sight and are unconfident about their appearance is offered by the **British Red Cross**, which trains members already skilled in therapeutic beauty care to teach make-up technique to blind and partially sighted women. Enquiries about this free service should be addressed to the local county branch of the British Red Cross. People with limited sight may also find it helpful to use a magnifying mirror when applying make-up, or shaving. A model with a choice of two different magnifications is available by mail order (price £49.95) from the *Partially Sighted Society*, which also sells at the same price a set of large magnifiers that can be fitted over a wall hung mirror.

14.4 Sleep disturbance

There have been a number of reports suggesting that people who lose their sight are more likely to suffer from sleep disturbances. This is thought to be caused by changes in the functioning of the pineal gland which is greatly influenced by the amount of light perceived by the eyes. The pineal gland produces a hormone called melatonin which affects sleep patterns. A research project led by Professor Alan Bird of Moorfields Eye Hospital is currently investigating the relationship between sleep and blindness, and it is hoped that the results of their research will lead to simple forms of treatment for those who are affected.

14.5 Visual hallucinations

Visual hallucinations are a not uncommon experience for people who have lost their sight. When the subject was first raised on the *In Touch* programme, a number of listeners responded with relief that others had similar, and often frightening experiences, 'seeing' objects and people very clearly that were invisible to anyone else. One elderly listener described a terrifying vision of men wielding knives; others saw more benign apparitions including bunches of flowers or lines of jumbled print. A neuro-ophthalmologist interviewed on *In Touch* said that it was a normal phenomenon after sight loss. The brain was trying to substitute visual images when the eye could no longer see. Although individual patients experienced such images for varied periods of time, they did eventually disappear. But they were not a sign of mental instability.

In Australia **Vision Victoria** runs a telephone support group for people in this situation. They encourage members to describe their hallucination and then to try to link it with a pleasant experience, and this is found to be helpful. For example, when one member repeatedly 'saw' strange purple shapes looming up, she was encouraged to think of them as luscious bunches of grapes. More information from *Jennifer Gibbons, Association for the Blind, 7 Mair Street, Brighton Beach VIC 3188, Australia.*

14.6 Diet and nutrition
14.6.1 Research into diet

As yet no one understands the causes of the two main conditions – cataract and macular disease – that lead to sight loss in older people in the western world. Over the years there have been many attempts to find dietary supplements that might prevent the deterioration of sight. Most attention has been focused on the value of anti-oxidant vitamins and minerals, as the retina is prone to oxidative damage due to the high level of polyunsaturated fatty acids in the photo-receptor membranes. Various research projects in the United States have examined the value of zinc and selenium as well as vitamins E and C and carotenoids. So far the most promising results have been reported by a team from the Harvard University Medical School led by an ophthalmologist Dr. Johanna Seddon. They found that increasing the consumption of foods rich in certain carotenoids (a substance found in dark green leafy vegetables such as spinach) might decrease the risk of developing macular disease. However, the report published in the Journal of American Medical Association in November 1994 stressed that the findings had been based on a relatively small study, and needed to be supported by further research.

14.6.2 Ways to lose weight

Quite a lot of blind people are overweight. This is partly due to lack of normal exercise; it is not easy to move about briskly when one cannot see properly. Sometimes over-eating may be an emotional compensation in response to the shock of sight loss. Apart from cutting down on fattening food, the main way to lose weight is by taking more exercise. A stationary exercise bicycle may be the solution for those who feel that going out for a walk is beset with too many hazards. Exercise bicycles cost from about £30 from sports shops or mail order companies. Gentler exercise which can even be done sitting down is described in **Feeling Good**, a cassette course based on the Medau method. This aims to stretch muscles gently, keep joints supple and help good breathing. The cassette is available (price £5.99 plus 99p p&p) from *Motivation Sound, 35a Broadhurst Gardens, London NW6 3QT* ✆ 0171 328 8305. Yoga instructors recommend exercises such as the head stand as a good way of losing weight, but an eye specialist should be consulted before trying it, as this particular pose may not be recommended for people with certain eye conditions. Otherwise the more gentle yoga exercises can do nothing but good. A monthly tape magazine which includes gentle yoga and relaxation exercises as well as advice on nutrition and articles on complementary therapies is available for an annual subscription of £4 from *Good Health Association for the Blind, 136 Holloway Road, London N7 8DD* ✆ 0171 609 3590.

General advice on diet is given in **Healthy Eating for Older People** available free in large print from *Foodsense, London SE99 7TT* ✆ 01645 556000 (quote ref PB 1526); braille and tape versions available from *RNIB Customer Services*. Some blind people have found slimming clubs helpful. Weight Watchers offer visually impaired members a cassette **Slim and Trim** which gives their current advice on healthy diet. Weekly membership costs £3.95 (£2.95 for over 60s). Tapes and details of local clubs are available from *Weight Watchers UK Ltd., Kidwells Park House, Kidwells Park Drive, Maidenhead, Berks SL6 8YT* ✆ 01628 777077. This tape and others with advice on diet are available from RNIB Cassette Library. The Scottish Braille Press has braille versions of the BMA's **Slimmers Guide** and **Slim and Enjoy It**. Talking bathroom scales are available from *Cobolt Systems* (£31.95).

14.7 First aid

Although a number of visually impaired people have successfully completed first aid courses, no one has yet documented first aid methods or materials that might be particularly helpful to people with little or no sight. One Red Cross trainer has indicated to *In Touch* that he would welcome the challenge of teaching first aid to

Putting in drops using
Autodrop (see 14.8 for details)

▲ Autodrop clips on to the top of most eyedrop dispensers and holds the bottle at the correct angle

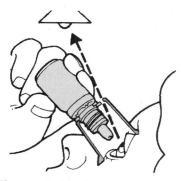

▲ The cup holds the lower lid open. There is a pinhole to direct the eyesight away from the descending drop

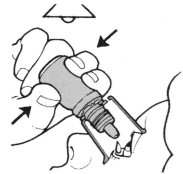

▲ One squeeze and the drop is delivered into the eye

visually impaired people. Anyone interested should contact *Barry Palmer, British Red Cross (Norfolk), Coronation Road, Norwich NR6 5HD* ✆ 01603 426361. A colleague has already run a special resuscitation course for visually impaired people in conjunction with the Norfolk and Norwich Blind Society. But the British Red Cross Society, which is now issuing brailled certificates to sighted first aiders so that blind people can check their qualifications, would also encourage visually impaired people to contact their local branch to see if there is a suitable course for them.

14.8 Taking medicines

Information about people who are eligible for free prescriptions is given in 5.13.1.

Identifying which medicines to take and when to take them is a problem faced by many blind people, especially those who have to take various medications throughout the day at different times. It is now usually possible to get tablets dispensed in blister packs which separate out the correct dosage for each day. However, for people who find it difficult to get tablets out of these packs, and particularly for those who need to take several different tablets at varying intervals throughout the day, it might be well worth investing in one of the **pill dispensers** into which a carer can put a daily, weekly or even three weekly supply of tablets. These dispensers not only serve as a reminder, but also make it easy for a carer to see if medicines have been forgotten. The RNIB sells a range of pill dispensers – details in the **Daily Living Product Guide** (see also photograph in the colour section). For those who still find themselves trying to distinguish two different tablets in identical containers, the general advice is not to take them out of the original bottles but to place them into two larger and differently shaped or coloured containers which can be easily distinguished. Some blind people put clothes pegs on the edge of these containers to indicate the number of times medicine should be taken, and remove them one by one as each dose is taken. There is also a medicine dispenser which screws onto a standard medicine bottle and measures out a 5ml dose without risk of spillage (*RNIB* £2.96). A talking thermometer is available from *RNIB* for £29.82. An easy-read thermometer which some people with partial sight may be able to decipher is available from *Boots* (£2.96).

14.8.1 Putting in eye drops

The administration of eye drops can be a tricky operation, but it is something that many people with failing eyesight have to learn to do for themselves. The illustration in this section shows the method recommended by Moorfields Eye Hospital. It is best to lie down before putting in eye drops. Curl the fingers of the hand not holding the eye-dropper bottle, and place the hand on the cheek below the eye so that the extended forefinger can comfortably reach to pull down the lower lid of the eye. This exposes a pocket between the lid and the surface of the eye into which the eyedrop can fall. The back of this hand becomes a prop for the other hand which is holding the eyedropper bottle. Hold the bottle between finger and thumb; rest the base of this thumb on the back of the curled fingers resting on the cheek. Look up, and squeeze the eye dropper bottle so that a drop enters the space between the lower lid and the eye. Shut the eye, rest for about a minute and then wipe off any excess solution on the eyelashes with a clean tissue.

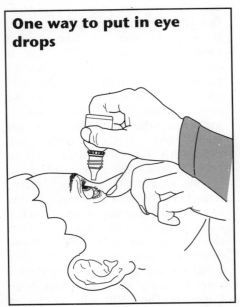

One way to put in eye drops

There are two devices that may help by holding the bottle in position and keeping the eye open. The RNIB sells the **Auto-drop** at £2.01 (see illustration in 14.7) but this does not fit bottles of Timoptol commonly prescribed for glaucoma. But the Timoptol bottle will fit into the **Easi-drop** guide sold by some chemists and also available by mail order (price £3.45 for two) from *Quote Force Ltd, The Old Post Office, Bucks Hill, Chipperfield, Herts WD4 9AT* ✆ 01923 263588.

262

14.9 Health care information

There is no reason to think that people with a vision loss have different health problems from sighted people, but those unable to read ordinary print will find that information on health matters is still limited in large print, tape or braille. A selection of **Family Doctor** and **BMA Healthcare Booklets** is available either in braille or on tape though rarely both. RNIB Customer Services have compiled a bibliography **Health and Fitness** listing a wide range of publications ranging from alternative therapies to sex manuals which are available in accessible formats. A number of tapes on health issues of particular interest to women, such as **Hormone Replacement Therapy**, are available from *Women's Health, 52 Featherstone Street, London EC1Y 8RT* ℘ 0171 251 6580. Audio cassettes with advice on coping with pain in general, as well as specific advice on coping with headaches & migraine or with back pain, have been produced in collaboration with the Pain Research Institute by Wendy Lloyd Audio Productions, who have also produced tapes on **Coping with Anxiety** and **Coping with Depression**. The tapes cost £7.55 each from *30 Guffitts Rake, Meols, Wirral L47 7AD*. There is an ever increasing range of **information tapes** on health issues being produced commercially and these are most likely to be sold in health food shops as well as in some chemists.

A **Health Information Service** on a freephone enquiry line, ℘ 0800 665544, has been set up by the Department of Health. The Department says the service is equipped to provide information on all kinds of health related matters, whether local or general. It can answer enquiries about particular conditions such as diabetes and where to get help with the cost of medication, the procedure for gaining access to medical records and information about support groups or which hospital has the shortest waiting list for a hip or a cataract operation. A similar service relating specifically to Wales is offered in Welsh or English on 0345 581490 (calls charged at local rate). Information about **hospital waiting lists** is also available from the *College of Health, St. Margaret's House, 21 Old Ford Road, London E2 9PL* ℘ 0181 983 1133.

14.9.1 Advice on sexual matters

The **Association to Aid the Sexual and Personal Relationships for People with a Disability** (SPOD) has a helpline, ℘ 0171 607 8851, which operates on Tuesdays and Thursdays from 10.30 a.m. to 1.30 p.m., and on Wednesdays from 1.30 to 4.30. SPOD has considerable experience in helping blind people with physical disabilities or those whose problems are caused by conditions such as diabetes.

The **Visually Impaired Gay Group** operates a 24 hour confidential helpline to offer advice and support to those who feel depressed or isolated, ℘ 01705 524739. A Scottish support group can be contacted on ℘ 01387 261679.

15 Everyday living

Given time and practice, people with deteriorating sight can learn to manage most of the ordinary tasks associated with running a household and dealing with their personal affairs. Memory, tidiness and an increasing awareness of information conveyed by the other senses all play a part. This chapter only gives outline guidance on how blind people manage and on the kind of equipment and services which can help, but it may serve to start people thinking about how they can solve some of their problems.

15.1 Sources of help

Rehabilitation workers (see the introduction to chapter 12) can show newly blind people the best way of coping with household tasks such as cooking and cleaning. Tuition in practical skills of this kind is usually included in the day rehabilitation courses run by some local social services, Resource Centres or voluntary societies for the blind. Such courses also provide the much valued opportunity to exchange ideas and experiences with others who have lost their sight.

15.1.1 Residential courses

Social rehabilitation courses are offered by RNIB at their **Skills Development Centre** in Torquay. The courses are intended for people who are not necessarily interested in taking up paid employment, or who are already over retirement age. Besides being taught daily living skills – how to move around safely indoors and out, how to make the best use of remaining vision and of other senses, plus communication skills including braille, Moon and typing – students receive individual counselling and support in coming to terms with loss of sight. Courses are flexible and vary in length to suit individual students. All students are offered up to two weeks' prior assessment to determine how much help they need and in which areas. The weekly charge is £455, but this should be paid by social services departments if they are unable to provide a rehabilitation service in the person's home area.

June Bretherton, a teacher who since losing her sight has concentrated on teaching practical living skills to newly blind people, runs some residential courses in different parts of the country. Full details from Mrs Bretherton at *98 Aldborough Road, Upminster, Essex RM14 2RS* ✆ 01708 458475 (see also 10.5).

15.2 Looking after your home

15.2.1 Housework

Blind people learn from experience to work systematically so that they do not go over the same place twice with a vacuum cleaner or broom. When washing floors, the lines of tiles or other floor covering can serve as guides, or a piece of paper can be

---

Key to media of publication ℗ clear print ➊ large print Ⓑ braille ➊ tape Ⓜ Moon Ⓓ disk

Where a full address is not given in the text, see 32 (Useful addresses)

used on smooth surfaces. Dusting is best done by first removing loose items to a safe place and then working over one small area at a time, starting at the back and moving across the surface from one side to the other; the person with sensitive fingers will be able to feel where the dust is. Polish should be sprayed into the duster.

Clothes can be washed quite satisfactorily by rubbing every item carefully, particularly areas likely to be especially dirty, such as shirt collars and cuffs. The clothes-line is safer if it runs along the length of the garden, perhaps starting at one side of the house, than across the width where it may be difficult to find without bumping into it. A rotary clothes-line has the advantage that the user can stand still while hanging up the washing. An apron with deep pockets to hold clothes pegs is also useful. An electronic **rain alert**, £8.76 from RNIB, is sensitive to moisture and sounds an alarm as a warning to bring in clothes (or the baby) from outside when the first drop of rain falls.

15.2.2 Domestic equipment

Points to look out for when buying an iron for a blind person are stability when it is rested on its heel, and as large a distance as possible between the parts which get hot and the control knob and, in the case of a steam iron, the filling hole. An **Iron guard** can be obtained from RNIB to help protect the user's fingers. It is a plastic buffer which fits round the hot plate of most domestic irons.

Reports in **Which?** magazine (available on cassette, see 19.4.1) on equipment such as irons, vacuum cleaners and washing machines take account of their suitability for anyone with special needs, such as blind and partially sighted people. The report on washing machines in the January 1995 issue included an assessment of the Zanussi FL1083 Amie, £459.99. It was specifically designed for ease of operation by visually impaired people, with features such as black controls on a white background, tactile programme progress indicator and user instructions on cassette. A braille overlay can be supplied for the programme control.

Braille or tactile adaptations can be made for the controls of many domestic appliances. The procedure for having this done is explained in RNIB's **Labelling Domestic Equipment** guide. Alternatively, depending on how much information the user needs, adaptations can be made to controls with the kind of materials described in chapter 17.

15.2.3 Timers

Timers to programme electrical appliances – lights, the washing machine, a recorder to tape a radio programme – to operate at selected times are available with a voice read-out to help blind people set them independently. The **Talking TimeSwitch** from *Portset* comes in three versions. The basic model, £135, has one socket and can be set to switch on and off daily for any period up to a maximum of 24 hours. The second model, £165, has one socket, can be set for up to seven days and has an alarm function. The third, £195, has the same features as the second but has two sockets so that it can programme two separate appliances. The **Talking Timestat** from *Cobolt Systems* has a thermostat in addition to its timing functions. One model (£49.95) has two independent timers, the other (£69.95) has seven independent timers. A 24 hour **mechanical timer** is available for £17 from RNIB.

15.2.4 Central heating programmer

Many people with poor sight have difficulty in operating central heating controls. The **SP30 electronic programmer**, designed with elderly and disabled users in mind, has large, easily distinguished control buttons which bleep when pressed. Details from *Sunvic Controls Ltd., Bellshill Road, Uddingston, Glasgow G71 6NP* ℘ 01698 812944. The programmer can be fitted in place of most conventional heating timers.

15.2.5 Sewing

Self-threading needles, where the thread is pushed through a spring in the top of the eye, and **needle-threaders** with a loop of very fine wire to guide the thread through the eye, are sold by most good haberdashery stores, and are available from RNIB. A more elaborate **automatic needle threader**, 98p from RNIB, has two funnels, one for fine and one for thick needles. The needle is inserted, eye end down, and a metal probe, released by pressure on a lever, pushes the thread through. Other useful haberdashery items include 'invisible' thread, iron-on Wundaweb (to save stitching hems) and velcro (as a substitute for zip fasteners). Imperial or metric tape measures marked with metal eyelets are available from RNIB.

Many blind people use ordinary **sewing machines**. Mrs Ve Appleby, a sewing instructress who taught dressmaking to blind people, says that the choice of a machine is a matter of individual preference involving the same considerations as for sighted people, such as the weight of the machine and whether the sequence of controls is easy to use and remember. She suggests a straightened out wire paper clip with one end bent up to form a flat hook for use in threading up machines where the cotton has to pass through rather small holes. A seam guide can be devised using double sided sellotape to attach it to the base plate.

Helpful techniques which Mrs Appleby has evolved are incorporated in her large print booklet, **Make a Skirt the Quick and Easy Way**, £1.55 from the *Partially Sighted Society.*

15.2.6 Do-it-yourself

Loss of sight does not necessarily mean that it is no longer possible to tackle carpentry and other jobs around the home. Some specially designed tools are available from RNIB – details in their **Learning Product Guide**. Articles about woodwork appear from time to time in **Arts and Crafts News** from *RNIB Leisure Service.* One totally blind man who runs his own business making garden furniture would be happy to advise other visually impaired handymen on how best to deal with particular tasks. Contact *John Clarke, JC Woodcraft, 54 Maple Crescent, Newbury, Berks. RG13 1LR* ℘ 01635 44042.

15.2.7 Home security

Opening the front door and being unable to recognise the caller is a major anxiety for any visually impaired person alone in the house. A **password** can be used to identify bona fide representatives of public utilities. The password is chosen by the customer and known only to the Gas, Electricity or Water company concerned (see also 15.6.2).

A **door chain** which is easy to slot into place is an excellent idea. Sometimes there are local schemes to fit these for elderly or handicapped people. It is recommended that a door chain should only be used when the householder is checking the identity of a caller. Leaving a door chain, or a door limiter, on at other times carries the risk that emergency services would be unable to gain access quickly in times of need. See also 26.6.6 for information about telephone-linked alarm systems.

Useful free leaflets are issued by the *Home Office, 50 Queen Anne's Gate, London SW1H 9AT:* **Practical Guide to Crime Prevention** 🕿 (*from Crime Prevention Publicity, Room 151*), **FPT1 Fire Safety in the Home** 🕿 and **FB6A Fire Safety Advice for Disabled People** 🔵 (*from Fire Safety Literature, Room 133* ✆ 0171 273 4145). The Scottish Office publication **Don't Give Crime an Open Invitation** 🔵🕿 can be obtained from the *Scottish Braille Press.*

British Telecom's leaflet on tackling the problem of **Malicious phone calls** is available on tape from *RNIB Customer Services.*

15.2.8 Home repairs and improvements

The House renovation grants system can help householders or tenants living in unsuitable or old houses which need repair or modernisation.

Renovation Grants (upper limit £20,000) can meet the costs of bringing a property up to a 'fit standard'. Although local authorities are required to make such grants to owner occupiers, and tenants responsible for repairs, the amount of the grant is means-tested, taking income into account and savings over £5,000.

Disabled facilities grants (upper limit £20,000) can be made in the same way to provide facilities or to cover work which needs to be done to make a house suitable for a disabled person, defined as anyone who qualifies for registration as handicapped by his local council. Blind and partially sighted people are therefore eligible.

Discretionary grants may be made to cover a wide range of works to make a home suitable for a disabled person's accommodation, welfare and employment. A grant may also be given for adaptation work to the common parts of a building containing flats.

Minor works assistance grants are discretionary, but can be made to householders over 60 years of age who receive housing benefit, council tax benefit or income support. The help can take the form of a grant or the provision of materials, in both cases up to a value of £1,080, to cover the cost of small but essential works of repair, improvement or adaptation. The total amount that may be given in respect of the same dwelling over a three year period is £3,240.

Full details of the grants will be found in the booklet **House Renovation Grants** issued by the Department of the Environment and available at local council offices. **RNIB Housing Service** can also advise. Locally based **Care & Repair** or **Staying Put** home improvement agencies are non-profit making and can act as intermediaries offering independent advice and practical help throughout the whole process of repairs or adaptations. Contact *Care & Repair, Castle House, Kirtly Drive,*

Snapshot

Nancy and Bill Crowhurst are in their 80s and both have poor sight. Nancy has a bad arthritic hip and Bill is not quite so steady on his feet as he used to be. "We'd got to the state where neither of us dared to get in the bath for fear we'd never get out," Nancy recalled. "Our doctor asked an occupational therapist from Social Services to call to see what could be done. She said: what about a walk-in shower?

"I thought it was a lovely idea, but my Bill wasn't so sure. How were we going to cope with the mess and the workmen, not to mention the bill. Still, that OT talked him out of it and said she'd get someone from Care and Repair to see us through.

"And they did. They helped us with all the form filling — it took ages. But finally we heard we'd got a Disabled Facilities Grant. Then the Care and Repair man brought round the chap who would do the work and the OT came along too, and we all decided where everything was to go. I can't say it was easy when they started work, but the Care and Repair man popped in most days when the workmen were here — even took us down to the pub for lunch when things were at their worst. Now it's just grand — fold-up seat, handrails and a non-slip floor. My Bill's that proud of it. You'd think it was his idea. But that's men for you, isn't it?"

Nottingham NG7 1LD ☏ 0115 979 9091 (England), or *Norbury House, Norbury Road, Cardiff CF5 3AS* ☏ 01222 576286 (Wales) for further details. In Northern Ireland enquiries should be addressed to *Mrs Y. M. Pickles, Staying Put Manager, Fold Housing Trust, 3 Redburn Square, Holywood, County Down BT18 9NZ*.

In Scotland the grant system is different, but improvement and repairs grants are available. The Scottish Office Environment Department's booklet **Improve your home with a grant** gives details. Further information can be supplied by *Care & Repair (Scotland), 53 Bothwell Street, Glasgow G2 6TS* ☏ 0141 248 7177 (see also 26.6.3).

15.3 Housing advice and assistance

Local authority housing departments have a duty to find housing for people who are in 'priority need, unintentionally homeless and who have a local connection with the area'. People in 'priority need' are defined as those who are vulnerable because of old age, or an overriding medical factor such as mental illness, handicap or physical disability. Visually impaired people threatened with homelessness should therefore approach their housing department in the first instance.

NEW **RNIB Housing Liaison Officers** work with visually impaired people who have housing problems, including homelessness. They can be contacted at *RNIB Tate House, Harrogate* and at *RNIB Garrow House, London*. **RNIB Housing Service** issues individual leaflets ❶❷❸ giving details of the Housing Service, Council Housing, Housing Associations and finding private rented accommodation. Single copies free. The Service has a small number of nomination rights with housing associations in London and the South East and can also arrange for tenancy agreements and other housing information to be transcribed ❶❷❸.

15.3.1 Specialist housing for people of working age

Action for Blind People has flats in south and central London and 58 flats in Epsom for single blind people and for couples where at least one partner is blind or partially sighted.

NEW **The Gift of Thomas Pocklington** is extending its housing provision. Instead of buying or building housing and then finding tenants, it is aiming to identify visually impaired individuals and families who need housing and wish to live independently. It will then try to provide housing to meet their individual needs. The houses or flats will be let on ordinary tenancies at affordable rents. Eight flats in Hammersmith have so far been occupied on this basis. There are new projects in Wolverhampton and Berkshire and plans for the Greater London area. A major building programme at Pocklington Close, Shepherds Bush includes a new block of 18 studio flats as well as upgrading the existing 50 flatlets for single men and women. Further details from *Paul L. Quin, The Gift of Thomas Pocklington.*

NEW The **Northamptonshire Association for the Blind** has six self-contained single flats in the Kingsthorpe district of Northampton which are particularly suitable for anyone living independently for the first time. Arrangements can be made for a rehabilitation worker to teach residents how to find their way round the area and other daily living skills such as managing their budgets. The flats are available on a short term rental basis for a period of two years. Applicants are put on the local authority housing list (after six months' residence in the case of people from other boroughs). Support from rehabilitation workers continues as residents move on to local authority accommodation. Enquiries to *John Wood, Secretary, Northamptonshire Association for the Blind, Wardington Court, Welford Road, Northampton NN2 8AG* ✆ 01604 719193.

RNIB has 23 self-contained flatlets and 5 two-bedroom flats at *Garrow House.* There is a licensed restaurant, recreation areas and facilities for guide dogs.

The **Star Housing Association** has 5 flats in Acton, a housing development of 12 single flats, 6 bungalows and 8 family homes at Colindale in North London, and nomination rights in 9 flats in Ealing owned by the Acton Housing Association. Enquiries to the agent, *Mrs D. K. McLoughlin, 5 Watford Way, London NW4 3JN* ✆ 0181 202 3858.

NEW A leaflet **L** **B** **T** giving details of specialist housing for visually impaired people is issued by RNIB Housing Service. Single copies free.

15.4 Keeping in touch

15.4.1 Telling the time

Choice of an **easy-to-see**, **talking** or **tactile** timepiece depends on whether the visually impaired person has much useful sight or is entirely dependent on touch or hearing. Examples are illustrated in this section and 26.9. A selection of clocks and watches is likely to be on display at Resource Centres. Models with **large**, **clear faces** can be obtained from RNIB and the Partially Sighted Society. Both stock **talking** clocks and watches which tell the time at the press of a button.

Watches (clocks in 26.9)

◄ Tactiwatch for deafblind people (RNIB) £15.23. The hours are announced by a series of pulses, followed by a pause. Then a long pulse indicates ten minutes, followed by the appropriate number of short pulses. For example, 9.25 is indicated by nine pulses, pause, then two long pulses followed by five short pulses.

Tactile watch (RNIB). Prices from £9.50 ▲

◄ Easy-to-See quartz watch (RNIB). £15.75. Aquamarine or black case and strap

Talking watch (RNIB) £10.95 ▼

It's 2.04 pm

Tactile clocks and watches are supplied by RNIB. These have specially strengthened hands and the hours are indicated by raised dots. The smaller the timepiece, the more sensitive the touch required. Watches all have a hinged glass front which opens up when a push button is pressed. For deafblind people, there is a **vibrating** timepiece which gives the time in pulses of varying duration.

RNIB's **Clocks and Watches** product guide and the Partially Sighted Society's brochure and catalogue (see 29.1) give details of models stocked.

Talking clocks and watches from commercial sources include the **Cobolt** range (also available from the *Partially Sighted Society*), the **Sharp EL640 talking clock/calculator**, £75 from *Dolphin*, the **Seiko** talking watch, £74.95 from *VISability* and a watch which also responds to a whistle, £9.99 from *Tandy* shops (mail order cat. no. 63-7020).

15.4.2 Keeping track of the days

In response to requests from *In Touch* listeners, Radio 4 announces the date and the day of the week regularly at 6.30, 7 and 8 a.m. during the Today programme, and in both the early morning and late afternoon shipping forecasts, as well as at 6 a.m. and closedown.

A **large print appointments-type wall calendar** and a **bold print page-a-week diary** (6″ x 3″ approx.) can be obtained from the *Partially Sighted Society* for £2.80 each. Some of the larger diaries sold at stationers have very clear, bold print.

E

15.4.3 Telephoning

Modern **push-button phones** are relatively easy to use by touch alone. Some models have a raised dot on the number 5 button to help locate the centre of the keypad. Many have facilities for storing numbers so that only one or two buttons need to be pressed to make the call. Some models have slightly larger buttons.

NEW **Dialtalk**, a pocket-sized keypad with bold black numbers on contrasting yellow buttons, can be used with any phone connected to a digital exchange. It voices each number as it is keyed in, and reads out the completed number when the speak button is pressed. To make the call, lift the receiver, place Dialtalk close to the mouthpiece, and press its send button. Other features include adjustable volume and the capacity to store ten numbers in the memory. Dialtalk is £34.95 from *Cobolt Systems.*

Phones with **extra-large key pads** include the **Binatone Easy-Button,**

Enlarged numeral dial ring

A cheap and simple solution to a common problem

ivory with dark grey numerals, £17.50 from the *Partially Sighted Society* and the **Audioline Tel 33**, dark grey numerals on white background, hearing-aid compatible, £29.99 at some BT shops and other telephone retailers.

Many blind people find a **cordless telephone** saves them the frustration of struggling to get to the phone before it stops ringing. Prices of BT's Freestyle range start at £69.99. High street stores and mail order companies offer a choice of other models.

An **enlarged numeral dial ring** can be stuck to a dial telephone. There is a choice of three types:

- rigid, black numerals on white, free from local BT offices.
- paper, white numerals on black: send 15p plus stamped, addressed envelope to *Surrey Voluntary Association for the Blind, Rentwood, School Lane, Fetcham, Leatherhead KT22 9JX.*
- flexible, white numerals on black or black numerals on white or yellow: 60p each from the *Partially Sighted Society.*

A dial by touch system is described in **Instructions for Telephone Dialling**, a free leaflet from RNIB. Notches cut on the dial by the figures 4 and 7 help locate the digits.

Public payphones. A free BT cassette explains how to use press-button cash payphones and phonecard phones. The listener is taken step by step over the layout of the call-boxes and the procedure for operating them. Copies of the cassette can be obtained from *Master Transcriptions.* A small notch is cut on the right hand side of BT Phonecards to help visually impaired people insert them correctly. The cards can be obtained in local shops and post offices.

Directory enquiries. People who are blind or have any disability which prevents them from using BT's printed phone books are entitled to use the **free directory enquiry service** on 195. To make use of the service, the caller has to be registered with BT and quote the personal identification number (PIN) he has been allocated. Ring 195 free at any time for an application form. Applications must be accompanied by a copy of a local authority certificate of blindness or partial sight, or certified by a recognised health care official. **NEW** BT will accept applications made on behalf of blind or partially sighted people by a local voluntary society. Once registered, the customer is given a card with his PIN in large print and braille. The service is available to Mercury customers on 195 or ℘ 0500 500 195 on similar conditions. Special easy-to-read application forms are available from *Mercury Customer Service* on Freephone 0500 500 194.

NEW There is no charge for calls to **Talking pages**, giving information about businesses and services everywhere in the country. Ring Freephone 0800 600 900.

A large print personal telephone numbers list could be made up using a Letraset kit, on sale at stationers. RNIB will make up lists of telephone numbers in Moon (see 18.3). A **talking address book**, two cassettes with indelibly recorded alphabetic divisions, costs £2.83 from RNIB.

Some blind people find it useful to be able to record calls such as directory enquiries, train times, directions for a journey, dial-a-recipe, etc. Though there is nothing to stop any subscriber who has a phone with a microphone socket from plugging in an ordinary tape recorder, it is an offence to make recordings of calls unless both the phone and the recorder are approved. One simple device, the **Telecorder**, is approved for use by blind and disabled people only. It costs £18 and can be used with any make of cassette recorder. Further details from the suppliers, *Applied Technology Centre Ltd., 19 Donegall Pass, Belfast BT7 1DQ* ✆ 01232 232480. Another option is a combined telephone/answering machine which also records telephone conversations. BT's **Response 300** is £99.99.

The **BT Guide for people who are disabled or elderly** (also in braille or on tape) gives information about telephone services and equipment to help people with a hearing loss or other disabilities as well as blind and partially sighted people. Product User Guides for many BT phones are available in large print, braille or on tape. For copies of any of this material or for further information and advice, contact BT Action for Disabled Customers Manager on **Freephone 150** (0800 800150 for non-BT lines).

Information on **Mercury** services and tariffs, etc. is available on cassette. The terms and conditions printed on the reverse side of the residential service application form are available in braille and large print. A Special Needs Brochure is available in large print from *Mercury Customer Service* Freephone 0500 500194.

15.4.4 Post

Within the British Isles, braille and Moon material, or specially recorded audio tapes and cassettes such as those made by talking newspapers or tape services for the blind, can be sent post free by or to registered blind people, or anyone able to produce a certificate signed by an ophthalmologist, doctor or ophthalmic optician stating that their close-up vision, with spectacles, is N12 or less. Equipment such as white sticks, tactile clocks and guide dog harnesses can also be sent post-free to and from recognised organisations dealing with blind people. Packages should carry an 'Articles for the Blind' label supplied by RNIB. Anyone making use of the concession should register with the local Royal Mail Customer Service Centre (listed in the phone book under Royal Mail). The concession does not apply to ordinary handwritten or typed letters, or to taped music, entertainment or personal messages. Normal additional charges are made for sending items registered post or recorded delivery.

As regards **overseas** destinations, RNIB have an agreement with Royal Mail International to provide a forwarding service so that blind individuals can send cassette messages abroad free of postage. All packages must bear the label P4558 (available at all post offices) which indicates that the contents are for blind people, and be marked **Cecogrammes**. Contact the *Overseas Tape Service* at RNIB Head Office. Otherwise postal concessions are available only to recognised organisations or institutions who have made special arrangements with Royal Mail. The concessions apply to periodicals, books and papers of any kind impressed in braille or Moon, and certain articles for use by visually impaired people. Packages up to 7kg are free of charge by surface mail to all destinations. Airmail packages up to 1 kg for destinations within Europe are free; there is a small charge for items over 1kg up to a maximum of 7kg. For airmail packages to destinations outside Europe, a small charge is made according to weight up to a maximum of 7kg.

Full details of postal concessions can be obtained from *RNIB Corporate Purchasing Manager* at Peterborough.

Collection of mail in rural areas: People living in remote areas can ask for their postman to collect letters and packages when he delivers the mail. Even if there is no mail to deliver on a particular day, anyone with a special need can leave a note on the door asking the postman to knock. As rural postmen generally deliver mail by van, the weight of parcels of braille books and equipment would not pose a problem. Requests for this service should be made to the postman or to the local *Customer Service Centre* (listed in the telephone directory under Royal Mail).

15.5 Shopping

The ideal shop for a visually impaired person is the old-fashioned corner shop where the proprietor knows the customers and their needs well. But such shops are diminishing in number, and blind people may be reluctant to pay the higher prices they charge in comparison with supermarkets.

15.5.1 Supermarkets

Self-service shopping presents obvious difficulties to a person unable to see the goods displayed. But supermarkets sell a wide selection of goods under their own brand name, and these are invariably cheaper than the branded goods of other companies though the contents are often identical in quality and quantity. Consistent buying of such goods is the most economical way of shopping and can compensate blind shoppers for being unaware of special offers.

Most of the larger supermarkets and chain stores expressed themselves, in response to an enquiry from *In Touch*, as willing to help blind customers if they made their needs known to an assistant or supervisor. Several stores would ask an assistant to help customers with their purchases, though it is obviously advisable, if at all possible, for blind shoppers to avoid busy periods when assistants are under great pressure.

As the use of bar coding in supermarkets becomes more and more common, price stickers on individual items, often difficult enough for people with normal sight to read, are being replaced by a large price tag on the shelf where the goods are displayed. The Institute of Grocery Distribution is trying to promote packaging which is easier to read and to open, as well as better store design and signs. It stresses the need for the trade to take account of the increasing number of older customers, a significant proportion of whom are likely to have poor sight. *IGD, Letchmore Heath, Watford, Hertfordshire WD2 8DQ* ℘ 01923 857141.

Some **Shopmobility** services for disabled people offer a free escort service, manned by trained volunteers, which blind and partially sighted shoppers might find helpful. The local Shopmobility should be listed in telephone directories, or contact *National Federation of Shopmobility, Maria Appleton, Telegraph House, Baillie Street, Rochdale OL6 1JH* ℘ 01224 484957.

Since 1980, Gateshead social services and the local Tesco supermarket have cooperated in running a **shopping service** for disabled people, including elderly people with impaired vision, who have difficulty in getting to the town centre. Customers are issued with catalogues and price lists, available in large print. They place their orders by telephone and the goods are delivered to their homes. The delivery charge is 50p, and the customer pays for the goods on delivery. Other retailers, including a chemist, are participating in the scheme. Further information from *Michael Lowthian, The Project Leader, Gateshead Shopping Service, Social Services Department, Civic Centre, Gateshead NE8 1HH* ✆ 0191 477 1011 ext. 2514.

> **I keep a tiny magnifier in my purse. It's a godsend in the supermarket when I really want to read the small print – you can't expect people to read the microwave instructions to you.**

15.5.2 Other commercially available goods

Shopping for goods other than the weekly groceries can also present a problem to people who are unable to see what is on offer, yet many commercially produced items can be of particular use to people with little or no sight. A selection of such items is displayed at some Resource Centres, including the *In Touch* kitchen (see chapter 16). Goods on sale in high street shops as well as equipment of special interest to visually impaired people are topics covered by **MerseyTape Extra**, one of the cassette magazines produced by Disability Network (see 19.4.4). Some specialist mail order companies are listed in 29.1.

15.5.3 Advice on shopping and credit

Cassette versions of **A Buyer's Guide**, information on consumer rights to goods and services and advice about buying items on credit, and **Moneyfax**, a guide to credit and debt, are available free from the *Office of Fair Trading, PO Box 2, Central Way, Feltham, Middlesex TW14 0TG*.

15.5.4 Release from VAT

Registered blind and partially sighted people and charities for the blind can buy certain goods without paying VAT on them. Under the 1994 VAT Act, these include equipment and appliances designed solely for blind or handicapped persons (group 12), alarm systems for home use (group 12), welfare vehicles for use by charities providing care to blind people (group 15) and recording equipment used by charities to produce talking books and newspapers, and the recorders they supply on free loan (group 4). Charities can obtain zero rating on certain stationery, principally headed notepaper and envelopes, provided it contains a suitable 'qualifying advertisement'. Information regarding these reliefs and the declarations which have to be issued to the supplier of the equipment can be found in leaflets 70/7/94 **VAT reliefs for people with disabilities** and 701/1/92 **Charities**, both available at local VAT offices.

15.5.5 Relief from import duty

Blind people can import certain articles free of the customs duties which would otherwise be due under the European Community's Common Customs Tariff. The goods must have been specifically designed for the blind. Application should be made to the Department of Trade and Industry on Form **DFA (BH) 89** obtainable from *DTI, ITP Division, Room 247, Ashdown House, 123 Victoria Street, London SW1E 6RB* ✆ 0171 215 6039.

15.6 Money matters

15.6.1 Banks and building societies

Telephone banking enables customers to pay bills, check balances and make other enquiries concerning their finances from home, doing away with much of the paperwork. This facility is offered by Alliance & Leicester Giro, Bank of Scotland, Co-op, Midland's Firstdirect division, NatWest and TSB, and, among the top five building societies, Alliance & Leicester, Halifax and Nationwide. Abbey National Direct handles mortgage applications by telephone.

It is always worth asking banks and building societies what other facilities they offer which make it easier for visually impaired customers to conduct their business. Listed below are some of the specialist services provided.

Cheque book templates – most high street banks; some, including Bank of Scotland, Barclays and NatWest, will issue to customers with poor sight the larger size company cheque books with templates to fit. Alliance & Leicester and Nationwide also issue templates to fit paying in books.

Talking statements – Bank of Scotland (synthetic speech ensures confidentiality).

Braille or large print statements – Bank of Scotland, Barclays, Lloyds, Midland, Royal Bank of Scotland, NatWest, TSB and the major **credit cards**. Halifax will provide braille mortgage statements and savings account statements. Halifax and Nationwide will make photocopy enlargements.

Correspondence – Lloyds and NatWest in braille or large print, Girobank in large print.

Cashpoints – bank staff would normally be willing to show a blind customer how to operate a cashpoint. NatWest Servicetills have audible prompts and operating instructions are provided in braille and large print. Bank of Scotland provide braille operating instructions.

Information – leaflets or brochures may be provided in braille, large print or on cassette.

15.6.2 Paying bills

BT can arrange for **braille** or **large print** copies of **telephone bills** to be sent a few days after the normal bill goes out. To register for this free service, call free on ✆ 0800 400454. Bills can also be read out to the customer over the phone before being posted. Under the **Protected Service Scheme**, if BT knows that a customer may be at risk without a phone, disconnection will be delayed if there is a nominee (friend, relative, neighbour, welfare worker etc.) to help resolve the problem. To apply for any of these services, ring Freephone 0800 800 150.

British Gas will arrange **braille** or **large print** bills, or for details of bills to be given by **telephone**. Alternatively the bill can be sent to someone whom the customer has designated to deal with his or her financial affairs. The customer can also nominate a close friend or relative to be contacted in case of difficulty. Contact the *Home Service Adviser* via any British Gas showroom or district office.

A similar service is offered by Electricity Companies, some of which are also able to provide bills in large print or braille. Contact the local company's regional headquarters, details of which are given on the electricity bill.

Water Companies keep a confidential register of customers with special needs such as bills in braille, large print, audio tape or by telephone. Contact the local Company.

RNIB Customer Services will send its bills in braille or large print if asked to do so. Full details are given in a free leaflet **Welcome to shopping with RNIB ⦿ⒷⓉ**.

15.6.3 Income tax

Local Inland Revenue offices can be approached, by telephone or in person, for help with filling in income tax returns as well as with other matters such as reclaiming tax on savings. Leaflet IR120 **You and the Inland Revenue** is available in large print from any Tax Enquiry Centre or Tax Office; a braille or cassette version will be posted on request. It explains how people can get help and information from tax offices, how to complain if they are not satisfied with the way their tax affairs have been handled, and includes the text of the Taxpayer's Charter. Photocopy enlargements of forms and other leaflets could also be provided. If necessary, a tax officer could come to a housebound blind person's home. Confidential help is also likely to be available from the Citizens Advice Bureau. Most high street banks would regard completing a straightforward income tax return on behalf of a blind person as part of the normal service offered to customers.

15.6.4 Drawing pensions

Signature guides for both old and new style pension and allowance books are 50p each from RNIB (see illustration in 18.1.6). Provision is made for anyone unable to sign his or her name to use a mark in lieu of a signature, but this must be witnessed, and the witness cannot also collect the money.

People who cannot go to the Post Office regularly to collect their pension can appoint an agent do this for them. **Leaflet AP1 A Helping Hand** from Social Security offices or by post from the *Benefits Agency Distribution and Storage Centre* gives details and explains how a close relative or friend can be appointed to act on behalf of the disabled and perhaps confused person they are helping.

State retirement pensions can be paid by automatic credit transfer (ACT) direct into a bank or building society account. People receiving Income Support can also have it paid in this way. It will be paid weekly in arrears. If the claimant is receiving retirement pension as well, this can be included in the weekly ACT payment, but if the claimant loses entitlement to Income Support, the pension will revert to being paid four-weekly in arrears. Enquiries to the local Social Security office or to the Pensions Direct helpline on ✆ 0191 203 0203.

15.6.5 Insurance

Insurance companies who have had no previous dealings with visually impaired people may be reluctant to accept them for household, travel and other policies on the same terms as sighted clients in comparable circumstances. But it should be possible to provide visually impaired clients with most of the usual benefits of personal accident cover at a normal premium, and there is no reason why visual handicap in itself should make any difference whatsoever to household or life insurance. One insurance broker who has had a number of visually impaired clients can advise on the choice of insurance companies with experience of the needs of blind and partially sighted clients. Contact *Brook Whitwell & Co. Ltd, 2 Osborns Court, High Street South, Olney, Buckinghamshire MK46 4AA* ✆ 01234 713535.

NEW A company offering household insurance specifically for visually impaired clients provides information in large print, braille or on tape and will correspond in any of these media. Further information from *VIP Insurance Services, Elizabeth House, 22 Suffolk Street Queensway, Birmingham B1 1LS Freephone* ✆ 0500 258080.

15.6.6 Making a will

A legal will cannot be drawn up in braille. Wills drawn up by people who do not see well enough to read print have to be read to them in the presence of witnesses, and a clause added to that effect. **NEW** RNIB provides a **free will making advisory service** from its London headquarters. It can supply free information booklets **L B T** and can put blind people in touch with a solicitor. See also 28.5.1 for details of an **advocacy service** for elderly people in residential care.

Blind and partially sighted people and anyone aged 70 or more are among exceptions to the rule that the cost of drawing up a will would not be covered by Green Form legal advice and assistance, a type of Legal Aid. To qualify, an applicant's disposable capital and income would need to be under certain limits. Details from a Legal Aid solicitor or the Citizens Advice Bureau.

15.6.7 Making a fortune!

NEW A free leaflet **How to play the National Lottery** is available in large print or on cassette from *RNIB Customer Services.*

15.6.8 Coping with cash

Some blind people find coin dispensers convenient for loose change. RNIB stocks flat plastic containers to hold five £1.00 coins, eight 50p coins, ten 20p coins, five 10p coins or ten 5p coins ate 68p each, and a key-fob coin holder with space for two £1.00 coins at 65p. A pound coin dispenser which holds six coins and is designed to fit a key ring costs £4.34 from the Partially Sighted Society.

Banknotes carry large coloured symbols: the £5.00 note a blue circle, the £10 an orange diamond, the £20 a purple square and the £50 a red triangle. New £10, £20 and £50 notes show the value in bold numerals at the top right hand corner of the front and back. A plastic measure to help distinguish banknotes currently in circulation is issued free by some high street banks.

15.7 Calculators

Easy to see calculator (white numbers on black buttons and large, angled display panel) £9.68 from RNIB

Talking calculator, £9.79 from RNIB

Talking calculator with earphone, £20.85 from *Cobolt Systems* or the *Partially Sighted Society*

Talking calculator, £19.99 from Tandy shops or mail order from *Tandy* (quote cat. no. 65-554)

Sharp EL640 talking clock/calculator, £75 from *Dolphin*

RNC Model TSC talking calculator (made to order adaptation of the Casio FX82 scientific calculator) £160 from *MWD Electronics, Mail Box Extension no. 111, 48 Market Street, Hoylake, Wirral L47 2AF* ✆ 0151 638 4493.

Coping with money

• Fold £10 notes in half and put a rubber band round £20 notes so that neither gets mistaken for a fiver

• Before going out shopping, collect all your loose change and make up £1–worth. Keep this in a separate purse or pocket. It's then easy to pay for something which costs less than £1 by removing the necessary coins.

From the In Touch Care Guide *101 Practical hints*. 1994. £2.50.

15.8 Further reading

A Guide to public services in the home 🄻🄱🅃, a free RNIB leaflet, includes information about BT's directory enquiry service and telephone numbers of Electricity Companies and Gas Regions.

The housing needs of visually impaired people. £10 from *RNIB Housing Service*.

The National Savings leaflet **Guide to savings for non taxpayers** is available on cassette (ring ✆ Lo-call 0645 645000).

The large print edition of Age Concern's publication **Earning Money in Retirement** is £13.95.

16 In the kitchen

Those who have lost part or all of their sight could be forgiven for thinking that cooking and preparing food is fraught with so much danger that all they could hope to do is to live off pre-packed and tinned food for the rest of their lives. However, very many visually impaired people have learned to cater not only for themselves but for their families. This chapter can only give some guidelines on ways in which to make the kitchen safer and easier to use; it is very important for a newly blind person to try to get tuition in cookery methods which should be on offer locally either from the social services department or the voluntary society. The list of resource centres (see 34) indicates places where equipment that might help visually impaired cooks can be examined.

> I keep this cheap little plastic magnifier on a string round my neck when I'm in the kitchen. I use it so much that I have to wash it up with the dirty dishes – and that's the one time I lose it!

It is not necessary to make radical alterations to a kitchen to make it suitable for a person with little or no sight. It is better to concentrate on a few adaptations to existing equipment – such as making cooker controls easier to manage – than to introduce totally new items which in any circumstances require a period of adjustment. Nor is it necessary to find specially designed items or gadgets. When the *In Touch* team pioneered the concept of a kitchen designed for visually impaired cooks at an exhibition to mark the programme's 20th anniversary in 1981, it was instructive that **out of over 200 items selected barely half a dozen were specially made for blind people**. The guiding principle then and now is to minimise clutter; a good storage system and the discipline always to put things back in the right place as soon as possible after use helps enormously, as does appropriate lighting and the use of colour contrast to make the most of any useful sight. The advice on lighting given in Chapter 3 is an essential starting point. Visually impaired cooks with residual vision need to judge for themselves the best position in which to install a spotlight or a fluorescent tube and also how best to make things more visible by putting them on a colour contrasting surface.

The principles which guided the design of the **In Touch Kitchen** are fully described in a large print book *In Touch at Home* (1986. Isis). The book is no longer in print, but is available in public libraries and a tape version can be obtained from *Calibre* or *RNIB Talking Book Service*. Modern kitchen units make it much easier to store equipment and ingredients methodically. **Phlexiplan Studio** is a range of kitchen units based on the In Touch Kitchen and designed specifically for visually impaired cooks. The storage cupboards, drawers and wall units with sliding doors, are outlined in bright red wood trim and have red pull handles. Worktops are

Key to media of publication P clear print L large print B braille T tape M Moon D disk
Where a full address is not given in the text, see 32 (Useful addresses)

Coping with the cooker

Bright orange, tactile 'Bump-Ons' are self-adhesive and are stocked by RNIB (see 16 introduction). Mark the 'off' position on each knob, as well as on the fascia panel, so you can line them up. The oven knob can be marked at the settings you most often use

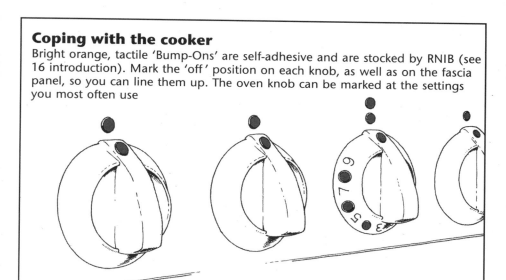

available in a number of colours including dark grey or plain white. Full details from *Phlexicare, 3/10 Shoreditch High Street, London E1 6PE ℘ 0171 247 5432.*

E

16.1 Coping with cookers

16.1.1 Adapting controls

One of the first essentials for a visually impaired cook is to ensure that the cooker controls can be easily managed. Partially sighted people should bear in mind that unless they can read the controls of a cooker at a safe distance they need to resort to tactile methods or a colour coded system. The RNIB issues a useful free leaflet on **Labelling Domestic Equipment ❶❷❸**. The easiest way is to use **Bump-Ons**. These are black, day-glo orange or transparent raised discs which are self-adhesive on grease free surfaces. The orange ones are particularly easy to see but the transparent ones have the advantage of not obscuring the control marks for the sighted people using the cooker. **Hi-marks** can also be used and do-it-yourself adaptations such as grains of rice, beads or matchsticks have also been used quite effectively by some people (see also chapter 17). It is usually best to get a sighted person to put the tactile mark in place but in consultation with the blind user. Bear in mind that it will be easier to feel marks if they are widely spaced out – it may only be necessary to mark the most frequently used settings. Specialist workers in social service departments or voluntary agencies may well be prepared to come and mark controls of cookers or washing machines. It may also be possible to buy replacement knobs that have tactile pointers. Many **Belling cookers** use knobs with pointers and these are often interchangeable with other knobs.

If a blind person does decide to buy a new cooker then the RNIB can arrange for the controls to be adapted with studs or braille. This should be discussed at the time of purchase with the shop, which should be asked to contact the manufacturer and arrange for them to send a duplicate set of controls to the RNIB to be marked up. No simple way of adapting oven timers has yet been brought to the attention of *In Touch*. The most exciting development for blind cooks is the long awaited talking microwave oven due to be produced by the summer of 1995 (see 16.6).

16.1.2 Lighting the gas

An elderly gas cooker fitted with a pilot light can be unreliable and expensive to run. Visually impaired people who want to continue using one would be best advised to turn the pilot light off altogether and use a spark ignition lighter instead. These are easily found in the shops. Some people have found it easy to use the **Long Flame Lighter** (Partially Sighted Society £5.88). The length of flame can be regulated, but to be used safely the tip of the lighter should be placed against the cooker burner before the control button is pressed. If the pan is put over the burner before lighting it, the pan can be safely centred and will also act as protection as the gas is being lit. Many people feel safer using only the back burners when first cooking without sight.

E

> ## Points to consider when choosing a kettle
> • The design and shape of the spout is vital. A good prominent spout can be more easily held over the edge of a mug or tea-pot. An elastic band wound round the spout about an inch from the end can help to hold it steady when pouring. Avoid the more streamlined types of spout which can slip all over the place when pouring!
> • Jug kettles can boil small quantities of water which is quicker and more economical. It is safest if someone is unsure about pouring only to put in the exact quantity – e.g. one cupful – required, so that there is no fear of spillage when the hot water is poured.
> • Jug kettles are made of plastic and in different sizes. Some may be lighter than conventional kettles. Lightest of all is a small travel kettle which might be worth considering for someone who has physical problems with lifting and manipulation.
> • Some jug kettles are cordless, which has the advantage that there are no trailing flexes to worry about. However it is worth checking how simple it is to relocate them on their base, as this is not always easy.
> • For people with partial sight it might be worth looking out for coloured models, (but jug kettles are usually white or cream).
> • Some people feel that the tall slim design of jug kettles makes them less stable, so if this is the case it is worth looking for conventional shaped kettles which are sometimes available in plastic and/or cordless.
> • The switch position needs to be considered. A switch on top of the handle is less likely to be knocked accidentally than one underneath the handle.

16.2 Dealing with hot liquids

People are understandably frightened of scalding themselves. One way of minimising this is to ensure that there is a flat surface alongside the cooker and at the same level, so that saucepans full of boiling liquid can be slid onto the work surface. Ideally the sink should also be alongside the cooker so that vegetables can be drained without having to be carried across the kitchen. Many blind cooks find it helpful to put their vegetables into a chip basket inside the pan, and this is simply lifted out when the vegetables are cooked. A small rust-resistant mesh wire cooking basket which has a heat-resistant handle can also be used (*Chester Care* £7.19) But there is no doubt that cooking vegetables or pasta in a microwave oven reduces many of the hazards. It is possible now to get special microwave vegetable and pasta cookers from most kitchen-ware shops and large supermarkets; these consist of a plastic bowl with an inner basket that has a handle for easy draining. But getting a kettle that is safe and easy to use is probably the first requirement, and the plastic jug kettles have much to recommend them. Someone who has real difficulty in pouring might like to consider an automatic tea maker, which dispenses hot water straight into a cup.

16.2.1 Making tea

The illustrations in this section show a safe way of making tea for those who want to avoid the short cuts of a tea-bag in a mug!

(**1**) Fill the teapot with cold water; note that one finger reaches into the teapot to feel when the water has nearly reached the top. (**2**) Pour the water into the empty kettle. This ensures that (**3**) when the boiling water has to be poured back into the teapot there will not be any surplus to overflow.

In order to pour the right amount of milk and tea into the cup use the **Sensa cup level indicator** *(Cobolt Systems* £3.75). (**4**) A sensor bleeps when the milk is half an inch from the bottom, and (**5**) a second sensor bleeps when the tea is half an inch from the top.

The **liquid level indicator** (*RNIB* £5.50) is an alternative device (see illustration in 16.4). It is also hooked over the side of a cup, but the tea must be poured in first. There is an intermittent tone and vibration when the cup is nearly full and it is time to add the milk. A continuous tone and vibration indicates that the cup is full. The gadget therefore has the advantage of being useful to anyone with a hearing loss.

When pouring in the milk and the tea it is important that both jug and teapot should touch the side of the cup. With a little experience most people find that they can discard the gadgets, but it is a good way of building up confidence in the early days. Eventually most blind people find that they can fill their teapot safely by judging the difference in the weight of the kettle or the changing sound of the water being poured. Some people find it helpful to count. Milk can be poured into the cup with a short sharp jerk of the wrist rather than by trickling which is more difficult to control. One quick tilt should be enough. When pouring from the teapot rest the spout on the edge of the cup and put one finger from the free hand lightly over the opposite edge of the rim. The finger will feel the warmth of the tea fractionally before it reaches the top of the cup. It is worth looking out for a teapot in a bright colour, and insulated models have the advantage of not being too hot to touch.

Making a cup of tea

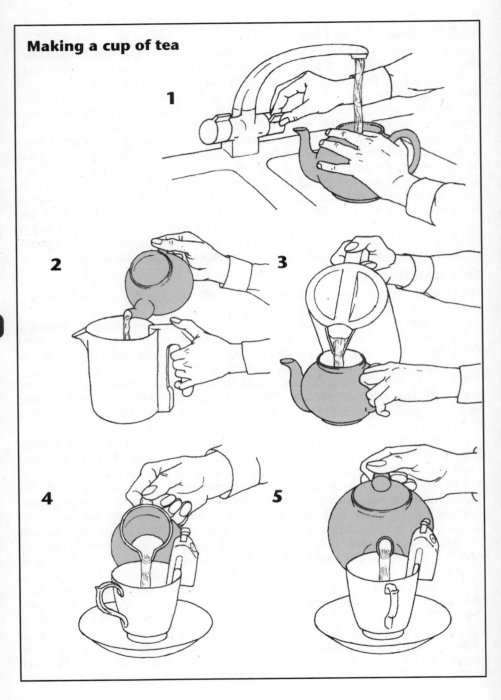

1

2

3

4

5

16.3 Cooking methods

16.3.1 Using the oven

Frying is probably the most frightening method of cooking for a blind person, and many visually impaired people avoid it altogether, and either grill their food or cook it in the oven. But before using an oven it would be as well to invest in a good pair of oven gloves, ideally ones which are long enough to protect the delicate skin on the forearm. The Heritage **extra fine oven glove** has aluminium foil incorporated into its lining. This enables the wearer to feel the item being held as the glove is not thick and bulky, though it is heatproof and long enough to cover the lower arm. The gloves can be obtained by mail order from *Heritage PLC, Bridge Works, Manchester Road, Altrincham, Cheshire WA14 4RL* ✆ 0161 929 0477. Price £10 a pair.

As oven cleaning is so difficult for anyone with poor sight, it is a wise precaution to put a large roasting tin underneath a dish containing any food that is likely to ooze or boil over and to put food into oven dishes that are slightly too big for their contents.

16.3.2 Frying

Some totally blind experienced cooks have demonstrated how with care they can fry safely, but a newly blind person might welcome the gift of an **electric frying pan**. This provides the safest method of frying because it is thermostatically controlled and the control knob can be easily marked with Bump-Ons or Hi-marks. Andrea Llewellyn, who teaches Living Skills at the Royal National College, recommends the Kenwood model as it is fairly deep, has straight sides and a high dome lid which make it suitable not only for frying, but for poaching, boiling, casseroling and stir-fries. Some electric frying pans are sold with a ceramic insert dish which can be used to convert them into slow cookers. Those who are determined to cook chips or other items in deep fat could consider the purchase of an electric deep fat frier, but these are quite expensive.

Features to look for include:

- Cool walls so that they are safe to touch when in use
- Controls that can easily be made tactile
- Non-stick/easy clean interior
- Push button opening for the lid
- Basket that can be lowered by the turn of a knob when lid is closed
- Basket handle that does not need to be removed when the lid is closed as these can be hard to put back in place
- Basket that rotates when cooking which means that less oil is needed, and it is therefore quicker to heat up
- Easy method to drain away oil
- Built in timer.

16.4 Food preparation methods

The most popular aid to slicing that *In Touch* has ever demonstrated over the years has been the high quality Swiss-made **DUX knife**, with a detachable slicing guide that can be adjusted according to the width required (see illustration in this section).

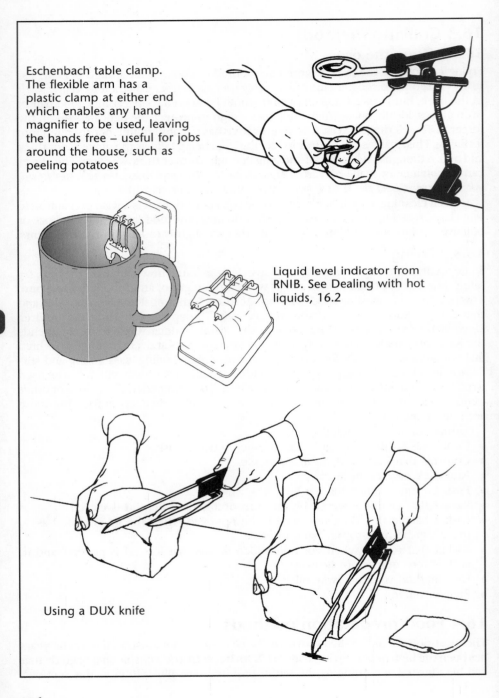

Eschenbach table clamp. The flexible arm has a plastic clamp at either end which enables any hand magnifier to be used, leaving the hands free – useful for jobs around the house, such as peeling potatoes

Liquid level indicator from RNIB. See Dealing with hot liquids, 16.2

Using a DUX knife

There is a very simple technique which is soon mastered. The knife needs to be pressed firmly against the cut side of the loaf. The bread is cut with the usual sawing movement until the guard touches the bread board. Then the wrist is raised slightly and the cut completed using the tip of the knife only. The knife is available by mail order from *Swiss Cutlery (UK) Ltd, 163 Parker Drive, Leicester LE4 0JP* ✆ 0116 235 1111. Price £23.44 (right hand version) and £24.55 (left hand version, illustrated). These are special prices to blind customers and cash with order is appreciated. RNIB stocks a similarly designed knife in right and left hand versions for £12.25.

It is possible to find in most good department stores a range of cutting and chopping gadgets which avoid the use of knives and protect the fingers. RNIB sells two types of vegetable choppers which prevent the fingers coming into contact with the blades. A good pair of **kitchen scissors** solves a lot of problems.

No one has come up with a perfect method for peeling potatoes, or other vegetables. Whichever method is used it is probably sensible, and possibly even more economic in the long run, to buy pre-washed and packed potatoes from the supermarket. These should be clean and free of blemishes so that it is possible either to boil them unpeeled, or bake them in their jackets. When a group of blind cooks was asked to assess different types of peelers, all preferred a horseshoe shaped peeler with a swivel blade. This type of peeler which is also ideal for other vegetables such as parsnips or carrots is stocked by the *RNIB* (£1.60) Those who benefit from magnification might consider installing a magnifying glass held in a double ended flexible clamp on their kitchen work top (see illustration in this section). The clamp costs £13.27 from the *Partially Sighted Society.*

Some blind people, particularly those who have had no experience of cooking with sight, have found it extremely helpful to invest in a food processor which can turn what used to be slow and tedious tasks such as slicing, chopping, grating, whisking or blending into a job that is completed in a few seconds. They are safe to use as all models have a jug-like bowl with a well-fitting lid that has to be locked into position before the appliance will operate, so there is no danger of food spurting out and being spilled. It is worth choosing a model that has a variable speed control and attachments that do not need to be assembled before use. Other design details to consider are:

- How easy is it to change the discs or slide in the different cutters?
- Is it simple to fit the lid into place on the bowl?
- Are the controls easy to operate and understand?
- Is the off button quick and easy to locate?

The speed of the operation is for some people offset by the need to spend time dismantling and cleaning the equipment. It is safer not to put the metal blade in the washing up bowl; it can be cleaned efficiently by holding it under running water.

16.5 Weighing, measuring and timing

When it is difficult to see the markings on conventional kitchen scales it is perhaps easiest to adopt the American-style method of measuring by cups. Many visually

Making things easier to find in the kitchen

- Wear an apron with a large deep pocket, into which kitchen tools can be kept ready at hand for when they are needed – and keep a damp cloth for mopping up spills immediately.
- Keep tools next to the place where they will be needed: a magnetic knife rack on the wall above the work top on which the chopping board is kept, a large container full of wooden spoons next to the cooker and a tray set out near the kettle with what is needed for making tea or coffee.
- It is often easier to keep things in drawers than on shelves. The contents of a drawer are more accessible and can be identified by touch without accident. One lady with poor sight lined a deep kitchen drawer with plastic foam and put all her cups into it.
- Use plastic boxes such as old ice-cream containers to divide up different types of items in kitchen cupboards.

impaired cooks set aside containers which they know contain a given amount. For example, a 150 gram yogurt pot holds ¼ pint or 5 fluid ozs of liquid, or 3 oz of flour. With the help of a sighted friend it is possible to mark up a set of containers suitable for the most commonly used quantities. The RNIB also sells a set of four stainless steel measuring cups suitable for measuring liquids from 50ml to 250ml. The largest cup could also be used for small quantities of dry ingredients. For very small quantities of liquid the RNIB can supply plastic syringes. The domestic set (50 pence) consists of a 1ml and a 20ml syringe. The small syringe will dispense liquid by drops (useful for flavourings) and the 20ml syringe has every 5ml position (equivalent to one teaspoon) marked by a groove on the flanges of the plunger. It comes with a nylon tube so that it can be used with deep containers. A 5ml general purpose syringe (50 pence) is supplied with a universal bottle opener.

People who do want the information that can only be got from conventional weighing scales could consider **talking kitchen scales** (*Cobolt Systems* £38.00). These can weigh up to 11lbs, announce the weight in imperial or metric form and claim to be accurate to within half an ounce. Traditional balance scales do not require any adaptations and many people find them easy to use. They are widely available but a model fitted with a pear-shaped scoop for easy pouring might be the best choice for someone with poor sight. A **kitchen timer** is particularly essential for visually impaired cooks who often rely on timing to judge when food is cooked. The RNIB stocks two mechanical timers, one of which has giant size raised black numbers on a white background. Both timers can be set by touch.

16.6 Microwave ovens

Probably the most popular piece of equipment for people who have lost their sight and with it their confidence in conventional methods of cooking is the **microwave oven**. Whether it is used just for reheating prepared food or for actual cooking, the microwave oven has the advantage that the inside is always cool. As all microwaves are table top models it is easy to take dishes out and for some people with limited

16.6 Microwave ovens

Probably the most popular piece of equipment for people who have lost their sight and with it their confidence in conventional methods of cooking is the **microwave oven**. Whether it is used just for reheating prepared food or for actual cooking, the microwave oven has the advantage that the inside is always cool. As all microwaves are table top models it is easy to take dishes out and for some people with limited sight it may be possible to see the controls. The promised advent of a **talking microwave oven** – due to be in production by the summer of 1995, should mean that one main obstacle to the use of microwave ovens has been overcome. Many of the microwave ovens currently available have electronic touch pad controls, which can be adapted with various types of tactile marks, but if the cook cannot see the digital read-out to check that instructions have been keyed in properly, there is always a risk of a timing error, which could render food inedible, or even cause it to ignite. Despite these difficulties many blind people have been using microwave ovens without any problems. The new talking microwave which is being developed by Cobolt will have a read-out which will repeat the programme that has been selected when the start button is pressed, so that any errors can be checked before cooking starts. It will also have a talking timer and a talking clock, and cost about £170.

From the point of view of a blind user, the microwave combination cookers and grills which are increasingly available do have a disadvantage; the inside of the oven will become hot when using the grill or the convection options. In some models there is an exposed element hanging down from the top of the oven in a position that can easily be touched when food is removed. While the additional features of the combined oven are very convenient, a straightforward microwave oven may be the better choice if simplicity and safety are the main considerations.

A labelling system designed to make the cooking of ready meals in microwave ovens safer and easier was introduced in 1992. All new microwave ovens are now marked with a letter (from A to E) according to their category for heating one portion quantities of food. Many microwaveable food packs such as ready meals are marked with guideline times for the most common categories of oven. People who already have microwave ovens can check the letter category that applies to their oven by consulting **The New Microwave Labels**, a free booklet published by the Ministry of Agriculture, Fisheries and Food, available in large print from *Foodsense, London SE99 7TT* ℘ 0645 556000, and on cassette or in braille from *RNIB Customer Services*. A freephone helpline run by the **Food Safety Advisory Centre** ℘ 0800 282407 can answer enquiries and give practical advice on microwave ovens in general. It is worth noting that the **Which?** reports on microwave ovens, published by the Consumers Association, now take account of their suitability for people with special needs.

16.7 Cookery books

A limited number of cookery books have been produced in braille, large print, Moon and on cassette. Full details of what is available can be obtained in a bibliography **Food and Cookery** from *RNIB Customer Services*.

There are not many cookery books produced for visually impaired cooks. The **RNC Large Print Cook Book** has some hints and tips for blind cooks. It is available (price £3.45) from *RNC Enterprises* or in braille and Moon from *RNIB*. **A Basic Microwave Cookery Book** (£2.50 large print, £1.50 tape) and **A Taste of Microwave Cookery** (£3.50 large print, £2.50 tape) are excellent books for absolute beginners compiled by rehabilitation workers in West Glamorgan. Contact *Ann Phillips, Social Services Department, 1 Heol y Gog, Gowerton, Swansea SA4 3BX* ℘ 01792 872375. Make cheques payable to the Resource Centre for Visually Impaired People.

A set of 12 **Look'n'Cook** large print cookery cards give simple and nutritious recipes devised by Doreen Chetwood (Partially Sighted Society. £2.00). These recipes use containers such as empty yoghurt pots for measuring instead of conventional scales.

16.8 Further reading

In Touch at Home. Maragaret Ford. Isis. 1986. Cassette version available from *Calibre* and *RNIB Talking Book Service*. Large print edition now out of print but still stocked in many public libraries.

RNIB Product Guide **Daily Living** has a range of cookery items.

The Cooker for you ❶ ❷ ❸ a free RNIB booklet which describes the range of gas and electric cookers available and useful features to consider when buying a new one.

17 Labelling and identification

Most people with little or no sight can manage to recognise items in their own homes by a variety of systems using touch, colour, shape and sometimes also by smell or sound. Even if sight is no longer sufficient to allow for comfortable reading of a large print book, it often is enough to enable two or three large print letters to be read on a label. A very basic knowledge of braille or Moon opens up opportunities to use tactile methods for labelling. It is not even necessary to know the whole braille or Moon alphabets; the ability to recognise the first ten letters of either of these alphabets (which double as the symbols for the numbers 1 to 10) would enable a keen bridge player to identify her playing cards, ensure that a newly blind person does not open a tin of peaches when he wants a bowl of soup and provide a way to keep a list of telephone numbers. This chapter aims to give a basic introduction to the methods and equipment that are available. It owes much to the ideas of Jessica Finch, a blind teacher who has an ongoing research interest in labelling – details at the end of this chapter.

17.1 Labelling for beginners

Even the simplest everyday object can be made into a **label** that can distinguish apparently identical items for someone who cannot see. An elastic band slipped around the marmalade jar distinguishes it from the jam; a small piece of Elastoplast on the handle identifies a toothbrush when its colour cannot be seen; a safety pin discreetly placed inside the cuff of a jacket or coat ensures that it can easily be distinguished from others. A paper clip can be an invaluable marker – one blind traveller always gives one to the booking office clerk to slip onto his return ticket.

Those who retain their colour vision can make use of this either by selecting similar items in different colours, or where this is not appropriate by adding a distinguishing colour. Brightly coloured electrician's tape can be bought in DIY stores; using different coloured strips on plastic containers in a freezer could help to identify the contents, e.g. red on meat, blue on fish, green on vegetables. It is also possible to get **NEW** **coloured bag closures** (from *Lakeland Plastics, Alexandra Buildings, Windermere, Cumbria LA23 1BQ* ✆ 01539 488100) which can be used to seal plastic bags as well as to identify their contents. Using different **coloured electric plugs** would ensure that the fridge or freezer are not switched off instead of the toaster or kettle. The different **coloured plastic folders** widely available in stationers can be used to separate personal documents or bills from other letters.

17.1.1 Identifying clothes

It is possible to learn to distinguish clothing by becoming more observant of small differences; the brown jacket can be distinguished from the blue by the number of buttons on its sleeve, or by keeping a small object like a pencil in one pocket. A green dress can be distinguished from a similar one in a different colour if a brooch is pinned to it. If it is difficult to tell the black shoes from the brown, some people tie the shoelaces together as soon as the shoes are taken off. A more sophisticated method is to buy flat shoelaces for the black shoes, and round ones for the brown – or simply to stick a tiny piece of sticking plaster inside the heels of the brown pair to distinguish them from the black. One well-organised blind man told the *In Touch* programme that he distinguished his trousers by keeping them on hangers that could easily be recognised by touch – brown pairs on wooden hangers, black on metal ones. Those who find it difficult to pair their socks might like to use the plastic **coloured sock clips** sold by RNIB (£4 for a pack of 12). The colours are identified by a series of small tactile dots and the clips can be put into the washing machine. A similar set of clips will also hang onto a washing line, and can be obtained from John Lewis stores (£1.95 for a set of five). For those who want to distinguish similar clothes in a number of different colours, it is worth getting the **colour indicating buttons** sold by RNIB. These are made in plastic, each distinctively shaped to represent 16 different colours e.g. cross for red, shamrock for green, star for blue.

17.2 Tactile markers

These colour indicating buttons can also be used in a variety of other ways to identify items such as cotton reels, knitting wools, shoe cleaning materials, or to distinguish the white hyacinth bulbs from the blue ones. The buttons can be stuck on with blu-tak or double sided sticky tape, or attached with wire, hat elastic or safety pins.

There are also various ways in which people can make tactile marks on equipment in common use around the house. **Bump-Ons** are small raised self adhesive plastic dots available in a range of sizes, shapes and colours (black, orange and transparent) which can be used to mark the controls of cookers, irons, washing machines or other domestic equipment. **Bump-Ons** are available by the sheet (with at least 56) from *RNIB* (price £3.61 transparent, £3.67 black and £4.63 orange). They can also be bought in bulk (at least 1000) from, *Castle Packaging Ltd, Bott Lane, Walsall WS1 2JG* ✆ 01922 25451 or 26664 (price per 1000 £32.06 for transparent, £56.65 for black or orange).

The RNIB also sells **Loc-Dots** which are small, clear, raised self-adhesive dots that can be used as a reference point on

Sound advice

The popularity of audio tapes both for information and entertainment, as well as the growing number of blind people who have compact disc players and computers mean that there is a very real need to devise ways of identifying cassettes and disks of all types. For people who do not know braille or Moon this can be a very real problem. When a listener challenged *In Touch* to come up with a method to enable a newly blind lady who did not know braille, to find the record she wanted to play from her large collection, the team found it difficult to think of an effective method other than re-organising the collection into small sections – by type of music or composer – and identifying each section with the colour/shape buttons. But the best advice was to learn enough braille to recognise numbers and then with sighted help arrange the records in a numbered order which is also recorded onto a tape.

The illustration (opposite) shows the various ways in which audio cassettes could be labelled.

Cassette labelling

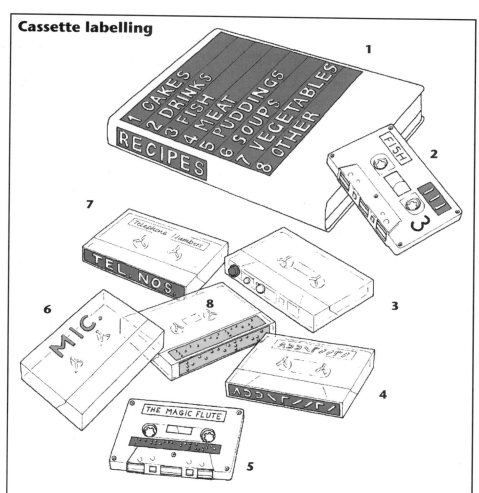

1 Cassette carry case (available from RNIB) labelled with raised large letters made by Dymo 2300 machine.

2 Labelling for non-braillists. Large handwritten label; raised numeral 3 made with Dymo 2300 and lines created with ordinary Dymo labeller.

3 Using different types of Bump-Ons to create a private code.

4 Moon labelling for a taped address list.

5 Braille labelling.

6 Hi-Marks lettering has to be placed on flat side of case as spine is not wide enough.

7 Label made with Dymo 2300 has to be trimmed slightly to fit spine.

8 Transparent braille labels can be used to allow print labelling to be seen hi-fi or central heating controls or to mark the home keys on a typewriter or computer keyboard. A pack of six costs £1.00. The **Velcro** dots sold in haberdashery stores can be used in a similar way and may be easier for less sensitive fingers to feel. One rehabilitation worker recommends the use of corn plasters as markers!

It is also possible to make tactile marks with **Hi-Marks**, a fluorescent orange paste which is dispensed from a small tube with a fine nozzle. It adheres to a variety of surfaces including metal, plastic, paper and fabric. As it is non-flammable when dry it can be used to mark the controls of domestic appliances such as cookers. The RNIB's free factsheet **Labelling Domestic Equipment** gives instructions on how this might best be done. Hi-Marks is available from either *RNIB* or the *Partially Sighted Society* for £3.50 a tube. Similar raised marks can be produced by **Slick Writers** which are widely sold in art or craft shops and stationers for about 99 pence. Slick Writers are produced in about 200 different colours and the distributor says that it should adhere to any fabric (except silk) as well as plastic, wood or metal surfaces. Distributed by *Inscribe Ltd, The Woolmer Industrial Estate, Bordon, Hampshire GU35 9QE*. Both Hi-Marks and Slick Writer require application by someone with good sight.

There are also tactile **self-adhesive markers** specially designed to be placed on the controls of a cassette player to mark stop, play, fast forward and rewind. These are available from the RNIB – £3.20 a set, but will only adhere to a perfectly clean, grease-free surface. It is also a good idea to mark side A of a cassette. Talking Newspapers do this with a small green cloth spot on the right hand side, and TNEL will sell sheets containing 64 of these for 50 pence. However, as TNAUK is using the green cloth spots to identify the source of their tapes as well as Side A, it is hoped that, to avoid confusion, anyone else using these green spots will not put them in exactly the same place on the cassette. **NEW** COTIS is planning to publish its guidelines on identification of cassettes in the summer of 1995 which hopefully will help to establish standard methods for anyone involved in producing tapes for blind people.

17.3 Ready-made labels

For those who can read a limited amount of large print there are several types of ready-made labels. **Self adhesive PVC labels** with black capital letters 1 cm high on a white or yellow background can be obtained for £1.50 per A4 sheet. This sheet provides various labels for food, electrical appliances, etc., as well as individual letters and numbers. It is also possible to get sheets with individual letters from *fingatip labels, Unit 26a, Lenton Business Centre, Lenton Boulevard, Nottingham NG7 2BY* ✆ 0115 942 0941.

Similar **self-adhesive paper labels** in smaller print – black letters on a white background – are available from *W.S. Duncan, 27 Sharps Lane, Dundee, Tayside* ✆ 01382 68024. They cost £1.50 a set (plus 25 pence if braille overprinting is required). Labels in extra large print can be made to order.

The brightly coloured magnetic letters and numerals sold in good toyshops can be used on metal surfaces such as fridge doors and serve some people as a message pad or to keep note of telephone numbers.

294

17.3.1 Braille labels

The alphabet sheets and ready-made labels described above can also be supplied overprinted in **braille** at no extra charge from *fingatip labels*. It is also possible to order labels made to individual requirement.

17.3.2 Moon labels

Both the RNIB and fingatip will produce **Moon labels** on request. As the Moon letters are variations of single shapes in different positions it is important to request that any Moon label has a Moon comma at the end, to ensure that it is read the right way up. The RNIB labels are free. fingatip can make Moon labels to individual order or supply self-adhesive PVC sheets embossed with the Moon alphabet so that people can make up their own (prices from 20 pence per sheet containing a single Moon alphabet). fingatip have also produced Moon letter tiles (similar to those used for playing scrabble). These are primarily intended for use as word building sets in schools, but the tiles are backed with Velcro and might also be useful for label making.

17.4 Home-made labels

17.4.1 Large print labels

It is obviously much more satisfactory to be able to make one's own labels. It is possible to create both letters and words by pricking out the shapes with a sharp pointed implement on plastic material. Jessica Finch has used plastic cut out of empty washing-up liquid containers; less adroit individuals may find it easier to use the sheets of **self-adhesive labelling foil** available from the RNIB. It is available in black which produces raised white dots which are clearly seen by someone with limited sight, but it may sometimes be better to use the transparent clear foil which allows the original label to be seen – an important consideration when sighted people are also using the same products. For those who can read a few letters in large print, very effective attractive looking labels can be created with the **Dymo 2300**, an industrial signmaker. This produces slightly raised letters ½ inch high on a ¼ inch tape. This signmaker costs £349 + VAT which puts it out of the reach of most individuals, though some voluntary societies have bought them to make labels for people in their areas. Details of stockists can be obtained from *Esselte Dymo, North Feltham Trading Estate, Spur Road, Feltham, Middlesex TW14 0SL* ✆ 0181 890 1388. Garages and workshops often have such signmakers and might be willing to make some labels for a visually impaired person on request.

17.4.2 Using braille

Braillists can use either hand-frames, or an adaptor for the Perkins braille writer, or a braille Dymo gun (a labelling machine) to produce labels. All these can take ordinary Dymo tape as sold in stationers, o-r black or clear 12mm tape available from the RNIB. *Techno-Vision* supplies this tape in a variety of colours, and also stocks the 9mm reels which are ideal for labelling computer disks. For general purposes the single line braille frame is ideally suited, but there is a frame with specially shaped clear labelling material to use when making **cassette labels** (see illustration in 19.7). These frames and materials are available from the RNIB as is the labelling adaptor for the Perkins, which slips onto the back of the machine. People who make a lot of labels might consider buying a **braille labelling machine** which works in a very similar fashion to the Dymo labelling gun. This machine is marked up with the ordinary alphabet as well as braille so that sighted non-braillists can use it without difficulty. It is available from *Techno-Vision* (price £38.00 inclusive of 10 rolls of tape) and from *RNIB* (price £32.75 with one free tape).

17.4.3 Using Moon

It is not easy for people to make their own labels using Moon. Some sighted people have managed to create simple Moon labels using Hi-Marks, but both the RNIB and fingatip will make Moon labels on request.

Useful hints on labelling

● Tear all the labels off the dog food tins to differentiate them from anything else in the larder.

● When staying in a strange house or a hotel, wind a thick rubber band round the outside door handle of your bedroom.

● To make sure that you never put shaving cream onto your toothbrush, always buy toothpaste in tubes with flip lids.

● To differentiate books of first class and second class stamps tear the corner off the cover of the second class ones.

● Sit new items in labelled old containers – label an empty washed carton of a particular flavour of yoghurt and then put the next full one in it.

17.5 Labelling materials

A full range of labelling materials is available from *RNIB* and from *fingatip labels*. The RNIB sells **tie-on labels** with one or two holes so that they can be attached with string, hat elastic or wire. Both these tie-on labels and a range of self-adhesive labels in various sizes can be brailled onto directly or marked with an indelible ink. fingatip sell thick tags (onto which braille, Moon or large print labels can be stuck) designed to be fastened on with rubber bands. For tins it is best to make labels using a **plastic faced magnetic rubber strip**. It is possible to emboss directly onto this strip, but some people prefer to stick a label made from the self adhesive-tape (see 17.4.1) onto the magnetic material. Magnetic labels can be used over and over again; **some well-organised blind shoppers take the label off as soon as a tin is used, put it into their shopping bag to serve as a shopping list and put the label onto the new tin before leaving the shop!**

Whatever the method used for making labels, it is important to find ways in which to cut down the work involved, either by limiting the number of items that actually need to be labelled or by finding ways of re-using labels for goods that are frequently bought. It may be possible to differentiate the self-raising flour from the plain by always buying the former in 3lb bags and the latter in 1lb packets, or similar food can be bought or stored in containers that are different in shape or colour. If custard powder is always bought in tins it will not be confused with the packet of cornflour. It will also help if it is possible to organise storage in the kitchen cupboards so that different types of food are kept separately. But this does mean that everyone who uses the kitchen has to be extremely tidy and well-organised! The simple methods described at the beginning of the chapter using rubber bands to distinguish similar objects are very effective for a limited number of items. It also depends on a good memory: was the single band on the tin of salmon or the tin of tuna, or the other way round? For more sophisticated labelling of a wide variety of items **it is hard to escape the conclusion that if at all possible one of the touch reading methods should be learnt and put into use**, ideally with the initial help of a rehabilitation officer.

17.6 Further reading

Jessica Finch has prepared extensive notes on all aspects of labelling. She will send a selection of information in return for an A4 addressed envelope with two first class stamps and a cheque for £2 made payable to Camsight. Write to *Mrs. Finch c/o Camsight, 5 Coles Lane, Oakington, Cambridge CB4 5BA.*

E

18 Reading and writing 300

19 Pleasures of listening 316

20 A beginner's guide to computers 334

F

18 Reading and writing

Many people with impaired vision can still read if print is clear enough and larger than normal. This chapter gives details of large print publishers, and of ways in which people can be helped to go on using their writing skills. The value of good lighting and other advice on making the best of remaining sight is dealt with in chapter 3.

For people who cannot see to read any kind of print, the tactile alternatives of braille and Moon give access to at least some of the wealth of printed material available. Both 'touch-reading' systems are described here, with details of the publishers who produce them and of the equipment used to write them.

Social services have a duty to provide both Moon and braille teaching as part of their rehabilitation service for blind people. Local resource centres or voluntary societies for the blind may have at least one person able to teach Moon or braille. RNIB has a **register of Moon and braille teachers**, some of whom are prepared to undertake postal tuition; enquiries to *RNIB Customer Services*. Teach-yourself packages are available as an alternative to learning with a teacher.

This chapter also gives details of electronic equipment which provides direct access to the printed word by converting it into other formats, including synthetic speech. Chapter 19 deals with reading matter on tape, chapter 20 with books on computer disk. A guide to transcription services which produce large print, braille and Moon from text in print or on computer disk is given in 33.

18.1 Large print

18.1.1 Large print books

F

Only a minute proportion of all books published are in large print. Titles that appear in large print are for the most part best-selling fiction and non-fiction, including popular romances, mysteries and Westerns, some produced with lightweight soft covers. The main outlet for large print books is through **public libraries**. The number and range of large print books on the shelves of branch libraries may vary, but large print books are included in library services to the elderly and housebound. Some libraries also provide a limited collection to be kept at residential homes and day centres for the elderly in their area. Librarians should be able to check whether any particular title has been published in large print.

The **National Library for the Blind** publishes a large print series named **Austin Books**. The series consists of about 300 titles concentrating on classics and standard English works, including history, travel, philosophy and popular science as well as novels. A catalogue is available on request. The National Library also has a collection of several hundred large print titles issued by commercial publishers, but now out of print. Books from both of these collections can be borrowed by arrangement through the local public library. The National Library now holds the National Large Print Collection originally deposited with the British Library.

Key to media of publication   **P** clear print   **L** large print   **B** braille   **T** tape   **M** Moon   **D** disk

Where a full address is not given in the text, see 32 (Useful addresses)

Large print books are relatively expensive and are rarely stocked by bookshops, but they can be obtained direct from the publishers, who will provide catalogues on request. The main commercial distributors of large print books in this country are:

Ulverscroft (over 4,400 titles in print)
Chivers (over 1,200 titles in print)
Magna (over 3,800 titles in print)
Isis (over 550 titles in print).

Some reference books are available in large print, among them the following dictionaries:

A new **Oxford Large Print Dictionary**, based on the Oxford Paperback Dictionary, 4th edition, to be published by OUP in September 1995 at £17.99

The **Little Oxford Dictionary**, 6th edition, £14.95 from *Ulverscroft* or from the *Partially Sighted Society*.

18.1.2 Other large print publications

Big Print is a 28 page weekly tabloid in bold typeface twice the size of normal newsprint. Half its pages are devoted to television and radio listings, the rest carries a selection of news and features and one page of sport. It is available by post only from *Big Print, PO Box 308, Warrington WA1 1JE Freephone ☏ 0800 124007*, quarterly subscription £12.80, annual subscription £48. Big Print is funded wholly by RNIB.

No British newspaper has yet followed the example of the **New York Times**, which publishes a weekly large print edition.

A large-type edition of **Readers Digest** magazine is available in the United States. A British reader would need to take out a subscription ($11.95 p.a., payable by international money order). Details from *Large-Type Edition, Readers Digest Fund for the Blind Inc., PO Box 241, Mount Morris, 61054 Illinois, USA*, fax 00 1 815 734 1246.

The World at Large, a 44 page fortnightly news magazine, is published in large (20 point) print by *World at Large Inc., 1689 46th Street, Brooklyn, NY 11204 ☏ 00 1 718 972 4000*, subscription to UK readers $63 for 24 issues. Most of the magazine is reproduced from US News and World Report but some articles are taken from Time Magazine and the

F

Christian Science Monitor, and it includes a crossword from the Los Angeles Times. A free list **L** **B** **T** of some **sources of large print material** can be obtained from *RNIB Customer Services* or *RNIB Reference Library*.

18.1.3 Christian religious publications in large print

Large print Bibles

Bibles are published in a number of large print versions, complete or in individual books. It is worth comparing different versions as type size and thickness of paper varies. Thin paper may allow print to show through from the next page and smaller print on thicker paper may prove easier to read. Large print Bibles published in **individual volumes** are not so heavy to handle.

Fixing your newspaper to a clipboard enables you to keep the right distance when using a spectacle mounted magnifier

The Gospels (Authorised Version and New International Version) and Psalms (AV) are published in booklet form in exceptionally clear heavy black type by *SGM International, Radstock House, 3 Eccleston Street, London SW1W 9LZ* ℘ 0171 730 2155. Prices vary from £1.00 to £1.50 for each booklet. The **Torch Trust** publishes the whole Bible (RSV, but St. Mark's Gospel also available in NIV) in giant quarter-inch block lettering. It is in 38 volumes, each of which can be purchased separately. Prices for registered blind and partially sighted people range from 35p to £1.50 per volume. The **Gideons** publish two large print editions of the New Testament and Psalms, one slightly smaller and one larger than the usual large print typeface, both available in either the AV or the NIV. They are normally provided free to homes for the elderly or hospital geriatric wards, but partially sighted individuals may obtain a free copy by writing to *Gideons International, Western House, George Street, Lutterworth, Leicestershire LE17 4EE* ℘ 01455 554241.

Other publishers of large print Bibles are:

Bible Society. AV, NIV, New King James, Good News, New Welsh Bible; 25% discount to registered visually impaired people.

Cambridge University Press. *The Edinburgh Building, Cambridge CB2 2RU* ℘ 01223 312393. Large (AV) and giant-sized print (AV, NIV, New Revised Standard Version).

Hodder & Stoughton. *338 Euston Road, London NW1 3BH* ℘ 0171 873 6000. (NIV).

Trinitarian Bible Society. *Tyndale House, Dorset Road, London SW19 3NN* ℘ 0181 543 7857. (AV). 25% discount to registered visually impaired people.

Large print prayer books

Order for Holy Communion, Rite A, based on new **Alternative Service Prayer Book**, on sale at good religious bookshops or mail order from *Church House Bookshop, 31 Great Smith Street, London SW1P 3BN*, price £3.50 plus £1.00 postage (cheques payable to *Central Board of Finance*).

The **Methodist Service Book** (£11.50), the **Sunday Service** booklet (£1.05), the bi-monthly devotional guide **The Upper Room** (annual subscription £7.50) and **Losing One's Sight**, a booklet compiled from personal experience (£2.00), all available in large print from the *Methodist Publishing House, 20 Ivatt Way, Peterborough PE3 7PG* ✆ 01733 332202.

Reading with a hand magnifier

Large-Print Prayer Book (£1.50) and **Large-Print Mass Book** (£2.00) published by *Catholic Truth Society, 192 Vauxhall Bridge Road, London SW1V 1PD* ✆ 0171 834 4392.

A Shorter Morning and Evening Prayer (£14.99), mainly for Catholics, published by *HarperCollins Religious, PO Box Glasgow G4 0NB* ✆ 0141 772 3200.

New Daylight Large Print, daily readings from the Bible, with comments, £3.50 each or £12 annual subscription for three booklets. Also available on cassette and in braille from *The Bible Reading Fellowship, Sandy Lane West, Oxford OX4 5HG* ✆ 01865 748227.

Large print hymn books

Mission Praise 1, £2.50, and **Mission Praise 2**, £4.00, both in giant print from *Torch Trust.* **Mission Praise Combined**, £14.95, words only and in large print from *HarperCollins Religious* (see above).

The **Ulverscroft Large-Print Hymn Book**, £3.95, a reproduction of the **Hospital Hymn Book** of the Free Church Federal Council and similar in size to an ordinary hymn book. 119 hymns, selected scripture passages and prayers and index with cross-references to six of the most generally used hymn books.

The New Standard version of **Hymns Ancient and Modern**, £9.75, and **The New English Hymnal**, £9.75, published in large, clear print by *The Canterbury Press, St Mary's Works, St Mary's Plain, Norwich NR3 3BH* ✆ 01603 612914.

Thora Hird's Praise Be! Notebook (from the TV series Praise Be!), £3.95 published by *Isis.*

Hymns for Today's Church, large print edition, £9.95 published by *Hodder & Stoughton* (see above).

F

Hymns and Psalms, soft back large print edition, £8.50 (£9.50 with spiral binding) published by *Methodist Publishing House* (see above).

18.1.4 Other religious publications in large print

For information on large print Hindu, Muslim, Buddhist, Bahai, Sikh and Jain Scriptures, contact *Bhadra Patel, Multi-Cultural Library and Information Service, Tooting Library, 75 Mitcham Road, London SW17 9PD* ✆ 0181 871 7174. The **RNIB Talking Book Service** has a wide assortment of religious material. Details of Hebrew Bibles and Jewish prayer books in large print can be obtained from Jess Clare at *Jewish Care*.

18.1.5 Large print song books

Ulverscroft publish two **Large-Print Song Books** (£3.25 each) containing hymns and carols as well as popular songs, 139 in the blue book, 240 in the red. The Large-Print Music Edition is £6.25 (blue), and £7.25 (red), with simple piano accompaniments and guitar chords.

A collection of 21 carols (90p) and a book of 27 popular music hall songs (80p) is produced in bold black type by disabled workers in Cambridgeshire. Both are available by post from *Jannet MacLachlan, OT Assistant, Social Services Department, Herlington House, Benyon Grove, Orton Malbourne, Peterborough PE2 5XS* ✆ 01733 394828.

RNIB publishes a large print **Carol Book** (£2.50) with the words of 50 well known carols. The Partially Sighted Society's **Large-Print Carol Book** (70p) contains 22 carols. A large print booklet with ten carols costs 50p plus postage from the *Bible Lands Society, PO Box 50, High Wycombe, Buckinghamshire HP15 7QU* ✆ 01494 521351 or 532593. A collection of 100 popular songs from traditional and folk to hymns and carols is available for £4.91 from *Toys for the Handicapped*.

18.1.6 Writing for people with some sight

Pen and paper

People with poor sight need to write in much larger letters than before and to use thick, dark writing implements. The use of felt-tipped rather than ordinary ink or ballpoint pens may make it easier for someone who can still see enough to read what he or she has written. As people with limited sight often have to write with the eyes (and nose) close to the paper, it is worth looking for felt-tipped pens which are water rather than spirit based. The *Partially Sighted Society* stocks **Berol** fibre-tip and roller-ball pens with black ink at 87p each (£2.20 for three). Other useful pens on sale at stationers include the **Edding 250** which can be used on paper or on a wipe-clean notice board and the **Papermate Tempo** with a nylon fibre tip.

Choose matt rather than shiny paper to write on. Large sheets encourage larger handwriting. As people with poor sight may find it difficult to write straight, it is worth considering **lined stationery** available from both RNIB and the Partially Sighted Society. RNIB supplies notepaper with raised lines, various types of **writing frames** which guide pen or pencil in a straight line and a plastic **envelope guide** with cut-outs for writing addresses. **Address templates** are issued free to their customers by Barclays and Lloyds banks.

At the very least, people with impaired vision need to be able to sign their names on documents, cheques, pension books etc. Banks and building societies usually supply templates for their cheques to help a person with poor sight fill them out in the right place. Two **signature guides**, one to fit DSS allowance books, one for other documents or letters, can be obtained from RNIB (see illustration in this section). See also 15.6 for further information about handling financial transactions.

Typing

If handwriting is difficult, the ability to type would be enormously helpful. Even if the visually impaired person cannot read what has been typed, at least the typed message can be understood by friends and relatives – or the milkman! Touch-typing is also a valuable skill for anyone considering the possibility of using a computer, as the basic lay-out of the keyboard is the same.

F

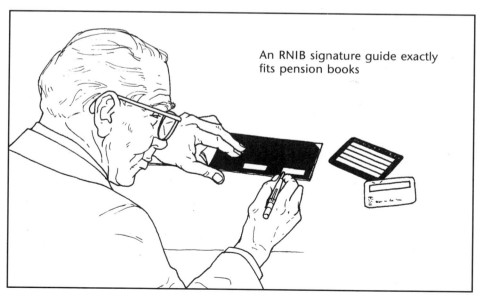

An RNIB signature guide exactly fits pension books

In some areas, typing is taught to newly blind people at a local rehabilitation centre. Otherwise a visually impaired student should be able to follow any ordinary class in an adult education centre, as everyone normally learns to type by touch. **Learning to touch type** (three cassette tapes and a booklet), £15 from *RNIB*, is a basic keyboard course for visually impaired people of all ages. For braille readers, Pitman's **Teach Yourself Typing** and several other books are available in braille from *RNIB* (see also 8.9). Beginners find it easier to locate the home keys when they are marked with pieces of sticking plaster or tactile dots (see 18.1.6). The typing position can be felt with the help of a tactile metal scale which can be made to order free by RNIB to fit the carriage of most makes of typewriter.

Partially sighted typists may find it helpful to use **copyholders** to hold text close to the eyes. Copyholders can be obtained from suppliers of office equipment. Some models are stocked by the Partially Sighted Society. The **Luxo** range includes copyholders mounted on adjustable, spring balance arms and with optional magnifying line-finder and clip-on light. Details from *Luxo UK Ltd., 4 Barmeston Road, London SE6 3BN* ℘ 0181 698 7238. Details of other models and manufacturers of copyholders are available from the Disabled Living Foundation and other disabled living centres (see 34). There are several illuminated 'industrial' **magnifiers** fitted to an adjustable arm, which would enable visually impaired typists to see their work enlarged, though because of their size the magnification is low. Details from the *Low Vision Adviser* at the *Partially Sighted Society.*

Changing to a larger than normal **typeface** might be worth considering if this would mean that a person with low vision could read the typescript. A choice of typefaces in various sizes is available for electronic typewriters, and can be obtained from suppliers of office equipment. Details are given in **Large Print Typewriters**, a free leaflet compiled by RNIB Employment Technology Unit. Carbon ribbons produce good, black print. To obtain the clearest possible typescript from ordinary inked nylon ribbons, they need to be replaced as soon as they begin fading as a result of wear and drying out.

People unable to afford a typewriter may find the local voluntary society willing to help with a grant or the loan of a machine, or the local social services department may be able to lend a machine. A student might get help from either the local education department, or from one of the educational charities (see 8.23). Details of help available through the **Access to Work Scheme** are given in 10.7.4.

18.2 Braille

This system of embossed script, which has been universally adopted by blind people, was invented by a Frenchman, Louis Braille, in 1824. It consists, in its English version, of 63 symbols which are variations on the dots of a domino six. Apart from the 26 letters of the alphabet, the symbols include eight braille punctuation signs and 27 contractions for common combinations of letters such as 'st' or 'th'. There are two grades – Grade One, in which every word is fully spelt, and Grade Two, the everyday form in which various contractions are used to express frequently recurring groups of letters and words and thus reduce, by one-quarter, the bulk of the braille.

Braille contractions vary in different languages, but by international agreement the signs used for phonetically similar letters of the alphabet are generally the same, regardless of language, at least in Europe. For information about how braille is used nationally and internationally, contact the *Braille Authority of the UK, Secretary, Stephen Phippen, c/o RNIB, Peterborough.*

To read braille by touch, a person has to develop a sensitivity in the fingertips which may not always come easily. It has been estimated that only a small proportion (about seven per cent) of the blind population can read braille but, given determination, age is no barrier. Many *In Touch* listeners have learnt braille when in their seventies and eighties and found they derived a great deal of pleasure from it. Most elderly people find writing braille easier than reading braille. Feeling the dots is the hard thing about learning braille, but even if braille reading is too slow for the enjoyment of books, it can be useful for other purposes, such as playing cards (see 21.5.2) or making labels (see chapter 17).

18.2.1 Learning braille

A number of teaching packs are available for adult students. They can be used with or without a teacher.

RNIB supplies:

- **Beginning Braille**, £7.50, by Dr. Michael Tobin: four braille booklets, four companion cassettes and print notes for teachers and learners. Most of the material is written in jumbo size braille, as beginners often find a larger cell easier to identify.
- **Fingerprint**, £7.50, by Nigel Berry: 10 cassettes and 11 volumes of standard size braille, with full coverage of Grade 2, with notes for teachers and a script of the cassettes in print and braille.
- **Braille Primer**, £9.50, updated 1992: designed for **sighted** students. (See 8.8.1 for details of recognised qualifications in braille.)
- **Check your Braille**, £2: designed to help braillists revise or check up on signs and basic rules of Grade 2 braille.

National Library for the Blind provides:

- **Braille made Easy – as Pye**, a first course in Grade One jumbo size braille, 20 lessons with cassette.
- **Upgrade your Braille – a second slice of Pye**, braille workbook and cassette leading to Grade Two braille.
  These courses are £3 each or can be borrowed from the Library.
- **Birmingham Braille Course**, £34, primarily for **sighted** learners: rule book and workbook in print; braille workbook in two volumes.

A few volumes of **short stories** in Grade One braille and about 30 volumes in Grade Two braille can be borrowed from the National Library. Each volume contains one story in jumbo braille followed by the same text in normal wide-spaced interlined braille, enabling the learner to check his or her progress.

A Newcastle social worker runs a **correspondence club** to give new braillists an opportunity to use their skills. Contact *Mrs Linda Watts, Social Services*

Department, Civic Centre, Barras Bridge, Newcastle-upon-Tyne NE99 2BM
℡ 0191 232 8520 ext. 6320. Pen-pals can also be contacted through the braille magazine **Progress**, published by RNIB.

NEW Students can practise their braille with the help of the **DotTest** computer program, £25 from *Dorton IT Support Centre*. Based on the first nine exercises in the course workbook, the program is designed for Archimedes computers, using six of the home keys and the space bar to mimic a braille keyboard. Alternatively an adapted Perkins brailler can be plugged into the computer.

Information on learning braille for adults 🄻 🄱 🄣, a regularly updated leaflet, is available free from *RNIB Customer Services*. See 8.8.1 for details of courses for children.

18.2.2 Braille writing equipment

Basic braille writing equipment is supplied by RNIB, including hand frames, manual braillers, braille paper and plastic braillon.

NEW M-Boss waterproof embossable material supplied by Blind Spot (UK) Ltd. is more expensive (about 18p a sheet) than braillon but has certain advantages. Unlike braillon, it can be used for double-sided brailling, the braille dots are clearer than on conventional braille paper, and the low-reflective surface makes it ideal for the dual-media production of braille and large print.

Hand frames

Braille is written by hand with a style or 'dotter' to indent the characters on the back of the paper, working from right to left. It surprises most people that writing in reverse comes quite naturally after a while, but it takes a much longer time and a lot of practice to acquire a reasonable speed. For writing on one side of the paper, there is a four line frame, £7.77, a single line guide, £5.20 and a two line giant dot frame, £1.05. Other frames can be used for writing on both sides of the paper. The Marburg range, £5.78 for the A4 size, produces interpoint braille, that is with the characters on the second side of the paper between the points of the characters on the first. The Tylor Tatlow seven line frame, £11.03, produces interline braille, with the characters on the second side of the paper between the lines on the first. Interpoint is more difficult to read at first because the lines are closer together.

Manual writing machines

All standard braille writing machines have six keys which represent the six dots of the braille cells, and the first three fingers of each hand are used for operating the six keys. It is not necessary to write in reverse as with the hand frames.

- The British-made **Stainsby** machine was for many years regarded as the standard braille writing equipment. The only major disadvantage of the machine, in the opinion of many users, is that it is too noisy. Stainsby machines can be used to emboss characters on both sides of the paper and are available in either interpoint or interline versions for £70, including case.
- The **Perkins** brailler is made in the United States. It is a heavier machine, but less noisy and much more sophisticated than the Stainsby. It has the considerable advantage of being an upward writer, so that the braille can be

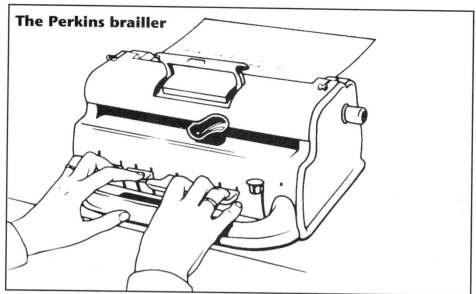

The Perkins brailler

read while the paper is in the machine. It produces braille spaced as for interpointing, but uses one side of the paper only. Its operation is rather different from the Stainsby, but not very difficult to learn. Unlike the Stainsby, it has a back-space key, a line spacer and a carriage return lever, all situated at the front of the machine. The Perkins costs £196.52 and comes in **standard** or **Jumbo dot** versions, or a **UniManual** model adapted for use with one hand. A Perkins has a carrying handle, but RNIB supplies a light weight-soft **carrying case** with adjustable shoulder strap for £10.30.

- The German made **Mini-Picht** upward brailler is also stocked by RNIB at £88.

- Fitted with **Braille-n-Print** and linked to a printer, a standard Perkins brailler will produce print at the same time as braille. Braille-n-Print, £625 from *Concept Systems*, accepts Grade 1 or 2 English braille, and Grade 1 braille in several European languages. It has a 24k memory. There is a standard version or a Slimline version which clips onto the Perkins to allow a degree of portability. Special software, £35 from *Concept Systems*, enables text to be word-processed on the Perkins if it is linked to an IBM compatible computer.

- The electronic **Mountbatten Brailler** is manufactured in Australia and distributed in this country by *RNC Enterprises*. It has six braille keys which do 6 or 8 dot braille, plus seven function keys, including an overstrike/rub-out facility. The brailler is mains/battery operated and it can be linked to computers, printers and modems. The standard model, £1,360, has 25k memory. The advanced model, £1,650, has 128k memory. A qwerty keyboard can be plugged into it enabling text keyed in to be converted into Grade II

F

braille. Interfaced with an appropriate computer and printer, it can be used to convert text into Grade II braille or braille into text.

18.2.3 Braille publishers

The biggest braille publishers are the **National Library for the Blind**, **RNIB**, the **Scottish Braille Press**, and the **Torch Trust for the Blind** which publishes evangelical Christian literature. All now have computer systems to do some of the work. Between 500 and 800 titles are published in braille each year.

The **National Library for the Blind** is the main source of braille books in this country. A large proportion of the titles it publishes, which include reference works such as the **Oxford Children's Encyclopedia**, are available for sale as well as for loan. A separate list of these can be obtained from the Library. Enquiries and requests for books can be dealt with by telephone or by post in braille or print.

RNIB publishes braille books on a wide variety of subjects from cookery to computers, plus examination papers and government leaflets such as DSS benefits leaflets. Complete catalogues are available on request. Details of new publications appear in **Spotlight** ❶❷❸ (fiction and general interest titles) and in **High Browse** ❶❷❸ (professional and academic titles), two monthly journals available free from RNIB. Over 30 other magazines are published in braille by RNIB, including **Radio Times** (Radios 1, 2 and 4), **3 FM** (Radio 3 and Classic FM), and **TV Times**, which list all national radio and television programmes, 29p each. BBC Worldwide schedules appear in the monthly magazine **London Calling**. Other periodicals range from news and current affairs, health and beauty, shopping information and a teenagers' weekly, to specialist journals for physiotherapists, lawyers and piano tuners.

The **Scottish Braille Press** publishes a popular novel each month in its **Thistle** paperback series. Its growing range of other publications includes books of knitting patterns and cookery recipes, which are very much in demand. It also produces six braille periodicals, including two weeklies, and prints and distributes another two dozen magazines on behalf of various organisations concerned with the welfare of blind people. It obtains sponsorship to produce braille versions of publications such as **Boots' Christmas catalogue** and Scottish Office publications.

The **In Touch Handbook** and **In Touch Care Guides** are published in braille by **In Touch Publishing**, an imprint of **Gwasg Pia**. Pia also publishes the annual **Budget Briefing**, and other occasional titles as sponsorship permits, often in association with other publishers and broadcasters.

Other braille publishers can be contacted through the *United Kingdom Association of Braille Producers, Secretary, Marie Brown, c/o RNIB, Peterborough*. The Association was formed in 1991 to promote braille and to provide information and advice for anyone involved or wishing to become involved in the production of braille.

18.2.4 Braille libraries

The **National Library for the Blind** holds over 400,000 braille volumes which can be borrowed free by all blind readers. Catalogues are available in braille and through the In Touch Gateway. Individual book lists can be compiled on request. Details of all new braille publications added to stock are included in the free **NLB Bulletin** 🅟🅛🅑 which comes out six times a year. **Hands On** 🅟🅑, the Library's free newsletter, is published twice a year.

The **RNIB Braille Library** is primarily intended to provide study material for blind students at universities or other places of further education and to meet the need of professional workers, but the books can be borrowed by any other blind person. The Library contains over 70,000 braille volumes and includes textbooks and other material in common use as well as a variety of books of academic interest. Information on the contents is held on computer database which can be consulted via *RNIB Customer Services*.

Some **local voluntary associations** keep small stocks of braille books, available on loan, which might be particularly helpful to beginners. The **Torch Trust for the Blind** has a lending library of evangelical literature in braille. Details of the **ClearVision** collection of young children's books are given in 11.5.4.

RNIB Customer Services can provide information on books, magazines and other material available in braille from RNIB and from other braille producers in this country and overseas. RNIB can also arrange the loan of books from overseas sources.

18.3 Moon

This touch-reading system was devised in 1845 by Dr. William Moon, who was himself blind. The embossed script, named after its inventor, is based on a simplified form of the Latin alphabet. It is therefore much simpler to learn than braille with its code of dots, and is generally considered easier to read for people with less sensitive fingertips. It has also been used in a number of special schools as a way of teaching reading to young blind children for whom braille is not an option. Moon has never been universally adopted, and is now little known outside a small minority of blind people in the United Kingdom. It is far bulkier than braille, and was until recently slower to produce, so much less literature is available than in braille.

Moon is produced by RNIB, which makes no charge to blind people for Moon books and other publications. Despite the cost in relation to the number of readers – it is estimated that there are about 700 active Moon readers – RNIB is committed to continue with the production of Moon. Their Needs Survey identified a group of 200,000 people with a severe visual disability who are unable to read any kind of print satisfactorily, and of whom only 10,000 use braille. This has convinced RNIB that there are many more potential Moon users.

About a dozen books are published in Moon each year, and 12 magazines. Titles include **Moon Weekender**, which is taken from the weekend press and includes a weekly summary of the news and articles on a variety of subjects, **Diane**, a women's magazine, and **Channels of Blessing**, a religious publication. **Moon Magazine** and **The Light of the Moon**, which both reproduce articles from national newspapers and magazines, are published monthly. Also available are weekly football and cricket fixtures and results in their appropriate seasons, the quarterly magazine **Come Gardening** (see 21.6.2), and the *In Touch* Care Guide **101 Practical hints for**

Using a Moon writing frame

living with poor sight. Enquiries about Moon are dealt with by *RNIB Customer Services*.

The **National Library for the Blind** keeps copies of all Moon publications, available on free loan to blind people. Their catalogue 🅟 🅜 lists over three thousand Moon titles. The bulk of these were published before Moon was produced by computer. This means that people who have learned Moon recently have to adjust to the old method of printing with the lines of text running alternately from left to right and right to left instead of all from left to right.

18.3.1 Learning Moon

Many older people have found it quite easy to learn Moon. Moon comes in two grades: Grade One is mainly uncontracted, that is, without abbreviations or short forms, and a selection of short stories, knitting patterns, devotional literature and some full-length novels are available. Grade Two Moon has 45 contractions which are not difficult to learn and are often a matter of common sense. A much wider range of books and magazines is available in Grade Two Moon. Even if people do not want to read books in Moon, a knowledge of the alphabet will enable them to use Moon labels (see chapter 17) and lists of telephone numbers.

Two self-teaching courses, **Journey Round the Moon** introducing the student to Grade One, and **Moon Journey: Phase 2** going on to Grade Two, are available for £2.00 each from *RNIB Customer Services* who will supply further details on request.

Moon Magazine carries advertisements from people seeking a pen-friend with whom they can correspond in Moon. **Mooncats**, a teaching pack for use with young children, has been developed at the University of Birmingham School of Education. It consists of a graded reading scheme, supporting cassettes and a teaching manual, and should be available later in 1995. Enquiries to *RNIB Customer Services*.

18.3.2 Writing equipment

The **Moon handframe** is portable enough to be carried in a handbag. It has rows of squares, 14 across and 8 down, in each of which a Moon character can be written with the stylus provided. The stylus is like a ballpoint pen without ink. The writing material is plastic embossing film on which the stylus forms a raised mark instead of an impression. The kit including a supply of the film is £3.00 from RNIB.

Prior to the appearance of the handframe in 1992, the only means of writing Moon by hand was with **Moonwriter**, a machine about the size of a portable typewriter. Characters are traced onto a special template with a style, which is operated by a finger inserted into a ring attached to the style. As each character is formed, a key is pressed to emboss it onto brailon (plastic) paper. Moonwriter did not prove as popular as had been hoped when it was launched in 1986. Though some people liked it, others found it heavy and slow to use. RNIB is selling remaining stocks of Moonwriter at £50.

18.4 Electronic reading equipment

18.4.1 Desk-top scanners

Self-contained **OCR** (optical character recognition) systems convert print or typescript into synthetic speech. Scanners can be found in some public libraries and resource centres (listed in 34) where they can be examined and used by the public. The three main systems currently available are listed below. All have a headphone jack so that documents can be read privately and without disturbing others, all can be linked to a cassette recorder, all have a memory and can be interfaced with another computer enabling text to be produced in large print or braille. The capacity of the memory varies from one model to another. Of the different synthetic speech systems used, DECtalk is generally considered to be the easiest to follow. Other details from the suppliers.

The Reading Edge with DECtalk speech, £4,495 from *Sight and Sound Technology*

An Open Book, £2,970 from *Dolphin Systems*, £3,995 with DECtalk from *Sensory Systems*

Robotron Text Reader TR320, £2,350, **Robotron Rainbow** with DECtalk speech, £2,936, both from *Techno-Vision Systems*.

Points to bear in mind when choosing an OCR system are included in assessments of current models carried out from time to time by *RNIB Employment Development and Technology Unit*. The results of these assessments and regularly updated **factsheets** ❶❸❼ on electronic reading aids are available from the Unit. OCR systems as an add-on to a personal computer are dealt with in chapter 20.

18.4.2 Optacon

This portable device consists of a small camera used to scan the line of print with one hand and a main unit housing an enlarged vibrating display of the images read by the camera. This is felt with the forefinger of the other hand. Various lens modules can be fitted to the Optacon to enable the user to read fine print, video display terminals and electronic calculator displays. Optacon can be connected directly to a personal computer. The Optacon demands a very sensitive touch. Learning to read with an Optacon requires a period of training followed by intensive practice. **Optacon training programmes** are available for work or study purposes through RNIB's Vocational College, and a number of schools for blind children give Optacon training to some of their pupils. The Optacon is made in California and can be obtained for £3,195 from *Sensory Systems*. Blind people who need an Optacon in their jobs may be able to obtain one on loan through **The Employment Service** (see 10.4.1).

18.4.3 Electronic dictionary/thesaurus

The American-made Franklin **Language Master** is available with synthetic speech in a special version for blind people. This battery-operated portable device resembles a calculator but instead of number keys it has a qwerty keyboard. It is about 14cm square and has a large screen with 6mm display characters. It contains the American Merriam-Webster dictionary and thesaurus. Other facilities include spelling correction and a number of word games. The Language Master Special Edition can be obtained from *Techno-Vision Systems Ltd* for £255 (£225 cash with order).

18.4.4 Electronic newspapers

Given a television aerial and an IBM compatible PC with speech synthesiser, braille display or large print software, a visually impaired person can have access to **The Guardian** newspaper at the same time as the print version would be delivered. The computer has to be fitted with a decoder card so that it can receive the text of the paper as it is delivered electronically during the night, and also with newspaper reading software allowing the user to find and read articles with a series of simple menus. Advertisements, Stock Exchange and unit trust prices and weather forecasts are not included in the text, but the system gives full access to teletext pages, which carry this information, and to television sound. To obtain the decoder card and associated software, contact *RNIB Customer Services*. The cost including the first year's subscription to the service is £655. The annual subscription for subsequent years is £160. Full details are given in **The RNIB Electronic Newspaper – your questions answered ⬤⬤⬤** a free leaflet available from RNIB.

The service is to be expanded to provide access to many other publications supplying news and information. A number of similar services are operating in other European countries. RNIB is among those involved in the further development of electronic newspapers and the delivery of a range of reading material in electronic form, through a joint Europe-wide research project supported by the EC 'TIDE' programme. Further information from *Mark Prouse, Technical Research, RNIB*.

18.4.5 Bulletin boards and the Internet

The rapid growth of worldwide computer to computer communications (see 20.11) is likely to have two implications for visually impaired readers. First, it will become easier and cheaper for ordinary people, including visually impaired computer users, to access **online information**. Second, it will become more worthwhile to do so. The current obsession with the technology of the new media will give way to concern for their content. More publishers and organisations will publish online as well as in traditional media. This is good news as online publications are innately accessible to visually impaired computer users (subject to the normal caution about graphic screen displays – see 20.8): they can be read using the usual screen access devices, or downloaded and then brailled or large printed. This is equally true of all online information, not simply that produced on visual impairment.

There are however a growing number of specialist services: examples are the **Ability** bulletin board associated with the British Computer Society's Disability Group – details from *Ken Davies* ✆ 01 594 826096 or send a stamped addressed envelope to *19 Latimer Road, Cinderford, Gloucestershire GL14 2PS*; the **Disabilities Access** Internet site which offers news and information for people with disabilities from charities such as RADAR, Scope, Skill and Dial UK – at http://www.pavilion.co.uk/CommonRoom/D-Access; and the **BBC In Touch Gateway**, modem line ✆ 01 222 222099, being launched by In Touch Publishing.

The In Touch Gateway, based around the online In Touch Handbook, offers a comprehensive service of news, information and comment on visual impairment from the leading blind welfare publishers. For full details see the Directory at the front of this Handbook.

18.5 Further reading

Blind Faith, a story based on the life of Dr. William Moon by Edna Stroud. £5.00 plus £1.00 postage and packing from the publishers, *William Sessions Ltd., The Ebor Press, York YO3 9HS*. Available in Moon from *RNIB* or on loan from the *National Library for the Blind*, and on tape from *RNIB Talking Book Service*.

Triumph over Darkness, the life and work of Louis Braille by Lennard Bickel. £7.95 from *Ulverscroft* or on loan from the *National Library* **B** , *RNIB Talking Book Service* **T** or *Calibre* **T** .

19 Pleasures of listening

This chapter is about the spoken word, the main source of information and entertainment for most visually impaired people, whether on radio or television or recorded on tape.

A survey carried out in 1993 of people with little or no sight showed that in the majority of cases, tape was the preferred medium for reading material. The survey was commissioned by NALSVI (National Association of Local Societies for the Visually Impaired). Of the 2,212 people who responded to the questionnaire, over half of them aged over 70, 43% preferred standard cassettes and 26% long playing cassettes such as those used by RNIB Talking Book Service.

Besides the growing number of books available from specialist tape libraries for the blind both in this country and abroad, many more spoken-word cassettes are being produced commercially and can be found on the shelves of public libraries. There is a wide range of national and local talking newspapers and magazines.

There is as yet no central register of all spoken word recordings, but public libraries should hold catalogues of commercially produced audio books, and RNIB Customer Services can provide some information about books and other material on tape, both from RNIB and from other specialist sources in this country and overseas.

19.1 Specialist libraries for blind people

In this country, the main source for the ordinary leisure reader is the **RNIB Talking Book Service**, holding over 10,000 titles. Its American counterpart, the **Library of Congress National Library Service for the Blind and Physically Handicapped**, which receives state funding, has over 72,000 of its own titles.

Unfortunately it is impossible to take advantage of the whole range of recorded books offered by British and overseas specialist libraries with just an ordinary commercial cassette player. RNIB Talking Book Service and the US Library of Congress are bound by the terms of their agreements with publishers to reproduce their books in limited editions and in non-commercially available form. British and American talking books are therefore recorded on special format cassettes that can be played back only on players provided by the respective libraries, but players and tapes are not interchangeable. RNIB records its talking books on **multi-track** Clarke & Smith cassettes which run about 12 hours. Most books are complete on the one cassette. American talking books resemble standard two-track commercial cassettes, but are recorded on **four tracks** and at half the normal speed; one cassette holds up to six hours of recorded material. Britain is the only English-speaking country which still uses the **multi-track format** for its talking books. Talking book services in Canada, Australia, New Zealand and the Irish Republic use the Library of Congress format. Many libraries for the blind in other countries use standard compact cassettes. Any move towards international standardisation has to take into consideration the possibility of tape being

---

Key to media of publication   **P** clear print   **L** large print   **B** braille   **T** tape   **M** Moon   **D** disk

Where a full address is not given in the text, see 32 (Useful addresses)

superseded by alternative modern technology, but no decisions have yet been made as to what format should be adopted for talking books in the future.

19.1.1 RNIB Talking Book Service

This is the service most widely used by blind people in Britain, with a membership of around 65,000. The books are recorded by professional readers; most are fiction and include standard favourites as well as classics, but there are many non-fiction titles and a small selection of children's books. About 600 titles are added each year, a tiny fraction of the 27,000 books published annually in Britain. Membership is open to anyone in the British Isles who has defective reading vision (i.e. who cannot comfortably read N12 or worse with spectacles) or who is registered blind. **Application forms** plus further details in large print, braille and on standard cassette can be obtained from the Talking Book Service. The **annual subscription**, currently £49, may be paid by the local authority social services department or by the local voluntary society for the blind. In Northern Ireland and a small but growing number of authorities in Great Britain the subscription is paid out of public library funds.

NEW Now that RNIB Talking Book Services issues invoices on 1st January, 1st April, 1st July and 1st October, regardless of enrolment date (and with the option of paying quarterly) new applicants are in effect offered a **free trial period** of up to three months. No charge is made if talking book players are returned before first subscriptions are due from members or from agencies paying on their behalf.

NEW In a two-year research project set up in January 1995, **corporate membership** of RNIB Talking Book Service has been taken up by **Gloucester County public libraries** to replace the payment of individual subscriptions by social services. This is the first public library service to do so. It means that visually impaired people in Gloucestershire can now borrow RNIB talking books through the local public library free postal cassette service. The new VIP unit which operates the service holds 2,500 of the most popular talking book titles as well as its own collection of 1,000 titles on standard cassette. Further details from *Jill Harvey, Assistant County Librarian (Specialist Services), Quayside House, Shire Hall, Gloucester GL1 2HY* ℘ 01452 425035.

Talking book players are provided on loan to members and are not available for purchase. They are specially designed for ease of use by totally blind people. The most recent model is significantly lighter than its predecessors, with improved controls, particularly those for selecting the track, and a device to help avoid tape spillage. Earlier models are still being issued to about half of new subscribers, but anyone with a particular need for one of the new models should contact the Talking Book Service.

For people who want to listen to talking books without disturbing others, RNIB supplies **headphones** and **stethophones** (from about £8 to £13, depending on the model) and **headphone plug adaptors** so that the headphones issued free by the British Wireless for the Blind Fund (see 19.8.1) can be used on a talking book machine. People confined to bed could use a **compact pillow speaker**, £2.99 mail order from *Tandy* (quote cat. no. 33-206) or from Tandy shops. Adaptations are provided free by the Talking Book Service for people who have additional handicaps, such as arthritic hands or hearing difficulties (see 23.2 and 26.3.3). For single additional payments, **Variable-speed** (£6.50) and a **rechargeable battery pack** (£25) are available as optional extras on the latest talking book players.

Servicing talking book players

Members of the Talking Book Service are normally put in touch with one of the 3,500 local volunteers who make no charge for servicing players which are not functioning properly, though if the fault is serious the player may be returned to the Talking Book Service for repair or replacement. In most cases, malfunctioning is the result of an accumulation of oxide on the playback head. This causes a drop in volume and sometimes makes the player stop. Dealing with this is a simple job, and if necessary the servicing volunteer should be willing to demonstrate how it is done. Disconnect the player from the mains. Remove the cassette and stand the player on its speaker by lifting it by the carrying handle at the back. A rubber wheel can be felt to the right of the slot where the cassette fits. The playback head is the smooth piece of metal to the left of the rubber wheel, with brass guides top and bottom. This is the area to be cleaned, with a rag dipped in methylated spirits, or a cotton bud.

19.1.2 RNIB Cassette Library

This collection of over 16,000 non-fiction titles covers a wide range of mainly academic subjects. The books are read by volunteers, often specialists in the subjects concerned. Recordings are mostly on standard C90 cassettes, but about 2,000 are recorded in the 4-track US Library of Congress format. The latest additions, with an X prefix in the catalogue, are available in standard or 4-track format. Customers may ask for new books to be recorded for addition to the Library, but must supply a copy of the book to be read. The service is open to anyone wanting access to print material for study or information purposes and is no longer restricted to students and teachers. Enquiries to *RNIB Customer Services*.

Material required urgently for work, study or leisure purposes can be taped by **RNIB Express Reading Service**. At least an hour's recording per day is undertaken for any individual until the reading is completed. Contact should be made by letter or telephone before first use of the service. Material is recorded on compact cassette, at standard or half speed, on two or four tracks, and can be tone-indexed. This is a system whereby bleeps inaudible at normal playback speed are recorded onto the tape to mark sections or chapters. The bleeps are audible only during spooling on a cassette machine with cue and review (see 19.7). Scotland is served by the **RNIB Recording Centre** based at the Resource Centre in Glasgow. The use of these services is free to individuals.

19.1.3 Calibre

This lending library of books recorded on standard cassettes offers a choice of about 4,000 titles, among them several hundred children's titles. The organisers record new fiction, and base their selections on best-seller lists as well as much-loved classics. The catalogue is available on cassette and in print. The library tries as far as possible to ensure that all members receive tapes within a day or two of returning their books.

318

Although the books are recorded in their own homes by volunteer readers (professional actors or actresses who give their services free) the quality of recording is very good. Membership of Calibre is free to individuals who can provide a photocopy of a certificate of registration as blind or partially sighted or a doctor's certificate stating inability to read printed books. Group membership at £35 a year is offered to schools, hospitals and other institutions, and allows four books to be borrowed at a time. Calibre also supply public libraries, but only for housebound delivery services.

19.1.4 Playback Service for the Blind

This comprehensive tape service based at the *Resource Centre for the Blind* in Glasgow (see 34) has accumulated a lending library of over 800 titles on cassette. They range from miscellaneous fiction and non-fiction books to cookery, specialist information for the visually impaired, DSS leaflets, and instructions for domestic equipment. A catalogue is available free **P** **T**.

19.1.5 Prince Michael of Kent Tape Library for the Blind

Formerly known as the Free Tape Recorded Library for the Blind, this library holds a collection of programmes made by the late Ron Hall, who was totally blind, on a diversity of subjects such as holiday travels and interviews with personalities. Additions to this collection are being recorded by Bill Cox, another visually impaired man. The library also contains recordings made in its own studio of popular novels and non-fiction. Membership of the library is free, but donations are welcome. Details from *Mrs. M. Bennett, Prince Michael of Kent Tape Library for the Blind, 105 Salusbury Road, London NW6 6RH* ✆ 0171 624 8844.

19.1.6 Feminist Audio Books (FAB)

A tape library of feminist, lesbian and women-orientated books not readily available from other libraries. The catalogue is available on cassette. Annual subscriptions start at £3.00 for unwaged members. Further details from *FAB, 52-54 Featherstone Street, London EC1Y 8RT* ✆ 0171 251 2908.

19.1.7 Other languages

A collection of about 1,500 **Welsh books** recorded on standard cassette is available on loan free of charge to all registered visually impaired people. Enquiries to *Rhian Evans, 1 Penlan, Carmarthen, Dyfed SA31 1DN* ✆ 01267 238225. Rhian Evans also issues a monthly cassette magazine of abstracts from Welsh language periodicals.

The Talking Library for Indian Blind has about 100 **Gujerati** and 60 **Hindi/Urdu** titles recorded on standard cassette. Annual membership is £5.00. Enquiries to *Narendra Mehta, 21 Hungerford Road, London N7 9LB* ✆ 0171 609 3590.

RNIB's Talking Book Service has some titles in Welsh, three in Gaelic and growing collections in Hindi, Urdu, Punjabi, Gujerati and Bengali. Other foreign language titles can be borrowed on behalf of readers through international library loan. Enquiries to *RNIB Customer Services.*

F

19.1.8 American libraries

The **Library of Congress National Library Service for the Blind and Physically Handicapped** has over 72,000 of its own titles, of which 11,000 are children's books, plus copies of several thousand more titles produced by other specialist libraries both inside and outside the United States. British readers can arrange through RNIB Customer Services to borrow books from the National Library Service. They will need an appropriate playback machine (see 19.7.1).

Blind people in this country can also borrow books from **Recording for the Blind**, a lending library of nearly 80,000 largely non-fiction titles intended primarily for blind and learning disabled students and others who cannot read standard print. Like its British counterpart, the recording is done by volunteers, and the service is available to any blind person, but the cassettes are all made in the Library of Congress format, so again a special playback machine would be needed. Further information and application forms for membership can be obtained direct from *Recording for the Blind, 20 Roszel Road, Princeton, New Jersey 08540, USA* ✆ 00 1 609 452 0606 or from *RNIB Customer Services*. The **Jewish Guild for the Blind**, despite its title, is not a sectarian organisation, and its tape library reflects current American tastes. The 1,600 titles are recorded on standard cassette, and can be borrowed by British readers. Full details from *Bruce Massis, Jewish Guild for the Blind, 15 West 65th Street, New York NY 10023* ✆ 00 1 212 769 6331.

19.2 Recorded books from commercial sources

An increasing number of audio books are on sale at ordinary book shops and other commercial outlets, but, because full length books are too expensive (around £20 to £30) to be popular with the general public, most titles are abridged versions of the original book. Over 12,000 titles including novels, biographies, educational subjects, and other non-fiction such as self-help (e.g. giving up smoking and stress relief) will be listed in the new combined Gramophone/Music Master **Spoken Word Catalogue** (June 1995. £12.95) from *R.E.D. Publishing Ltd., Paulton House, 8 Shepherdess Walk, London N1 7LB* ✆ 0171 490 0049. It will also be available on CD ROM (updated every two months) from the publisher.

19.2.1 Publishers of unabridged audio books

Unabridged audio books are mainly distributed through public libraries, but can be obtained direct from the publishers who will supply catalogues on request.

Assembled Stories. *60 Orchard Road, Brentford, Middlesex TW8 0QU* ✆ 0181 568 1019. About 24 titles, general fiction.

Chivers. About 1,000 titles in stock, including popular fiction, world classics and 150 children's titles.

Complete Listener. *Field End Cottage Studios, 8 Apple Street, Oxenhope, Keighley, W. Yorks. BD22 9LT* ✆ 01535 645983. About 100 titles, mainly classic fiction.

Cover to Cover Cassettes Ltd. *PO Box 112, Marlborough, Wiltshire SN8 3UG* ✆ 01264 337725. Specialise in 19th century classics. About 40 titles in stock plus about 45 children's titles.

Isis. General fiction and non-fiction including travel, history and biography. Over 800 titles.

Magna Story Sound. Over 150 titles, popular fiction and non-fiction.

Ulverscroft. Over 900 titles in stock, mainly popular fiction and non-fiction.

TNEL. (see 19.4.1). Some collections of short stories on C90 cassettes, including 12 previously unpublished children's stories.

The BBC Radio Collection. Catalogues from *BBC Enterprises, PO Box 190, Peterborough PE2 6UW* ✆ 0181 576 2236. Over 400 titles including some unabridged short stories as well as the edited readings of full length books broadcast on BBC Radio. On sale at BBC and other bookshops. See also 19.2.3.

19.2.2 Lending libraries

Public libraries

Audio books stocked by **public libraries** are largely commercially produced, but some libraries have a collection of spoken word cassettes specifically for blind readers. These may be augmented by specially recorded material, perhaps of local interest. Other libraries may restrict the loan of audio books to people who cannot read ordinary print, but the more usual practice is to exempt them from any borrowing charge. Audio books are likely to be included in domiciliary and mobile services, and a number of libraries run a **free postal cassette service** for visually impaired people in their area (see also 19.1.1). Catalogues of audio books may be provided, sometimes on cassette as well as in print. There are facilities, including headphones, for listening to cassettes in some libraries, and cassette machines, usually specialist models such as the Easiplay (see 19.7.1), may be available for free loan to visually impaired people who could not afford them and could not use cheaper ordinary models.

The **Poetry Library** at the South Bank Centre has a collection of twentieth century poetry on cassette. Membership and postal loan is free of charge to blind people. Enquiries to *Mary Enright, Poetry Librarian, The Poetry Library, Level 5, Red Side, Royal Festival Hall, London SE1 8XX* ✆ 0171 921 0943/0940.

Commercial postal lending libraries

Titles from a range of publishers are stocked and are also available for purchase from:

Storyline. *20 Carrbrook Crescent, Stalybridge, Cheshire SK15 3LP* ✆ 01457 834406. Annual subscription £9, weekly charge per cassette 80p. Mainly unabridged titles, including general fiction and non-fiction, poetry and plays, autobiography and some children's titles.

The Talking Book Club. *11/12 Lettice Street, London SW6 4EH* ✆ 0171 731 6262. Annual subscription £7.50; rental from £1.25 for two or three weeks, depending on number of cassettes. Over 2,000 mainly unabridged titles. General fiction, classics, thrillers, non-fiction, children's titles.

Travellers' Tales. *Great Weddington, Ash, Canterbury, Kent CT3 2AR* ✆ 01304 812531. Annual subscription £20; from £6.40 for minimum hire of 4 tapes for first week, 7p per tape per day thereafter. Classics, the Bible, biographies, fiction including romances and thrillers, non-fiction, poetry, plays and children's titles. Over 2,500 unabridged titles.

Isis. Membership free to blind and partially sighted people. Isis rent their own unabridged titles for a period of 30 days at a charge which varies with the number of cassettes. For a four-cassette book this would be £6.25 inclusive, for an eight-cassette book, £10.45.

19.2.3 Mail order companies

Unabridged as well as abridged audio books are also supplied by:

Morley Audio Services. *Elmfield Road, Morley, Leeds LS27 0NN* ℘ 0113 253 8811. Catalogue on request.

The Talking Bookshop. *11 Wigmore Street, London W1H 9LB* ℘ 0171 495 8799. Catalogue on request.

Bags of Books. *1 South Street, Lewes, Sussex BN7 2BT* ℘ 01273 479320. Specialise in children's titles. Catalogue in return for 4 x 25p stamps.

In Touch Publishing. BBC Radio Collection titles supplied with braille or large print labels. **Opening Books ❶❷❸** catalogue on request.

19.3 Religious literature on tape

Bibles

Authorised Version. The Old Testament and the Gospels can be borrowed from *Calibre* and the complete Bible or the New Testament and Psalms can be borrowed from *RNIB Talking Book Service*. The Bible is also on sale from *Isis* at £169.36 complete or in sections. Genesis and Psalms & Proverbs are £7.99 each from *BBC Radio Collection* (see 19.2.1). The complete Bible read by American voices is available for £77.95 (budget edition with no special packaging £45.00, New Testament only £15.95) from *Metropolitan Tabernacle, Elephant & Castle, London SE1 6SD* ℘ 0171 735 7076.

Revised Standard Version. Old and New Testaments from *Torch Trust* and *RNIB Cassette Library*; New Testament from *Calibre*.

New English Bible. *RNIB Talking Book Service.*

Revised English Bible. New Testament, £39.95, *BBC Radio Collection.*

New International Version. New Testament on 15 cassettes, £3.95 each or £39.95 for the complete set from *Bible Society* (50% discount to registered visually impaired people).

Good News Bible. 5 cassettes of readings, £5.95 each, from *Bible Society.*

New King James Version. New Testament and portions of the Old Testament free in English and 40 other languages from *Bible Alliance Inc., PO Box 621, Bradenton, Florida 34206, USA* ℘ 00 1 813 748 3031. Proof of visual impairment required.

Sources of free devotional material

Torch Trust for the Blind. The Trust has a free lending library service of Christian literature on cassettes, including devotional, fiction, missionary and study books, and several magazines.

Anglican Readings. *Graham Winterbourne, Flat 8, Uffculme Court, Ashley Road, Uffculme, Devon EX15 3AY* ℘ 01884 840285.

St. Cecilia's Guild for the Blind. *Sister Frances Hayes, St. Roses Convent, Orange Hill Road, Burnt Oak, Edgware, Middlesex HA8 0ST* ℘ 0181 906 0408.

The Society of St Vincent de Paul. *743 Marfleet Lane, Hull HU9 4TJ* ℘ 01482 792582.

Taped Ministry. *William J. Bell, Finlas, 20 Myrtle Avenue, Lenzie, Dunbartonshire G66 4HS* ℘ 0141 776 2111.

Anchor Recordings Ltd. *72 The Street, Kennington, Ashford, Kent TN24 9HS* ℘ 01233 620958 (free loan to registered blind people).

19.4 Talking newspapers

In most parts of the country there are groups of volunteers who produce **digests of the local press** on standard cassette and distribute them free to local blind, partially sighted and severely handicapped people. The cassettes generally appear once a week. Some local talking newspapers also provide magazines and personal tape services. The talking newspaper movement grew rapidly from its beginnings in the early 1970s, and there are now about 500 established projects. The co-ordinating body is **TNAUK (Talking Newspaper Association of the UK)**, a registered charity whose aim is to make a taped newspaper available to every visually impaired person in the country. Information on existing groups and help with starting new ones can be obtained from TNAUK in return for a stamped, addressed envelope. Local talking newspapers and magazines are listed in the **Guide to Tape Services for the Handicapped** (4th edition, 1993, £5 from TNAUK) together with national talking newspapers and magazines, and some specialist journals, tape libraries and tape reading services.

19.4.1 National press

A National Newspaper and Magazine Service is provided by TNAUK. They will consider taping any periodical, given a minimum of 6 subscribers – or less, if financial support is obtained from the publishers. Extracts are already provided on standard cassette of over 180 publications including all the Sunday newspapers, weekly digests of most of the dailies and numerous magazines, plus **Radio Times, TV Times** and the complete text of **Which?** The individual membership fee of £15 per year gives a choice of any number of titles. TNAUK provides **Insight tapes**, 60 minute cassettes giving details of the magazines it tapes, including subject matter and cover price of the print originals. Further information and order forms can be obtained from TNAUK. The scheme operates from studios in Heathfield and Inverness, using selected volunteers for reading and a small paid permanent staff.

Many public libraries around the country are now stocking a range of the taped periodicals produced by TNAUK. The cassettes are copied and distributed by **TNEL (Talking Newspaper Enterprises Ltd)**, a subsidiary set up to help fund TNAUK.

An alternative selection from the **Observer** is available for an annual subscription of £3.50 from the *Cultural Society of the Disabled Tape Service for the Visually Handicapped, 4 The Square, Ugborough, Ivybridge, Devon PL21 0NT* ✆ *01752 892532.* Taped digests from a variety of national journals are distributed free to blind people by **Playback Service for the Blind** (who also do a complete version of **Which?**) and by the **Tape Recording Service for the Blind**, *24 Catherine Street, Dumfries DG1 1HZ* ✆ *01387 253927.*

A tape version of **The Voice**, the weekly newspaper which covers items of particular interest to the **Afro-Caribbean** community, is available free from *RNIB Ethnic Minorities Department.*

19.4.2 Daily talking newspaper

AIRS News, the only daily talking newspaper in the country, includes world, European and national news. The service is offered nationwide at an annual subscription of £50 by **AIRS** (Access to Information and Reading Services), *The Central Library, Prince Consort Road, Gateshead NE8 4LN* ✆ *0191 477 3478.*

19.4.3 Asian language talking newspapers

The fortnightly **Bhol Chal** (Talking To) covers local, national and international news, with original articles as well as material taken from the printed press. The main language used is Urdu, but articles in Punjabi and Gujerati are also included. Bhol Chal is distributed free by the *Cathedral Centre (Susan Crow), Captain Street, Bradford BD1 4AH* ✆ *01274 308707.*

NEW Fortnightly Gujerati and Punjabi talking newspapers are produced by the *Royal Leicestershire Society for the Blind.* Besides local news they contain national and international news, articles on subjects such as health, and Indian folk stories and poetry. Annual subscription is £5.00 each; free to Leicestershire residents.

NEW Three taped periodicals are available in Urdu, Punjabi, Bengali and Gujerati for an annual subscription of £40 (free to residents in the Birmingham area) from *Birmingham Royal Institution for the Blind.* **Talking Eyes** monthly includes news, reviews, health, community and other general information, plus poetry and short stories; the six-monthly **Talking Pamphlet** gives the latest information on services for visually impaired people; **Talking Issues** appears three times a year and addresses the kind of problems visually impaired people experience in their dealings with authorities such as housing departments. Contact *Birmingham Royal Institution for the Blind Vision Services, Cowley Centre, 23 Gravelly Hill, North Erdington B23 6BT* ✆ *0121 373 1336.*

NEW **Kiran** weekly (Gujerati) and **Roshni** monthly (Hindi) both contain articles from the national and international press, information on health, welfare and social security, short stories, play readings and listeners' letters. The tapes are free to visually impaired people from *Brent Asian Visually Handicapped Group, 8*

Cameron House, 80 Pound Lane, London NW10 2HT ✆ 0181 451 4354 or contact
Jhatish Malde ✆ 0181 907 1304 *(evenings).*

19.4.4 Special interest and other journals

Cassettes circulated by the **Society of Blind Lawyers** include **Law Society
Autumn Refresher Lectures** and the fortnightly **Lawyers' Tapes** with
material, selected by a solicitor, covering case reports and articles from legal
periodicals and the legal press. Both are available to non-members as well as
members. Details from *John Wall, 20 Cleveland Road, Worcester Park, Surrey KT4
7JH* ✆ 0181 330 1290.

A cassette version of **Social Work Today** is available from *RNIB*.

The **British Computer Association of the Blind** fortnightly cassette contains a
selection of articles from leading British data processing papers and journals,
including those of the British Computer Society.

A cassette version of the quarterly braille magazine **Theological Times**, with
articles from well-known clerical publications, is available from *RNIB*.

Magazines specialising in subjects such as **personal computers, audio and
hi-fi, amateur radio** and various kinds of **music**, are recorded by *Monument
Tape Services,* annual subscription £6.00 per publication.

For a cassette version of **What's Brewing**, the monthly journal of the Campaign
for Real Ale, contact *CAMRA, 34 Alma Road, St. Albans, Hertfordshire AL1 3BW*
✆ 01727 867670.

Two weekly publications for lesbians and gay men provide coverage of
international and national news and events: **Capital Gay on Tape** from *CGOT,
c/o 66 Marchmont Street, London WC1N 1AB*, and **Pink Paper on Tape** from
72 Holloway Road, London N7 8JZ (from August 1st 1995) ✆ 0171 608 2677.

Members of **Disability Network**, annual subscription £5.00, can receive two
fortnightly tapes, **MerseyTape** (national news and current affairs) and
MerseyTape Extra (features, competitions, reviews of equipment of interest
to visually impaired people), and **MerseyTape Monthly** (short stories, poems,
recipes and features). MerseyTape incorporates **Disability Network News**
every quarter.

Talkback, a monthly tape magazine with articles of general interest to visually
impaired people, is distributed free by *Talkback Magazine Service, 163 Valley
Way, Stevenage, Herts. SG2 9DD* ✆ 01438 746700.

BT Soundings a monthly magazine with articles of general as well as of specific
interest to visually impaired people. 50p a copy from *RNIB Customer Services;*
also distributed through *TNAUK National Newspaper and Magazine Service* and
to St. Dunstaners.

Weekend Listener. General interest including news of events and exhibitions,
personality interviews, holidays and travel and articles by **Which?** magazine
reporters. £16.95 for 50 issues from *MT Audio Publications Ltd., MT Studios on
the Common, The Pantiles, Tunbridge Wells, Kent TN2 5TE* ✆ 01892 544796.

19.5 Tape correspondence clubs

The tape equivalent of pen-pals is available to any blind person who owns a cassette recorder. It may be possible to find suitable contacts through a tape correspondence club. The **Chatterbox Recording Club**, contact *Mr. R. Armstrong, Welland, Stafford Street, Telford, Shropshire TF2 9DT* ℘ 01952 616410, has special-interest groups such as classical music, jazz and a ladies' section. **Disability Network** also runs a penfriend club.

19.6 Tape reading services

For material not already available on tape from existing sources, there are a number of services besides RNIB (see 19.1.2) which offer audio transcription services nationwide. They are prepared to read anything from books, leaflets and magazine articles to recipes, knitting patterns and instruction leaflets. It is worth asking for a sample tape and checking how long the job will take.

19.6.1 Voluntary groups

With the help of volunteer readers, a free service for visually impaired people is offered by:

ADA Reading Service, *Mrs. Audrey Artus, 6 Dalewood Rise, Laverstock, Salisbury, Wiltshire SP1 1SF* ℘ 01722 326987.

Braille Bureau, *County Hall, West Bridgford, Nottingham NG2 7QP* ℘ 0115 982 3823 ext. 3157: also read technical and mathematical material (sighted customers charged 50p per cassette).

Cadwell Recording Services for the Blind: also undertake some work in four-track Library of Congress format. Charge for supplying blank cassette tape. Full details available free in print or on cassette.

Monument Tape Services: also offer a copying service to other organisations and will copy open reel to cassette.

Playback Service for the Blind: also read German and Spanish.

Some **Resource Centres** will record material on request for blind people in their area. It is also worth asking any local voluntary society for the blind or people involved in local talking newspapers. **Public libraries** may be willing to tape material for visually impaired readers. Those which have electronic scanning equipment (see 18.4) may be able to record the synthetic speech output onto cassette.

19.6.2 Professional services

Some services normally charge a fee. They are listed below together with the approximate charge to a commercial organisation for a basic reading of **10 A4 pages** of straightforward English text. Additional charges would be made for multiple copies and distribution of tapes. Charges may be different for other categories of customers, and may vary according to the type of material to be read and the style in which the reading is presented.

AIRS *Central Library, Prince Consort Road, Gateshead NE8 4LN* ✆ 0191 477 3478. £17.50 (direct to cassette) £36 (studio recording); professional readers. Copying and distribution undertaken.

Blind Spot (UK) Ltd. £80 (studio recording); professional readers. Scripting service. Copying and distribution undertaken.

Braudio Transcriptions *Michael Gray, 8 Morpeth Terrace, North Shields NE29 7AN* ✆0191 258 6324. £11 (direct to cassette); experienced reader. Copying and distribution undertaken.

Disability Resource Team. £20 (tone indexed studio recording); professional readers. Urdu, Hindi, Gujerati, Turkish, Bengali, Chinese and some European languages, technical material. Copying and distribution undertaken.

Greater London Association of Disabled People (GLAD) *Ms B Zipser, 336 Brixton Road, London SW9 7AA* ✆ 0171 274 0107. £12 (direct to cassette); experienced readers. Copying and distribution (limited).

Huddersfield Library *Mrs Eileen Cartmell, Princess Alexandra Walk, Huddersfield HD1 2SU* ✆ 01484 424959. £5.00 (direct to cassette) plus postage and packing; volunteer readers. Short documents only. Copying and distribution undertaken.

Lilac Recording and Copying Service *Bill Cox, Lilac Cottage, Moorhouses, New Bolingbroke, nr. Boston, Lincs. PE22 7JL* ✆ 01526 342918. £15 (studio recording); experienced reader. Copying and distribution undertaken.

Master Transcriptions. £200 (studio recording, DAT technology); professional readers. Welsh, most European languages, Chinese; copying, distribution and marketing undertaken.

NOSITE *Wallsend People's Centre, Frank Street, Wallsend, Tyne & Wear NE28 6RN* ✆ 0191 263 0005. £85 (direct to cassette); experienced reader. Copying and distribution undertaken.

Tactile Audio Braille Services Ltd. (TABS) *YPI Buildings, 83-93 George Street, Hull HU1 3EN* ✆ 01482 585383. £5.00 (direct to cassette); experienced reader. From £25 (studio recording); professional readers. Copying and distribution undertaken.

TNEL. £50 (studio recording); professional readers. French, German, copying and distribution undertaken. Profits from work done for commercial customers are remitted to TNAUK (see 19.4).

Waltham Forest Transcription Service *Michael Flood, Media Resources Co-ordinator, Town Hall, Forest Road, Walthamstow, London E17 4JF* ✆ 0181 527 5544 ext. 4854. £30 (direct to cassette); professional readers. Urdu, Hindi, Punjabi, Bengali, Gujerati, Chinese, Greek, Turkish and other languages. Copying and distribution undertaken.

19.7 Recording and playback equipment

There is no reason why a blind person should not just seek the advice of a local specialist radio, television or hi-fi shop when buying a cassette machine. Angus

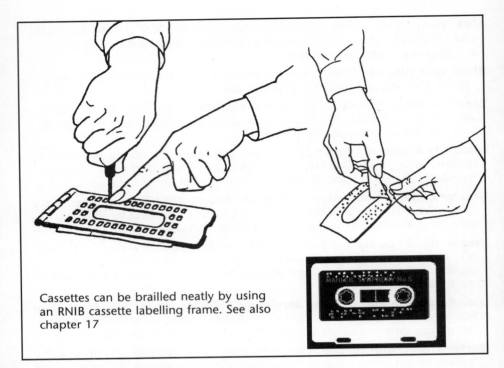

Cassettes can be brailled neatly by using an RNIB cassette labelling frame. See also chapter 17

F

McKenzie MBE, who is himself totally blind and an expert in the field of sound reproduction, suggests that, besides checking the **quality of the sound** reproduction, certain other points should be taken into account, particularly when choosing a machine for an elderly blind person:

- **Controls** should be easy to operate and positioned in such a way that they can be clearly identified by touch, or at least separated, to prevent the wrong one being used in error.

- The extent to which **volume** can be increased without distortion is worth noting, as older people often suffer from a hearing loss. For them, a **headphone socket** on the machine would be essential.

- There should be a **pause button** and **tone control**.

- If the machine is likely to be used for recording as well as listening purposes, the automatic limiting control should be effective enough to cope with sudden and unexpected variation in the sound being recorded.

- **Cue and review**, which means being able to hear the high-pitched chatter as the tape is spooled through, is a useful aid to locating particular passages without having to listen through the whole cassette. Gaps between items are easily spotted, as well as tone indexing bleeps (audible only during fast wind) such as used in the cassette **Radio Times**.

- **Autostop** on playback saves unnecessary wear on the machine if the listener fails to switch off at the end of a cassette.

Autostop on wind is less important. Some machines take longer than others to rewind cassettes. Fast winding is heavy on batteries and should be avoided unless the machine is run off the mains. Other features worth considering are the facility to play back at different speeds and voice activated recording.

19.7.1 Cassette machines from specialist sources

Easiplay, £49 from the manufacturers, *Clarke & Smith*, is a specially designed playback machine for standard cassettes. It resembles a toaster with a broad base. The bright yellow contrasting controls are designed to be clear and simple for an elderly blind person to use. Optional extras are a remote switch, £4.00 and a lightweight headset, £5.11.

RNIB stocks a **Philips** desk-top cassette recorder, £50.83 which plays standard 2-track cassettes. It is mains/battery powered and facilities include cue and review, variable speed, built-in microphone and socket for external microphone. Lightweight 'Walkman' style machines which will play **4-track** as well as standard cassettes are stocked by RNIB: the **Talkman III** player with variable speed, £49.80, and two player/recorders, the **Talkman IV**, £125, and the American Printing House **Handi-Cassette**, £122.57. Features include cue and review, tone indexing and variable speed facilities.

The 4-track **APH 3-5196** desk-top machine is £238 from *Hagger Electronics, Unit 22, Business Centre West, Avenue One, Letchworth, Herts. SG6 2HB* ✆ 01462 677331. It has voice and tone-indexing facilities and variable speed playback. Hagger can fit it with pitch adjustment for about £55, depending on the age and condition of the machine, to make listening easier when cassettes are played slower or faster than normal. The APH **Handi-Cassette** is among other cassette recorders stocked by Hagger. Their price is £156, but a quantity discount is available.

19.7.2 Cassettes

Some manufacturers distinguish the sides of cassettes with an embossed A and B, or one or two dots, or even braille in the case of some Fuji cassettes. Hagger Electronics supply cassettes on which side 1 is indicated on the housing by a tactile symbol, the shape of which varies according to the length of tape. See also chapter 17. TapeSense offers blank tapes at **discount prices** to registered blind and partially sighted people and to registered charities working with them. Enquiries to *Nicky Phillips, The Persula Foundation, 202 Long Lane, London SE1 4QB* ✆ 0171 357 9298.

19.7.3 Pocket recorders

Many blind people find **microcassette pocket recorders** convenient for note taking, messages, letters, etc. Prices start at around £30. Details of more expensive, specially modified pocket cassette recorders are given in a factsheet available in large print or braille from *RNIB Employment Development and Technology Unit.*

Pocket recorders with an **electronic chip** instead of a cassette can be used to store brief messages. **VoicePad**, £39, has a capacity of 120 seconds (eight 15-second or four 30-second messages). It can be programmed to repeat a selected message from five minutes to 21 hours ahead, or to repeat a message if it is moved. It is supplied by *Lineplex, Fairmile House, High Street, Ripley, Surrey GU23 7SD* ✆ 01483 211858. **Talking mini memo**, £5.24 from *RNIB*, will take one message of up to 20 seconds. It is operated with just two buttons, record and playback.

19.8 Broadcasting

19.8.1 Radio

Radio is obviously the perfect medium for blind people. All registered blind (though not partially sighted) people over the age of eight who lack a suitable radio set are eligible for one on free permanent loan under the terms of the **British Wireless for the Blind Fund**. The sets currently being issued (see illustrations in this and the colour section) are two Roberts radios, the **RP26B** with presets on one medium wave, one long wave and four FM stations and the **R701**, a smaller battery/mains portable radio, and the new specially designed **Clarke & Smith Model 1318** mono radio/cassette recorder (£95 from the manufacturers).

Blind people who already have one of the Fund's radios may exchange it for the new radio/cassette recorder. If they have one of the radio/cassette recorders previously distributed by the Fund, they can exchange it for a radio, but not for the new radio/cassette recorder.

The Fund issues its radio sets through local agencies, usually either the local voluntary organisation for the blind or the local social services department. The local agency should be approached if a radio or cassette player issued by the Fund is in need of repair; in many areas there are volunteers who undertake servicing and can

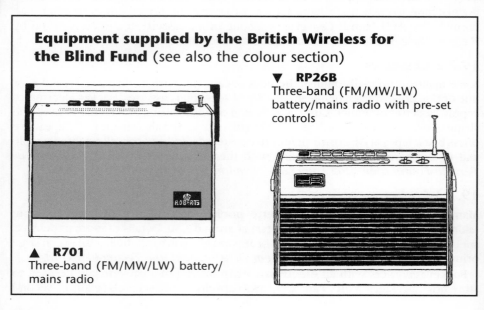

Equipment supplied by the British Wireless for the Blind Fund (see also the colour section)

▼ **RP26B**
Three-band (FM/MW/LW) battery/mains radio with pre-set controls

▲ **R701**
Three-band (FM/MW/LW) battery/ mains radio

330

obtain spare parts free of charge from the Fund. The Fund also supplies through the local agencies four **free PP9 batteries** a year or four sets of LR14 or LR20 batteries to any blind person who has one of the Fund's sets. In addition, the local agency can buy from the Fund further supplies of batteries at concessionary prices. As this agreement is left to the discretion of the local agency, the availability of cheap batteries varies considerably around the country. **Free headphones** are issued by the Fund to those blind people who cannot listen to their radios without disturbing other people and to those who have a slight hearing loss. (Further information about aids to help people with a hearing loss to listen not only to their radios, but also to television and talking books, is given in 26.3.3).

Radios with preset push button tuning are the easiest for blind people to use. Angus McKenzie says that presets on FM are the most important, but with the advent of new national commercial stations, they are also important on MW. He stresses the value of good FM reception, especially if the radio is to be used downstairs in an area where there may be an obstacle in the way of the signal from a transmitter. A shoppers' guide to reasonably priced portable radios with presets is given in **Pleasures of Listening**, the In Touch Care Guide (In Touch Publishing. 1992. £2.50). See 15.2.3 for details of talking timeswitches which can set equipment to record radio programmes.

19.8.2 Television

Modern technology has the potential to make **television** and **video** more accessible to people whose sight is too poor to see the pictures on the screen. Verbal commentary describing the action taking place during silent intervals of a television programme is already available to blind people in the United States and Japan. The possibility of providing audio description on television in Europe is being investigated by AUDETEL, an EC-supported consortium which is developing the technology for an extra sound channel to carry commentary. **RNIB's Broadcasting Officer** assists with the AUDETEL project and campaigns for improved services in general for blind people from public service and independent broadcasters. Under discussion, for example, are guidelines for programme producers about the amount of information given as text on screen rather than verbally. Further information from *RNIB Leisure Service*.

A **TV sound receiver** enables blind people to listen to the sound content only of television programmes, and as the set receives no pictures, there is no need for a TV licence. The receiver is

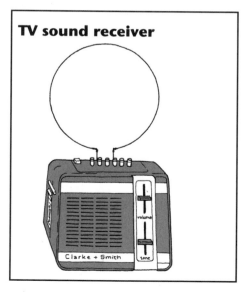

TV sound receiver

Clarke + Smith

easy to use once it has been tuned; a simple push-button operation is all that is needed to switch channels.

The British Wireless for the Blind Fund distributes a Clarke & Smith TV sound receiver free to registered blind people who do not have access to a television set. The same model can be obtained from RNIB for £90. Repairs and service of the Decca set originally distributed by RNIB can still be undertaken by *D & S Electronic Services, Building 15, Unit 4, Stanmore Industrial Estate, Bridgnorth, Shropshire* ✆ 01746 766641. For repairs to the Marconi set distributed by RNIB during the 1980s, contact *RNIB Customer Services*.

A **Rediffusion sound tuner** is suggested by Angus McKenzie as an alternative to the Clarke & Smith set. He recommends the model available from *Display Electronics, 32 Biggin Way, London SE19 3XF* ✆ 0181 679 4414. The version with a built-in speaker costs £45, but Mr. McKenzie says better sound reproduction can be achieved by adding an external speaker to the Telebox B-ST version, £43. Both are special prices for visually impaired customers.

Connected to a television aerial, **NICAM decoders** can be used to receive television audio output in digital stereo sound. One model is designed for use by blind people, with audible signals on the controls and automatic tuning. It costs £203 from *Portset*.

Television sound can also be received via **Talking Teletext** (see below) and via the equipment provided for subscribers to the RNIB Electronic Newspaper (see 18.4.4).

Blind people who have an ordinary television set get a **reduction of £1.25 on their television licence**. The local authority will supply a certificate of blindness which should be shown when paying for the licence and then kept to use again in future years.

19.8.3 Teletext

The Ceefax and Oracle teletext services carried by television channels include news, weather, sports and business coverage as well as radio and television programme details. A synthetic speech read-out of these services can be obtained with **Talking Teletext**. This 8″ x 10″ unit has a simple keypad to access television channels and teletext pages. The user does not need a licence as Talking Teletext can be plugged directly into a domestic aerial. It is supplied by *Portset*, the makers, in three versions. The basic model, £599, gives a page by page read-out. The version which also gives full television programme sound is £649. The version costing £685 has several additional features, including continuous read-out of all sub-pages of the section selected. Serial and parallel ports can be added to Talking Teletext so that it can be linked to a compatible computer or to a large print or braille printer.

A personal computer fitted with an **adaptor card** can be used to access Teletext. The card supplied by *Portset* is £188. Others are supplied by *Dolphin Systems* (£175) and by *Techno-Vision Systems* (£195, or £295 for a special version to fit Eureka A4 and other devices with an RS232 port). The equipment provided for subscribers to the RNIB Electronic Newspaper (see 18.4.4) can also be used to access Teletext.

19.8.4 Programme details

Radio and television programme details are available on cassette from TNAUK, in large print in *Big Print* (see 18.1.2) and in braille from RNIB (see 18.2.3).

For the benefit of visually impaired viewers, daily telephone listings of their programmes are provided by:

- Carlton (London and South East England) on 01426 927958
- Central (West Midlands and Central England) on 01426 952900
- Meridian (Southern England) on 0345 573041
- S4C (Wales) on 01222 741414

A free weekly large print guide to Central programmes can be obtained from *Sam O'Sullivan, TV Line, Central TV, Broad Street, Birmingham B1 2JP* ✆ 0121 634 4391.

19.8.5 Video

An **Audio Described Home Video Service** was launched by RNIB in 1994. Among titles available so far are **Pretty Woman**, £10.99, **Dead Poets Society**, £10.99, **Bambi**, £14.99 and **Hear My Song**, £10. Also stocked are documentary titles without description but which have sufficient narration for visually impaired people to follow the story. Further information from *RNIB Customer Services*.

19.8.6 TV and video remote controls

Remote controls with large, clear contrasting buttons are on sale at television and hi-fi retailers; John Lewis, for example, stocks a **One For All** model at £19.75. A kidney shaped **Fox Zappa** in orange, yellow or green with contrasting buttons costs £19.88 from *Willow Vale Electronics, 11 Arkwright Road, Reading RG2 0LU* ✆ 01734 876444.

F

19.9 Radio amateurs

Many blind people get a great deal of enjoyment out of operating short-wave radio sets. Nearly half the members of the **Radio Amateur Invalid and Blind Club** are visually impaired. The Club will put blind amateur radio enthusiasts in touch with local representatives and radio clubs who will help them wherever possible with the initial installation of equipment as well as with any necessary repairs and maintenance. The Club has a limited amount of equipment which it can lend out in special circumstances. Blind people wishing to obtain a transmitting licence can get their study material in the form of a cassette course, and the Licensing Authority is prepared to allow blind candidates to take an aural examination in their own homes. Special arrangements are also made for the 12 wpm Morse test. Details of Club membership from the *Hon. Membership Secretary, Mrs. Shelagh Chambers, 78 Durley Avenue, Pinner, Middlesex HA5 1JH* ✆ 0181 868 2516.

Full membership of **St Dunstan's Amateur Radio Society** is restricted to St Dunstaners, but other visually impaired people are eligible for associate membership. Details from *Ted John, 52 Broadway Avenue, Wallasey, Wirral L45 6TD* ✆ 0151 638 5514.

20 A beginner's guide to computers

Computers can bring enormous benefits to visually-handicapped people. With quite a simple home computer, a blind person can produce faultlessly typed letters, print the envelopes, and keep file copies in an accessible form, or have a personal address list and telephone directory instantly to hand. Larger and faster computers can become reading machines, through which blind people can read books stored on compact disk, and even printed text; and the machines can be connected through the telephone network to make contact with other computers all around the world.

Computers are for all ages, not just for the young. Blind people in their 70s and 80s have enjoyed mastering the new 'information technology', and relish the independence it has brought them. Of course the very young take the new technology completely in their stride, and in schools and colleges it is used for vision training and academic work. In the field of employment, computers have made as many changes for visually-handicapped people as for their sighted colleagues, and nowadays people in many lines of business, from piano tuners to office workers to engineers, use computers as a matter of course. And last but not least, computers can be used simply for fun – either for games, or by learning to program, or produce all manner of music and strange sounds.

This chapter examines the three ways in which visually-handicapped people can read a computer screen: through artificial speech, enlarged screen display, or electronic braille. It surveys the range of computer equipment available, and gives guidance on choosing and using it.

F

The tables in this chapter (see 20.13) list much of the specialist equipment that is available for visually-handicapped users. Much of it is suitable either for home or the workplace, but funding is rather more likely to be obtained for a system that is needed for work. Details about the help available through **Access to Work** are found in 10.7.4; references to sources of help for educational needs are found in chapter 8. There may also be some limited help from charities (see 30). But for those relying on their own resources, it need not cost a fortune to buy a computer, and this chapter shows how costs can be kept down without lowering standards.

20.1 Getting started

People starting computing from scratch need to think carefully about what they want a computer to do. If they want simply to be able to write and print letters, and keep handy lists of phone numbers or recipes, they need a less powerful and therefore cheaper machine than someone who plans to run a CD-ROM drive or a scanner. And someone who wants a basic machine now but intends to buy a CD-ROM drive or scanner later on must make sure that the new machine has scope for expanding its capabilities.

Key to media of publication   **P** clear print   **L** large print   **B** braille   **T** tape   **M** Moon   **D** disk

Where a full address is not given in the text, see 32 (Useful addresses)

Reg Jackson took up computing in his seventies and uses a computer regularly for all his correspondence – and to amuse his grandchildren!

There is perhaps one other word of caution to be added before a novice takes the plunge. Many complex tasks can be accomplished effortlessly by a computer. That is true. It is not true that they can be accomplished instantly without effort on the part of the user. Beginners may take far longer to produce a letter using a word processing program than they would take to put a sheet of paper in the typewriter and type it. Instruction books are notoriously full of jargon. The frustration felt when the computer refuses to do anything except display incomprehensible error messages is considerable, and only surpassed by the irritation of knowing that nearly always the operator, not the machine, is at fault! But all beginners, sighted or sight-impaired, suffer in the same way, and thousands of visually-handicapped novices have succeeded and found their computer skills well worth the effort of learning. In the words of one user who took up computing in her 60s having been nearly blind for five years, 'This marvellous machine has made me literate again.'

20.2 The equipment

Hardware means all the equipment that you can touch, like the monitor or the keyboard; software covers instructions needed to make computers work. A personal computer comprises a variety of both. By far the most widely used sort of personal computer is the **IBM-compatible PC**, and this will be the best choice for the vast majority of beginners. The original PCs were made by IBM and PC was their own trademark, but then many other companies started making computers that were compatible, that is, they could use the same software as the PC. There are over five million PCs in Britain alone, and there is an enormous amount of software available for them. Among non-PC machines, the **Apple Macintosh** is the most widely used for business and home computing; it is newer in design and by no means inferior to the PC, but radically different, with unique software. The machines can be made to output speech and enlarged display, though currently not electronic braille. But they are far less widely used, and beginners are strongly advised to start with a PC if possible.

335

A PC is described by a number denoting the power of its microprocessor, or driving engine. The standard current machine is the 486; the less powerful 286 computers are no longer made, and new 386s are extremely rare. The fastest machine to date is the **Pentium**, ('586'), which is still very expensive, and a home user is unlikely to need the extra speed it offers. However, much the same comment was being made about 486s only a couple of years ago. The computer industry changes with bewildering speed.

PCs are called 'desktop' or 'notebooks' (formerly 'laptops') depending on whether they are portable or not. Notebooks, which can fit into a briefcase, seem at first sight the most attractive choice; neat, battery powered, and capable of being adapted for a visually-handicapped user. They are however costly to buy, vulnerable to rough treatment, and expensive to insure and to repair, should anything go wrong. Unless portability is a must – as for a student, or someone who needs to do computer work while travelling – a desktop model is cheaper, and will suit a beginner well.

Though there are many makes of PC, they all have the same basic components: a keyboard, a display unit or monitor, a processing unit, plus a printer. The keyboard is like that found on a typewriter, with some additional specialist keys. The monitor resembles a television screen. The printer produces an inkprint copy of the results of the computer's work. The processing unit, which looks like a simple box with all the other items plugged into it, is where the work is actually performed.

20.2.1 The processing unit

The processing unit has a memory, which is the computer's temporary work area; this works in conjunction with a hard disk (used for permanently storing completed work, and for holding the programs that make the machine run) and with a slot for inserting small 'floppy' disks (used for loading in or taking out additional information as required). Older machines, made without a hard disk, had to have all their programs and information loaded into them from floppy disks each time they were used. Floppy disks, which are actually squarish and rigid, come in two sizes – the standard 3.5" kind, used by modern machines, and the older 5.25" size.

Hard disks come in many sizes, measured in units called **megabytes** (Mb – a megabyte is roughly a million bytes, and a byte can hold one character of text). Most new machines have anything from 130Mb to 730Mb hard disks. Computer memory is also measured in megabytes; 4Mb is considered the minimum for modern machines. But many older computers with smaller hard disks and memory can give good service, and should not be dismissed altogether (see 20.3.2).

20.2.2 The keyboard

The keyboard normally presents few problems. To use it efficiently it helps to be a touch typist, and for anyone with little or no sight this is almost an essential skill, but one not too difficult to achieve. There is now even a computer-based **Touch Typing Tutor** (£24) supplied by the **Research Centre for the Education of the Visually Handicapped** at Birmingham University (see 18.1.6 for details of other touch-typing courses). A number of the suppliers mentioned in 20.13 sell large print keytop labels (around £8.00 for white on black, around £14 for a wider choice of colours or with a braille overlay.) Some specially designed computers have a **braille keyboard**, or offer one as an optional extra. If so, it will almost always be laid out in the same way as a Perkins keyboard.

20.2.3 The monitor

Difficulties are more likely to arise over the monitor. Some partially-sighted users can read a standard screen by working very close to it. A movable **monitor arm** costing around £30 can be helpful; it supports the screen on a platform at eye level and can be slid forward close to the user or pushed back out of the way when not required. For others there is a variety of solutions to be tried. Good contrast is always needed, and some people can see certain screen colours better than others; it is worth remembering that the pre-set colours which computer programs display can usually be altered by the user to something more readable. Some users find a monochrome monitor works best, but beware of old cheap mono monitors, which may well not be capable of running modern screen-enlarging software. Be cautious about old monitors in general, as they may not conform to modern low-radiation standards. A large lens for magnifying a whole standard screen up to four times, the **Compu-lenz**, (£485), is supplied by *Specialist Optical Source Ltd, 57 Dukes Wood Drive, Gerrards Cross SL9 7LJ* ✆ 01753 888411. Simply buying a large monitor is a very expensive way to gain legibility.

20.2.4 The printer

There are many makes of printer, but only three basic sorts: dot matrix; inkjet or bubblejet (which are the same for all practical purposes though not identical technically); and laser. Dot matrix printers are noisy when working and their print quality can never be as good as print produced by the other two kinds. But they are cheap to buy, typically between £120 and £220, and cheap to run, with printed output costing under 1p for an A4 sheet. Inkjet or bubblejet printers typically cost from £250 upwards. They produce good quality very dense print – even colour, if required – and are quiet and quick to use. They are expensive to run, because their ink is costly; each A4 sheet costs from 5p to 10p, depending on ink cartridge prices. Laser printers are the dearest kind to buy, though the price is dropping fast and the cheapest are now well under £400. The 'toner' (ink) and renewable parts they need are expensive, but these consumables will last a lot longer than either a bubblejet's ink cartridge or a dot matrix printer ribbon. Small lasers typically produce an A4 sheet for 2p. Laser printers are easy and quiet to operate and can produce high quality print in many kinds of typestyle. They are especially good for those needing large print, and specialist programs such as **Large Print Express** (Pia. £95) enable a variety of different sizes of large text to be easily printed from a single word processor document.

Whatever type of printer seems most suitable, the user must be able to operate it easily unaided, so several important points need to be checked. First and foremost, are the buttons that control it easy to use? Push-buttons with a positive action are usually preferable to touch-pads embedded flush with the printer's case. How easy is it to get paper and envelopes in straight? Many models have trays which hold a pile of stationery and feed it in automatically, but if the individual sheets must be inserted by hand, some printers make this practically impossible for someone with little or no sight. For those needing large print, will their chosen printer produce this easily using their favourite software? Printer models change as quickly as clothing fashions; it is wise to consult either experienced blind users, RNIB, or the **Foundation for Communication for the Disabled (FCD)**, to get up-to-date advice before buying.

20.2.5 Programs

The programs, or sets of instructions that make the computer work, are stored on the computer's hard disk ready for use, or loaded into the machine from floppy disks. The most fundamental bit of software, one the computer must have but its owner rarely has to worry about, is the operating system, which underlies all the practical programs that the user works with from day to day. New computers usually come with the two commonest operating systems, **DOS** and **Windows**, ready loaded; in fact current machines will run without Windows, but not without DOS, which all other programs need. The practical programs the user deals with are called 'applications programs', and three main sorts concern the beginner: the **word processor**, for typing and printing any text from a three line memo to a novel; the **database**, a kind of electronic card index for storing and sorting lists, such as names, addresses and phone numbers; and the **spreadsheet**, a flexible calculation chart for working out anything from mortgage repayments to the cost of a wedding reception. The user has to learn how to operate the different kinds of programs – for instance which keys to press to make the word processor check spellings, or to find the right phone number in the database list – but once the basic instructions are mastered, the program does the rest.

It is possible to try out certain programs, known as **shareware**, before deciding to buy. Shareware programs include examples of word processors, databases and spreadsheets, and their quality ranges between brilliant and appalling. But they are exceedingly cheap to acquire – up to £5.00, merely to cover distribution costs – and are widely available through mail order. However, the version obtained this way is an 'evaluation copy', and may not be complete. After a trial period a registered version must be bought, complete with latest improvements, printed manuals and after-sales support. Details of how to do this are always included with the shareware copy.

20.2.6 Specialist equipment and programs

Visually-handicapped users will probably need some specialist hardware in addition to the standard equipment described above, and certainly some specialist software. A **speech synthesiser** can make the computer 'talk', and it needs a **screenreader** program so the user can instruct it how to read out all or part of the screen. For braille readers, an **electronic braille unit** can display the screen's contents in braille a line at a time; or a braillist might also require a **braille embosser** and translation program, so that the computer can print braille script. Large-text software can magnify the words displayed on the screen, thus making them much clearer for a partially-sighted person.

Which of these specialist systems to choose depends on the user's eyesight, personal preference, and finances. As no hardware is needed for **screen magnification programs**, this tends to be a cheaper choice than speech or braille output. Electronic braille is by far the most expensive option, and usually only chosen by those in work for whom government funding can be arranged.

20.3 Getting the equipment

Having decided whether to read the screen through speech, large display, or electronic braille, the user can choose between two basic options: buying a complete package of computer hardware and software which is all ready to use, or a self-assembled system, where the computer and the necessary adaptations and software are bought piece by piece. Maybe just the adaptations need be purchased, if there is a machine already in the family.

20.3.1 A package

This is the easiest way of buying a computer system, if finances allow. Many specialist suppliers sell a variety of packages, each built round a commercially available computer, with adaptations to make it either speak, display braille, or magnify the screen's contents. The package can include a printer or braille embosser, and whatever other specialist hardware and software the customer wants. But just as buying a fitted kitchen from a kitchen designer costs much more than buying the sink, fridge, cooker and units and installing them yourself, so inevitably buying a ready-made computer package carries a higher price tag than assembling the equipment piecemeal. However, anyone choosing a package will have the peace of mind of knowing that all the component parts of the system work together well, and if they do not, there is only one seller to contact to get things put right. Many specialist suppliers offer additional advantages, such as manuals on tape, in braille or in large print, and after-sales support such as helplines.

There are also packages consisting of equipment specially designed for braillists, with a braille keyboard, and perhaps built-in speech. They are portable, some indeed being pocket-sized 'note-takers', ideal for making and storing a quick braille note ready to be read later. They vary in the amount of information they can store, whether they have speech or braille output, and whether they can be used to store or retrieve data from a PC (see 20.13.3). They tend to be expensive, though specially designed equipment is exempt from VAT, and if they meet a person's specific needs precisely, it is money well spent.

20.3.2 A self-assembled system

It is quite feasible for a visually-handicapped person to buy all the various components of a computer system from different sources, including the specialist adaptations needed to make it usable. It is not a road to be recommended for the lone novice for it can be full of pitfalls. It is not always easy to get individual parts of the system to function together properly, and if the finished system does not work, how can the newcomer tell which vendor of which component to complain to? Having said all that, plenty of visually-handicapped people have bought a good system, including enlarged text or speech, costing under £1000, assembled with the help of an experienced friend.

The commercial equipment can be bought in local shops, or more cheaply still by mail order through computer magazines. When buying hardware from a distant supplier, it is worth considering also buying on-site warranty. New equipment carries a statutory guarantee, but should anything go wrong with bulky or fragile items it is a distinct advantage to have a repair engineer come to the equipment, rather than having to return goods to the supplier. Incidentally the temptation to economise by doing without a monitor should be resisted. The blind user may manage happily without one, but sighted helpers will be rendered helpless.

Buying a second-hand computer can help keep costs down, but it is about as problematical as buying a used car, and a beginner will need expert help. Alternatively, adapting a machine already owned by someone in the family is well worth considering as a cheap option, though this can have problems too if the computer is old; a five-year-old model is considered a veteran! Not all modern speech and enlarged-screen systems can be run on old machines, even PCs, and many non-PCs are not straightforward to use with speech or enlarged-text display. But even a very elderly BBC computer long discarded by the children can be pressed into service. Contact the *Research Centre for the Education of the Visually Handicapped (RCEVH)* at the University of Birmingham, which can sell software and offer advice to make a BBC machine usable.

20.4 Choosing a screenreader and speech synthesiser

The screenreader is the more important of these two elements, because it is the program which enables the user to control how the screen is read out. It is wise to pick a screenreader first, then choose a synthesiser which works with it. The chart below (20.13.1) differentiates between complete speech systems, and synthesisers and screenreaders which can be bought separately, but note that not all synthesisers work with all screenreaders.

Most screenreaders can be instructed to speak either the full screen, a section of screen, a line, a word, or individual letters, and speak keys as they are pressed. There are many more sophisticated features, like the ability to read out a complete document continuously no matter how long. Commands can be entered either through the keyboard or through a separate keypad, depending on the screenreader chosen. Several practical questions need to be asked when choosing a screenreader. How easy is it to pick out and read any part of the screen? How good is it at speaking changes on the screen, such as the appearance of unexpected error messages? Is it easy to change its reading speed? Does it work with a synthesiser whose sound the user likes?

The synthesiser may be housed in an external box complete with speaker and headphone socket, which plugs into the computer; or it may be just a printed circuit board or 'card' which fits inside the processing unit, with an external speaker and headphone socket. A few can work from battery power as well as mains: for example

340

the **Juno**, the **SpeakOut** and the **Artic Transport**. These truly portable models are ideal for use with notebook computers.

When choosing a synthesiser, its 'voice' is not usually the crucial feature. More important is its compatibility with a chosen screenreader, and its individual features, such as portability and price. Having narrowed down the field, the user can then consider voices. It takes time to adapt to synthetic speech, with its odd intonations and occasional mispronunciations. **DECTalk** synthesisers are considered the best for voice quality and variety. **Apollo 2** and **Infovox** speak good non-American English. But all have their individual features. The RNIB sell a cassette (price £1.45) with sample readings by a dozen popular synthesisers to help buyers choose.

20.5 Choosing a large (enhanced) character display

There is an increasing choice of programs for enlarging the screen's display (see 20.13.2). Depending on eyesight, some are easier to read than others, and only the user can decide which is most suitable. Some systems give a much wider range of magnification than others; but the more the characters are enlarged, the less of the screen's contents can be seen at once, so it is important to have a program that will switch back and forth easily between the enlarged display and the 'real' screen. If the user can manage with only two times magnification, the **Magic 2** program at £80 is good value; most other programs are between £200 and £450. As usual, it is vital to ensure that the chosen system will work with the user's favourite programs. Before coming to any decision, the user should try out several systems. Suppliers will normally provide free demonstration disks of this type of software, so the programs can be run to show off all their features, but only for a limited time, often fifteen minutes.

F

20.6 Choosing a braille display

Electronic braille display is only for those with plenty of funding available (see 20.13.4). But braillists may prefer the screen's contents presented in braille, especially if they are working with computer programming languages, which include symbols that are not always read well by speech systems. The braille display unit plugs into the computer and displays a line at a time through a line of braille cells. The dots are formed by minute plastic pins, one at each dot position, which are moved up and down electronically. Different systems offer different line lengths, mostly representing half or a full screen width.

20.7 Choosing a braille embosser

Braille embossers are expensive and noisy, and usually more appropriate for the workplace than for home; home users wanting an electronic brailler may well prefer the smaller and relatively cheap **Mountbatten note-taker** (see 20.13.5). Speed, noise, ease of operation and quality of braille produced are all important factors governing embosser choice. Servicing arrangements should also be carefully checked. Before finally choosing an embosser it would be wise to discuss its suitability with RNIB, or with the **UK Association of Braille Producers**. Contact the secretary *Marie Brown* ℘ 01733 370777.

A **braille translation program** will also be needed. When choosing, it is important to bear in mind that the program that may be an excellent choice for the competent braillist keying in his own material, may be quite wrong for his assistant or colleague, who does not know one dot from another but needs to put documents into braille. At another level, professional braillists are likely to require a highly sophisticated program which will meet their most esoteric demands. **Braille Maker Express** is an automated, easy-to-use program aimed particularly at non-braillists who want to produce good, straightforward braille, and at braille users who require fast output with a choice of braille formatting options. Amongst other programs, **BrailleMaster** allows highly competent braille readers to decide how the text should be translated, either from the existing built-in braille codes or according to their own private code (see 20.13.6).

20.8 Choosing programs

Having acquired the computer system and the special programs needed, it is time to consider applications programs. Most people want to start by producing letters, so a word processor will probably come first and a good basic one can be had for under £50. All word processors enable the user to add, delete, copy and move text around, control page layouts, and produce a variety of typestyles. Virtually all have a spelling checker to help identify spelling or typing mistakes. FCD offers **LetterPerfect** and **Galaxy**, which both have all these features, for £39 each, and supply step-by-step instructions on tape, on floppy disk or in large print, which makes them especially good for beginners. The Foundation also sells two more specialised word processors: **Eye Relief** (from £215), which displays the text in large characters, though it can only be printed out in normal size, and **Flexiwrite**, a simple word processor which displays double sized text (£40). FCD can also advise on databases and spreadsheets.

A relatively recent problem facing blind computer users is that more and more programs are going over to 'Graphical User Interface' (GUI). This horrible jargon describes programs that display messages on the screen not only in words, but in pictures, called icons. The sighted user can communicate by way of these, using a small control device or 'mouse' to move a pointer around the screen. To tell the computer to print, for example, the pointer can be moved to touch a picture of a printer. Though there are ways round this for blind users, graphical programs pose other technical problems which make them rather difficult, and sometimes impossible, to use with speech and electronic braille. But they are visually attractive and easy for sighted people to learn, and so are becoming standard. Microsoft **Windows**, the GUI operating system which allows other graphical programs to run under its control, is routinely installed along with DOS on new computers. Windows is posing a serious problem to blind users who rely on speech or braille output, especially in work situations, where a blind person may have to switch from familiar programs to new software that is much harder to access.

Several screenreaders have been written to make Windows programs speak, or produce electronic braille (see 20.13), and they have made it possible for blind users to operate many Windows-based programs with reasonable success. They are all expensive and need experienced handling, so they are not for the beginner. But as new Windows versions keep being produced, like the long-awaited **Windows 95**, new screenreaders will have to be developed to keep pace. Much effort is being devoted to the problem in Britain, Europe and the United States. For the current British situation, which is constantly changing, contact *RNIB Employment Development and Technology Unit*, who produce a regularly updated technical bulletin, **Windows Briefing ❶ ❸ ❼**. Single copies are free to individuals.

Windows is less of a problem for partially-sighted people. Windows-based word processors make it easy for users to enlarge the text they are typing in and printing out, and inexpensive shareware programs can be found which enlarge the size of the mouse pointer and magnify some of the screen's messages and menus. And for an overall solution, there are several enlarged text programs that work with Windows software (see 20.13.2).

A valuable introduction to Windows for reasonably experienced computer users is **Window Concepts ❶ ❸ ❼**, by Sarah Morley, published by RNIB for the multinational GUIB Consortium. Based on research involving visually handicapped people, it aims to describe how Windows works without the visual explanations and jargon normally present in Windows instruction books. It is available free from the author, Sarah Morley, at *GUIB Project, Psychology Division, University of Hertfordshire, Hatfield AL10 9AB*.

20.9 Try before you buy

With specialist computer equipment it is extremely important to get 'hands-on' experience in the literal sense, yet this is far from easy. There is no one place where the complete range of hardware and software that can help visually-handicapped people is available to be tried out and compared. Instead there are many different showrooms and resource centres throughout Britain, each having a different selection of equipment, and would-be buyers must investigate as best they can with the time and energy at their disposal.

Most specialist suppliers have a demonstration area at their headquarters. Some take part in occasional exhibitions around the country, and home demonstrations can be arranged. A selection of computer equipment can be examined at the **RNIB's Resource Centre, London**, but it is wise to make an appointment before visiting. Staff in their **Employment Development and Technology Unit** are also ready to advise though their prime responsibility is to help people with applied technology for employment. Visits are available by appointment. Many smaller resource centres have computer equipment for the use of their visually-handicapped members, though this will usually be from a few manufacturers only; the list of resource centres at the end of this book shows which have hi-tech equipment.

The **Research Centre for the Education of the Visually Handicapped** at Birmingham University holds demonstrations every Thursday when there is an opportunity to examine a wide range of computers and ancillary equipment. Many of the programs have been devised for children, but adults would also find a visit worthwhile. An annual exhibition of hi-tech equipment is organised at different centres by the **British Computer Association of the Blind**. Members of the **Association of Visually Handicapped Office Workers** hold occasional conferences where new equipment is examined and mutual problems discussed.

The **Foundation for Communication for the Disabled** is a registered charity offering independent advice on alternatives to conventional methods of writing or communicating. It sells a selection of hardware and software, but gives advice covering the whole specialist range, and if necessary is prepared to make a home visit. Where there is a real problem in meeting the cost of a system it can also advise on possible sources of funding.

The **ComputAbility Centre** is a national charity which provides a comprehensive information service for people with disabilities. It offers a consultancy and an assessment service. It has open days once a month which offer visitors (by appointment) a general introduction to computing, and an opportunity to discover what is available. There is a free telephone advice line ℘ 0800 269545. More details from *Bill Fine, PO Box 94, Warwick CV34 5WS* ℘ 01926 312847.

20.10 Reading by computer

Few blind people read braille fluently, and books on tape have the great disadvantage that it is impossible to browse or to find a particular reference quickly. Books stored on computer disks can offer a useful alternative.

20.10.1 CD-ROM

CD-ROM stands for Compact Disk Read Only Memory. To use it a computer needs a CD-ROM drive (from £150 – but many modern machines have them already built in). Into this drive are slotted CDs, looking like audio compact disks, which can hold the equivalent of 2,000 average sized books or a twenty-volume encyclopaedia. The lightning speed with which a computer can search through a CD far surpasses the ability of a sighted person to skim through a book, and as soon as the reference is on the screen it can be read in speech, braille or enlarged text.

More and more CD titles are now being published in graphical formats, which are more difficult to access with speech or electronic braille (see 20.8). When choosing books from the growing number of CD catalogues, it is vital to check whether the chosen title is in a DOS-text non-graphical format, or a Windows format. So many CDs are designed to be read using Windows software that numbers of blind people are already using Windows screenreaders to handle them, and finding the results quite acceptable, and undoubtedly this is the way of the future for those who want to explore the enormous range of CD books. But some popular titles are still available in DOS-text versions such as the **Software Toolworks (Grolier) Encyclopaedia** 1992 (£45), **Desktop Bookshop** with its many hundreds of classics (£75) and the **Oxford English Reference Library** (£85) all from FCD and Dolphin Systems.

20.10.2 Books on floppy disk

Books can also be stored on floppy disks, and can be loaded from them onto the hard disk and read there. Examples are the **Concise Oxford Dictionary 1991** (£50) and **Thesaurus** (£50), and **Collins English Dictionary** and several two-way language dictionaries (£69 each) obtainable from F.C.D., who will also advise on how straightforward they are to use. **The Good News Bible Computer Concordance** and **New Testament** can be obtained on disk; further details from the *Bible Society*. The **In Touch 1995-96 Handbook** (In Touch Publishing. £19.95) is available on floppy disk, with a text search facility, for registered blind and partially sighted readers.

20.10.3 Reading by OCR

Optical Character Recognition systems (OCRs) are among the most exciting recent developments because they enable printed text to be copied into a computer and stored there in a form readable by a blind user. The OCR machine is a scanner plus its recognition software. The scanner can either be a self-contained 'stand-alone', used mostly by public libraries (see 18.4.1), or a cheaper option is to plug a commercially available scanner into a fast PC provided it has enough memory and room within the processing unit for an additional 'card'. This is one area where a user is advised to buy a scanner together with its appropriate OCR software from a specialist supplier, who can give advice on matching it with the rest of the computer system (see 20.13.7). **Flatbed scanners**, resembling small photocopiers, are most suitable, because they can copy a whole A4 sheet of print at once. Beware of small hand-held scanners, which are temptingly cheap (from about £60); they are next to impossible for blind users, because they only scan a page in sections, and therefore must be moved precisely and evenly over different portions of the text so that their software can stitch the segments together into a complete page ready for reading.

Scanners cannot read handwriting, but books and typescripts can be scanned successfully, and also magazines, if the user is prepared to tackle a variety of page layouts. Above all, blind scanner users can enjoy the independence of reading their printed mail unaided.

20.11 Long-distance computer communication

A computer can be used to communicate with other computers via the telephone lines of the world. Two things are needed: a small device called a modem attached to the computer and the telephone socket, and software specially designed for communications, compatible with the user's own system. There is plenty of shareware communications software to try, but getting just the right program to harmonise with speech, enlarged text or electronic braille is attended by the familiar problems that always arise when combining different components into a smoothly running system. Advice from both sighted and visually handicapped users will probably be needed, but once the teething troubles are over the user has access to literally a world of contacts and information. The infinite possibilities of the Internet are beyond the scope of this handbook (but see 18.4.5), but many people start with a strictly practical use for their modem – gaining access to **Bulletin Board Systems**. Many companies and individuals run these BBSs, holding on their computers perhaps shareware software, or collections of useful information on many topics. A modem user, having registered and paid a small subscription, can dial up the Bulletin Board and by following the instructions on the screen can read information, and transfer or 'download' data or software onto their own machine. The only extra cost is the charge for the phone call. **NEW** The BBC **In Touch Gateway** is a bulletin board run by the publishers of the **In Touch Handbook**. In addition to the Handbook itself, subscribers can access and search information from many other sources and organisations concerned with visual impairment. More details in the Directory section.

20.12 Learning to use the equipment

20.12.1 Training courses

Training opportunities for people aiming for employment can be found in chapter 9. Local colleges of further education often have computer courses and sometimes have special groups for visually impaired people, or they can provide support for a visually impaired person in a sighted group (see 8.15). Adult Education classes are frequently run for beginners and can be a good place to meet like-minded people. See also mobile training units (9.6.2). Suppliers of specialised equipment often include training sessions in the purchase price, or offer them as an optional extra. When the equipment is being provided by the Department of Employment for work, it may be prepared to pay for some training. Local resource centres with computer equipment can sometimes arrange lessons for beginners. The **RNIB's Employment Development and Technology Unit** has a list of trainers, some of whom are visually impaired, who can provide one-to-one intensive courses. For those prepared to teach themselves, **tutorial cassettes** can be obtained on loan from RNIB Cassette Library. Titles include **WordPerfect**, **WordStar**, **Supercalc**, and many others.

20.12.2 Further advice and help

NEW The RNIB have established a network of 'computer volunteers' throughout the UK, who will help visually-handicapped home computer users in choosing and using equipment and in troubleshooting, though they cannot undertake training. Contact *Lynda Fowle, RNIB Technical Research, London*. The knowledge and expertise of visually handicapped user groups can be a rich source of advice. The following are glad to help with advice on hardware and software, and the problems and solutions their members have found:

The **British Computer Association of the Blind** promotes the interests of visually impaired people in the computing field. It publishes a quarterly newsletter **L** **B** **T**, and through RNIB, a fortnightly tape magazine, **Datatape**. It also organises specialised training courses. It is affiliated to the British Computer Society. Full membership (£18 p.a.) is open to visually impaired computer professionals or computer students. Associate membership (£7.50 p.a.) is open to visually impaired people who demonstrate an active interest in computers.

346

The **VDU Computer User Group** issues a quarterly cassette journal, **Computer Talk**, which reviews new hardware and software packages for PCs. The group has a small software library including some talking games and a few simple utilities, but not commercially available software. One of the group's most important aims is for members to be able to help each other. Membership is free; simply provide a C90 cassette and postal wallet for the magazine. Contact *Mike Cassidy, 137 Almond Road, Gorleston on Sea, Great Yarmouth, Norfolk NR31 8EN* ✆ 01493 440860.

The **Jotta Users Group** has a telephone advice service. Contact *Frank Cosgrove, 8 Wandsworth Road, Heaton, Newcastle on Tyne NE6 5AD* ✆ 0191 265 6345.

The **VersaBraille Users Group** includes users of VersaBraille 1 and 2 note-takers (now out of production), who keep in touch to discuss common problems and give practical help. Contact (in braille) *Derek Troll, 35 Chandlers Close, Feltham, Middlesex TW14 9PG* ✆ 0181 751 4167 (bulletin board, answerphone and fax).

The **Eureka A4 User Group** circulates a quarterly newsletter issued on a Eureka disk. To join the group, send a Eureka disk with brief personal details and return address to *Eleanor Tew, 7 Turkey Court, Vivary Road, Taunton, Somerset TA1 3JN* ✆ 01823 272863.

A new group for **Apple Macintosh users** is in process of being set up. Contact *Iki Nahaboo, 30 St Thomas Drive, Pinner, Middlesex HA5 4SS* ✆ 0181 420 1338.

20.12.3 Useful reading

A good starting point is the excellent series of factsheets issued by the **RNIB's Employment Development & Technology Unit**, containing clear, detailed and regularly updated information about specialist equipment and software. Each factsheet deals with a different aspect of computing – for instance personal computers, speech systems, and enlarged text systems – and includes lists of suppliers and current prices. Other subjects covered include note-takers, scanners, and non-PC computers. Single copies are free to individuals ❶❸❼❶. Voluntary societies can obtain a pack of 20 print factsheets plus technical bulletins and reports, and quarterly updates, for £60 p.a.

FCD produce a free large-print booklet, **Information Technology for People with a Visual Impairment**, which gives beginners guidance on choosing a suitable computer, and also covers large print and speech systems, printers, and programs.

RNIB Customer Services can supply a bibliography on computing in braille and on tape, though nothing like the choice available in print. Several magazines are available, based mostly on articles taken from the print computer press. RNIB produce two in braille and on floppy disk: **Compute-It**, monthly, on a wide range of computing topics, and **Access-It**, bimonthly, on specialist technology for visually-handicapped users. The **Talking Newspaper Association** produce **PC Today** and **Acorn Computing** monthly on cassette. **The Whistler**, a free quarterly information cassette sponsored by Dolphin Systems, which includes users' reports on hardware and software. Send a good quality C90 cassette and self-addressed wallet to *The Whistler, 11 Yarnton Close, Nine Elms, Swindon, Wiltshire SN5 9UQ.*

20.13 Computer information tables

20.13.1 Speech systems

Speech for DOS

Item	Notes	Supplier	Price
Apollo 2 synthesiser	External mains powered speech synthesiser	*Dolphin, FCD*	**£385**
Apollo 2 Speech system	External synthesiser with HAL5 screenreader	*Dolphin FCD*	**£580**
Artic Business Vision system	For PCs, screen reading software and Synphonix synthesiser card	*Concept*	**£695**
Artic Business Crystal Vision system	As above, with DECTalk synthesiser	*Concept*	**£995**
Artic Transport 615BV system	For PCs, pocket battery synthesiser and built-in screenreader	*Concept*	**£853**
Audiodata system	Audio box for PCs, with 12-key pad and slider for screen navigation	*Sensory Systems*	**£3,660**
DECTalk Express synthesiser	Portable speech synthesiser	*Alphavision*	**£650**
DECTalk PC 4.0 synthesiser	Internal PC speech card	*FCD, PVS, Alphavision, Sight & Sound, Techno-Vision, Aptech*	**£650**
Dolphin PC2 Europa synthesiser	Internal PC speech card	*Dolphin, FCD*	**£295**
HAL5 screenreader	Dolphin's newest screenreader; minimum requirement 386 PC with 4 Mb RAM	*Dolphin*	**£240**
HAL4 screenreader	This older screenreader works with less powerful PCs and many long established applications	*Dolphin*	**£165**
IBM Screen Reader 2	Works with DOS and OS/2. Supports many synthesisers	*Papworth*	**£780** (DOS); **£1,142** (OS/2)
JAWS for DOS screenreader	Supports many popular synthesisers	*Sight & Sound*	**£399**

Continued on next page

Key to abbreviations

FCD	Foundation for Communication for the Disabled
PVS	Professional Vision Services
RCEVH	Research Centre for the Education of the Visually Handicapped
RNC	Royal National College for the Blind

For suppliers' addresses, see 32

* Index printers are distributed by Alphavision, Concept †, FCD, Dolphin †, Pia, PVS, Sensory Systems †, Sight & Sound and Techno-Vision †

† = Authorised service centre

F

Speech for DOS continued

Item	Notes	Supplier	Price
Juno-SP synthesiser	Portable rechargeable synthesiser	Dolphin, FCD	**£405**
Keynote Gold/ Mastertouch system	Keynote gold speech card for PCs plus Mastertouch screenreader. Optional Mastertouch tablet for easy screen navigation	Sensory Systems	**from £1,395**
Magniread system	Infovox synthesiser and Magniread screenreader	PVS	**£650**
Microtalk Classic system	Internal synthesiser and ASAP screenreader for PCs	PVS	**£830**
Microtalk Portable synthesiser	External synthesiser with ASAP screenreader for PS/2 machines and portables	PVS	**£920**
MultiVoice synthesiser	External version of DECTalk, Battery or mains	Aptech	**from £995**
OutSPOKEN screenreader	For Macintosh Plus computers which have built-in synthesiser	Alphavision, FCD	**£315**
ScreenPower Speech system	Keynote Gold or DECTalk synthesiser with ScreenPower screenreader	Sensory Systems	from **£1,395**
Speak-Out synthesiser	Portable battery or mains powered synthesiser, works with Vocal-Eyes and Window-Eyes screenreaders.	Alphavision	**£525**
SpeechThing synthesiser	Works with Tiny Talk screenreader to form budget system costing about £150. Still under development; contact suppliers	FCD	approx. **£70**
Tiny Talk screenreader	Inexpensive screenreader, low memory requirement, supports several synthesisers and Soundblaster cards	FCD	**£80**
Vocal-Eyes screenreader	Supports most speech synthesisers	FCD, PVS, Alphavision	**£350**

Speech for WINDOWS

Item	Notes	Supplier	Price
JAWS for Windows screenreader	Works with many popular synthesisers	Sight & Sound	**£695**
OutSPOKEN screenreader	PC version of OutSPOKEN for WINDOWS. Works with most synthesisers	Alphavision	**£495**
ProTalk for Windows screenreader	Supports Apollo and other synthesisers	PVS, VISability	from **£600**
ScreenPower for Windows screenreader	Supports wide range of braille and speech access devices. Includes training.	Sensory Systems	**£2,995**
Window Bridge screenreader	Supports Apollo and DECTalk synthesisers. Integrated enlarged text.	FCD, Sight & Sound, PVS	**£495**
Window-Eyes screenreader	From designers of Vocal-Eyes.	Alphavision	**£450**
WinVision screenreader	Runs with Business Vision screenreader, for use with Artic Transport and DECTalk synthesisers	Concept	**£1,300**

F

20.13.2 Large (enhanced) character displays

Item	Notes	Supplier	Price
Artic Magnum Deluxe	DOS text 2x-16x, Windows -32x	Concept	£399
Audiodata Large-Print with Audiobox	Speech plus 2x-16x magnification of text. Hardware system	Sensory Systems	£4,095
InLarge	2x-16x magnification for Macintosh computers. Text and graphics software	Alphavision	£99
Lunar 2 for DOS	2x-8x magnification of text with some graphics. Allows a single line of enlarged text to move across centre of screen, or lines can be wrapped round	Dolphin, FCD	£195
Lunar for Windows	Up to 8x magnification of screen. Follows the pointer automatically	Dolphin, FCD	£290
Lunar 2 and Lunar for Windows combination		Dolphin	£350
Magic Deluxe	1.4x-12x magnification in DOS. Best used with mouse. 8x Windows magnification	FCD	£234
Magic 2	Cut-down version of Magic Deluxe. Magnification to x2 only	FCD	£80
Magnicomp v4.2	2x-16x magnification for DOS and Windows	PVS	£750
Magnus for Windows	Windows only screen enlarger, magnifies up to 8x.	FCD	£140
SE (Screen Enhancer)	4x-16x magnification of text. Mouse controlled. Limited Windows magnification	FCD	£320
Vista	2x-16x magnification of DOS and Windows applications. VGA monitors only. Supplied with special VGA replacement card for PCs. Can be used with existing CCTV to give split screen magnified printed text with monochrome PC display.	Sensory Systems	from £2,340
Visulex LPDOS	Large display software for DOS and Windows. Adjustable magnification and colour.	Alphavision, FCD	£445
Zoomtext	2x-16x magnification of DOS text	Pia, Sight & Sound, FCD, Pulse Data	£350
Zoomtext plus	As above, plus Windows magnification	Pia, Sight & Sound, FCD, Pulse Data	£450

F

20.13.3 Notetakers and portables (specially designed)

Item	Notes	Supplier	Price
Braille Lite	Braille input; 18 cell display, speech, text editing, spell checker, calendar, calculator etc	*Sensory Systems*	**£2,995**
Braille'n Speak	Braille input. Integral speech synthesiser. Text editing facility	*Sensory Systems, PVS, Concept*	**£895**
Braille'n Speak 640	As above, but more memory, diary, spell checker etc.	*Sensory Systems, PVS, Concept*	**£1,095**
David	PC with braille input, braille display, speech output. 230-500Mb hard disk, 8Mb memory	*Sight & Sound, Sensory Systems*	from **£8,500**
Eureka A4	Portable note-taker, database, word processor with Perkins braille input and speech. Advanced user and music models available	*Techno-Vision*	**£1,468** to **£2,253**
Jotta Popular	Personal organiser and talking word processor. Braille input	*Pathway*	**£570**
Jotta Professional	Extra facilities such as diary, telephone, calculator etc.	*Pathway*	**£925**
Keynote Companion	Compact PC based QWERTY pocket computer with Keynote Gold speech built-in. Word processor, calculator, database and e-mail software included. LCD screen. External PC compatible floppy disk drive	*Pulse Data*	**£1,500**
Notex 486	Notebook PC. Silent braille keyboard. 42 cell braille display	*Alphavision*	**£5,950**
Type'n Speak	As Braille 'n Speak above, but QWERTY keyboard. Built-in word processor and spell checker	*Sensory Systems*	**£1,295**

F

20.13.4 Electronic (paperless) braille displays

Item	Notes	Supplier	Price
Alva Braille Terminal ABT-80	85 cell display	PVS	£7,900
Alva Braille Terminal ABT-40, ABT-20	43 and 23 cell displays for portable and laptop computers	PVS	£2,200 to £4,500
Audiodata 80 Brailleline	84 cell display plus speech for PC, AT and PS/2	Sensory Systems	£10,950
Braillex IB 80	80 cell display in one row	Alphavision	£9,695
Braillex 2D	80 cell display plus vertical display showing screen data structure	Alphavision	£12,695
Brailloterm	20, 40 or 80 cell display for desktop computers	VISability	from £4,995
Convertibraille	40 cell display for laptops	VISability	£5,975
Inka	Integrated keyboard access. 40 cell display. Speech option	Sight & Sound	from £5,500
Keybraille	45 cell display. Battery powered, can be used with portable PCs	Concept	£4,635
Minibraille	20 cell display. Ideal for small portable PCs and Braille'n Speak	Concept	£1,995
Multibraille	One 84 cell display, 2x42 or 2x82	Concept	£7,295 to £11,585
Powerbraille 40/80	Range of displays for laptop or desk top PCs	Sensory Systems	from £5,500 to £7,800
Windots	Allows Windows screens to be displayed in braille. Works only with Braillex 2D display unit	Alphavision	£1,795

20.13.5 Braille embossers

Embosser	Speed	Supplier	Price
Braille Blazer	Speed: 10-15cps. Portable, 6 dot only	Sensory Systems	£1,095
Braillo Comet	Speed: 40-100cps with graphics capability, 6 and 8 dot. Software included	Sensory Systems	£2,795
Index Basic–S	Single sided	* See Key in 20.13.1	£1,695
Index Basic–D	Double sided	* See Key in 20.13.1	£2,250
Index Everest	Speed: 100cps double sided, single sheet feeder	* See Key in 20.13.1	from £2,595
Mountbatten	Stand-alone electronic brailler. Add-ons allow use as a PC embosser	RNC Enterprises, Concept	from £1627
Porta-Thiel	Speed: 10cps. Portable	Pia, Techno-Vision, PVS, FCD	£995
Thiel Beta X3	Heavy duty embosser. Speed: 130cps	Pia, Techno-Vision, Alphavision	£7,800 approx.
Versapoint	Speed: 40 cps. Optional graphics. Continuous sideways printing	Sensory Systems	£2,660

F

20.13.6 Braille translation programs

Program	Notes	Supplier	Price
Braille Maker Express 2.5	Grade 2 braille automatically from WordPerfect, WordStar and Word for Windows	Pia, Concept, Sight & Sound, Pathway, FCD	£95
Braille Maker Transcript	Grade 2 braille plus clear and large print, which can be printed to varying low vision needs.	Pia, Sight & Sound, Pathway	£175
Braille Maker Professional 2.5	All the above plus maths and languages	Pia, Concept, Sight & Sound, Pathway, FCD	£495
BrailleMaster	Eureka A4 version	Techno-Vision	£130
BrailleMaster	PC version for DOS programs	Techno-Vision, PVS, Alphavision	£260
BrailleMaster v6	For DOS and Windows	Techno-Vision	£285
Centre Text to Braille	For BBC, Nimbus; PC version available	RCEVH	£17
Cipher	For PCs and Index embossers	Dolphin, FCD, Sensory Systems	£101
Duxbury	For PCs. Macintosh version available	Sensory Systems, Sight & Sound	£450
Megadots	Braille Desktop Publishing and translation for DOS text. Includes word processor	Alphavision	£395
Text to Braille 3	For Archimedes computers	Dorton IT	£30

F

20.13.7 OCR reading systems

Item	Notes	Supplier	Price
Open Book	For PCs. HP 3P scanner with Open Book software. Automatic page orientation	PVS, Dolphin	from **£1,225**
OSCAR	For 486 PCs. HP 3P scanner plus OSCAR software. Automatic page orientation	Sensory Systems	**£1,595**
Reading AdvantEdge	Scanner with Kurzweil recognition software. Automatic page orientation	Sight & Sound	**£1,105** to **£2,605**
Recognita Plus 2.0	For PCs with 4Mb memory. HP 3P scanner with simple-to-use Auge menu software	Alphavision, Concept , PVS, FCD	from **£625**

Leisure   G

21 Recreations   355

G

22 Holidays   374

21 Recreations

The leisure-time interests of blind and partially sighted people are as varied as those of the rest of the community. They have successfully taken up pursuits as diverse as photography, choreography, and pigeon racing. Visually impaired sportsmen and women have distinguished themselves at national and international levels. Many would rather join in the activities of ordinary local clubs and societies than be segregated into a special club for the blind. Often, the most appropriate way of helping visually impaired people to participate is to provide transport to clubs of their choice, where they can, if necessary, use adapted equipment such as braille playing cards.

RNIB Leisure Services provides information and advice about a wide range of leisure pursuits and supports projects initiated by other agencies. Assisting the Manager of the department are four development officers. The **Leisure Officer, Recreation**, is responsible for the development of all home and local activities, including gardening and crafts, especially for elderly people. **The Leisure Officer, Arts**, is responsible for the development of all arts activities including drama, museums, art, sculpture etc., and the **Music Officer** is responsible for encouraging increased participation in the performance and appreciation of music. There is also a **Broadcasting Officer** (see 19.8). A range of directories, reports and information packs are provided, including one specifically for older people, giving more details of different aspects of participation and of particular organisations. For information about physical education and leisure activities for children, see 8.14 and 8.16.

British Blind Sport helps blind and partially sighted people in all matters relating to physical recreation. The aim is to encourage blind people to take part in a wide range of sports and recreation in the community, including less popular sports, and to help provide special facilities where these are needed. British Blind Sport selects and trains teams for European, World and Paralympic championships. It acts as a pressure group to ensure that the needs of visually impaired people are taken into account when sports and recreational facilities are planned in the community, and will try to help them with any problems regarding sports or recreation. It has established a central register of information and produces a quarterly magazine, **Participation** ⊤.

21.1 Arts and crafts

Many visually impaired people successfully take part in art and craft work. **ADVISE**, a panel of specialist teachers, aims to promote the development of art, craft, design and technology for all blind and partially sighted people. ADVISE is recognised and supported by RNIB and VIEW (Visually Impaired Education and Welfare). Further details from *John Everett, Director, Art Department, Royal National College for the Blind*. Mr. Everett will gladly advise any blind or partially sighted person who wishes

Key to media of publication ⊕ clear print ⬤ large print ⬤ braille ⊤ tape ⊛ Moon ⊙ disk
Where a full address is not given in the text, see 32 (Useful addresses)

to pursue an interest in arts and crafts on how to set about it. At the Royal National College, students with varying degrees of sight loss are producing BTEC, GCSE and A-level work, using many different media and materials, including collage, clay, pottery, textiles, photography and jewellery as well as drawing and painting. A few registered blind students have gone on to art college.

Carole Agger, an artist who became totally blind in 1990, developed techniques which have enabled her to paint again despite her loss of sight. Her techniques to enable blind people to create some very simple paintings are described in **Beyond the Horizon Line**, a learning pack consisting of an audio cassette and support information in braille and large print. It costs £12.50 from *Crossborder Arts, Unit 1, Peterborough Arts Centre, Orton Goldhay, Peterborough PE2 5JQ* ℘ 01733 234583.

Local groups such as **Art to Share** in Nottingham provide opportunities for visually impaired and sighted people to share their experience of the arts, thereby increasing their mutual enjoyment and interest. For example, discussion groups may be organised at exhibitions with the participation of the artists whose work was on view, as well as adult education classes, workshops, music recitals, and visits to museums, art galleries and historic houses. Details from *RNIB Leisure Services.*

> **'Drawing isn't a matter of what you see, it's a question of what you can make other people see'**
> – Edgar Degas, 1834-1917, who had monocular vision, a squint, corneal ulcers and other eye conditions which combined to give him a distorted visual field and 'a cloudiness in front of my eyes'.

The **Richard Attenborough Centre for Disability and the Arts** aims to pursue the understanding and practice of touch as a cognitive experience for both visually impaired and sighted people. It provides extended arts courses for people with disabilities and researches into disability and alternative approaches to the arts. It also produces written material and mounts exhibitions on a regular basis. For details of forthcoming courses, publications and information about the Centre's work, contact the *Richard Attenborough Centre, University of Leicester, University Road, Leicester LE1 7RH* ℘ 0116 252 2455.

The **Living Paintings Trust** is a charity which aims to make well known works of art more accessible to blind people in their own homes. Albums, each containing tactile representations of ten works of art, are available on loan free of charge together with descriptive commentaries on tape.

RNIB's journal **New Beacon** carries a regular feature, **Leisure for all**, which includes information on the arts. **Arts and Crafts News**, another RNIB publication, contains tips and suggestions for tutors and students about a range of arts and crafts. RNIB Leisure Services also produces a range of information packs and reports on the arts, including **A taster of the arts** and **Painting, Photography and Sculpture**.

21.1.1 Handicrafts

Visually impaired people interested in handicrafts such as **basket-making**, **weaving**, **carpentry** etc. should be able to get help in developing their skills from their local authority or voluntary society, one or other of which in most areas will run craft groups especially for blind and handicapped people. Materials are usually provided at discount or trade rates. To find out what is available in any given area, contact the local social services.

21.1.2 Knitting

About 100 **clear print knitting patterns** are produced by Wendy Wools. They are available from local Wendy Knit Shops or direct from *Department CP, Carter and Parker Ltd., Guiseley, Yorkshire LS20 9PD,* who will send a list of the patterns in

Knitting using a spectacle-mounted intermediate telescope

return for a stamped, addressed envelope. A large print version of this list is available for £2.00 from *Mr. F. K. Peachey, The Thorns, Pantile Lane, Brampton Road, Madley, Herefordshire HR2 9LU* ✆ 01981 250481. Individual knitting patterns could be enlarged, brailled by one of the transcription services (see 33) or recorded on tape by one of the tape reading services (see 19.6). A selection of knitting patterns in braille and Moon can be obtained from *RNIB Customer Services* and in braille from the *Scottish Braille Press*. Braille and Moon knitting patterns and some **crochet** patterns can be borrowed from the *National Library for the Blind* together with braille books about knitting.

A **Knitting Information Pack** ❶ ❸ ❼ is available from *RNIB Leisure Services.*
NEW A **knitting starter pack** with tactile or large print row counters, needles, needle gauge and a cassette of information about patterns costs £9.00 from *RNIB Customer Services.*

A cassette entitled **Better Knitting Made Easier** was recorded by Audrie Stratford, an experienced knitter. She gives instructions for knitting methods and designs that should be easy even for an inexperienced blind person to follow. The cassette can be borrowed free of charge from *Jewish Care Communications Department, 85 Lordship Road, London N16 5BF* ✆ 0181 880 2244. It is also available from *Calibre.*

Knitting machines are used by a number of blind people. Some have been taught by craft teachers, and there is no reason why instructors who train sighted people should not also be able to teach blind people to use knitting machines.

21.1.3 Needlework

A free cassette version of the monthly **Needlecraft** magazine can be obtained from *Talkback Magazine Service* (see 19.4.4).

21.1.4 Photography

Enlarged photographs can help people with limited sight to see objects which would otherwise be nearly invisible to them, and some visually impaired people have themselves become very successful amateur photographers. See 22.4 for details of residential photography courses.

The **Disabled Photographers' Society**, which has some blind and partially sighted members, is a registered charity set up by photographers who take a special interest in the problems of disabled people wanting to take up photography. They would be happy to try to help any visually impaired members with advice on the choice of equipment and how to obtain it. Membership is £5.00 per annum for individuals, £15 for groups. Contact the Society at *PO Box 130, Richmond, Surrey TW10 6XQ*.

21.1.5 Museums, art galleries and other places of interest

While this country has so far no permanent exhibition for blind people, such as the one at the Museum of Arts and History in Brussels or the Tom Gallery in Tokyo, there has been a growing awareness of the needs of people with little or no sight who want to be able to enjoy works of art and other museum exhibitions. **Discovering Museums – a guide to museums in the United Kingdom for blind and partially sighted people ❶❷❸** (1993. £9.95, RNIB) covers nearly 450 museums and art galleries, and gives details of provisions made to allow visually impaired visitors access to their exhibits. Even at museums and art galleries not listed in the guide, it is worth enquiring whether any help can be provided for a visually impaired visitor. RNIB Leisure Services (Arts) can provide advice on how best to make such an approach. Among museums and art galleries which now provide facilities, details of which were not available when the guide was compiled, is the **National Portrait Gallery**. Visitors to their Later 20th Century Galleries are offered a tactile floor plan, a large print black and white illustrated guide, permission to touch six of the sculptures, thermoforms of four of the paintings with tape commentary, large print and braille captions for some of the exhibits, and the loan of magnifiers.

The **Cathedrals through Touch and Hearing Trust** has enabled blind and partially sighted people to appreciate the architecture and artefacts at a number of cathedrals. Wooden models and ground plans conveying the shape, size and structure of the buildings can be touched and explored while listening to a descriptive commentary on headphones. Taped guides, provided on free loan with a personal stereo for use in the cathedrals, give details of history, architecture and acoustics together with sounds of organ, choir and bells. Cathedrals with some or all of these facilities are Canterbury, Coventry, Chichester, Durham, Exeter, Gloucester, Hereford, Lichfield, Lincoln, Norwich, Peterborough, St. Albans, Salisbury, Winchester, Worcester and York. Further information from *Professor John Hull, School of Education, University of Birmingham, Edgbaston, Birmingham*

B15 2TT ℘ 0121 414 4836. The taped guides are suitable for home listening, and are on sale at cathedral gift shops or from Professor Hull, or can be borrowed from *Calibre* and some county libraries. Braille and large print guides to many of the cathedrals can be borrowed from the *National Library for the Blind*, and the braille guides can be bought from the Library for £1.00 each.

The free annual guide to **National Trust** properties, **Information for Visitors with Disabilities**, is available in large print and on cassette. It indicates whether large print, taped or braille guides are provided at the properties. The guide is updated annually and is free, in return for an addressed adhesive label stamped with minimum postage, from *Dept. IT, The National Trust*. The Members' Magazine is available on cassette free of charge to visually impaired National Trust members. Many of the 16 Trust Regions in England, Wales and Northern Ireland provide a taped version of their newsletters for members living within their boundaries.

English Heritage Guide for Visitors with Disabilities lists staffed properties county by county and includes information useful to visitors with visual impairments. It is available free in large print, braille or on cassette from *English Heritage, Portica House, Addison Road, Chilton Industrial Estate, Sudbury, Suffolk CO10 6YJ* ℘ 01787 311868. The large print version is in separate booklets, one for each county.

Soundalive tour tapes are designed to be used when visiting English Heritage and other sites, but are also suitable for home listening. There are 100 tapes to choose from, including titles as diverse as Audley End (a Jacobean mansion near Saffron Walden), Corbridge Roman site (Northumberland), HMS Belfast (London), Overlord Embroidery (the D-Day museum at Hastings), Warwick Castle and Wigan Pier. Visually impaired individuals can obtain the tapes from the *Talking Newspaper Association* for £2.95 each or one different tape a week at an annual subscription of £12.50.

Advice on ways of making museums, art galleries, arts venues and heritage sites more accessible to visually impaired people can be obtained from a consultant, himself registered blind, who produces audio guides and tactile plans and images. Contact *William Kirby, 11 Eastgate Street, Winchester SO23 8EB* ℘ 01962 854003.

21.1.6 Further reading

DAM (Disability Arts Magazine) quarterly ❶❷ includes audio-description of illustrations. Annual subscription £12. Further details from *DAM, 10 Woad Lane, Grimsby DN37 9NH* ℘ 01472 280031.

The **NEW** **Arts and Disability Directory** (3rd ed. 1994) ❶❸❷ gives information advice to disabled people interested in participating in the arts. Free to visually impaired and other disabled people from the *Arts Council, 14 Great Peter Street, London SW1P 3NQ* ℘ 0171 973 6511.

What Colour is the Wind? (£5.30. 1992.) by Sue Blagden and John Everett, art tutors at Queen Alexandra College and the Royal National College, describes their work with visually impaired students and the techniques they use. From *National Society for Education in Art and Design, The Gatehouse, Corsham Court, Corsham, Wilts. SN13 0BZ* ℘ 01249 714825.

Art horizons 1990, a report on the first European Blind Union conference on topics such as access to museums and art galleries and audio description in the theatre, cinema and on television. RNIB. 1992. £6.00.

Museums Without Barriers: a new deal for disabled people. Fondation de France/Routledge. 1991. Survey of projects providing improved access for people with disabilities.

An **Arts pack** is available for £10 from the *British Journal of Visual Impairment.* It contains articles on visually impaired people and the arts published in the Journal between 1981 and 1993.

21.2 The performing arts

21.2.1 Dancing

There is no reason why a visually impaired student who wants to take up dancing should not join ordinary classes together with sighted students. A check by the *In Touch* office indicated that applications from blind students would be treated sympathetically by adult education institutes, which would try to help them follow the courses of their choice if at all possible. Dancing classes are run by some local voluntary societies for the blind.

Blind and partially sighted dancers have for some years taken part in performances given by the **Amici Integrated Dance Theatre Company** which runs regular workshops in London and occasionally goes on tour with its productions. Enquiries to *Barbara Lawrence, 13 Dane Road, London W13 9AQ* ✆ 0181 840 4874 (evenings).

Visually impaired and sighted dancers train and perform together in **Touchdown Dance**, a company which uses a free flowing dance technique known as contact improvisation. As well as touring, the company holds workshops at various locations in the UK and Europe. Further information from *Katy Dymoke, 111 Huddersfield Road, Saddleworth, Lancashire DL3 5NU* ✆ 01457 876770.

The **Royal Opera House** runs free dance classes for visually impaired people whether beginners or with some experience of dancing. Details from *Darryl Jaffray, Head of Education (Ballet), Royal Opera House, Covent Garden, London WC2E 9DD* ✆ 0171 240 1200.

21.2.2 Drama

Participation in amateur dramatics can be a valuable activity for visually impaired people, not only as a new interest but also as a way of restoring confidence for those who have lost their sight. A number of visually impaired people have joined ordinary local drama groups. Apart from classes at adult education centres, there are many amateur dramatic groups. Details of local ones can be obtained from the public library.

There are some blind drama groups including **The Venturers**, who also welcome sighted members; details from *Valerie Slade, 170 Cambridge Road, Seven Kings, Ilford, Essex IG3 8NA* ✆ 0181 599 4256, and the **Kellett Players**, run by *Mr B. Naylor, 85 Stonegate Road, Leeds LS6 4HZ* ✆ 0113 278 2307.

A low vision aid consisting of a spectacle frame with a built-in telescopic system for distance viewing. Various caps can be fitted for different working distances

The **National Association of Drama with the Visually Handicapped** organises annual **summer schools** and weekend workshops in the spring and autumn. It publishes regular newsletters 🅛 🅑 🅣. It can offer advice on setting up a drama workshop, and if necessary provide a tutor. Details from *Norman Machin, 153 Homefield Road, Sileby, Leicestershire ℘ 01509 812754.*

Graeae, the only British professional theatre company of disabled performers, aims to employ disabled performers and to offer training to those who are new and inexperienced. Blind and partially sighted actors have taken part in the company's productions, including a play by Marie Oshodi, who is herself blind. The company produces a mixture of Theatre in Education programmes, small scale touring productions and theatre skills workshops. Further information from *Graeae, Interchange Studios, Dalby Street, London NW5 3NQ ℘ 0171 267 1959.*

An information pack, **Performing Arts** 🅛 🅑 🅣, is available from *RNIB Leisure Services.*

21.2.3 Theatres

Over 20 theatres can now provide live **audio description**, relayed on headphones, of the action on stage. A list of theatres 🅛 🅑 offering audio description and other facilities for visually impaired patrons can be obtained from *RNIB Leisure Services.*

21.3 Music

RNIB Music Services is run by three full-time specialist staff covering the areas of education (see 8.13), leisure and the production of braille music. Three free information packs 🅛 🅑 🅣 are available from the *Music Officer, RNIB Leisure Services:* **Making Music and Performing for Visually Impaired People,**

Music Appreciation for Visually Impaired People and **Music for Leisure for People with Severe Disabilities**.

Contact with blind and partially sighted musicians and music lovers can be made through either the *Music Officer, RNIB Leisure Services* or the *Visually Impaired Musicians Association.*

NEW The **Inner Vision Music Company** has been set up to help visually impaired musicians in this country, regardless of culture and musical style. It commissioned a study of the problems they face as a first step towards establishing how best their needs could be met. The results of the study **L B T** are available for £5.00 from *Agnes Meadows, Flat 6, Braunton Mansions, 28 Rosebery Avenue, London EC1R 4SY* ✆ 0171 833 5828.

21.3.1 Large print music

Most large print music produced in this country is aimed at children and is unlikely to serve the needs of an adult musician. Large print music stocked by the American Library of Congress can be borrowed through the National Library for the Blind. One **music shop** which has proved helpful to people wanting to obtain large print music available in this country is *Bell & Crane Music, 154 Sidwell Street, Exeter, Devon* ✆ 01392 436258. It also runs a **mail order service**.

Music can be specially copied onto large-sized music manuscript paper – supplies can be obtained from the Partially Sighted Society – or enlarged, using a photocopy enlarger. The National Library for the Blind provides a **music enlargement service** for which it makes a charge of 10p a sheet. The Partially Sighted Society's Sight Centres and many other Resource Centres have **photocopy enlargers**, as well as public libraries and local high street print shops.

John Strachan's DIY design brings the music closer

NEW Following an agreement between RNIB and the Music Publishers' Association, photocopy enlargements can be made for individuals without infringing copyright if permission is obtained from the publisher. Some publishers may be able to provide enlargements. Further information is given in **Music in large print** (RNIB/MPA. 1994), £3 from *RNIB Education Centre*.

NEW The use of computer technology (MIDI – Musical Instrument Digital Interface) in the production of large print music as well as in the composition of music is explained in an information pack **Introduction to MIDI for Visually Impaired People ❶❸❼**, £1.50 from *RNIB Leisure Services*.

Some partially sighted musicians could be helped by **adapting music stands** to bring the music closer. Several schools with partially sighted pupils have made their own music stands. A rest which brings music to within a few inches of the pianist's face was designed by *John Strachan, 16 Chapel Meadow, Gilberdyke, Brough, N. Humberside HU15 2UN ✆ 01430 441131*. Mr. Strachan will provide details on request (see illustration in this section). The local **REMAP** group is another possible source of help. Good lighting is also important when reading music (see 3.9 and 3.10).

Information on Music for People with Partial Sight, a large print resource paper updated in 1995 (£3.60), and a quarterly taped newsletter **Music News** (in return for two blank C90 cassettes) plus other information and advice can be obtained from the *National Music and Disability Information Service, Foxhole, Dartington, Totnes, Devon TQ9 6EB ✆ 01803 866701*.

21.3.2 Braille music

Braille music is no more difficult to learn than any other specialist braille code. RNIB Music Services Manager can advise on suitable books for learners to use.

Braille music is produced in this country by RNIB. Production is centred on the requirements of people in the fields of education and employment, but as much material as resources allow is produced for leisure needs. Contact *RNIB Customer Services* for details of what music is available in this country and overseas. Newly published braille music is listed in **High Browse ❶❸❼** and **Spotlight ❶❸❼** monthly magazines, available from RNIB, and in **Braille Music Magazine**, a monthly journal with articles of interest to both amateur and professional musicians. RNIB also publishes a braille magazine concentrating on rock, pop and jazz music.

Braille music can be borrowed from the *National Library for the Blind*. Catalogues are available in print and braille. The collection includes almost all the music in RNIB's Braille Music Catalogue as well as much from earlier years and from other sources. The National Library is the UK agent for the American Library of Congress and holds **catalogues of braille music** which can be borrowed from them.

Braille Music: an international survey, published in 1986, was compiled by John Henry, a blind harpsichordist. It gives information, arranged by country and by instrument, about sources of braille music around the world. It costs £1.00 in braille (to registered blind people), £10 in print or on cassette, from the *National Library*. The braille version can be borrowed from the Library.

RNIB Customer Services can arrange for music to be transcribed if it is not otherwise available. A private service for urgent transcriptions from braille into print is offered by *Stephen Gardiner, Hillside, St. James Park, Tunbridge Wells, Kent TN1 2LG* ✆ 01892 538881.

21.3.3 Opportunities for singers

Blind singers often join sighted choirs if they are expert at reading braille music. There are some choirs for visually impaired singers. They include a long-established choir in **Leeds**, contact *Development Officer for the Sensory Impaired, Social Services Department, Merrion House, 110 Merrion Centre, Leeds LS2 8QA* ✆ 0113 247 8593, and the **Visionaries**, contact *Society for the Blind of Dewsbury, Batley and District, 64 Daisy Hill, Dewsbury, West Yorkshire WF13 1LJ* ✆ 01924 465801. Another small group which has been active since the 1950s is the **Dorset Blind Choir**, contact *Miss M. Curtis, 10 Maclaren Road, Bournemouth, Dorset B89 2UZ* ✆ 01202 514083.

21.3.4 Inner Vision Orchestra

This orchestra of blind and partially sighted musicians comes from many different cultural backgrounds. They provide concerts and entertainments either singly or in groups. Further details from *Balluji Surivastav, 33 Northolme Road, London N5 2UU* ✆ 0171 354 5709.

21.3.5 Blind bellringers

A visually impaired person wanting to learn bell ringing can find an experienced teacher through the *Association of Church Bell Ringers (David Thorne or Anne Carpenter), c/o Ringing World, Penmark House, Woodbridge Meadows, Guildford, Surrey GU1 1BL* ✆ 01483 569535. One blind bellringer has suggested forming an association of blind campanologists throughout the country so that they can exchange concerns and advice. Contact *Henry Brugsch, 17 Kent Close, Kidderminster DY10 1NS* ✆ 01562 820090.

21.3.6 Events and concerts

A guide to access and facilities for disabled people at 50 music venues in London is available free in large print or on tape from the *Music Officer, RNIB Leisure Services.* **Talking Notes** presented live by professional broadcasters and musicians are provided on headphones at the **Royal Festival Hall**, the **English National Opera** at the London Coliseum, the **Royal Opera House**, Covent Garden, the **Glyndebourne Touring Opera**, **The Anvil**, Basingstoke, and are being considered for opera performances at the 1995 **Edinburgh Festival**. At concerts, Talking Notes replicate the printed programme and provide commentary on platform activity; in the opera house they give a synopsis illustrated with descriptions of sets, costumes and activity on the stage.

A monthly tape bulletin gives programme details of events and concerts taking place at the **South Bank Centre**, the **Barbican**, the **Royal Albert Hall**, **St. John's, Smith Square**, the **Wigmore Hall**, the **Coliseum** and the **Royal Opera House**, Covent Garden. The bulletin is compiled two months in advance by the *Disability*

Resource Team, annual subscription £6.00. A braille selection of South Bank Centre events is available from the *Music Officer, RNIB Leisure Services.*

NEW Information about forthcoming events is available in accessible formats at some venues outside London. These include the **Warwick Arts Centre** (**L** **B** **T** from the Box Office), the **Symphony Hall, Birmingham** (**T** from Birmingham Royal Institution for the Blind's Resource Centre) and, following a request from a blind patron, a monthly listing in braille of events at **St David's Hall, Cardiff** is available for reference at the box office.

21.3.7 Concessions for visually impaired music lovers

Under the terms of a legacy, RNIB has tickets at a nominal price for most Royal Albert Hall concerts. These are available to visually impaired music lovers and guides accompanying them. **NEW** Other venues which offer concessions include the South Bank Centre (free seats for guides accompanying blind patrons) and the London Coliseum (seats at £10 each, usually in the front stalls). Further details from the *Music Officer, RNIB Leisure Services.*

NEW The **English Chamber Orchestra** offers a 20 per cent reduction for a blind or partially sighted patron and guide (25 per cent for groups including visually impaired people) for performances given at the Barbican, and hopes to extend the arrangement to performances at other concert halls. Enquiries to *Membership Secretary, ECO, 2 Coningsby Road, London W5 4HR* ℘ 0181 840 6565.

21.3.8 Recorded music

Taped extracts from **Gramophone** magazine are available monthly from the Talking Newspaper Association (see 19.4.1). Details of other cassette magazines with articles of interest to music lovers are given in 19.4.4.

21.4 Writing

One year courses on tape, **Starting to Write** (introductory level) and **Poetry** (second level) can be obtained from *Open College of the Arts, Student Services, Houndhill, Worsborough, Barnsley, S. Yorks. S70 6TU* ℘ 01226 730495. Second level **Short Fiction** will be available shortly.

The **New Playwrights Trust** provides its newsletter and other information on tape. Membership for registered visually impaired people is £7.00 a year. Further details from the *New Playwrights Trust, Interchange Studios, Dalby Street, London NW5 3NQ* ℘ 0171 284 2818.

A group of blind writers based in Glasgow runs an annual **residential course** for visually impaired writers at Newbattle Abbey College, Dalkeith, usually in early May. Enquiries to the Chairman, Nick Larkin on ℘ 0141 954 8140 or *c/o Glasgow & West of Scotland Society for the Blind, 2 Queens Crescent, St. George's Cross, Glasgow G4 9BW.* The group produced a collection of short stories and poetry called 'A New Vision', available in print for £2.50 or on tape (4 cassettes) for £7.00 from *Mr. Larkin.*

An information pack on **Creative writing** **L** **B** **T** is available from *RNIB Leisure Services.*

21.5 Indoor games

21.5.1 Bingo

NEW A bingo board and pre-printed large print or braille cards are now available from RNIB so that visually impaired people can play with family and friends at home or at a local club, but not at commercial bingo halls. The cards are slotted into the board, which has 15 holes to display the numbers and contrasting yellow caps to cover each number when it is called. The board is £3.50 and the cards £2.63 a set of 50.

Large print washable plastic bingo cards, with big bold black numerals on a white background are £18.74 a pack of 20 from *Toys for the Handicapped.* The cards are used with water-based marker pens.

Some clubs for blind people play a version of bingo based on dominoes. In one method of play, there are four players to a table and each player has seven dominoes. A caller sits at the top table and has a full set of dominoes, which are shuffled thoroughly. Domino 6/4 is always called first to start the game, and every person who has that number places it in the middle of the table. The first person to have seven dominoes out calls 'house' and the caller checks the dominoes.

In another version, players sit two to a table, and one set of dominoes (double blank to double six) is allowed to each table. Each player draws nine dominoes, leaving ten in the box. The same nine may be retained for each game, or the set may be shuffled and re-dealt. The player places the dominoes face upwards immediately in front of him or her and turns each one over when that number is called. The caller has a complete set of dominoes which are shuffled and placed face downward on the table. They are picked up at random and, after being called, placed to one side in numerical order so that checking is easy. The caller continues until a player has had all his or her numbers called, and when this happens the player cries 'bingo!'

21.5.2 Card games

Good stationers, department stores, etc. are likely to stock **large print playing cards** made by well-known manufacturers. A range of large print cards is stocked by the Partially Sighted Society. Standard size cards with large index are £2.22 a pack, £3.66 with giant numbers, giant size cards £9.79. RNIB **Easy-to-see** standard size cards with large symbols are £1.70 a pack.

RNIB Easy-to-see playing cards with **brailled** symbols are £1.84, standard print cards £1.80 a pack. RNIB also stocks brailled **Happy Families** and **Uno** cards. A knowledge of the braille alphabet only is needed to be able to use these cards. All are suitable for sighted and blind people playing together, as the cards are otherwise standard in design and size.

21.5.3 Chess

Special chess sets for blind players, including a pocket set, are available from RNIB; white and black are distinguished by a point on either the black or white pieces, and all pieces have small pegs at the bottom so that they can be plugged into holes on the chessboard. The black squares on the board are raised, and the white slightly sunk.

The **Braille Chess Association** serves visually impaired chess players, whether braillists or not. It organises the British Championship for the Visually Handicapped and other over-the-board tournaments in this country and abroad. It offers advice on all matters concerning chess, including techniques by which blind players can use chess computers. Information is supplied on cassette as well as in braille, and members have access to the Association's comprehensive tape library of chess material. The Association welcomes beginners as well as experts and arranges postal chess games between members both in Britain and abroad. Full details from the secretary, *Stan Lovell, 7 Coldwell Square, Crossgates, Leeds LS15 7HB* ✆ 0113 260 0013.

The American chess magazine **En Passant** can be obtained on cassette from *Cadwell Recording Services for the Blind*, annual subscription £2.00. The **Braille Chess Magazine** is published quarterly by RNIB, 77p a copy.

21.5.4 Other board games

A variety of games including **draughts, beetle, dominoes, cluedo, backgammon, noughts and crosses, solitaire** and **monopoly** 🅛🅑 are available from RNIB. There are modifications to the usual designs so that blind players can distinguish the pieces, but all are suitable for blind and sighted players to play together. None of the adaptations requires any knowledge of braille. On the dominoes, for example, the pips are raised so that they can easily be felt, and in draughts white draughtsmen are smaller than black, and the black squares on the board are slightly sunk. A wooden domino holder designed by a blind man, John Broughton of Lincoln, is also available from RNIB.

Some board games stocked by RNIB, including **Ludo** and **Snakes and Ladders**, use a colour-coding system devised by another blind man, John Slade, in which different shapes indicate different colours.

Extra-large dice with very clear markings can be obtained from *Ways & Means*. **Tactile dice** are available from RNIB.

An adapted **Scrabble** set, £24.15 from RNIB, has letters and values in print and braille. The letter tiles fit into embossed squares on the board, and the dots are distinct enough to be felt even by people whose sense of touch is poor. To play the game effectively demands a good knowledge of the braille alphabet and a good memory. RNIB's **Large print scrabble**, £16.22, has an $18\frac{3}{4}$″ square board and 1″ square tiles.

21.5.5 Large print crosswords

Two collections of **Daily Mirror** crosswords, £1.95 each from the *Partially Sighted Society*.

An extra large print crossword puzzle book and a large print collection of **Daily Telegraph** cryptic puzzles, £3.14 each from *RNIB*.

Jumbo Print Crossword Book (60 puzzles compiled by Terry Pitts Fenby) £3.99 from *Age Concern England* or from bookshops.

Extra Large Print Crossword Book, £4.95 from *Jennie Janes, 29 Pynchon Paddocks, Little Hallingbury, Herts. CM22 7RJ* ✆ 01279 724529.

Large Print Crosswords and Large Print Puzzles bi-monthly magazines, £1.55 each from newsagents or from *Nexus Media Ltd., Warwick House, Swanley, Kent BR6 8HY* ℘ 01322 660070 (℘ 0191 510 2290 to arrange subscription).

NEW Jumbo Print Crossword Book for Gardeners by Terry Pitts Fenby, £4.99 from *Grub Street Publishing Ltd., The Basement, 10 Chivalry Road, London SW11 1HT* ℘ 0171 924 3966.

21.5.6 Braille puzzles

NEW Conundrum, a monthly braille magazine published by RNIB, includes crossword and other puzzles such as brain-teasers, anagrams and word searches. A braille **crossword kit** consisting of a board with square recesses and cubes with different symbols on each face is available from RNIB for £45.

Braille crossword puzzles are included with other word games and brain teasers in the free introductory pack supplied by the Braille Puzzle Club. For an annual fee of £18, members then receive a puzzle pack each month which includes at least ten crossword puzzles. Contact *Frank Ellis, 66 Beckwith Crescent, Harrogate HG2 0BH* ℘ 01423 562613.

21.5.7 Quiz games

A series of quiz tapes, originally designed for amusing families on boring car journeys, can be obtained from RNIB for £2.00 each. Topics covered are General Knowledge (3 tapes), Sport, Pop Music, Entertainment (television and cinema) and Junior General Knowledge (2 tapes).

Recreational Activities for Deafblind People, an information pack produced by RNIB Leisure Services, gives details of a number of suitable indoor games. For details of games suitable for blind children, see 6.7.

21.6 Outdoor pastimes

21.6.1 Angling

Many people continue to enjoy fishing despite poor sight, and totally blind fishermen have won cups in local contests. Local clubs are likely to be sympathetic to the needs of blind anglers, and pleased to help them if at all possible. Fishing-tackle shops can usually give addresses of local clubs, but in case of difficulty the *National Federation of Anglers, Halliday House, Egginton Junction, Derbyshire DE65 6GU* ℘ 01283 734735, may be able to help.

A braille edition of **Teach Yourself Fishing** (two volumes, catalogue nos. 25149/ 50) is £2.22 from *RNIB*.

21.6.2 Gardening

This is one of the most popular leisure-time pursuits for visually impaired people. Information and advice can be obtained from *Horticultural Therapy, Goulds Ground, Vallis Way, Frome, Somerset BA11 3DW* ℘ 01373 467072 (24 hour answerphone), the national charity for disabled gardeners and those who work with them. It co-ordinates services for blind and partially sighted people. The **Advisory Committee for Blind Gardeners** organises residential weekend courses for blind gardeners and seminars for sighted people on gardening with the blind. The quarterly magazine **Come Gardening** is produced on cassette (to be returned within the quarter) and in braille, annual subscription £3.00 each, or £5.00 for both. The Moon version is free. Subscribers to the magazine have free use of the **cassette library for blind gardeners** containing recordings of handbooks issued by the Royal Horticultural Society and others, as well as extracts from weekly and monthly gardening journals. The library does not lend cassettes but will make copies if subscribers provide the blank cassettes. All enquiries and subscriptions (but no cassettes) to *Horticultural Therapy*.

Gardening Without Sight ⓛ Ⓑ Ⓣ Ⓜ by Kathleen Fleet, £2.50 from RNIB, is an invaluable source of information on gardening methods and tools for blind and partially sighted people.

21.6.3 Rambling

A competent blind walker should be able to join in local groups organised by the Ramblers' Association, though it might be advisable to bring a sighted companion, at least on the first occasion. For details of local groups, and a large print fact sheet, contact the *Ramblers' Association, 1-5 Wandsworth Road, London SW8 2XX* ✆ 0171 582 6878.

Groups of blind ramblers can get help in planning routes from officials of the Forestry Commission, who can sometimes provide guides. Those interested in exploring their own part of the country should enquire about this sort of help from regional offices. Addresses and telephone numbers can be obtained from *The Forestry Commission, 231 Corstorphine Road, Edinburgh EH12 7AT* ✆ 0131 334 0303.

Rangers in National Parks can also help with outings in rural areas. Each National Park has its own information service, the addresses of which can be obtained from *National Parks and Planning Branch, The Countryside Commission, John Dower House, Crescent Place, Cheltenham, Gloucestershire GL50 3RA* ✆ 01242 521381.

Many nature trails in all parts of the country now have facilities enabling blind visitors to walk through them independently. Details can be supplied by *RNIB Leisure Services*. The British Naturalists Association occasionally arranges rambles for blind people, with an Association member as a guide, at nature reserves where they have branches. Enquiries to the Association at *1 Bracken Mews, Chingford, London E4 7UT*. Details of nature reserves which have not been adapted for blind visitors but which might be able to provide a guide to accompany a blind person can be obtained from *The Wildlife Trusts, Witham Park, Waterside South, Lincoln LN5 7JR* ✆ 01522 544400.

Ⓝ **Bird song**: there is now a taped guide to the Royal Society for the Protection of Birds nature reserve at Radipole Lake in Weymouth, Dorset, the first of its reserves to provide this facility. For further information about RSPB reserves and details of bird song cassettes they supply, contact *RSPB, The Lodge, Sandy, Bedfordshire SG19 2GL* ✆ 01767 680551. A series of **teach yourself bird sounds** cassettes, based on habitat (e.g. gardens, rivers and wet meadows, sea cliffs, etc.) are available for £6.99 each from *Waxwing Associates, Little Okeford, Christchurch Road, Tring,*

Ⓖ

Herts. HP23 4EF ℘ *01442 823356.* **Night of the Owls,** an information pack including braille descriptions, feathers and tactile outlines of owls and hawks and a cassette describing and explaining the sights and sounds of the night, is £11 from the *Hawk and Owl Trust, c/o Zoological Society of London, Regent's Park, London NW1 4RY.*

21.7 Sport

Visually impaired people are active in a wide range of sports including **horse-riding**, **sailing**, **skiing**, **water skiing** and many others. Blind and partially sighted people who have contacted local sports groups have found relatively little difficulty in joining in, provided instructors first understand their problems. There are also throughout the country a number of sports clubs specifically for blind people. Some games have been adapted, or specially devised, so that visually impaired people can play them. Details can be obtained from *RNIB Leisure Services* or from *British Blind Sport.*

British Blind Sport has sub-committees for **archery**, **athletics**, **bowls**, **cricket**, **football**, **goalball**, **judo**, **swimming** and **tandem cycling**. It has a database listing virtually every visually impaired group undertaking sport in the country and can put anyone interested in touch with their nearest club or activity. It organises 'Have a Go Days' all round the country in areas not normally served by organised provision, giving the opportunity to try out new sporting activities. Bowls, golf and tandem cycling are among the most popular activities.

21.7.1 Bowls

The **English National Association of Visually Handicapped Bowlers** sets out to promote interest in the welfare of visually impaired bowlers, providing where possible teaching amenities and financial help, and it acts as a liaison with other national and international organisations. The annual main events are the three open tournaments for visually impaired bowlers held at Hastings, Lowestoft and Weston-super-Mare, and a national tournament held at different venues each year. Addresses of local clubs, some useful hints on coaching new players, and other information about the Association can be obtained from the *Hon. Secretary, Mr G. Rawlinson, 11 Wordsworth Road, Clevedon, Avon BS21 6PQ* ℘ *01275 875969.*

The **Scottish Association for Blind Bowlers** has about 30 clubs from Inverness in the north to Ayr in the south. Each club plays its own domestic competitions, and the Association arranges various events in Scotland as well as participating in the British Championships every two years. Further information from the *Hon. Secretary and Treasurer, Mr James Bircham, 8 Holmlea Place, Kilmarnock KA1 1UU* ℘ *01563 32287.*

There are also national bowls associations serving visually impaired people in Wales and in Northern Ireland. Details from *British Blind Sport.*

A free information pack, **Bowls for visually handicapped people**, about playing and coaching bowls and setting up a club, can be obtained from *RNIB Leisure Services.*

21.7.2 Golf

English Blind Golf runs two regular 'clinics' near London where professional training can be arranged for groups of blind people wishing to play golf. Elsewhere it can put blind people in touch with their nearest golf professional. Golf clubs can be provided with information and advice, such as how to guide a blind golfer. Some 25 or 30 blind golf tournaments are held each year. Further information from the Chairman, *Ron Tomlinson, 93 St. Barnabas Road, Woodford Green, Essex IG8 7BT* ✆ 0181 491 7543.

Ron Tomlinson can supply details of associations for visually impaired golfers in Scotland and Northern Ireland.

21.7.3 Tandem cycling

Many blind people enjoy cycling, riding tandem with a sighted person. A particularly popular event is the **tandem marathon** for blind people, held annually in Lincolnshire by a local group, *BOLD (Blind Outdoor Leisure Development), Alan Wedgbury, 44 Main Street, Gedney Dyke, Spalding PE12 0AJ* ✆ 01406 363057. There are other local groups specifically for blind tandem enthusiasts, but the **Tandem Club** has members all over Britain, and the Club's Disabilities Liaison Officer would be willing to try to put a blind person in touch with a sighted tandem enthusiast in his or her own area. Contact *Mrs. Miriam Woodland, 85 Salford Road, Aspley Guise MK17 8HY* ✆ 01908 282485. The Tandem Club's journal is available on cassette from *Cath and Simon Pike, 23 Hardy Road, Wheatley, Doncaster DN2 4DP.*

The **CTC** (Cyclists Touring Club) is also glad to try to help visually impaired cyclists and put them in touch with sighted cyclists. CTC members are able to call upon the resources of the national office, for example for technical and touring advice, including lists of cycle hire firms that have tandems. Details of local district associations, some of which already have blind members, are available from the *CTC, 69 Meadrow, Godalming, Surrey GU7 3HS* ✆ 01483 417217. CTC's magazine, which sometimes contains articles or information about tandems, is available on cassette.

G

21.7.4 Team games

Blind and partially sighted people play **cricket** with a number of changes to the normal rules. The game is played on a wicket of only 18 yards, using a size 5 football that has ball bearings to make it audible. The rules are also adapted: for example the ball must bounce once before the crease for a partially sighted batsman, and twice for a totally blind batsman. The game has to be played without too much extraneous noise as the level of sound is as important to a visually impaired player as light to a sighted cricketer. Fourteen teams are currently playing, with friendly matches most weekends throughout the season. Further details and information about clubs from the General Secretary of the British Blind Sport Cricket Sub-Committee, *Anthony M. Hegarty, 8 Rockells Place, Forest Hill Road, London SE22 0RT* ✆ 0181 693 6097 (evenings). A free information pack **Cricket** is available from *RNIB Leisure Services.*

Making cricket better

Unlike in test matches, we use a large white rattleball, the size of a football.
At every ball it should go: Bowler – Ready?
Batsman/woman – Yes. Bowler – Play.
You can choose underarm or overarm.
The ball should bounce once, about two big strides in front of the wicket.
Blind fielders are allowed to take a catch after two bounces.
Partially sighted can have one bounce, and sighted must catch as in county cricket.
More powerful is more runs. Sixes, fours and other runs are decided together.
Remember, even big, strong players are not always right.
More important matches have umpires. Here blind players may use runners.
Don't count Leg Before Wicket.
If you lose the ball then link arms in a line and walk down the playing area.
My favourite cricket is played with my friends in a special outdoor mesh cage.
This has a concrete floor and wooden boards at each end, to help sounds.
Some of us don't need lights, and can play late at night.
It's more fun if you don't cheat.

▶ **Steven Morris**, aged 10, writing in *VISability*, Spring 1994

Five-a-side football is another adapted game. Clubs or groups of blind or partially sighted people prepared to form a team can obtain details from the British Football Association for the Visually Handicapped. Contact *Andy Kalavazides, 34 The Uplands, Ruislip, Middlesex HA4 8QN* ℘ 01895 623749.

Goalball is the only team game to be played exclusively by visually impaired men and women. It is played on a 18 x 9 metre indoor court with a 1.3 metre high goal spanning its full width at each end. There are two teams of three players and the object is to get the ball past the opposing team and into their goal. There are both national and international goalball tournaments. Further information from the Chairman of the British Blind Sport Goalball Sub-committee, *Roger Clifton, 54 Hatherley Road, London E17 6SF* ℘ 0181 521 3359. A free information pack, **Goalball**, is available from *RNIB Leisure Services*.

A group of blind people formed a **darts** team which plays against sighted darts teams – and sometimes wins! The blind players are not expected to start and finish on a double, and a sighted caller tells them where on the board the dart has landed. Further information from *Gary Hatt, 2 John's Lane, Morden, Surrey SM4 6EU* ℘ 0181 640 9704.

21.7.5 Snooker

A 'do-it-yourself' drilling kit for producing braille-coded snooker, pool and billiard balls has been devised by Mark Stewart. A snooker or pool kit costs £15.50, a kit for both is £19.50 (both prices plus postage and packing) from Mr Stewart at *IDEAS, 23 Sebright Avenue, Worcester WR5 2HH* ℘ 01905 358652. Mr Stewart developed a game called **potball**, in which snooker rules are adapted so that a blind player can play against a sighted player.

21.7.6 Spectator sports

Some football and cricket clubs make special arrangements for blind spectators. Clubs with facilities for relaying match commentaries to patients in local hospitals often allow blind people to sit in the commentary box or adjoining stands where they can hear the commentary on headphones. Free passes may be issued to local blind people. Details about any particular club's arrangements can be obtained from the club secretary.

Discovering Sports Venues – A guide for blind and partially sighted people who enjoy spectator sports **L** **B** **T**, £2.50 from *RNIB*, gives details of facilities at football, cricket, rugby league, rugby union and horseracing venues throughout the UK and at racecourses in Eire.

Football results, league tables and fixtures are available weekly throughout the season from the *Scottish Braille Press* **B** and from *RNIB* **M**.

A group of blind people organises regular trips to **race meetings** throughout the year. Arrangements may be made for members of the group to meet trainers, jockeys and other racing personalities. Those living outside the London area must be prepared to make their own travelling arrangements to the rendezvous point in London. Further details from *Len Williams, 8 Coverdale Road, London NW2* ℘ *0181 451 0309.* **NEW** A similar group has been established for the North of England. Contact *Len Floyd, 68 Coldwell Road, Crossgates, Leeds LS15 7HA* ℘ 0113 232 6311.

21.7.7 Sport tapes

Football Monthly, Sporting Life Weekender, Yachting World, **Golf Monthly**, **Angling Times** and **The Cricketer** are among the taped magazines available from the *Talking Newspaper Association* (annual membership £15). For younger sports enthusiasts, the Association tapes **Sportsview**, a general review of the sports scene, and **Sliding Tackle**, about football, both at an annual subscription of £5.00.

Taped sports magazines, including **The Cricketer** and a weekly digest of Sunday newspaper sports pages (annual subscription £10 each) plus the free loan of titles from a tape library of about 300 books about sport, are available from *Sports Tapes for the Blind, Derek Heyes, 38 Fearnhead Avenue, Horwich, Bolton BL6 7LJ* ℘ 01204 693868 (evenings).

Wisden Cricket Monthly can be obtained on cassette for an annual subscription of £6.00 from *Lois Leven, 48 Tenby Avenue, Kenton, Harrow, Middx. HA3 8RX*.

Over 100 sports titles can be borrowed from *RNIB Cassette Library*, over 30 from *Playback Service* and about 25 from *Calibre*.

22 Holidays

22.1 Specialist hotels in the UK

Hotels listed in this section cater specifically for blind and partially sighted holidaymakers from all parts of the country. Sighted friends and relatives, including children in many cases, are welcome. Though most hotels accept unaccompanied visually impaired people – some have arrangements with local volunteers to act as escorts – hotel managers suggest that a blind person is more likely to enjoy a holiday in an unfamiliar environment if accompanied by a sighted guide. Deafblind guests are accepted only if accompanied by a sighted person.

The hotels are not equipped to cope with guests unless they are in reasonable health, but almost all will provide special diets (for diabetic people, for instance) and with advance notice can arrange for a district nurse to give injections or administer eye drops for a blind guest. Guests could also arrange this through their own doctor.

Hotels vary in size and accommodation provided. Most claim to have guide rails, stair guards, lifts, grab-rails in baths and so on, to help avoid hazards which might worry elderly blind holidaymakers. Henshaw's Belmont Hotel and Halifax Society's Holiday Home have some accommodation specially adapted for wheelchair users. Action for Blind People and RNIB provide brochures giving details of their holiday hotels. All hotels will accept guide dogs, but some may not permit them in the dining room.

The weekly charges quoted below are for full board (unless otherwise stated) during the main summer season of 1995. Out of season charges may be considerably lower. Discounts are offered for group bookings. Hotels usually ask for a small deposit on booking, and for full payment about three or four weeks in advance (eight weeks for RNIB hotels). It is advisable to book as early as possible. Bookings for the summer season usually start immediately after Christmas.

Blackpool, Lancashire: RNIB Century Hotel

406 North Promenade, Gynn Square, Blackpool FY1 2LB ✆ 01253 354598. £154. Open Easter to Christmas and New Year.

Blackpool, Lancashire: The Henderson

1 Wimbourne Place, South Shore, Blackpool FY4 1NN ✆ 01253 341217. £165. Open April to October and at Christmas.

Bognor Regis, Sussex: Russell Hotel (Action for Blind People)

Kings Parade, Bognor Regis, Sussex PO21 2QP ✆ 01243 823572. £175. Open February to Christmas and New Year.

Clacton-on-Sea, Essex: St Anne's Holiday Home for the Blind-Deaf

26-28 Harold Road, Clacton-on-Sea, Essex CO1 6AJ ✆ 01255 420595. £140. Open all year.

Key to media of publication ❶ clear print ❶ large print ❶ braille ❶ tape ❶ Moon ❶ disk

Where a full address is not given in the text, see 32 (Useful addresses)

374

☼ Eastbourne, Sussex: RNIB Palm Court Hotel
15 Burlington Place, Eastbourne, Sussex BN21 4AR ✆ 01323 725811.
£175. Open Easter to October and Christmas/New Year.

☼ Fleetwood, Lancashire: Halifax Society for the Blind Holiday Home
Apply to *Halifax Society for the Blind, 3 Wards End, Halifax HX1 1DD* ✆ 01422
352383. £97. Open April to October.

☼ Llandudno, Gwynedd: Belmont Hotel (Henshaw's Society for the Blind)
21 North Parade, Llandudno, Gwynedd LL30 2LP ✆ 01492 877770.
£190. Open March to Christmas and New Year.

☼ Llandudno, Gwynedd: Oakwood Hotel
Dee Cockburn, 21 St. David's Road, Llandudno, Gwynedd LL30 2UH ✆ 01492
879208. £129 (dinner, bed and breakfast). Open all year.

☼ Scarborough, North Yorkshire: RNIB Alma Court Hotel
West Street, Scarborough, North Yorkshire YO11 2QL ✆ 01723 372934.
£154. Open May to September. Hotel to close at end of 1995 season.

☼ South Devon: Cliffden (Guide Dogs for the Blind Association)
Dawlish Road, Teignmouth TQ14 8TE ✆ 01626 770052.
From £162 for guide dog owners, from £247 for non-guide dog owners
(dinner, bed and breakfast). Open all year round. Own purpose designed
swimming pool. Guests must be guide dog owners or accompanying a guide
dog owner.

☼ Strathyre, Perthshire: Sir Andrew Murray House
Apply to *Elizabeth Hamilton, Central Regional Council, Social Work Services,
Drummond House, Wellgreen Place, Stirling FK8 2EG* ✆ 01786 442157.
5 self-catering suites, each with large twin bedroom and cooking facilities;
separate kitchen and dining room available for party occupying all suites.
Weekly charge £100 for suite with private sitting room, £80 each for other
four.

☼ Weston-super-Mare, Avon: Lauriston Hotel (Action for Blind People)
6-12 Knightstone Road, Weston-super-Mare, Avon BS23 2AN ✆ 01934 620758.
£189. Open mid-February to Christmas and New Year.

In **London**, all year round hotel accommodation at **RNIB Garrow House**, North
Kensington, consists of four single rooms and one double room with ensuite
bathroom and kitchen facilities. Bed and breakfast is £25 a night for a single
room; weekly charges by arrangement.

See 22.8 for details of Lions holiday home in **Great Yarmouth**.

The **Torch Trust for the Blind** provides accommodation to visually impaired
people who seek Christian fellowship while on holiday. Torch House, the Trust's
Leicestershire headquarters, offers house parties at Christmas, Easter, June (for
older people) and August (for families and for younger adults). The Trust's other
property in **Sussex** is open all year to anyone in need of a quiet holiday or respite

G

care. Enquiries to *Little Torch, 4 Hassocks Road, Hurstpierpoint BN6 9QN* ℘ 01273 832282.

22.2 Accommodation at residential homes

Residential homes for blind people are usually better equipped than hotels to accommodate guests who need more care and attention because of their age and other disabilities such as hearing loss. All four RNIB homes provide accommodation for short-term guests, including self-catering in some cases. Charges and other details on application.

☼ Harrogate, North Yorkshire: RNIB Tate House
28 Wetherby Road, Harrogate, North Yorkshire HG2 7SA ℘ 01423 886927.
2 self-contained flats, 1 with double bedroom, 1 with single bedroom.

☼ Hove, Sussex: RNIB Wavertree House
Furze Hill, Hove, Sussex BN3 1PA ℘ 01273 733376.
Self-contained flat with 1 double and 1 twin-bedded room.

☼ Westgate-on-Sea, Kent: RNIB Westcliff House
Sea Road, Westgate-on-Sea, Kent CT8 8QP ℘ 01843 831697.
Self-contained flat with kitchen, bathroom, living room and 3 bedrooms.

☼ Weston-Super-Mare, Avon: RNIB Kathleen Chambers House
c/o Earlfield Lodge, 28 Trewartha Park, Weston-Super-Mare, Avon B23 2RR
℘ 01934 612955.

☼ Llys Onnen Home for the Blind, Abergele, Clwyd
Apply to *North Wales Society for the Blind, 325 High Street, Bangor, Gwynedd LL57 1YB* ℘ 01248 353604. Single rooms £107.50 per week for short-term guests.

Other residential homes for visually impaired people may be able to take short-term guests. A complete list of specialist homes in England and Wales can be obtained free from RNIB. Someone who needs temporary accommodation during the absence of relatives, for example, but who is too frail to travel any distance, may find that the local authority can offer a place in one of its own old people's homes.

22.3 Group holidays

Many local voluntary societies and social services arrange group holidays for blind, partially-sighted and physically handicapped people. Generally a hotel or boarding house is taken over by a party for a week or a fortnight, either early or late in the holiday season. Transport is provided and entertainments and outings arranged. This can be a very friendly, happy holiday, and a good way for a person whose sight has only recently deteriorated to take the first big step of leaving known surroundings and yet have the support of friends made amongst blind people in the neighbourhood.

The **Hampshire Association for the Care of the Blind** arranges a **foreign group holiday** each year and accepts visually impaired people without escorts and from any part of the country. Anyone who would like to be placed on the circulation list should contact the Association at *25 Church Road, Bishopstoke, Eastleigh SO5 6BL* ℘ 01703 641244. Group holidays are run by some Rotary Clubs (see 22.8).

22.4 Residential courses

Summer schools and other residential courses on a range of subjects are held specifically for visually impaired people, either on their own or with a sighted companion, at the following centres. Courses vary from a few days to a week, and are likely to include visits to sites of interest in connection with the particular field of study.

Avon, University of Bristol

Choice of courses includes archaeology, horticulture, geology, literature, architecture, natural history; June/July. Funding being sought for creative writing weekends spring and autumn. Enquiries to *Jo Emslie, University of Bristol, Disabilities Unit, Department for Continuing Education, 8-10 Berkeley Square, Clifton, Bristol BS8 1HH* ℘ 0117 928 7176.

Dorset, Kingcombe Centre

Countryside and wildlife; choice of courses from spring/early summer to autumn. Enquiries to *Nigel Spring, The Kingcombe Centre, Toller Porcorum, Dorchester DT2 0EQ* ℘ 01300 320684.

Hampshire, Lord Wandsworth College

Suggestions for fields of study welcome; time of year varies. Enquiries to *Brian Barton Memorial Fund, Farnborough College of Technology, Highfield Centre, Highfield Avenue, Aldershot GU11 3XZ* ℘ 01252 336090 or *Bridget Wright* ℘ 01252 517816.

North Yorkshire, University of York

Photography, religious history, architecture; choice of courses, usually in August. Enquiries to *Kathy Christopherson, Centre for Continuing Education, Goodricke College, University of York, York YO1 5DD* ℘ 01904 434620.

NEW Pembrokeshire, Stackpole Centre

Courses organised by Share Music, a charity which aims to enable people with disabilities to take part in various musical activities in the company of musicians and helpers; first course specifically for visually impaired people July 1995. Enquiries to *Simon Labbett, RNIB Music Officer.*

South Yorkshire, Doncaster College

Local history, music, literature, art, drama, outdoor activities, sports; June/July. Enquiries to *Karen Sharp, Doncaster College, High Melton, Doncaster DN5 7SZ* ℘ 01302 553915.

Staffordshire, Wedgwood Memorial College

Contemporary social and cultural studies; time of year varies. Enquiries to *Derek Tatton, Principal, Wedgwood Memorial College, Barlaston, Stoke-on-Trent ST12 9DG* ℘ 01782 372105.

Annual residential **drama schools** are held in Loughborough (see 21.2.2) and **writer's courses** at Newbattle Abbey, Dalkeith (see 21.4). **NEW** **Gardening weekends** are organised by *Horticultural Therapy* (see 21.6.2).

Time to Learn, a directory of learning holidays in England and Wales, indicates course organisers who have stated that they welcome blind or partially sighted students. In other cases, visually impaired people should approach the principal of the college offering the course of their choice. The directory, currently £4.25 per issue, is published biannually in January and August by *NIACE (National Institute of Adult Continuing Education), 21 De Montfort Street, Leicester LE1 7GE* ✆ *0116 255 1451.*

22.5 Activity holidays

There are opportunities for blind and partially sighted people of all ages to participate in activities ranging from sailing or pony trekking to drama or dancing. Arrangements may be made by a local voluntary society or the initiative taken by an enterprising rehabilitation worker. Some schemes are open to people from anywhere in the country.

The **Guide Dogs Adventure Group** was formed to enable blind and partially sighted people of all ages to extend their horizons through the courses and holidays it organises in the UK and overseas. A fund exists to assist visually impaired members who might otherwise be unable to participate. Activities have included skiing, tandem riding, golf, bowling, rock climbing, sailing, ballroom dancing, wine-tasting, cookery, judo, drama, rambling, roller-skating, mountain biking, windsurfing, driving, camping, ice skating, fishing, abseiling, canoeing, caving, parascending, shooting and listening to bird song. Sighted help during activities is provided by volunteers and highly trained full time staff. GDAG membership is open to anyone who is visually impaired (guide dog owner or not). The cost to individuals is £2.00 plus annual subscription, currently £12. Terms for group membership are based on £6.00 multiplied by the average number of people in the group. Members receive a quarterly newsletter **L B T** which includes details of forthcoming holidays and trips. Enquiries to *GDAG, Hillfields, Burghfield, Reading RG7 3YG* ✆ *01734 835555.*

NEW One of the aims of the **Paul Vander-Molen Foundation** is to 'enable people with disabilities to fulfil their adventurous aspirations'. The Foundation was established as a memorial to an explorer who died of leukaemia in 1985 at the age of twenty-eight. It encourages expeditions to incorporate disabled people in their teams, and has helped many people with disabilities to take part in expeditions. Enquiries to *Mrs. Vander-Molen, The Model Farm House, Church End, London NW4 4JS* ✆ *0181 203 2344.*

The **Hampshire Association** (see 22.3) organises a number of activity weekends and weeks ranging from hill climbing and canoeing to rambling. Outside the main season, **RNIB holiday hotels** at Blackpool and Eastbourne (see 22.1) offer activity weeks centred round a particular theme, such as rambling or cultural activities. A number of **outdoor activity centres**, such as the Stackpole Centre in Pembrokeshire and the Calvert Trust in Northumberland, offer adventure holidays for people with any kind of disability. Details from *RNIB Leisure Service.*

Sailing has become popular with many visually impaired people, from beginners to those qualified to take part in top class international racing. RYA Sailability has pioneered structured sailing courses, both theoretical and practical, which lead to RYA certification. Cruising weeks are held for beginners and more experienced sailors at various venues around the country. There are opportunities to crew on the Lord Nelson, a square rigger. Dinghy and keelboat courses are held at the Island Sailing Club in Devon and at other venues. Further information and advice from *RYA Sailability, RYA House, Romsey Road, Eastleigh SO50 9YA ℘ 01703 627400.*

Blind and partially sighted young people are occasionally offered the opportunity to take part in a **working holiday** at National Trust properties where volunteers help with tasks such as woodland conservation. Enquiries to Valerie Wenham at the *National Trust.*

The Central Bureau for Educational Visits and Exchanges indicates in a number of its publications whether a visually impaired young person could participate: **Working Holidays**, **Volunteer Work** (guide to medium and long term voluntary service), **A Year Between** (guide to work training and travel), **Study Holidays** (guide to language courses in Europe), and **Teach Abroad** (guide to teaching opportunities worldwide). **Home from Home**, the Bureau's guide to agencies which can arrange for young people to stay with families in other countries, indicates which of these agencies can help young people with disabilities. *Central Bureau for Educational Visits and Exchanges, Seymour Mews House, Seymour Mews, London W1H 9PE ℘ 0171 486 5101.*

22.6 Help with independent arrangements

NEW In a pilot project starting in May 1995 **Henshaw's Society for the Blind** are providing a **national holiday service** for visually impaired people who wish to stay at a mainstream holiday hotel. Accommodation can be arranged at about a dozen hotels so far, all of which have been inspected to ensure that they are suitable for guests who are blind or partially sighted. These hotels are situated at seaside, city and country resorts in England and Scotland, but it is hoped to cover all parts of the UK as more inspected hotels are added to the list. Enquiries to the *Holiday Services Organiser, Henshaw's Manchester Resource Centre.*

NEW A similar national service is planned for the autumn of 1995 by **Action for Blind People**. They already offer package holidays on Jersey at eight mainstream hotels which they have identified as being suitable for visually impaired people. Travel can be arranged by ferry from Weymouth or from any one of 25 airports. Half board charges for the 1995 season, including return flight from Gatwick, range from £284 to £383 per adult per week. Full details from *Martin Morris* at Action for Blind People's London office.

Holiday Care Service, a registered charity, offers support and advice to disabled and older people, one parent families, carers and people on a low income. It has information about provision in the UK and abroad for blind and disabled holidaymakers, including activity and special interest holidays. Some 1,500 hotels and self-catering establishments inspected against national accessibility standards are listed in the **NEW** 1995 **Holiday Care Guide to Accessible Travel in the UK** (Hobsons Publishing. £9.95. Credit card orders ✆ 01403 710851). It indicates where guide dogs are welcome and information available in large print and braille. Details are included of accessible places of interest. Members of Friends of Holiday Care Service (annual subscription £10 for individuals) are entitled to discounted rates at many inspected establishments. The Holiday Care AWARDS scheme aims to promote good practice in mainstream tourism. Anyone who has had an enjoyable holiday is invited to contact the Awards Secretary for a nomination form. *Holiday Care Service, 2 Old Bank Chambers, Station Road, Horley, Surrey RH6 9HW* ✆ 01293 774535 (Minicom 776943) or 822221 for reservations.

RADAR (Royal Association for Disability and Rehabilitation) publishes two annual guides for disabled people, **Holidays in the British Isles** (£7.00) and **Holidays and Travel Abroad** (£5.00). Both indicate whether guests may bring guide dogs to the hotels and boarding houses listed, as well as giving other information of interest to disabled holidaymakers in general.

The **AA Guide for the Disabled Traveller** (pub. 1995, £3.99, but free to members) gives similar details about AA-recommended hotels, guest houses and farm houses together with information on tourist attractions, motorway service areas and advice on foreign travel.

NEW **Pets Welcome**, published by Farm Holiday Guides (December 1994. £3.99 from W.H. Smith and other bookshops) lists hotels that accept dogs.

NEW The **Youth Hostels Association** say that guide dogs are accepted at any of their hostels, given advance notification to the warden. *YHA, 8 St. Stephens Hill, St. Albans AL1 2DY* ✆ 01727 855215.

22.7 Holiday hotels for the blind abroad

Information and advice about specialist holiday facilities abroad may be available from organisations of or for blind people in the appropriate country. Their addresses can be obtained from *RNIB Reference Library*. There are specialist hotels where visually impaired guests from the UK are known to have been welcomed in the following countries.

☼ Bulgaria
Accommodation at two resorts on the Black Sea coast and at four in the mountains. Excursions, sightseeing and translators can be arranged. Enquiries to *Morfi Scarlatov, Union of the Blind in Bulgaria, 172 Naicho Tzanov Street, 1309 Sofia* ✆ 00 359 2-22 34 35.

☼ Denmark
NEW A centre near Billund airport in Jutland. Apply to *Fuglsangcentret, Sondermarksveg 150, DK-700 Fredericia* ✆ 00 45 75 911555.

☼ Finland
NEW Holiday homes in Helsinki and in northern Finland. Enquiries to *Nakovammaisten Keskusliitto, Makelankatu 50, SF-00510 Helsinki* ✆ 00 358 039 6041.

☼ **France**

Purpose-built holiday centre near Royan, Charente Maritime, open from June to September. Enquiries to *Comité de la Charente-Maritime, 20 Rue Gambetta, 17000 La Rochelle* ✆ 00 33 46 41 26 03. The Comité say the centre is popular with British visitors.

☼ **Germany**

Recreation and cure centres on the Baltic coast, in the mountains and elsewhere in Germany. Details from *Deutscher Blindenverband, Bismarckallee 30, D53173 Bonn* ✆ 00 49 228 35 40 37.

☼ **Italy**

Holiday centre near the sea, a few miles from Pisa and from Livorno station: *Le Torri, via Orchidee 44, 56018 Tirrenia PI* ✆ 00 39 50 32 587.

☼ **Sweden**

Holiday hotels for visually impaired people include one near Stockholm open all year. Enquiries to *Synskadades Riksforbund, SRF FRITID, S – 122 88 Enskede* ✆ 00 46 8 39 90 00.

☼ **Switzerland**

(NEW) Recently re-opened *Hotel Solsana, CH-3792 Saanen/Gstaad* ✆ 00 41 308 9494 in the Bernese Oberland 1150 metres above sea level.
Internationales Blinden-Centrum, 8597 Landschlacht ✆ 00 41 72 65 1212 in a small village on Lake Constanz near the German frontier.
Camps de Vacances-Retraite (Christian meetings) arranged by *Mission Evangelique Braille, Av. Louis-Ruchonnet 20, 1800 Vevey* ✆ 00 41 21 921 6687.

Blind and partially sighted people applying for a new or replacement **passport** can have a braille label reading 'passport' attached to it. They should indicate in the 'other information' section of the application form if they would like this done. Current passport holders can obtain the label from their regional passport office. There is no charge for this service. Guide dogs taken outside the British Isles are subject to six months' quarantine on re-entry.

G

22.8 Help with the cost of holidays

Local authorities have a duty to arrange holidays for disabled people assessed as being in need of them (see 4.4.1, 7.8). But according to a recent survey (Stackpole Trust, 1994) provision is often only made for respite care, and most authorities are unable to fund holidays at all. Visually impaired people who cannot afford to go on holiday should nevertheless approach their **local social services department**. They may be able to help blind people in special need of a holiday, particularly if recovering from illness or after a bereavement, and should at least be able to supply information on charities which fund holidays. **Local voluntary societies for the blind** are nearly always willing to contribute something towards the expense of a holiday, or will even meet the full cost in cases of real need.

Service organisations such as Rotary and Lions may also be able to provide practical and financial help. Some **Rotary Clubs** run group holidays. The address of the appropriate Club or District Secretary is available from *Rotary International,*

Kinwarton Road, Alcester, Warwickshire B49 6BP ✆ 01789 765411. **Lions Clubs** have their own holiday home for the blind at Great Yarmouth, with room for about 25 people. Blind visitors need to be able to climb stairs, as there is no lift, and to be in reasonably good health as staff are unable to provide much in the way of medical attention. Accommodation is mainly in twin-bedded rooms. Blind guests and their guides are sponsored by local Lions Clubs, which are responsible for making all arrangements, including travel, and pay the whole cost. Addresses of local Lions Clubs can be obtained from *Lions Clubs International, 257 Alcester Road South, Kings Heath, Birmingham B14 6BT* ✆ 0121 441 4544.

The **Handicapped Aid Trust**, a charitable fund set up during the 1981 International Year of Disabled People, helps disabled people with the expenses of a carer or guide when making independent arrangements for a holiday abroad. A blind person who cannot afford to pay the expenses of a companion, and cannot obtain sufficient financial help from other sources, may be able to draw on this fund. The minimum age for applicants is 17. The Trustees meet twice a year to consider applications and to allocate the funds available. Applications should be made, by 1st February for holidays between 1st April and 30th September and by 1st August for holidays between 1st October and 31st March, to *Handicapped Aid Trust, 17 Bowland Place, Lytham St. Annes, Lancs. FY8 3QJ* ✆ 01253 780011.

22.9 Further reading

Articles about holidays appear from time to time in **New Beacon**; the January issue regularly carries a feature on holidays. **NEW** The January holidays feature is available in February as a separate information pack **L B T** from *New Beacon* or from *RNIB Leisure Service*.

NEW Guidebooks to **London, Paris** and **Venice/Turin** **L B T** are £2.50 each from *RNIB Customer Services*.

Large print Berlitz guides, published in 1988, to London, Amsterdam, Paris and Venice are £3.95 each from the *Partially Sighted Society*.

Nothing ventured, a Rough Guide Special (1991. £7.99) is a collection of tales by disabled travellers who have visited countries all over the world. Several of the contributors are visually impaired.

23 Physical disabilities

According to the RNIB survey on blind and partially sighted adults in Britain, 35% of visually impaired people experience difficulties in hearing normal speech in a quiet room, even when wearing a hearing aid. In addition to the hearing problems, 67% of visually impaired people have another permanent illness or disability. The following sections give some indication of ways in which visually impaired people might find help in coping with additional physical disabilities. As hearing difficulties are reported to affect nearly 50% of very elderly visually impaired people, detailed advice on coping with a dual sensory loss is given in chapter 26 (Helping older, frailer people), while advice for deafblind people can be found in chapter 24.

An increasing number of organisations set up to advise and support people with a disability are aware of the needs of people who are unable to read information in ordinary print. Some are making information available in large print or on tape, or say that they will do so if demand justifies it. Elsewhere, as noted below, telephone helplines are likely to be staffed by volunteers who would be able to find and read the required information.

23.1 Aids

Caring for someone who has been diagnosed as having CMV retinitis is likely to be an extremely challenging task. It is necessary simultaneously to cope with a sight-threatening infection for which treatment can be unpleasant but has to be continuous if total blindness is to be averted, and with the implications of the diagnosis. The improved treatments now available to anyone who is HIV positive mean that people often have had no significant illness until CMV retinitis is diagnosed. Active CMV infection indicates that a person's immune system is not functioning effectively, and is an Aids diagnosis. Although the life expectancy of people affected by CMV is longer than it used to be (in the USA some people have survived up to four years after the initial diagnosis) there is no avoiding the realisation that remaining life may be limited.

It is not surprising therefore that the most important help to offer is emotional support coupled with prompt practical assistance in the tasks that the patient considers to be priorities. The helplines run by the main Aids charities are available to give support and counselling; many are run by people who are themselves HIV positive but they will not necessarily be familiar with help available for people with sight loss. The **National Aids Helpline** is available 24 hours a day on ℘ 0800 567123 and the **Terrence Higgins Trust** has a helpline daily from 12 noon to 10 pm on ℘ 0171 242 1010 and both should also be able to give information about local support groups. **Body Positive**, which aims to counsel people on living with Aids, also offers a counselling helpline ℘ 0171 373 9124 from 7 to 10 on weekday evenings, as well as from 4 pm to 10 pm on Saturday and Sunday. It is also publishing a booklet on CMV retinitis due to appear in July 1995. Details from *51a Philbeach Gardens, London SW5 9EB*.

Everyone who is diagnosed as having a CMV infection in the eye will need to have medication for the rest of their lives and up till now this has meant that the patient

Mark, a 38 year old freelance writer had been diagnosed as HIV positive (as had his partner) three years ago. Apart from one attack of PCP pneumonia from which he had made a good recovery, he was in good health. He was devastated to learn after a routine screening at his clinic that he had CMV retinitis in his right eye and had already lost quite a bit of vision. Unfortunately his left eye, though unaffected by CMV, was a lazy eye and useless for any fine work. The initial treatment as well as the implications of the diagnosis led to a period of depression which only began to lift after he was visited by a rehabilitation officer who told him about software which would enable him to enlarge the screen on his personal computer and make it much easier for him to see what he was writing. For speed he decided to buy this rather than wait for an assessment by the Employment Services, though he agreed to a referral to the low vision aid clinic to help with reading in the future. Once he was able to write again, Mark was prepared to have some basic mobility lessons so that he could at least go out independently in the daytime. Peter, his partner, came to one session to get some ideas about how to give Mark some guidance when they both went out together in the evenings. Though some lessons had to be cancelled because he felt too exhausted, Mark gained enough confidence to go down alone to the local shops. He refused to take his symbol cane out of his bag, however, because he felt it was too much of a stigma! Peter bought him a microwave cooker, on which the rehab. worker marked the essential controls so that Mark could heat up some food during the day, and they are now discussing ways in which Mark's extensive CD and record collection could be labelled using large print Dymo. After being told that talking newspapers do national titles as well as local papers, Mark has taken out a subscription to get Private Eye and two Sunday papers. Twice a week Mark and Peter are seeing a local counsellor who is helping them to cope with their situation.

had to have a permanent line – or catheter – surgically inserted into the chest, so that after the initial hospital treatment to combat the infection, the patient can administer his own medication at home. In March 1995 a tablet version of Ganciclovir, one of the two drugs used to combat CMV, became available but doctors are still uncertain whether the oral treatment is as effective as treatment by infusion, and it would be advisable to consult a doctor who is aware of the latest research findings on this subject.

H

There are two methods most commonly used for the intravenous administration of drugs: a **Hickman line** which is a flexible plastic tube connected through an incision in the chest into a large vein, leaving a portion of the line external and accessible for drug administration; or a **Port-a-cath type line** which involves planting the entire device under the skin and into a vein. The drugs are then infused via a needle through the skin into the Port. Many people prefer the Port-a-cath as unlike the Hickman it does not leave the patient with a length of tube dangling permanently from the chest which is understandably perceived by patients as damaging to their body image. Which device to choose is up to the individual concerned, but if sight is already affected then thought needs to be given to ensure that if at all possible the incision is made at a point where he is most likely to see well if he is to administer his maintenance therapy at home.

Some patients with poor sight have learnt to infuse themselves in order to maintain independence. The maintenance dose of medicine can be administered by a drip bag, which works on gravity (like a blood transfusion) but this means that the patient has to sit or lie still for several hours. Alternatively there is a device that looks a bit like a baby's feeding bottle and works by pressure so that there is no need to be connected to a drip stand and immobilised whilst receiving medication. People can even carry it around in a pocket while travelling about! However these systems – particularly the commercial versions – are very expensive though they would probably be the easiest for people with poor sight to administer unaided. Community nurses are available both to teach people how to cope with this very demanding regime, or to do it for them if there is a danger that poor sight or other disabilities mean that they are not likely to carry out the procedures correctly. Alternatively partners, friends or relatives can be taught how to do this safely, though they would still need considerable support from community health services.

Adaptations in the home are no different than for anyone else with poor sight, but someone who does not have a shower in their bathroom should consider having one installed as they make it easier to maintain the high standards of cleanliness needed to avoid infection with a permanent line into the chest. Those taking the oral medication need to swallow about 20 tablets a day and it might help some people to set out their tablets daily in one of the extra large pill containers (see photograph in the colour section) so that both they and their carers can see at a glance how much of the daily dose has been taken.

23.2 Arthritis

The dual handicap of limited sight and poor hand movement because of painful or swollen fingers presents a challenge to the affected individual in many aspects of daily living. The solutions may require the joint efforts of an occupational therapist, a rehabilitation officer and perhaps also the help of the local **REMAP** panel, whose members bring engineering and other practical skills to devise one-off solutions for individuals where no ready made equipment is suitable. This may mean finding a way for those who have difficulty in raising their hands up to their face to get their glasses on and off, or adapting a low vision aid so that it can be manipulated by someone with limited hand movement (see illustration in this section) But often problems can be overcome with simple gadgets available from specialist suppliers such as *Keep Able, Chester Care* or *Ways & Means* which sell a wide range of products to help people with disabilities (see also 26.4). Adaptations for talking book machines are described in 19.1.1. The **square talking alarm clock** available from *RNIB* may be easier for people with limited movement to use than some of the other models. **Arthritis Care** (annual subscription £4.00) does provide its quarterly newspaper on tape and suggests that visually impaired people make use of their free helpline for information (0800 289170 weekday afternoons). It is also considering putting

A hand focus telescope (3x and 2x) for distance use. The focus is adjusted by gentle pressure on the face; no fine finger movements are needed. £42 plus VAT. Details from *Sussex Vision, Unit 8a, Wayside, Commerce Way, Lancing, West Sussex BN15 8SW* ℘ 01903 851951

some of its information leaflets on to tape or producing them in large print. Details from *Arthritis Care, 18 Stephenson Way, London WN1 2HD* ℘ 0171 916 1500.

Rheumatoid arthritis may sometimes affect the tear glands and result in an inadequate tear flow, so that the eyes feel dry, gritty and sore. This can usually be remedied by the frequent administration of artificial tear drops.

23.3 Diabetes

23.3.1 Insulin therapy

Nowadays there are much easier options if poor sight makes it very difficult to use the traditional syringes.

A diabetes nurse or health professional will be able to advise, but even if mixed doses of insulin are needed people should be able to find alternatives which will deliver a dose close enough to their prescription to be appropriate.

Penject is used with a BD 1 ml syringe. A helper draws up a complete syringe full of insulin (100 units), generally enough to last for several days, and dials the right dose. The user has only to press a plunger to administer the correct amount. It cannot be used with mixed doses. The helper would need to draw up two syringes.

For complete independence, many blind people are using **pen injectors**. They are convenient to carry, resemble a fountain pen, and can be used with a quick, unobtrusive, single-handed action. The insulin is supplied in a cartridge which is screwed into place in much the same way as an ink cartridge into a fountain pen. The insulin dose is dialled in increments of one or two units either by pressing a plunger and counting, or by twisting a cap and counting the clicks. Pen devices can hold cartridges of short-acting, intermediate-acting and premixed insulins.

Counting the cost of diabetes

Free on prescription
Blood testing strips *(except those used in Talking Hypocount B)*
Click-count syringe
Diastix urine test strips
Disposable plastic syringes with attached needles
Glass preset syringe
Insulin cartridges for pen injectors
Preloaded pens

Free from manufacturers or a diabetic clinic
Terumo dose guide
B-D Magniguide

Free through a diabetic clinic or health professional
Novo Nordisk NovoPen II
Becton Dickinson BD Pen

Obtainable by purchase only *(suppliers' addresses opposite)*

Autopen	**Owen Mumford**	**£22.95**
BM Test BG Blood test strips	**Boeringher**	**£24.26**
(for use with Talking Hypocount)		**for 50**
Centrepoint Funnel needle guide	**D.E.P.T.H.**	**£12.00**
28 gauge disposable needles	**Novo Nordisk and**	**£9.80**
for pen injectors	**Beckton Dickinson**	**for 100**
30 gauge disposable needles	**Novo Nordisk**	**£12.80**
for pen injectors		**for 100**
Hypo-test audio urine meter	**Hypoguard**	**£94.50**
Penject	**D.E.P.T.H.**	**£29.95**
Strip Guide	**D.E.P.T.H.**	**£4.25**
Syringe magnifier	**Hypoguard**	**£1.77**

Talking blood glucose meters

Talking Hypocount B blood glucose meter	**Hypoguard**	**£280**
NEW One Touch II	**LifeScan**	**£250**

Novo Nordisk's **preloaded pen** is perhaps the ultimate in simplicity. It is a plastic self-contained insulin pen. Once the pen's 300 unit insulin supply is exhausted, it is thrown away and a new pen used. The insulin dose is selected by twisting the pen barrel until the tactile indicator points to the correct number of units on the scale on the side of the cap. The start position is clearly indicated and as the barrel is turned it clicks in two unit increments. The clicks can be heard and felt. When the correct dose has been drawn up the user has only to press a plunger. Human Mixtard 10, 20, 30, 40 and 50 preloaded pens are available, as are Actrapid pens and Human Insulatard pens.

Addresses of suppliers

- **Becton Dickinson UK Ltd**
  Between Towns Road, Cowley,
  Oxford OX4 3LY ℘ 01865
  748844

- **Boeringher Mannheim**
  Bell Lane, Lewes, Sussex
  BN7 ILG ℘ 01273 480444

- **Diabetes, Education,
  Prevention, Treatment and
  Health (D.E.P.T.H.)**
  75 Purley Parade, Woodford
  Avenue, Gants Hill, Ilford,
  Essex IG2 6UU ℘ 0181 551
  6263

- **Hypoguard (UK) Ltd.**
  Dock Lane, Melton,
  Woodbridge, Suffolk IP12 IPE
  ℘ 01394 387333

- **LifeScan**
  Enterprise House, Station
  Road, Loudwater, High
  Wycombe, Bucks HP10 9UF
  Lo-call ℘ 0345 121200

- **Owen Mumford Ltd.**
  Brook Hill, Woodstock,
  Oxford, Oxon. OX20 ITU
  ℘ 01993 812021

- **Novo Nordisk
  Pharmaceuticals Ltd.**
  Novo Nordisk House,
  Broadfield Park, Brighton
  Road, Pease Pottage, Crawley,
  West Sussex RH11 9RT
  ℘ 01293 613555

- **Terumo Corporation**
  1st Floor Offices, 62 Mount
  Pleasant Road, Tunbridge
  Wells, Kent TN1 IRD ℘ 01892
  526331

Preloaded pens can be supplied on prescription from GPs and hospital clinics. Pen injectors are supplied free through diabetic clinics and health professionals, but the needles have to be purchased.

People who prefer to use the traditional syringes and need only a low magnification to make the calibrations legible can obtain plastic magnifiers to fit the barrels of different plastic syringes. **Magniguide**, a combined **scale magnifier and vial guide**, fits the B-D 0.5ml and 1ml Micro-Fine syringes. A low vision aid which leaves the hands free is an option when higher magnification is needed (see 3.3).

Both Terumo and Becton Dickinson issue free **dose and vial guides** which fit their 0.5ml and 1ml syringes. These are slotted plastic strips which are easily cut to size with scissors at the correct dosage and act as templates so that the correct dose is drawn up and the needle is automatically inserted in the centre of the bottle cap. Other alternatives when sight is very limited are a glass **preset syringe** or a metal **click-count syringe** when mixed doses are needed. Both syringes can still be supplied on prescription, but people often find them unacceptably heavy and awkward compared to plastic syringes.

23.3.2 Home Monitoring

NEW A new version of the **One Touch II** voice synthesizer which connects with the One Touch II blood glucose meter was launched in April 1995. The complete pack costs £250, the voice synthesizer alone costs £211.20. Full details from *LifeScan Customer Helpline* ℘ Lo-call 0345 121200.

Talking Hypocount B (£280) blood glucose meter has an integral voice

H

389

synthesizer and visual read-out. The difficulty lies in getting the blood sample on the right place on the testing stick. Some people find the **Hypoguard strip guide** helpful. Talking Hypocount must be used with BM Test BG test strips which cannot be obtained on prescription.

Urine can be checked for glucose level by using **Hypo-test**, an audio urine meter. Operation is simple: a Bayer Diagnostics Diastix is placed in a socket and the instrument gives the result of the test by means of a buzzer code.

23.3.3 Counting the cost in cash

There seems to be little logic behind which items are on free prescription, which are provided free by manufacturers and those which need to be purchased privately.

To add to the confusion, an item which one patient with diabetes has to buy privately, such as a blood glucose audio meter, may sometimes be supplied free to another at the discretion of the local diabetic clinic or through money raised by a local BDA group. The table in 23.3.1 indicates the items substantially visually impaired diabetic people may use and the likely expense involved.

23.3.4 Counting the cost in human terms

The **Diabetes Control and Complications Trial**, a large study carried out in America, showed that very close control of blood glucose can play an important part in reducing the risk and severity of complications. The risk of patients developing new eye disease was reduced by 76% and the deterioration in the vision of patients with mild to moderate retinopathy was dramatically reduced.

In the trial, the 'close control' included self-monitoring of blood glucose at least four times a day and insulin injections at least three times a day, with monthly clinic visits. Unfortunately, together with the benefits, the risk of hypoglycaemia increased threefold. It was also a regime which people with diabetes often feel could 'take over' their life-style. However, as the Chairman of the British Diabetic Association, Professor Harry Keen states **'There is now absolutely no doubt that if people tighten up on control they substantially reduce the risk of developing eye and kidney and nerve disease.'**

Yet people who already have a substantial visual loss are not provided with the equipment which would help them achieve that control. The audio blood glucose meters needed cost over £250. Even the test strips, essential for one model, have to be purchased. Sighted people can buy a blood glucose meter from around £25, and the strips are free on prescription. The Department of Health states: **'Some items are not available on free prescription because of the increase they would cause to the Drugs Bill.'**

23.3.5 Sources of information

The **British Diabetic Association** offers advice and help to everyone with diabetes. In **Balance on Tape** the BDA try to include as much as possible of their bi-monthly magazine **Balance** as well as news and articles of particular interest to those with a visual loss. Both the tape and printed versions are included in the £12.00 annual subscription (pensioners, unemployed and disabled people £3.00).

NEW **Diabetes and Visual Impairment: information for people with diabetic retinopathy** **O T** (British Diabetic Association. 1995) describes the more serious forms of retinopathy and how these are treated. It deals with common problems, describes equipment and gives tips on its use. Contact Freephone 0800 585088 for a free copy.

NEW A number of BDA leaflets and booklets on different aspects of diabetes, including retinopathy, are available on tape, with large print versions on request. Contact Freephone 0800 585088 for the current list.

BDA leaflets on **What is diabetes?**, **Sensible slimming**, **What diabetic care to expect** and **Dietary recommendations** are available in braille from *RNIB Customer Services*. The BMA Family Doctor Booklet **Life with Diabetes** (Scottish Braille Press) can be borrowed from the *National Library for the Blind*.

23.4 Hearing problems

A front facing microphone can be supplied in all the different power NHS behind-the-ear hearing aids. This is the preferred microphone position for people with poor sight as it helps to indicate the direction from which the sound is coming, particularly sound coming from the front.

A hearing aid in both ears should also be considered for visually impaired people with mobility problems, especially if there is a hearing loss in both ears. A second hearing aid may restore the ability to locate sound, such as the direction of the traffic flow. **Venting the ear moulds,** by making a small hole in them, has been shown to help some people as it enables them to hear low frequency sounds such as traffic noise more naturally and prevents these sounds from drowning out the high frequencies. These questions should be discussed with the specialist and the hearing aid technician when the aid is being fitted. If clinically necessary the specialist can prescribe an aid for the other ear. Some visually impaired people might find the whole process of obtaining a second hearing aid simpler if they ask either their mobility officer or a rehabilitation worker to contact the hearing aid department on their behalf, or even to accompany them on a hospital visit.

At the specialist's discretion, a commercial hearing aid may be fitted if it is considered more appropriate than the standard NHS model. **NEW** **In-the-ear aids** may be particularly helpful for people with mild and moderate loss and these can be provided through the NHS. The aid, being tiny, may be more difficult to manipulate than the usual behind the ear model, but it is likely to enable the user to identify the direction of sounds much more accurately. It is also worth noting that a visually impaired person who requires a hearing aid can be prescribed a reserve aid. Details of how to get this on the NHS are given in DHSS circular C291 dated 30.3.1980.

23.5 Multiple sclerosis

Blurring of vision and double vision are not infrequently experienced by people with multiple sclerosis. The visual disturbances can occur suddenly without warning, and continue for days or weeks at a time. The nature of these visual problems coupled with their unpredictability can add up to a very intensely distressing experience, which is not liable to be easily solved with any kind of optical aid. However, if the double vision persists over a long period it may well be worth consulting an optometrist or an orthoptist to see if the addition of a prism to a pair of glasses would help (see 23.7). While no one would claim that the visual disturbance could be diminished simply by a sympathetic listening ear, the people staffing the Multiple Sclerosis Society's 24 hour helpline would understand the feelings of someone who woke up in the early hours of the morning to find they could not see properly. Contact ℘ 0171 222 3123.

*eye*OPENER

'Guiding people is about giving them information. Whisking people along in wheelchairs denies them the right to learn about their environment. If they have no idea where they are going, and with whom, they will not be able to demonstrate that they would rather be somewhere else.'
RNIB Multiple Disability Information Service

The Multiple Sclerosis Society produces its regular publications on cassette as well as in print. Details from the Society at *25 Effie Road, London SW6 IEE* ℘ 0171 736 6267.

23.6 Stoma care

NEW In response to requests from people with impaired vision who are wearing some kind of permanent pouch or appliance after operations to remove part of their digestive or urinary systems, taped information is now provided by the three support organisations: the *British Colostomy Association, 15 Station Road, Reading RG1 1LB* ℘ 01734 391537, the *Ileostomy Association, PO Box 23, Mansfield Notts. NG18 4TT* ℘ 01623 28099, and the *Urostomy Association, Buckland, Beaumont Park, Danbury CM3 4DE* ℘ 01245 224294. Most hospitals will have a specialist stoma nurse who should be able to advise a visually impaired patient about the type of systems which might be easier to use with limited sight. In case of any difficulty contact the *Stoma Care Nursing Forum* at the *Royal College of Nursing, 20 Cavendish Square, London WC1M 9AE* ℘ 0171 409 3333.

23.7 Stroke

Normally the two sides of the brain each form a separate picture of half of what the eyes see and the two pictures are joined together to give a total view. When part of the brain is damaged by a stroke the person may see only one half of the world (see the sight simulations in the colour section). Some people may suffer from double vision because the nerve supply to the eye muscles has been affected by the stroke, so that the eye movements are no longer co-ordinated. Some people also suffer from visual inattention, which means that they ignore everything on one side. This is not the same as a field loss, though the effects may seem similar. It is most common with people whose stroke has affected the right side of their brain so they will ignore everything and everyone to their left, which might mean that they would only comb the hair on the right side of their head. These problems singly, or in combination, are perplexing for the person concerned and their carers, and not easy to overcome.

Once carers understand why this is happening it is possible to develop strategies to overcome some of the problems, such as rotating a plate halfway through the meal so that all the food is seen. But it is also important to encourage someone in this situation to continue to turn in the direction affected by the field loss. Putting the telephone on the 'blind' side will ensure that when it rings the patient will turn towards it; though it is probably wiser to put the glass of water or the cup of tea on the other side! Suggestions to overcome the problems of reading with a field loss are given in chapter 3. One man who found reading very difficult after experiencing a stroke told *In Touch* that he discovered it made it easier to turn his book upside down!

Orthoptists, whose skills and training may be relevant to help people who have experienced a stroke, are not as much in evidence as physiotherapists, though the **British Orthoptic Society,** *Tavistock House, Tavistock Square, London WC1H 9JP* ✆ 0171 387 7992, should be able to advise enquirers how to contact one in their area. But it is very important that the patient, or carer, makes sure that any vision problems are made known to the doctor or physiotherapist treating the patient. Sometimes a stroke may affect a person's ability to move their eyes in certain directions. This movement is usually recovered with time but if a physiotherapist is not aware of the problem then it might hinder their therapy.

NEW It may be possible to overcome the problems caused by double vision by adding a thin plastic prism onto the patient's glasses. The prism has the effect of joining the two images into one. This can only be done in consultation with an optometrist or an orthoptist. Putting a patch over one eye is not recommended as this may prevent or retard spontaneous recovery. Some people may be able to reduce the double vision by adopting a different head posture. But this needs to be done carefully, and only in a sitting position, as for some stroke patients turning the head may cause problems with balance.

A stroke may also cause loss of feeling in the face and eye. This may affect a person's ability to blink, which is a normal reflex protection for the surface of the eyes. This may result in eyes becoming red and irritated. Some people lose the ability to control their eyelids so that they either do not open or shut properly. In these cases it is very important to get medical advice about ways of protecting the surface of the eye either by lubrication, or additional lid coverage, particularly at night. If the eyelids droop to such an extent that they obscure vision this can be corrected surgically.

If in addition to a visual field loss the stroke has left the individual with limited hand movement so that holding a book or turning a page are difficult, then it might be better to try listening to taped books with either an Easiplay machine, described in 19.7.1, or a talking book, which can be adapted to make it very easy to operate with gentle pressure. Details on request from the *RNIB Talking Book Service.*

23.8 Wheelchair users

People with poor sight who need to use wheelchairs do not have the option of wheeling themselves about, so it would be helpful for a carer to read the RNIB Focus factsheet **Guiding blind people who are wheelchair users**. This gives simple but easily overlooked ideas which would enable the blind wheelchair user to be informed about the journey. The pusher should not only describe the route as they are going along, but place a hand on the appropriate shoulder to indicate left or right turns. It also points out that the wheelchair footrests should never be used to push doors open.

Sonic headlights to enable a totally blind man to steer his electrically propelled wheelchair were designed some years ago by a REMAP volunteer. Contact **REMAP UK** for details. RNIB Multiple Disability Service, the Guide Dogs for the Blind Association and the Royal Hospital and Home, Putney are attempting to design a mobility aid that might be particularly useful for blind people with limited hand control who are wheelchair users. If developed, the device would need to be small and discreet and be able to give warnings of changes in surface level, such as steps down.

H

24 Deafblindness

Sense estimates that 21,000 people in the UK have a dual sensory loss, a figure based on surveys in Wales, Lincolnshire and Devon. The majority are elderly, but about 1,500 people were born with varying degrees of deafblindness during the rubella outbreaks of the 1960s. Their dual loss is often combined with brain damage and heart defects. Nowadays, rubella damage is substantially reduced but deafblindness due to congenital causes, including premature birth and birth trauma, still persists. In addition, a proportion of young deaf people gradually lose their sight through retinitis pigmentosa. Known as Usher syndrome, this genetic condition results in deafness from birth and gradual loss of sight in late childhood.

Deafblind people are not usually totally deaf and totally blind. Deafblindness has been defined as a combination of vision and hearing impairments which create unique problems in communication, mobility, education, accessing information and understanding the surrounding world. That definition is easier to appreciate when translated into the words of a profoundly deaf young man with Usher syndrome: 'It feels like I'm living in a box and someone is slowly closing down the lid.'

24.1 Communication

This is the lifeline of deafblind people, and keeping the lines of communication open is vitally important. There are no 'right' or 'wrong' methods; whatever is acceptable to a deafblind individual is 'right', though it helps to know a little about their remaining sight. For example, someone with tunnel vision, as often happens in advanced retinitis pigmentosa, must have the signs made within their field of view.

24.1.1 Using signing

When messages written with a thick, black, felt-tip pen fail as a means of communication, alternatives include tracing letters using the deafblind person's forefinger, and the widely used **deafblind manual** and **block alphabet**.

The deafblind manual is similar to the manual alphabet for deaf people but the letters are formed on the deafblind person's hand. Block alphabet (sometimes known as **Spartan**) is even simpler: capital letters are traced on the person's palm. A leaflet illustrating both methods can be obtained from the **National Deafblind League**, and RNIB issues a small card showing both manual alphabets. Practised senders and receivers can achieve relatively high speeds of communication by using the manual. Block alphabet, although slower, has the advantage that anybody can transmit a message without learning a new alphabet. **Hands-on signing** is an adaptation of sign language for people who also have very poor vision.

Recently, opportunities to learn how to communicate with deafblind people have increased and training courses are offered which lead to a certificate in **Communicating and Guiding Skills with Deafblind People**. Level 1 involves a short written examination, followed by a practical examination conducted by a

---

Key to media of publication ❷ clear print ❶ large print ❸ braille ❶ tape ⓜ Moon ❶ disk
Where a full address is not given in the text, see 32 (Useful addresses)

deafblind examiner. This requires candidates to demonstrate guiding and social skills and tests candidates' ability to communicate in the deafblind manual and in block alphabet. The result is a qualification which enables a helper to communicate effectively when, for example, taking a deafblind person shopping.

Level 2, an advanced certificate in interpreting for deafblind people, includes a written examination on the needs and difficulties of dual sensory loss, and four practical tests. These involve role play, a transmitting speed test of 40 wpm, a paraphrasing speed test at 100-120 wpm and a receptive skills test at 15 wpm.

The Council for Advancement of Communication with Deaf People on which RNIB, RNID, Sense and the National Deafblind League are all represented, is the examining body for these courses and sets the curriculum. It also trains deafblind and sighted people as examiners. A **Directory of Interpreters** (£12.00) includes interpreters for deafblind people. A training and resource video and audio-cassette pack **Touch and Go** (£95.00) can also be supplied together with a free leaflet **Finding classes and centres offering courses in British Sign Language and Communicating with Deafblind people**. Contact *CACDP, Pelaw House, School of Education, University of Durham, Durham DH1 1TA* ✆ 0191 374 3607.

Four day courses are run by Julie Brown, who is herself deafblind. Contact *Communication Works, PO Box 439, Beaconsfield, Bucks HP9 2QY* ✆ 01494 431664. The **National Deafblind League** are also able to provide courses for CACDP qualifications, and short basic courses tailored to suit consumers' requirements are available on request. Contact *Jill Johnson, Director of Services, 18 Rainbow Court, Paston Ridings, Peterborough, PE4 7UP* ✆ 01733 573511.

24.1.2 Using braille

For braillists, some of the new computer technology is making communication a little easier. An electronic braille display (see 20.6) linked to a laptop computer allows a deafblind and a sighted person to talk to each other. At a much more basic level **Brailtalk** (£9.95) is a slim pocket-sized hinged plastic case which opens to display the braille alphabet embossed beneath the corresponding raised print letters. Intended to be used as a communication card, the sighted person 'talks' by moving the deafblind person's fingers over the letters. Obtainable from *Electronic Aids for the Blind*.

24.1.3 Using the telephone

Deafblind people can talk to each other on the telephone by accessing the telephone network through a modem connected to a personal computer. Outgoing messages are typed and relayed down the telephone line. Incoming messages appear in large print on the computer screen or on an electronic braille display (see 20.6). With additional equipment, users can access Teletext.

Deafblind people can also use this system to talk to hearing people who have an ordinary telephone. This is done through the **Typetalk Relay Service** run by the Royal National Institute for Deaf People and funded by British Telecom. Calls are made via a Typetalk Service operator who types the response so that the deafblind person receives it on their terminal in braille or large print. Typetalk is a worldwide, 24 hour service, 365 days per year.

Braille systems are expensive to set up, due mainly to the high cost of the electronic displays. Systems for large print users cost around £1,500. **Hasicom** (Hearing and Sight Impaired Communication), a section of the National Deafblind League, can provide equipment on loan and supports users. Details from the *National Deafblind League.*

Due to the length of time it takes to type an outgoing message or receive a call in braille, telephone bills can be high. The **Text Users Rebate Scheme** provides a 60% rebate on both BT and Typetalk bills. Full details from *Typetalk, John Wood House, Glacier Buildings, Harrington Road, Brunswick Business Park, Liverpool L3 4DF* ✆ 0151 709 9494 (voice enquiries) 0800 500 888 (registration enquiries, text).

24.1.4 Using 'objects of reference'

This method of communication is described in **Objects of Reference** (Revised edition. 1994. £3.50. RNIB Book Sales). It is used with adults as a way of introducing communication, to aid comprehension and the development of sign or spoken language skills. More details from *RNIB Multiple Disability Service.* See also 7.3.

24.2 Benefits

People who are deafblind should claim **disability living allowance** or **attendance allowance**. Details will be found in 5.4 and 5.5.

Blind people who have 'no useful hearing' are likely to qualify for the middle rate care component of DLA. The DSS Guidance to adjudication officers suggests that people should be considered as having 'no useful hearing' when 'residual hearing, even when using artificial aids is, in practice, insufficient for oral communication, so that some other form of communication (lip-reading, sign-language, etc.) has to be used'. When care needs are being assessed, it is considered that the combination of these impairments means that a deafblind person is likely to be unable to avoid common dangers both in and out of doors.

There are additional criteria to be met if a deafblind person is to qualify for the higher rate mobility component of DLA. He must 'be unable to walk to his intended destination out of doors without the help of another person. The degrees of disablement resulting from loss of vision and loss of hearing must amount to

100% and 80% respectively.' 100% blindness is defined 'as vision less than 6/60 (see 4.7) using both eyes (with glasses if appropriate) or where finger counting is not possible beyond one foot. The whole field of vision must be assessed. 80% deafness is defined as an inability to hear a shout beyond one metre using both ears (with aids) out of doors. The person's ability to understand should be tested rather than ability to react to noise.' It is felt that this degree of disability can only be assessed by experts and the **Benefits Agency Medical Service** may be asked to arrange for sufficient evidence to be collected.

It is important that deafblind people get good advice regarding benefits. Not only may they fail to apply, but they may be satisfied with too low a level of award. **Sense** and **RNIB Benefit Rights Team** would be happy to advise.

24.3 Local authority services

These are provided for deafblind people by social services departments. Deafblind people are, however, in the unfortunate position of being a very small minority, requiring a highly specialised and personal service, calling on skills found in workers for the deaf and workers for the blind but rarely common to both.

Two major reports: **Breaking Through** (1988. RNID, RNIB, Sense, National Deafblind League) and **Sign Posts** (1990. Department of Health, Social Services Inspectorate) drew attention to the paucity of services for deafblind people and made recommendations regarding staffing, the establishment of guide-help schemes and the provision of service information.

Progress following these reports is slow but there are some encouraging signs. Sunderland Social Services employ a specialist rehabilitation officer and has a forum which includes deafblind people. The Borough of Wandsworth employ a care manager for deafblind people. A communicator/guide service is provided to enable deafblind people to gain access to information and communicate with other people, as well as getting out and about. An RNIB consultant is available to help local authorities and voluntary agencies for the deaf and for the blind to develop services for deafblind adults. Details from *Brian Peaker, RNIB Tate House, 28 Wetherby Road, Harrogate HG2 7SA* ✆ 01423 885967.

NEW A joint **RNIB/Sense** three year project began in November 1994. It aims to persuade local authorities to promote and develop guide-help schemes. RNIB is concentrating on local authorities from Cheshire, Derbyshire, Nottinghamshire and Humberside northwards to the Scottish border. Sense concentrates primarily on the Midlands and the South. Further details from *John Wadsworth, Development Officer, Guide Help Schemes for Deafblind Adults, RNIB Tate House* or *Graham Hicks, Sense.*

24.4 Rehabilitation

Sense Usher Services aim to help those who have Usher syndrome, their families, and all connected with them, towards a better understanding of the condition, and where to go to get advice and support.

Ashley House, Sense Midlands offers a rehabilitation service for people losing their vision due to Usher syndrome and other eye problems. Areas covered include daily living skills, communication, environmental adaptation and mobility. Enquiries to *Usher Services, Ashley House, 4 Church Road, Edgbaston, Birmingham B15 3TD* ℘ 0121 456 1564.

Every effort will be made to ease communication problems at RNIB Skill Development centres (see 10.5.2). Manor House has staff who can communicate using the deafblind manual, Spartan, and British Sign Language. Young deafblind people have successfully completed courses at **RNIB Redhill College** and **Queen Alexandra College** (see 9.6.3).

Social rehabilitation help is offered at **Rainbow Court**, the headquarters of the National Deafblind League in Peterborough. Accompanied deafblind visitors are welcome to stay in their guest flat. Through meeting the deafblind tenants in the League's flats, visitors are encouraged to find ways of overcoming their double disability. Tenants are ready to help a newcomer with informal instruction in any of the means of communication mentioned earlier. They can also help with braille or Moon and advise on daily living problems (see also 25.1.11).

Help with mobility problems can be provided by rehabilitation workers. The **Guide Dogs for the Blind Association** have successfully trained people with a substantial hearing and sight loss to be guide dog owners.

24.5 Employment

Although RNIB Employment Network and PACT teams would do their best to help a deafblind person train and find work, it is not easy. The inclusion of the services of an interpreter amongst the help that can be offered through **Access to Work** (see 10.7.4) is a step forward. A free leaflet **What we think people with a sight and hearing impairment do for a living ... ❶❷❸** (RNIB Customer Services) gives grounds for hope. It describes the jobs held by five people with dual sensory loss, and illustrates what people can achieve with support.

24.6 Equipment and publications

RNIB will band any of its symbol, long canes or smooth finish white walking sticks with red reflective tape free of charge. This indicates that the user is deaf and blind. RNIB's liquid level indicator can detect two different levels of liquid – full, and almost full – by vibrating as well as bleeping. See 16.2 and illustration in 16.4.

Ways of telling the time include a tactile clock with a vibrating alarm unit (RNIB £25.46) and **Tactiwatch** (RNIB £15.23) which tells the time by a series of vibrations or buzzes (see illustration in 15.4.1). A vibrating alarm **Sentinel** (RNIB £28.50) can be used with the same tactile clock, the door bell or telephone.

RNIB also supply a Vibrating door bell (£28.35). A transmitter unit with push button is fixed to the door frame. The receiver is carried by the user. When anyone comes to the door they press the push button on the transmitter and the receiver unit (a small bright yellow box) both rings and vibrates.

H

A **breeze bell** system uses oscillating fans, wall-mounted where they will easily catch the householder's attention. They are activated when the doorbell is pressed. A switch at the front door stops the fans when the door is opened. This system has the big advantage that no equipment need be carried around – and the disadvantage of creating draughts on a cold day.

The **sound monitor (Tam)** is a lightweight device worn like a wrist-watch. The control box is put in the user's pocket. It detects environmental and speech sound signals which are processed to produce an identical pattern of vibrations on the wristband. With practice, the wearer distinguishes between everyday sounds and is made aware of the ringing of the doorbell or the telephone. Tam also enables users to detect pauses in conversations and to judge the appropriate moment at which to speak, as well as monitoring their own voice levels. Both Tam and breeze bells can be installed and provided by social services departments. More information from *Royal National Institute for Deaf People* and the *National Deafblind League.*

The RNID factsheet **Visual and Vibrating Indicators** gives details of an adapted smoke detector and adapted fire alarms.

A few special publications relay the daily news. The Birmingham Royal Institution for the Blind Resource Centre has for many years produced a daily braille digest of the early morning news, but consideration is now being given to producing a weekly news sheet and widening the circulation area. Contact *BRIB* for the latest details. The National Deafblind League issues **Snippets** twice weekly for braille and large print readers. The Harrogate and District Talking Newspaper produces a braille summary of **local news**. Details of Moon publications will be found in 18.3.

24.7 Holiday hotels and residential homes

Deafblind guests, if accompanied by a guide, are welcome in the holiday hotels mentioned in chapter 22. **RNIB** has residential homes in Harrogate and Burnham-on-Sea. **RNID** also has residential homes at Bath and Canterbury which can meet the needs of deafblind people especially if they use British Sign Language. **St. Anne's Holiday Home for the Blind-Deaf**, Clacton-on-Sea is described in 22.1. Applications for **Rainbow Court**, a block of 12 flats, are welcomed from deafblind people wanting a permanent and independent home of their own. A ground floor flat is available. Details from the *National Deafblind League.*

H

25 Adults with complex needs

This chapter looks at the problems of adults whose very severe disabilities, generally present from birth, are complicated and magnified by visual loss. Many will have severe or profound learning difficulties, others will also have substantial hearing loss. All have great difficulty in communicating and most have had few opportunities to exercise choice. They are described as having 'multiple disabilities' and nobody knows how many people there are in this situation.

Some were born blind many years ago, classified as 'ineducable' and in consequence have spent most of their lives in institutions. Others, whose parents resisted 'putting them away', have grown to middle-age sheltered but unstimulated, functioning well below their capability. Now their parents are no longer able to care for them, they are faced with the cold reality of life and have no skills to cope.

Younger people may well have been educated at a school for blind children but because of their limited skills, and lack of appropriate support, have been unable to cope with the transfer from a sheltered environment to a sighted world. Some adults with learning difficulties lose their sight through eye disease or the ageing process. They may now be in their thirties or forties, prematurely aged, with deteriorating sight and other complications. There are also a small number of people who were born sighted and of average ability who are profoundly disabled through progressive disease, accidents or head injuries. Some people with multiple disabilities also have 'challenging behaviour' usually caused by lack of communication, self care or mobility skills.

Those long and negative descriptions are countered crisply by Gill Levy, RNIB's Multiple Disability Services Information Officer. **'Everything is possible. Almost anyone can be helped.'**

25.1 Can sight be improved?

This question, which has been posed throughout this book, is just as relevant to the needs of people with multiple disabilities as it is to the retired professor with ageing maculopathy. In fact, the question is more urgent. People with multiple disabilities need as much information as possible to make sense of their world. The professor, with his wealth of knowledge and experience, can if necessary manage with less. A free RNIB leaflet **Looking for eye problems in people with learning difficulties** gives carers and staff tips on spotting sight problems that would benefit from a visit to an optometrist.

Staff and carers alike may feel that nothing would be gained by a sight test, but techniques developed at the Visual Assessment Unit of the Department of

Snapshot Gregory displayed a wide range of self-injurious behaviour when left alone. Once he was taught to change the music tapes of his personal stereo, he would be calm and relaxed for long periods, without hurting himself in any way.

Optometry, University of Wales College, Cardiff now make meaningful results possible. **How to get the best out of sight testing of adults with learning disabilities and/or no obvious means of communication** (RNIB. 25p.) gives details and makes the point that a new pair of spectacles may only be part of the answer. People may need motivating to wear them. 'There need to be real rewards for seeing – particularly if seeing can be hard work. One man found that he could differentiate between the various chocolate biscuits on a plate when wearing specs – he now refuses to go anywhere without them.'

NEW In 1988 **Kent Association for the Blind** in association with Maidstone health authority introduced the post of Vision Therapist to work with people with learning disabilities and sensory loss. A county-wide survey followed, aiming to investigate current services, to demonstrate examples of good practice and to encourage local and health authority fundholders to invest in such services in future. As a result, several new posts for specialist workers have been created. Full details will be found in **Development Project 1992-94: Investigating the needs of people with Learning Disability and Visual Impairment**. Ann Lewis. Kent Association for the Blind. November 1994.

25.2 Services for adults with multiple disabilities

In recent years there has been growing recognition of the needs of people with learning difficulties and sensory impairments. An increasing number of specialist workers for visually impaired people are now ready to work with them. In Birmingham, for example, **Vision Services** is introducing a peripatetic development officer to work in the community, assessing and providing practical help to people in their own homes, in residential settings and at day centres.

Key to media of publication **P** clear print **L** large print **B** braille **T** tape **M** Moon **D** disk

Where a full address is not given in the text, see 32 (Useful addresses)

seeABILITY provides assessment services for several London Boroughs as well as resettlement programmes for people moving into the community after many years in long-stay hospitals. **Sense** is monitoring the provision of services to multiply disabled people through Community Care legislation and leads **Challenge**, a consortium of eight disability organisations, which aims to secure better services for young people and adults with a sensory impairment and severe learning disabilities and who may have challenging behaviour and need a high level of intensive service provision over a prolonged period. Locally, the community team for people with learning disabilities (sometimes still known as the community mental handicap team) is a good source of support (see chapter 7).

25.3 Opportunities at school-leaving age

Continued education between the ages of 19 and 24 can trigger unexpected progress and achievements. Details of funding by the Further Education Funding Council in local and in specialist colleges are given in 9.1. This funding can continue until the student's 25th birthday. However, funding for students with severe learning difficulties who would not be able to cope with schedule 2 courses, but would still benefit from further education, is more difficult to obtain and the situation varies in different parts of the country. Contact *RNIB Student Support Service, RNIB Multiple Disability Services* or *Sense* for advice and information.

NEW The FEFC is at present (1995) reviewing further education provision in England for students with disabilities and learning difficulties with the aim of ensuring that these students can take a full part in further education.

In recent years employment possibilities have widened. **Mencap Pathways** and a number of other agencies now run special supported employment schemes for people with severe disabilities. The local Disability Employment advisor (DEA) who can be contacted through the local Jobcentre should be able to advise, and RNIB Multiple Disability Services can give more details.

Where further education or employment is not an option, an automatic assumption that the only alternative is a place at a local adult training or a social education centre should be resisted. Many visually impaired people with multiple disabilities would fit in happily in such a setting; others would not. A full assessment, co-ordinated through the young person's social services department, and trial visits are needed before a decision is made. An individual care programme drawing on a range of different sources of help might be an option, or possibly a residential 24 hour programme may be the best way forward. Funding of the care programme is the responsibility of the local authority. See 25.5.

25.4 Specialist centres

The following centres all provide residential care, though attendance on a day basis is generally possible.

Henshaw's College, *Bogs Lane, Starbeck, Harrogate HG1 4ED* ✆ 01423 886451 provides on campus a number of specialist departments including a unit for deafblind young people and an independence centre for students aged 16 and over who have additional disabilities and learning difficulties. A supported housing scheme provides sheltered living accommodation. There is a special unit with nursing care for young people suffering from Juvenile Battens disease.

Insight Homes Ltd *141 Tennyson Avenue, Harrogate HG1 3LE* ✆ 01423 520680 provides community based residential accommodation for visually impaired young adults who need full-time care support. A range of large and small houses in Harrogate and Redhill allow progression towards a more independent lifestyle. A wide range of provision includes following programmes at Henshaw's College or RNIB Redhill College, or a combination of workshop, work experience and home based tuition. Day care is available.

The **Leigh Centre**, *48a High Street, Glastonbury, Somerset BA6 9DX* ✆ 01458 834986 provides community based long-term accommodation for people with sensory and other disabilities in four houses in Glastonbury, and has a three bedroom house which offers respite care to children and adults. Residents have 24 hour programmes in a structured environment which aids natural learning.

Oakwood, *(BRIB) 66 Wood Lane, Harborne, Birmingham B17 9AY* ✆ 0121 428 5070 provides accommodation for 34 people with multiple disabilities, including sensory impairment, in three units and two group homes.

Poolemead Centre, *Watery Lane, Twerton-on-Avon, Bath BA2 1RN* ✆ 01225 332818, run by the Royal National Institute for Deaf People, provides a wide range of rehabilitation, habilitation and long-term support to deaf and deafblind people, including those with additional disabilities. Accommodation is in self-contained units. The Education and Day Services unit provides occupational opportunities and preparation for work as well as recreational facilities. There is also supported housing and group homes available for those who can live independent lives with the occasional support of the warden.

The **Royal Leicestershire Society** has adapted a bungalow to provide accommodation for six people who have learning disabilities and a visual impairment. The residents are supported by a team of specialist workers. The Society, in conjunction with the Leicester Housing Association Ltd., is currently developing three bungalows each housing five people with additional disabilities.

Royal School for the Blind, *56-66 Highlands Road, Leatherhead, Surrey KT22 8NR* ✆ 01372 373086 is the national headquarters of seeABILITY, which provides residential and day services to adults of 19 and over who have a visual impairment and a range of other disabilities such as learning disabilities, head injuries, or physical disabilities.

The residential services offer a variety of accommodation for 130 people, including flats for 8-10 people, community homes for 2-5 people, and 1 and 2 bedroom flats. Residents are supported according to need and services range from 24 hour provision to minimal support. The emphasis is on developing maximum potential and independence, with individual programmes which include mobility and orientation, rehabilitation, daily living skills, basic education and a wide range of creative and leisure opportunities.

(NEW) Recent developments include the opening of new community homes, provision of assessment, rehabilitation and support services to visually impaired people in their own homes, and work with health authorities to re-house residents of long-stay hospitals. The development of a specialist nursing home for young people with serious degenerative diseases is under active consideration.

NEW **Sense Barnet,** *Anne Wall Centre,* is a purpose built centre for deafblind adults with learning difficulties. It provides residential accommodation for 20 people in four five-bedroom flats. The centre includes a hydrotherapy pool and a sensory room. Details from *Sense head office.*

Sense East, *The Manor House, 72 Church Street, Market Deeping, Peterborough PE6 8AL* ✆ 01778 344921 is the regional centre of Sense East. Manor House is the base of further education provision. All students live in small group home settings, living as independently as possible. The courses combine academic activities with vocational training and practice in daily living skills. A respite care facility for people over the age of 16 is available. Sense East is continuing to develop a number of group homes throughout the region to provide long-term accommodation. Other services include the Family Support Service, offering guidance, support and advice to families and carers of a deafblind person.

Sense Midlands, *Princess Royal Centre, 4 Church Road, Edgbaston, Birmingham B15 3TD* ✆ 0121 456 1564 (voice or text) provides a regional advisory service to families, deafblind people and professionals working with them. An adult service department offers a range of residential provision and learning opportunities for deafblind and multiply disabled sensory impaired adults based on individual need. A national information service and day service is provided for deafblind people in the Birmingham area.

Sense Scotland *Unit 5/1, 8 Elliot Place, Glasgow G3 8EP* ✆ 0141 221 7577 provides residential care and training in four family groups for twenty young people aged 16 and over who are deafblind, and/or blind and deaf with additional handicaps. Training for independence involves using many community resources, including the local Further Education college. Day centre and residential provision includes total communication, daily living skills, mobility, pre-vocational work and leisure pursuits.

Vision Homes Association, *4 Church Road, Edgbaston, Birmingham B15 3TD* ✆ 0121 455 8868 aims to provide and promote the provision of residential accommodation throughout the country for adults who have vision impairment and multiple disabilities. It also aims to provide or promote continuing education in social and daily living skills as well as pursuing ways of improving facilities and services for these adults and their families.

VHA currently manages two projects, providing home to 21 residents, and is working towards the development of another.

The Wilberforce Home, *187 Tadcaster Road, York* ✆ 01904 706106 caters for blind people who are between the ages of 16 and 35 on admission, and have additional serious physical handicaps. Application forms from the *Superintendent, E. W. Roberts.*

Non-residential training/rehabilitation services include:

The Elizabeth Gunn Centre (BRIB) *54 Woodville Road, Harborne, Birmingham B17 9AX* ✆ 0121 428 5000 ext. 5892. This day centre provides social education for 55 people from the West Midlands who have multiple disabilities including dual sensory loss. Members follow individual programmes which include music, swimming, and social education.

RNIB Springfield Service, *Springfield Road, Bishopbriggs, Glasgow G64 1PN* ✆ 0141 772 5588, is a purpose built environment offering individual training/ rehabilitation programmes to people with complex needs. Students attend part-time on a time-limited basis, usually to develop communication, independence and mobility skills and increase confidence in all areas of life. The Service, which can be wholly peripatetic, also works with staff and carers so that people continue to receive help which addresses their visual disability after they have left Springfield and moved to a less specialist resource.

25.5 Paying the fees

At 18 years of age, young people who have a continuing need for community care services, or who require them for the first time, have a right to an assessment of their needs under the **NHS and Community Care Act 1990**. If that assessment identifies a need for residential care and help is needed to meet the residential element in the fees, then the local authority is responsible for paying them in full when an appropriate placement has been found. A means-tested contribution from the resident will be collected.

If the prospective resident does not like the offered placement, or has a particular one in mind, the authority can be asked to arrange a place in that specific centre. The authority is obliged to do this, providing that the accommodation is suitable for the person's assessed needs, a place is available and the centre in question is willing to enter into a contract on the authority's normal terms and conditions. The accommodation should not cost more than the authority would usually expect to pay for residential care for someone with similar needs. If the accommodation is more expensive, but someone is willing to 'top up' the local authority's contribution and can show that they will be able to continue making these payments for the duration of the resident's stay, the authority is obliged to arrange the placement.

In 1993, Mark Hazell, a young man with Downs Syndrome, successfully took Avon County Council to court over their choice of his residential placement. Avon Social Services had offered four alternative placements after assessment, but he and his family was not happy with any of them, as he wanted particularly to live in the centre of his choice. They used the complaints procedure (see 4.4.9) without obtaining a change in Avon's recommendations, but were given leave to apply to the High Court for judicial review. At the review, Avon County Council claimed that lack of funds had not influenced its decision, but it was being forced to pay more unnecessarily because Mark wanted to go to one home rather than another. The Hazell family argued that pleading financial constraint as a defence from providing needs-led care was unlawful. The Judge supported them, and ruled that Mark had developed a psychological need to go to the home and that 'assessment of Mr. Hazell has to be based on current needs'. (R v Avon County Council, Ex parte M (1994) 2 FCR 259.)

When applying for help with the fees, the first step is to approach the social services department where the young person lives for the necessary assessment (see also 27.3). Funding for the vocational element in the fees may be provided through the Further Education Funding.

Local authorities have powers under the **Children Act 1989** (Section 24) to provide after-care for young people who have received services from them before the age of 18. They must provide advice for people under 21 who were looked after by the local authority after the age of 16, or accommodated on their behalf by a voluntary organisation. Assistance in cash or kind may be given to anyone who qualifies for advice, and education and training grants may continue beyond the age of 21.

25.6 Support for staff and carers

RNIB Information and Practice Development Service on Multiple Disability is a resource for staff and carers of people aged 19 and over who have visual and learning disabilities. An information officer can respond to individual requests for information on a wide range of topics, such as assessment, communication and rehabilitation. A newsletter, **Focus**, is issued three times a year (annual subscription £5.25). A series of **Focus Factsheets** include: Understanding and using sight – issues for work with people with severe disabilities; Challenging behaviour; Improving environments; Stereotypical behaviour; Minimising problems in eye surgery, and Planning individual leisure activities. A full list of publications and prices can be found in a free annually updated booklet **RNIB Multiple Disability Services** which also gives details of training courses.

NEW **RNIB Consultancy on Multiple Disability, Scotland** offers advice and support to staff working in health, social work and the private and voluntary sector. Consultation can include assessment of functional vision and its relationship to other impairments. Ways to improve the quality of life include advice on personal care skills and communication techniques, and simple ways of improving the environment.

25.7 Training for staff

RNIB Training Service provides individually designed in-house training packages for a wide range of staff groups in statutory, private and voluntary organisations. Each year, a programme of short courses is organised at different venues in the UK. Contact *Mark Gray, RNIB Training Service on Multiple Disability, Birmingham* or *Rhona Paterson, RNIB Consultancy on Multiple Disability, Scotland.*

Training courses leading to the **RNIB Certificate in Multiple Disability** are validated with the Welsh National Board for Nursing and can be linked to NVQ, SVQ, and CCETSW courses. Students should register with RNIB Training Service, who will locate a trainer in their area. Staff wishing to become trainers are allocated a place on one of a series of regular courses, which licence the trainer to deliver the RNIB certificate. This costs £2,500 for which the trainer receives a full resource pack and material to train 10 students. Further details from *Mark Gray.*

Sense provides training nationally for anyone working (in a paid or voluntary capacity) with deafblind or multi-sensory impaired children and young adults. Courses are held regularly at centres in London, Birmingham and Peterborough, and an in-house course design and delivery service is also available. Further information from the *Training Officer, Sense Headquarters*.

The **Council for People with Learning and Sensory Disabilities (CHANGE)** is a national body with representatives of statutory and voluntary organisations in health and social services, together with individuals with special expertise. It has area committees in the South, Wessex, the Midlands and the North. One of its aims is to produce distance learning training packs for staff who are required to assess the needs of multi-handicapped people. More details from *Phillipa Bragman, Sense Headquarters*.

25.8 Giving people choice

Giving people choice is the dominant theme that runs through all work with people with multiple disability. The outsider might consider that to be a very tame ambition. **But the ability to make choices, to accept or reject, is the bedrock of progress. It is something that has been denied for many years to some of the most vulnerable members of society**.

Snapshot

James liked to be left alone after lunch. He would lash out with both fists at anyone who came near. However, after he had received mobility training and could move around the day centre independently, he would quietly walk away from staff members and other service users who wanted to disrupt his daily half-hour siesta.

He now had a choice of ways of dealing with unwelcome attention.

25.9 Further reading

COPE: A compendium of post-16 education and training in residential establishments for young people (£17.50) is a useful reference book, revised biannually (latest edition April 1994). It covers a wide range of disabilities and lists schools where there are residential facilities and which have a reasonably wide catchment area. It includes establishments where the common goals are 'preparation and training for adult life'. Details from *Wiltshire Careers Guidance Services, Support Services Unit, County Hall Annexe, Bythesea Road, Trowbridge, Wiltshire BA14 8EZ* ✆ 01225 777442.

26 Helping older, frailer people

Most blind and partially sighted people are registered when they are between 80 and 89 years of age. Some are, literally, fighting fit and determined to continue living independently, organising any outside help they need for themselves. Much of the **In Touch Handbook**, especially the **Everyday Living** chapter, is intended to meet their needs. Many, however, are in poor health, living alone, just managing, hoping against hope to remain independent. This chapter looks at their needs. It aims to show that, by sharing the older person's perspective, the desire for independence can be achieved and some of the anxieties felt by carers can be eased, whether they be good neighbours, old friends or relatives.

Six ways to help people hear better

- Attract the person's attention before beginning the conversation
- Try to position yourself so that you are fairly close and on the same level as the person to whom you are talking
- Make sure the light falls on your face
- Speak distinctly. If it is necessary to speak more slowly than usual, continue to maintain a normal rhythm of speech
- Change the form of words used when a phrase cannot be heard
- Do not shout!

26.1 Can sight be improved?

Although poor sight is common amongst very elderly people, that does not mean it is inevitable. Any helper can check whether an elderly lady has cancelled her newspaper because she is weary of reading about gloom and doom, or because she cannot see the print. An offer to make an appointment to see an optometrist and provide a lift and moral support when the date is fixed may be all that is necessary. Admittedly, hopes may plummet when the new spectacles are tried at home. They may not seem as effective as when they were worn in the consulting room. A discussion on how home surroundings differ from the consulting room is likely to reveal a huge difference in lighting levels. An adjustable lamp, a fluorescent light, perhaps a higher wattage bulb in the centre light with a very simple shade, may be all that is needed to make it worth wearing the new spectacles.

Yet the fact must be faced that for many elderly people the closing years of life will be spent in a world of blurred outlines and indistinct faces, where objects are never quite where they seem to be, where kerbs disappear and the depth of steps cannot be judged accurately. To be hesitant and slow-moving in such a situation, resistant to change and new ideas, and cautious in contact with strangers – all these are natural and self-protecting reactions which would-be helpers should appreciate. New ways of doing things and new equipment can produce hazards rather than help. Sharing the problem and discussing the alternatives are ways of producing appropriate solutions. Perhaps a grandson would give the ceiling a coat of white emulsion, and to avoid getting under his feet, perhaps grandma could spend the day with her friend, who might demonstrate the rather nice reading lamp she says is so useful.

26.2 Hell's grannies?

> **Snapshot**
>
> **Not just a matter of age ...**
> 'When can we go and have a drink?' a little boy asked his mother. 'When we get your grandma off the back of that motorbike' came the reply. Grandma was one of a group of visually impaired people belting up a mile-long runway at speeds of up to 90 miles an hour in an event organised by Preston & North Lancashire Blind Welfare Society, the British School of Motoring and the Gold Star Motorcycle Association. Two gentlemen achieved the same speeds as their ages: 86 and 87 miles per hour.
> ▶ Comment by a carer

> **Snapshot**
>
> **Not just a matter of age ...**
> 'Mum's 85 and we're both at the end of our tether. She can't see television, she can't read the newspaper any more, she can't hear the radio properly. She mishears most of what people say and can't always move fast enough to get to the toilet in time. I'm lucky in that someone comes in every morning from Home Care to see if she's all right when I'm at work. But when they have holidays, everything goes haywire. Either no-one comes or two turn up at once, mum gets into a state, and it takes days to pacify her. She's not well enough to go out and she says life isn't worth living. I feel like agreeing with her.'.
> ▶ Comment by a carer

26.3 Can hearing be improved?

This may seem a curious question to ask in a book concentrating on the needs of people with little or no sight and who are generally regarded as having excellent, if not superlative, hearing. Yet estimates of hearing loss, based on Institute of Hearing Research data, indicate that over half the population in the 71 to 80 year old age group have some degree of hearing loss and at least 20% have a loss which is moderate or worse. **It is therefore very likely that significant loss of sight amongst older people is going to be accompanied by hearing difficulties**.

When sight deteriorates, problems with hearing loom much larger. Even without formal training in lip-reading most people to some extent automatically supplement the sound of the voice with information gained from watching the speaker's face. Age-related maculopathy, which affects the sight of many very elderly people, makes it very difficult if not impossible to distinguish people's faces. So it is more important than ever for helpers to remember to speak clearly and slightly more slowly than usual, and to make sure that the light is falling on their face rather than the listener's.

26.3.2 Using a hearing aid

Helping an older person to see a doctor is the first step to obtaining a hearing aid through the National Health Service. When a hearing aid is in use, an offer to return it to the Hearing Aid Centre for a check-up is likely to be appreciated. Hearing aids are supplied through the NHS in various strengths, including medium, high power and very high power models, so a change of model is always a possibility if hearing has deteriorated. When all else fails, the old-fashioned ear trumpet or speaking tube can be supplied.

26.3.3 Listening to radio, talking books, tape recorders and television

Using headphones

This is the simplest solution, and often a very effective one. **Headphones** with a mono/stereo switch and a volume control are issued free by the **British Wireless for the Blind Fund** (see 19.8.1). All their radios have a headphone socket.

NEW RNIB Talking Book Service issues a free leaflet **Headphones and Accessories** listing headphones which can be purchased from them and which are suitable for use with talking book players (see also 19.1.1).

NEW Talking book players can be fitted with a variable speed control and an electronic track change indicator, and can be converted to give a higher treble

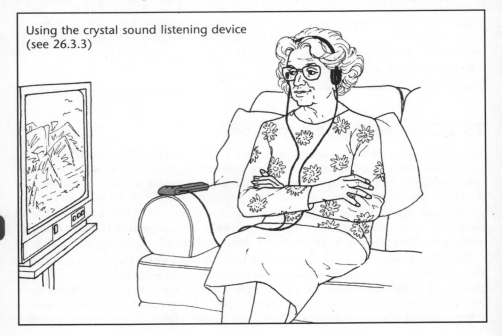

Using the crystal sound listening device
(see 26.3.3)

412

response. Details in **Notes for talking book users who are hard of hearing** from *RNIB Talking Book Service.*

Using a listening device

NEW Crystal (Sound Advantage. From £27.50) is a new portable TV/audio and general listening device developed by RNID for people with a wide range of hearing losses (see illustration in this section). It can be connected to the television or radio with either an extension microphone or a direct connection lead, but as it has its own microphone it can be just placed close to sound source. The user listens through light-weight headphones. Other people in the room can listen in the normal way. Full details in **Solutions**, the mail order catalogue of Sound Advantage, *1 Metrocentre, Welbeck Way, Peterborough PE2 7UH* ℘ 01733 361199.

Five ways to help people see better
- Offer to clean their spectacles or magnifying glass
- Notice if their spectacles are sliding down their nose and offer to tighten sidearm screws or ask the optometrist for help
- Offer to climb up and give the electric light bulbs or fluorescent light tube a good clean
- Ask if it would help if you took the net curtains down – and at the same time give them a wash
- After finding a mislaid item, place it on a contrasting background

Using an induction loop

A **room loop** allows users to move freely round the room and listen to the radio or television through a hearing aid whilst the volume remains at a level which suits other listeners. Most NHS hearing aids, and some privately dispensed aids, have a **T position switch** which means they can be used in this way. A length of insulated wire needs to be run around the room and connected to a loop amplifier. The microphone is placed near the sound source. By moving the switch to the T position, the user can hear sound directly, bypassing the hearing aid microphone.

   The Loop System – a Guide for Hearing Aid Users is a free Factsheet issued by RNID giving full details. Details of **personal induction loop systems** will be found in **Solutions**. These anchor the listener to his chair as the loop is connected to the loop amplifier, and other people in the room may not be able to listen as well.

Using an infra-red system

This is a more expensive, wire-free system. A transmitter is attached to the sound source and sends the sound signals to the listener by means of invisible infra-red light. The light is picked up by a receiver and is changed back into sound. Most systems mount the receiver into a headphone unit powered by batteries.

   Unfortunately, all these systems, whilst successfully preventing the user hearing unwanted background noise, also block out sounds such as the telephone ringing or

---

Key to media of publication ❶ clear print ❶ large print ❸ braille ❶ tape ❶ Moon ❶ disk

Where a full address is not given in the text, see 32 (Useful addresses)

someone knocking at the door. There are various ways of tackling this problem. A second hearing aid could be worn, switched to the normal position. Or a second microphone can be plugged to the loop amplifier, to pick up the sound of a bell, telephone or conversation. Advice should be obtained from RNID or the local hearing aid clinic.

When there is sufficient vision, a flashing light can be obtained to work with the telephone or doorbell. **Sound Advantage**, the marketing division of RNID, lists over 100 listening devices (not hearing aids) in its catalogue.

Social services departments or hospital hearing aid clinics may be able to assess, advise and possibly provide listening aids and install induction loops.

26.3.4 Tinnitus

Not being able to hear properly is frustrating enough, but many hard of hearing and deaf people have to cope with the added burden of constantly hearing sounds they do not want to hear. Noises in the head or in one or both ears is known as **tinnitus**. Sometimes the noises are almost unbearable. A **Tinnitus Helpline** ℘ Lo-call 0345 090210 is operated by RNID who supply a stress management tape on tinnitus.

26.4 Can daily living be made easier?

Adaptations to the home as well as aids to daily living, such as bath aids, toilet frames, grab rails, long handled shoe horns and raisers to increase the height of chairs or bed can often be supplied on loan through social services departments (the social work department in Scotland, the health and social services board in Northern Ireland). Contact the local office direct for an assessment.

Equipment for an Easier Life: A guide to products and where to get them is written especially for older people and those caring for them. It gives details of a wide range of household items from shower seats to a mini jug kettle that is light to lift. All were tested and found useful by older people. A copy and a large print version, if requested, is free on receipt of a large stamped addressed envelope. Contact *RICA*.

Anyone having difficulty in using the controls of a talking book player can have them modified. The track change lever and the on/off switch can be extended. Alternatively, an on/off foot switch can be supplied. Details from *RNIB Talking Book Library*. If pulling the plug from the mains socket is difficult, a brightly coloured **plug with a handle** from *Keep Able* makes the job easier. **Extendaplug**, a device that enables the socket to be raised to waist height without involving rewiring, is supplied by *Ways & Means*.

When an individually designed aid is needed, rehabilitation workers, occupational therapists or a local **REMAP** panel may be able to help. REMAP brings engineering and other skills to bear on 'one-off' problems. For example, when arthritis in the neck, shoulders and arms made it impossible for a lady to lean back to put in her drops, they devised an applicator which she could use without tilting her head back.

See 15.6.8 for ideas on ways people with very poor sight can identify money and 15.6.4 on how to become an agent when someone is unable to collect social security benefits because of physical disability or incapacity.

26.5 Helping people in a crisis

For very elderly people, continuing independence is often precarious. Registration or a sudden sight deterioration may cause the balance to be tipped disastrously. Any older person who has just been registered blind or partially sighted will be thinking, though probably not saying, 'Am I going to go completely blind?' 'How am I going to manage?' 'Will they make me go into a Home?'

Time is needed to adjust and to have an opportunity to bring some of these fears into the open. Relatives and friends also need to give themselves time to come to terms with the situation, and to find out what help can be provided. Older people are by nature resilient; they have lived through two world wars, economic depression and unemployment, and have experienced all the joys and sorrows that are intermingled in a long life. The strengths derived from these experiences can enable them to cope with this new setback, provided that courage is not sapped and self-confidence destroyed by the well-meaning attitudes of those around them.

Snatching away the mildewing loaf with the comment 'You can't eat that' may prevent an upset stomach, but the damage to morale is not repaired so easily. Sorting out the bread bin together while discussing the shortcomings of the modern bakery industry is a way of helping constructively. In much the same way, appropriate help given quickly at the time of crisis – a signature guide, a large print dial for the telephone, a radio or even a white stick – has a virtue far beyond the value of the aid. It conveys the message: 'You're not alone, and we believe you can manage'.

Nowadays the aim of all services is to enable older people, despite poor sight or any other impairment, to live independently as long as possible. Care in the community, that is, the provision of help and support to enable people to continue to live in their familiar surroundings, is not only a very effective form of care, but it is the type of help most older people prefer. No official is automatically going to think that a blind person must go into a home. Indeed, if help is needed to meet residential home fees it is now required that all the options be explored before such a drastic decision is made.

26.6 Living independently
26.6.1 Help in the home

Running a home single-handed can be hard work, especially for older people. In addition, anyone with poor sight has to concentrate extra hard all the time, which in itself is very tiring.

The **home care service** (often still referred to as the home help service) is provided through local authority social services departments as part of their community care provision. The doctor, health visitor or social worker can arrange for a worker to visit to discuss what kind of help, and how much, is needed. The service may be free for people receiving income support, but more often there is a charge which may be flat-rate or means tested.

How much help is allocated is decided through an **assessment**. A social services worker talks through what the older person feels is needed, and listens to the views of carers. When the person is very frail, a great deal of support may be offered: help with getting up in the morning, dressing, check visits during the day, provision of meals and help at bed-time. At its best, the service will be comprehensive and will mesh in with help from the community nurse, voluntary agencies and the carer. See also 4.4.5.

When help is not offered, or is felt to be inadequate, it is important to remember that the complaints procedure can be used (see 4.4.9). This may well bring results. The local voluntary society for the blind should be willing to act as an advocate.

26.6.2 Meals

In most areas, a **meals-on-wheels service** brings a hot dinner to the home perhaps twice or three times a week or, in some areas, every day. The cost is generally subsidised. Alternatives include **Ready meals** or long life meals which have the advantage that they can be stored at room temperature in the larder for between six and twelve months. Frozen meals are an obvious option and in some areas they are supplied through WRVS or social services. A basic microwave cooker (see 16.6) can solve a lot of problems for a carer. With a little ingenuity it should be possible for a carer to leave a meal which can be heated up by the use of one switch.

Another solution is to join a **day centre** or **luncheon club**. **Age Concern** and **WRVS**, as well as social services departments, run centres where there is the chance to have a hot meal, and to benefit from the chiropody, hairdressing and social activities that are often also provided. Transport should be provided for people who cannot reach the centre without it. Social workers or health visitors can explain what facilities there are locally.

26.6.3 Help with heating costs

Older visually impaired people who move slowly are inevitably liable to suffer from the cold. The twin fears of expensive fuel bills and of accidental fire also combine to make them particularly at risk. **Grants** to meet the cost of buying a safer appliance may be made from the Social Fund to people who receive income support (see 5.11.2). Some voluntary societies for the blind make winter heating grants. For example, in 1994, Walsall Society for the Blind, made annual grants up to £70 to people on low incomes. A social worker, health visitor or community nurse will know about local sources of help.

Grants to meet the cost of having doors and windows draughtproofed (up to £128.50) and the loft, pipes and water tanks insulated (up to £198.70) are made through the **Home Energy Efficiency Scheme**. People who are aged 60 or over or who receive income support, housing benefit, family credit, council tax benefit, disability working allowance or disability living allowance can get this help, whether they rent, own or are buying their own home. Local Network Installers specialise in doing the work and advising on energy efficiency. Details from local Council offices or the **Energy Action Grants Agency**, *Freepost, PO Box 1NG, Newcastle upon Tyne NE99 2RP* ✆ Freephone 0800 181667, 9.00 a.m. – 5.00 p.m. weekdays.

Keep Warm, Keep Well 🄛🄟🄣, an annual publication, includes details of the Scheme as well as information on **Renovation Grants** and **Minor Works Assistance** grants. These are awarded at the discretion of local councils and could include help with heating installations or home insulation. Free print copies from *Winter Warmth Line* Freephone 0800 289404 (England and Wales), Freephone 0800 838587 (Scotland) and Freephone 0800 616757 (Northern Ireland). Audio cassette copies from *Talking Newspaper Enterprises*.

26.6.4 Help with heating appliances

It is important not to undermine self-confidence when discussing heating. **Coal fires** can look dangerous to the outsider, but many visually handicapped people manage them perfectly safely: a life-time's experience of laying and lighting fires is not wiped out because eyesight has dimmed. The provision of a good **fireguard**, (an essential also for a very old gas or electric fire which has no effective guard of its own) is a more positive method of helping than immediately suggesting a different form of heating.

Other visually impaired people are very frightened indeed of open fires. A **gas fire** or an **electric fire** with controls fitted at the top are possible alternatives. See 17.2 for ways of marking controls. Gas fires should have a 'flame supervision device' that turns the gas off if it is left unlit or goes out. A **Home Service Advisor** can advise on choosing a gas appliance, arrange for controls to be marked so that they can be set by touch and provide suitable adaptors if turning the controls is difficult. Contact the *District Gas Office* for this free service.

As people age, so do the appliances bought in middle years, which can now present serious safety hazards. An evening spent checking plugs, cables and fittings could be an important contribution by a family member.

Central heating probably poses fewest problems. Some programmers can be adapted with tactile markings. RNIB and British Gas may be able to help (see also 15.2.4).

For warmth at night, **over-and under-electric blankets** are easy to use. A fleecy underblanket is another solution. Details of blankets and heating pads can be obtained from the *Disabled Living Foundation* (see 34). A **hot-water bottle** which does not need to be filled is stocked by RNIB. The Snuggler (£10.50) is filled with a gel pack which can be heated in a microwave and keeps warm for several hours.

Help with meeting the cost of buying a safer appliance may be made through the Social Fund (see chapter 5.11), or a **Disabled Facilities Grant** (see 15.2.8). Help may also be available through the local voluntary society for the blind, social services, or local organisations such as **Lions** and **Round Table**.

26.6.5 Avoiding accidents

Most people assume that very poor sight must make people more accident prone. They forget it also makes people slower, more cautious, and forces them to concentrate and to do one thing at a time. To an outsider, the home may seem full of hazards but because every awkward step and every piece of furniture is familiar, people are often safer in their own home than if moved to a modern, uncluttered environment. A room may be so filled with furniture that it enables someone who is unsteady to get about safely, as everything is within grabbing distance. To tidy the room and provide a walking frame may well cause problems rather than solve them.

It is, of course, sensible to take some precautions. The stairs, kitchen and bathroom tend to be where accidents are most likely. See 12.1.1.

Photographs in the colour section show how contrast and ingenuity can make life safer without making major alterations.

If possible, lighting levels should be consistent throughout the house, as elderly eyes are slow to adapt to changes in light level. Fitting an outside light on the back step might be an appreciated Christmas or birthday gift for the person who still has to get the coal in, or who cannot be persuaded to have an indoor toilet.

The cooker is often a major anxiety, especially when it is a vintage model. It is tempting to try to substitute a small table top electric cooker, or a microwave oven, for the ancient gas stove. But often an older user needs the reassurance of old, remembered things – her hands go almost automatically to the correct controls and long custom sets the pans centrally above the burners. A **'click' ignition gas lighter** might well be welcomed instead of matches, but a new cooker would be wisely resisted.

British Gas keeps a **GasCare Register** for people who are over 60 or who have disabilities. The Home Service Advisor or the District Office (listed under Gas in the telephone directory) can arrange this. Special services which can be provided include an annual **free gas safety check**, braille or large print bills, and the password scheme. The customer chooses a password which is known only to the meter reader so that his identity can be checked before letting him into the house. Details in **Our Commitment to Older or Disabled Customers** 🅟 🅣, free from British Gas showrooms or District Offices.

See 12.1.1 and 15.2.7 for other ideas on living safely.

See chapter 14 for details of safe ways of taking medicines and putting in eye drops.

26.6.6 Calling for help

There are sophisticated ways of calling for help, but the simplest ones are often the best. The good neighbour who keeps an eagle eye on curtains, lights and milk bottles and has time to 'drop in' during the day is best of all. Often blind people will be happy to devise their own system of signals which will indicate 'all is well'.

Often, though, a **telephone** may be a necessity. Particularly suitable telephones include models which have extra large key pads and a memory in which to store the most frequently used numbers (see 15.4.3). BT will fit **extension bells** free for people with poor hearing.

BT and **Mercury** can also supply telephones that amplify incoming speech. People using a hearing aid with a T position switch may find a telephone fitted with an **inductive coupler** helpful. This gives clearer incoming speech as the pick-up coil in the listener's hearing aid receives the call directly.

Help towards installing a telephone and paying the rental may be provided by social services (see 4.6). **Telephones for the Blind Fund** (see 30) or the local voluntary society for the blind may help.

However, it is only too possible for an emergency to happen out of reach of a telephone. **Telephone-linked alarm systems** allow the user to call for help by pressing a button on the telephone or on a portable control small enough to be hung round the neck, clipped on clothing or worn as a wristwatch. This activates the telephone to ring the number of a friend, relative or a special emergency centre automatically.

The **Research Institute for Consumer Affairs** recommends that people should first find out if their own local authority provides an alarm service. **Help the Aged's Seniorline** Freephone ✆ 0800 289404 can advise.

A **Guide to Community Alarms** (1993. £1.95 from RICA or Help the Aged) contains independent comparative test results on 15 systems and includes details on how to get an alarm, features to look for and a buying guide.

26.7 Living with relatives

It is always sad when people have to give up their own homes and move in with relatives, however welcoming and caring these may be. On both sides there is likely to be a good deal of apprehension, and it is often helpful for both parties to discuss the issues involved – and the alternatives – with a social worker before a decision is made.

Once the decision is made, careful joint planning is needed. The stress of moving and the new surroundings are likely to be very confusing, and people may feel their sight is if anything, worse, especially if they have no mental picture of their new home. The route from bedroom to toilet may be crucial, and a rail along the passage wall to act as a guide might relieve some anxiety. If space can be found, the bedroom should be large enough and warm enough for use as a bed-sitting room – a place to retreat to in order to listen to radio or talking book, and where privacy is ensured with the certainty that no one is watching. This room should be very much the visually handicapped person's kingdom, to be arranged as he or she desires it, even though the arrangement may not be aesthetically agreeable to others. Some blind people love a multitude of ornaments and photographs, while others prefer a regimented order which may give the room a bleak and spartan air. Where the elderly guest shares the living room, a **low vision aid** (see 3.3.4 and illustrations in chapter 3) may enable television to be watched without blocking the screen for others. For the hard of hearing, a **listening device** (see 26.3.3) may be especially welcome.

It is just as important, however, to make the newcomer feel at home. It is no kindness at all to insist on doing everything on their behalf, for no one wants to be a passenger. Modern kitchen gadgets may be unfamiliar, but vegetables can be prepared in the old-fashioned way and it is still a help for the busy housewife if she has only to check the potatoes are all peeled, rather than do the whole job herself. Some older visually impaired people become shoe-polishers in chief, others are teachers-extraordinary, for what child can resist reading aloud to someone who really wants to know what the letter says? Cleaning the cutlery, polishing the brass, dealing with the plain ironing, even becoming senior dishcloth knitter to the family and neighbourhood gives status and self-respect. Sharing problems – solving a crossword clue, what to do with the leftovers, how to cope with a grandchild – can be mutually rewarding. The blind person generally has much time to think and meditate with few distractions and so may complement the busy carer's lack of time. When a listener to *In Touch* enquired how one occupied one's mind when 90 years of age and housebound, suggestions from blind people ranged from crocheting in bright wool on a contrasting background, to recording reminiscences of early life on tape for the benefit of younger members of the family, or oral history groups.

26.8 Ideas for carers

26.8.1 Serving meals

Meals in bed can be difficult to manage unless there is a stable surface to take the dishes. A bed table may be the answer, but even an ordinary tray can be used more easily if the plates are held in position by **non-slip mats** (*RNIB* £3.70). Not being able to see clearly what is on the plate is enough to make anyone lose one's appetite so it is important always to say what is on the plate, adding if necessary, 'the meat is at 6 o'clock, the potatoes at 9 o'clock'. The photographs in the colour section illustrate simple ways of making the meal easier to see.

Food is less likely to be pushed off plates with coloured borders. Snap-on white polythene **plate surrounds** (*Ways & Means*. £1.58) can be clipped to circular plates. Red, deep blue and yellow light-weight plastic **Medici System** plates (*Ways & Means*. £6.30) also have a deep rim.

Dishes where meat and vegetables are combined, such as casseroles, are easier to eat. Sandwiches are easiest of all, and toasted sandwiches can be both nourishing and tasty. While it is tempting to leave cold food covered with transparent film, this can often be difficult to remove, and aluminium foil might be preferred.

26.8.2 Dressing

Some older people with little or no sight find it very difficult to cope with ordinary clothes fastenings such as hooks, buttons or hard-to-reach zips. **The Special Collection** is a mail order catalogue issued in January and August specialising in attractive, easy-to-wear clothing. Contact *J. D. Williams Group, Special Collection, 53 Dale Street, Manchester M60 6ES* ✆ 0161 236 5511.

26.8.3 Confined to bed?

The position of the bed in the room should be considered. Many older people are troubled by glare, and will see much better and feel much happier if the daylight is not shining directly at them, so they may prefer the bed alongside or at an angle to the window. A good light over the top of the bed, or clipped to the headboard, may make some activities possible – if the switch is within arm's reach.

On the bedside table, items which are easily knocked over can be anchored by **dycem mats**, or by **blu-tak**. A glass of water is likely to be visible if the glass is in a brightly coloured **plastic holder**, or beaker. The many things that can so easily be lost in bed, or be out of reach, can be stowed safely in a shoe-tidy. This useful set of pockets, generally found in haberdashery departments, can be hooked on the nearside of the bedside cupboard, or the top section can be anchored firmly between mattress and bedbase. The **Pyramid talking clock** may be much easier to use than a tactile model if hearing is good (see illustration in 26.9).

26.8.4 Passing the time

Listening to the radio is always a stand-by, and the preset push-button models distributed through the **British Wireless for the Blind Fund** may solve many difficulties. The tape services described in chapter 19 may be enjoyed. The new free radio cassette recorder issued by the Fund has easy to use controls. Unfortunately, the new **Easiplay** (see 19.7.1) cassette recorder is not free, but for the very elderly it has two great advantages: the cassette is inserted in the same way as toast into a toaster, and it automatically reverses the tape and switches off (see also 26.3.3).

A number of the games stocked by RNIB can be played in bed, as counters have been replaced by pegs. Books of **large print crosswords** (£1.95), beautifully clear **large print playing cards** (from £2.22) and **Patience cards** (£3.17) with giant numbers are stocked by the Partially Sighted Society.

Braillists have fewer problems. Some very elderly people enjoy learning **Moon**, a simple, easy to feel, embossed script (see 18.3). Handwriting is possible with a **Millard writing frame** (RNIB £3.89) which provides a firm surface when writing in bed.

Crafts can often still be enjoyed with the help of a good light and perhaps a favourite magnifier used with a table clamp (see illustration in 16.4). A free **Leisure Pack** of knitting ideas is available from *RNIB Customer Services* and **Art and Craft News** 🅛🅣 issued quarterly by RNIB Leisure Services often includes ideas for simple crafts.

The items listed above are illustrated in the colour section.

26.9 Nursing services at home

The home nursing service is well known, and the community nurse is a very familiar friend to many blind people. Nowadays, their work is often supplemented by home carers from the social services department (see 4.4) Sometimes there is also a night nursing service for elderly people who are gravely ill. Incontinence can be a heart-breaking problem, but help should be available through the community nurse or health visitor. The **Incontinence Advisory Service Helpline** can put callers in touch with their nearest incontinence advisor ✆ 0191 213 0050, Mondays to Fridays 9.00 a.m. – 6.00 p.m. **The Continence Foundation** issues a range of useful leaflets and booklets. Details from *2 Doughty Street, London WC1N 2PH.*

Clocks (watches in 15.4.1)
(Details in 15.4.1)

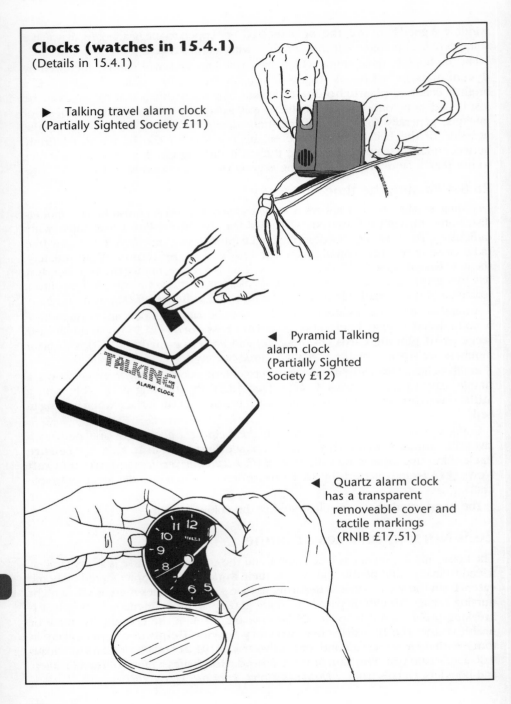

▶ Talking travel alarm clock
(Partially Sighted Society £11)

◀ Pyramid Talking
alarm clock
(Partially Sighted
Society £12)

◀ Quartz alarm clock
has a transparent
removeable cover and
tactile markings
(RNIB £17.51)

Serving a cup of tea

- Place the cup and saucer where it is most likely to be seen and say what you are doing. Put the teaspoon on the far side of the cup
- Do not fill the cup to the brim
- Never offer the cup 'out in the air'. Reaching out for a cup of hot liquid when sight is poor and judging distances difficult, is a recipe for disaster. Instead, place the cup and saucer into the person's hands – after saying what you are going to do

Locating a cup of tea

- Run your fingers along the edge of the table to make sure you are sitting square
- Place your hand flat on the table and then loosely clench your fist
- Move your fist forward very gently. Your knuckles reach the saucer first and stop you knocking the cup over

Some local authorities provide a **laundry service**, and **home nursing equipment** such as bath aids, commodes, bed cradles and aids to prevent pressure sores or special beds. Some nursing equipment, including wheelchairs and commodes, can often be borrowed through the local Red Cross medical depot. **Wheelchairs** for long-term use can be supplied free through the District Health Authority on the recommendation of the patient's family doctor.

26.10 Care in hospital

Being confined to bed in hospital can be, in the experience of *In Touch* listeners, very frustrating. Much depends on the personality of the patient, for the extrovert who is able to tell staff and fellow patients about his or her poor sight may have no problems at all. Others may not be so fortunate, and will find that their cup of tea has been put on the bedtable without their being aware of it, that staff neither introduce themselves nor explain what they propose to do before they do it. A booklet **Helping Visually Handicapped People in Hospital** (RNIB 50p) describes these problems and suggests ways to solve them.

Everyone looks forward to returning home, but for very elderly people this can be another event which tips the balance between independent living and residential care. Community Care provision should enable older people to make appropriate choices, in full knowledge of the alternatives available and the help that can be provided. When discharge is being considered, a social worker will be involved and should consult patient, carer and other relevant people, so that everybody is involved and an acceptable **care plan** made.

26.11 Help for carers

With the best will in the world, both carers and cared-for need to get away from each other occasionally. Community care legislation emphasises that the needs of the carer must always be taken into account when a care plan is made. Carers have a right to ask for an assessment of their needs. Such help might include introducing an elderly person to a local club for older or visually impaired people, providing day care at a local day centre or residential care home, or arranging a short stay at the home to enable the carer to have a holiday. When nursing care is needed, it might include a short stay in a respite care bed in a local hospital.

The **Carers Recognition and Services Bill** currently going through Parliament (May 1995) would give them the right to have their needs assessed and appropriate services provided. More details from *Carers National Association, 20/25 Glasshouse Yard, London EC1A 4JS* ℘ 0171 490 8818. See also 4.4.5 and yellow pages.

26.11.1 Financial help

Full details will be found in **Caring for Someone?** (FB31) **B** a booklet summarising the statutory and voluntary sources of help for carers, free from social security offices or through Freephone ℘ 0800 868868 (see also 5.6).

26.11.2 Mutual support

Carers often feel very isolated. The **Carers National Association** offers information and advice to all carers and campaigns for better services. A bi-monthly magazine for members (annual subscription £3.00) is issued. Carer groups meet locally. More details from *Carers National Association* ℘ 0171 490 8898 (Carers line 1.00 p.m. – 4.00 p.m. weekdays).

The local voluntary society for the blind may also be a source of support, but as yet there appear to be few initiatives in this respect. **Carers are rarely represented and so the needs of very frail, very elderly and housebound visually impaired people tend to be overlooked as there is no-one to speak for them or the people who look after them**.

26.12 Further reading

Clubbing Together **L** , Geraldine Holloway. A handbook for organisers of clubs for older visually handicapped people. (Partially Sighted Society. £1.25).

Information Pack for Older People includes information on leisure activities. Contact *RNIB Leisure Services*.

Caring at Home (£6.95). **NEW** A handbook for people looking after someone at home, brings together information about help in the home, legal matters, time off and where to go for help. Copies from *BEBC, PO Box 1496, Parkstone, Poole, Dorset BH12 3YD*.

I

26.13 Telephone help line

Seniorline is a freephone information service for older people, their relatives, carers and friends. ℘ 0800 289 404 10.00 a.m.–4.00 p.m., Monday to Friday.

27 Residential accommodation

Moving house is always traumatic and is certainly not a decision to be taken lightly. Poor sight in itself is no argument for moving home; more often it is a good reason for staying put. Yet the problems of continuing to live alone can become insuperable when the family home is too large, too isolated or too inconvenient, and the garden is a constant source of anxiety. This chapter looks specifically at the housing needs and options of frailer people who may also be well over pension age.

27.1 Sheltered housing

People who feel that they would be able to live independently, if the conditions were right, may wish to consider sheltered housing. A group of flats or bungalows, each with a bedroom, living room (or bedsitting room), kitchen and bathroom, is linked to a warden by an alarm system and intercom. There is usually also a communal lounge where residents can meet, and often a laundry room and guest room is provided. In 'very sheltered accommodation' there will be a communal dining room as well as personal help given to residents in their flats. This type of housing is provided by local authorities, housing associations and private developers. Waiting lists for local authority sheltered housing tend to be long and in practice vacancies often go to Council tenants living in houses that are too large for them. Priority is also given to people with disabilities whose present accommodation is very unsuitable. The local housing department can give details and supply application forms. Written support from a doctor and social worker is likely to give some priority to the application.

Housing Associations run many sheltered housing schemes designed to meet the needs of elderly people. Applicants living in their own homes or in privately rented accommodation or who wish to move to a different area may stand a better chance of being rehoused by applying to one of these. The local housing department should be able to give details of Housing Associations within its area and RNIB Housing Service can provide information.

Private developers also provide this type of accommodation either for renting or purchasing. Single copies of factsheets on **Sheltered Housing for Sale**, **Rented Accommodation for Older People** and **Housing Schemes for Older People Where a Capital Sum is Required** can be obtained free on receipt of a large stamped addressed envelope, from *Age Concern England*.

27.1.2 Specialist sheltered housing

A limited amount of housing is provided especially for older blind and partially sighted people. The **Gift of Thomas Pocklington** provides single and double flats at Pocklington Court, Roehampton, Pocklington Place, Birmingham and at Pocklington Rise, Plymouth. All the flats are purpose built. Meals and warden support are available. At Roehampton around 120 hours of weekly care support is also provided to the 30 residents through a contract with the local social services department. It is planned to extend this type of care support to Pocklington Place and Pocklington Rise.

Key to media of publication ❶ clear print ❶ large print ❶ braille ❶ tape ❶ Moon ❶ disk

Other voluntary societies for the blind in Blackpool, Ipswich, Leicester, Manchester, Norwich and Worthing have similar schemes. **Willowbrook** is a housing development in Coventry. It was built by The Guide Dogs for the Blind Association in conjunction with the Coventry Churches Housing Association. Designed with the needs of visually impaired people in mind, twelve flats are designated for past or present guide dog owners. Applications should be channelled through GDBA's Regional Controllers.

27.2 Residential care

There can come a time when the worries and responsibilities of living alone, or with a very frail partner, become too much. In recent years many local authority homes have closed and the number of homes especially for blind people has fallen. At the same time there has been a big increase in the number of private residential care homes and nursing homes.

RNIB Accommodation with Care Support Service aims to raise the quality of life of older people who are living in housing with care, residential care, or nursing homes. Branches in Yorkshire, Kent and Somerset provide an outreach service which offers training and advice on good practice. **NEW New Independence** (£165 plus £12.50 for workbooks) is a training package for care staff. It consists of six modules covering topics such as 'Vision and Ageing', 'Changing the Environment' and 'Activities of Daily Living'. Details from *RNIB Accommodation with Care Support Service*.

NEW Helping Residents to Hear (25p) is a useful factsheet from *Counsel and Care* relevant to the needs of elderly visually impaired people with a hearing loss.

27.2.1 Private residential care homes

Social services departments in England and Wales (social work departments in Scotland) are responsible for the registration and inspection of all residential homes caring for four or more residents. In England and Wales (but not Scotland) residential homes with three or fewer residents are under less rigorous regulatory control. The only basis on which such a home may be refused registration is that a person involved in running it is not a fit person to do so. Local social services offices can provide a list of all the homes in their area. All homes should be able to provide a brochure and be willing to arrange a 'trial stay'. Many older visually impaired people, especially if they retain some useful vision, find they can fit in happily when the home is in their old neighbourhood.

27.2.2 Specialist residential care homes

Most specialist homes for blind people are able to accept residents from any part of the country, particularly if it would enable the person to be nearer to relatives. Major

---

Eight Rules for Care Staff
- Say who you are
- Say what you are doing
- Talk directly
- Talk slowly and clearly
- Stand where you can be seen
- Answer questions
- Touch for attention
- Say when you are leaving

From: *New Independence*, an RNIB training package

agencies include **Action for Blind People** with homes in Horley, Surrey and Croydon. The **Catholic Blind Institute**, which does not limit its help to Catholics, has accommodation for 77 residents at *Christopher Grange, Youens Way, East Prescot Road, Liverpool L14 2EW* ✆ 0151 220 2525. When built in 1972, the complex of four houses pioneered the use of texture, colour, lighting and sculpture in design for blind people.

The **Gift of Thomas Pocklington** has purpose-built homes in Plymouth, Birmingham and Northwood. A modernisation programme has been completed at Northwood and Birmingham and is in progress at Plymouth. Accommodation consists of single rooms with ensuite facilities and a few double rooms for couples. **North London Homes for the Blind** has two homes on the Sussex coast. Contact *Honeywood House, Station Road, East Preston, Sussex BN16 3AL* ✆ 01903 770339. **RNIB** has four residential homes situated in Hove, Westgate-on-Sea, Harrogate and Burnham-on-Sea. **Henshaw's Society** purpose designed home in Pendleton, Manchester provides personal care and support individually for residents in their own flat whilst encouraging them to retain independence for as long as possible. See also the photographs in the colour section.

RNIB can supply a regional or national list of all specialist homes for blind people.

27.2.3 Local authority homes

Every local authority in England and Wales has to provide residential accommodation for people 'who by reason of age, infirmity, or any other circumstance are in need of care and attention which is not otherwise available to them'. Local authorities in Scotland have similar responsibilities. A few local authorities have homes especially for blind people. Local social services departments can give details, and deal with admissions, to all the local authority homes in their area.

27.2.4 Nursing homes

Nursing homes differ from private residential care homes in that they must have a trained nurse on their staff, and on duty day and night. A residential care home provides the nursing care that a competent relative might offer. In a nursing home clinical nursing procedures are available. Sometimes a home may be dually registered, as a care home and a nursing home. The District Health Authority keeps a **register of all nursing homes** and will supply lists on request. Few homes for blind people offer nursing care, though the **Gift of Thomas Pocklington** homes at Northwood, Birmingham and Plymouth cater for people who are very frail and very dependent. **Essex Voluntary Association for the Blind**, *29 Moulsham Street, Chelmsford, Essex CM2 0HS* ✆ 01245 352560, has nursing homes at Frinton-on-Sea and Wanstead for blind and partially sighted people. Permanent residents, convalescent and holiday guests are welcomed from any part of the country. **Action for Blind People**, the **Catholic Blind Institute** and **Henshaw's Society** provide nursing care at Cooper Lodge, Horley, Surrey, Christopher Grange, Liverpool and the Lotte Hobson home, Manchester respectively.

Mrs. Brown is 75 years old, very frail and registered blind. She lives with her daughter who is in poor health, and social services have agreed that she needs residential care. She has found a home charging £200 per week, which is within the limit her social services department has set for her.

When she lived with her daughter, her income was £100.95 per week **1**
Mrs. Brown moves and is delighted to find her allowance increased to £183.25 **2**

Personal allowance (step 1)	£45.70
Higher pensioner premium (step 3) (see 5.8.3 – paid due to registration)	£24.70
Attendance allowance	£30.55
Total 1	**£100.95**

Social Services tell her she must pay £170.15 towards the home's fees. They will pay the home £29.85.
Mrs. Brown does the arithmetic in her head. 'That means the home gets its £200 and I've still got £13.10 in my purse.'

Personal allowance	£45.70
Higher pensioner premium	£24.70
Severe disability premium	£34.30
Residential allowance	£48.00
Attendance allowance	£30.55
Total 2	**£183.25**

Four weeks later, she gets a letter from the DSS and everything seems to be changed. Her income has been reduced to £118.40 **3**

Personal allowance	£45.70
Higher pensioner premium	£24.70
Residential allowance	£48.00
Total 3	**£118.40**

'I can't stay here', Mrs. Brown tells the social worker. 'They've cut my money.'
'Not to worry', says the social worker. 'We were expecting that. We'll make up the difference. We'll pay the home £94.70 instead of £29.85.'
'But what about my £13.10?' asks Mrs. Brown.
'You'll keep that just the same because we'll only expect you to pay £105.30 to the home' says the social worker.
'Well, it sounds mad to me' retorts Mrs. Brown. 'And it's enough to worry a body to death, but at my time of life I'm not going to give them that satisfaction!'

27.3 Paying the fees (SSCC1 **Ⓑ**, DHCC1 **Ⓑ**)

Anyone needing financial help to meet the fees for residential or nursing care must contact their local social services department and ask for an assessment of their care needs. If residential care is felt to be appropriate, the department will pay the home's fees and collect a contribution from the resident based on his or her income, but leaving £13.35 per week personal allowance. People with more than £8,000 in capital (property, savings and investments), are expected to pay the full fee. The person's home is counted as part of their capital unless it is lived in by their partner or by a relative who is either aged 60 or over, or if younger, is disabled. In any of these circumstances, the value of the property **must** be ignored. Local authorities also have discretionary power to ignore the value of the house if a friend or relative who gave up their home to look after the prospective resident is still living there. People with less than £8,000 savings get help following a financial assessment. This is similar to the assessment for income support described in chapter 5. Possible entitlement can be checked out by using the **income support charts** (see 5.8.6). Complete steps one, three and five and add a residential allowance of £51 per week (£57 in Greater London). This is the level to which income support can 'top up' existing income. If there is still a short-fall, the local authority will make up the difference in order to meet the fees and leave the resident with £13.35 per week personal allowance.

People living in a residential care or nursing home before April 1993 have 'preserved rights' to special levels of income support. They can claim this help any time up to three months before their savings fall to £8,000.

NEW From April 1995, these special levels are £197 for homes registered to care for elderly or physically handicapped pensioners. Registered blind people over pension age and pensioners who qualify for the higher rate of attendance allowance can claim help with fees up to £227. Homes which are registered to care for physically handicapped people under pension age or for people who become disabled before reaching pension age have a higher limit of £267. The limit for residential care homes in Greater London is £34 higher. The levels set for nursing homes caring for people over pension age is £295 and, for people under pension age, £331. The Greater London maximum increase is £39. These are the levels to which existing income, assessed according to the income support rules, can be 'topped up'.

27.4 Choosing a home

27.4.1 Choosing independently

Anyone with resources sufficient to pay the fees is, of course, free to choose where to go, and no social services assessment is needed. Attendance allowance or disability living allowance care components will continue to be paid indefinitely if the criteria are still met (see 5.5). It is also possible to claim income support and use this to help pay the fees. In these circumstances, the residential allowance can be paid, as can the severe disability premium if the resident is also entitled to attendance allowance.

Counsel and Care provides free and confidential advice and an information service for elderly people, carers and professionals. It can advise on funding and ways to access money from other charitable funds. It has an extensive database on private care and nursing agencies throughout the country and visits all registered private and voluntary homes in Greater London.

27.4.2 Choosing under community care provision

Local authorities are required to allow people to choose their residential home but, not surprisingly, there are some limitations. Normally, after assessment, a particular home or homes will be suggested. The local authority may have special arrangements with certain homes, including specialist homes for blind people.

If, however, the prospective resident does not wish to enter the home suggested, but has another in mind (even in another part of the country), the local authority is obliged to meet their wishes. The only provisos are that the 'preferred home' is willing and able to admit the resident under the social services department's usual arrangements and the cost is not more than the authority would normally pay for someone with the same needs.

Local authorities are often guided by the special rates listed in 27.3, but some will pay more. If the preferred home is too expensive for the local authority to meet all of the charge, a relative, charity or friend can make up the difference.

27.5 Complaints

In order to be registered under the 1984 Registered Homes Act all residential homes in the voluntary and private sector and all nursing homes in England and Wales must satisfy the registering authority (the social services department or district health authority) that they are providing a certain standard of care. In Scotland private and voluntary residential care homes are registered by social work departments under the Social Work Scotland Act 1968, as amended by the Registered Establishments Scotland Act 1987. Nursing homes are registered by Health Boards under the Nursing Homes Registration (Scotland) Act 1938. Serious complaints about any home, if they cannot be resolved by discussion with the staff or proprietor, should be referred to the registering officer. The complaints procedure regarding the way local authority social services staff have carried out their duties is described in 4.4.9. Tenants wishing to lodge a complaint about a Housing Association can telephone the **Housing Association Tenants' Ombudsman Service** ✆ Lo-call 0345 125973 for an information leaflet ❶ and a complaints form.

27.6 Further reading

Getting and Paying for Care is a useful free booklet from Age Concern England. Their factsheets **Local authority charging procedures for residential and nursing home care** and **Finding residential and nursing home accommodation** give more detailed information. Single copies free on receipt of a stamped addressed envelope.

The Benefits of Caring (Philip Boyd. Third edition, 1994. £6.95). A comprehensive and detailed description of all relevant financial benefits. *Inside Communications Ltd., Banks House, 23 Warwick Road, Coventry CV1 2EW* ✆ 01203 252246.

28 Ideas for volunteers

Blind people are as varied in their needs and interests as their would-be helpers, but matching volunteers with blind people in need of their help can demand skills more normally associated with matchmakers! However, when the right people are brought together it can be a mutually rewarding experience. This chapter suggests some of the ways in which a volunteer's time and skill can be used to good effect. It is based on the experiences of blind and partially sighted people and volunteers in all parts of the country. Also, as so many of the most effective volunteers are themselves visually impaired, the chapter includes some suggestions from an experienced blind volunteer.

The four people described here are all volunteers who have chosen to do something for blind people, but they are also doing things that they themselves enjoy, and this is perhaps **the first and most important factor for any would-be volunteer to consider. 'What do I like doing and what will I get out of it?'** This is not selfish, because no volunteer is going to be saintly enough to continue for long doing something which is not to his/her taste. The relationship between blind people and someone who undertakes to provide a service for them on a voluntary basis is a reciprocal one. Helpers can get as much out of it as those they are helping – but this is most likely to happen when they are appropriately matched. So volunteers need to be honest with themselves about what they are looking for. The newly bereaved are often advised by well-meaning friends to get out of the house and do something for someone

Volunteers don't just read to the blind

- John is devoted to exercise; every evening after work he goes out for a 5 mile run around the local park with his blind neighbour who is hoping to be selected to represent Britain in an international sports event.

- Harold took early retirement from his job as a technician, and now spends about two days a week visiting blind people who would like someone to tune their pre-set radios, or get their talking book machine to work properly.

- Shirley who is 65 was feeling rather lonely after her husband died and was persuaded to go as an escort on a summer school which was teaching natural history to blind people; she got so enthralled with the subject that she has now enrolled at a local adult education class to learn more herself and is on the waiting list for next year's summer school for blind students in case anyone needs an escort.

- David who is 19 spent two very energetic weeks in the summer after he finished his A level exams helping at an activities holiday for deaf-blind youngsters. He came back very tired but is thinking of applying for a job as a care assistant in a Home for young adults with visual impairments and learning difficulties before going to college in a year's time.

'I wanted to become involved because, working shifts, I found I had spare time and I wanted to use it in a worthwhile way. I visit two people: Frank who is deaf and blind and Christine who is blind and mentally handicapped. I visit Frank every week, and Christine once or twice a month. I might help with any jobs they cannot manage – rent books, Christmas cards, letters. We may go to the pub, for walks, to meet my friends or just sit and talk. My visits provide company and something to look forward to on a regular basis. Being involved has increased my confidence and it provides me with company and friendship when all my friends are working and I'm at a loose end. I feel good being able to help and give.'

▶ **Belinda Duckers**, a volunteer in Macclesfield.

else, but that is unlikely to make them ideal visitors for housebound blind people. However, they might be very welcome at the weekly talking newspaper where volunteers are needed for copying, packing and posting the cassettes and there is a lot of lively chatter and the opportunity to make new friends!

The sections that follow outline the range of opportunities that exist for those who feel that they would like to do something to help blind people. Almost every voluntary organisation listed in this book is likely to welcome an approach from someone with an interest in their activities and some time to spare. The local library should be able to give details of any local voluntary organisations, or one could start by contacting the nearest resource centre (see 34). A number of voluntary organisations for the blind now employ someone to co-ordinate the activities of volunteers – and it is they who have the delicate task of matching the needs of local blind people with the skills offered by volunteers.

28.1 Working in groups

Not all volunteers have the time or inclination to do something on their own with a blind person, particularly if they have never known someone with a visual problem. It is often easier to start by working within a group, and there is plenty of scope. Most towns of any size have a club or a craft group for visually impaired people, who are mostly very elderly. Volunteers who can teach crafts or play the piano or any other musical instrument are always likely to be needed, but there is no end to the skills that can be used. One newly retired volunteer found himself leading a weekly current affairs debating group. Another is teaching basic computer skills to a small but enthusiastic group with an average age just over 70, and a lady with a lifelong passion for keeping fit is coaxing the members of her local blind club through a series of gentle armchair exercises.

Key to media of publication ⓟ clear print ⓛ large print ⓑ braille ⓣ tape ⓜ Moon ⓓ disk

Where a full address is not given in the text, see 32 (Useful addresses)

How to guide a blind person 1

▶ The blind person grips her sighted guide's arm just above the elbow, and walks half a pace behind

◀ No need to push a blind person into a seat! Once the guide's hand is on the back of the chair, a blind person can slide her hand down the guide's arm to locate the chair, and then move into it unaided

How to guide a blind person 2

◀ Guiding an older blind person downstairs

▶ Guiding a blind person through a narrow space

434

Pet Hates

The *In Touch* programme has always been made and presented by blind journalists and broadcasters who, like all other visually impaired people from time to time, encounter well-meaning but not always appropriate behaviour from sighted people. Here are some examples they find particularly irritating.

I hate it when...

* People help me onto a train, which I can actually manage unaided, but then leave me to find an empty seat, which is not easy if you are blind. *Peter White*

* People who I have just met start quizzing me about my eye condition. 'What's wrong? Have you had it always?' I'm not embarrassed about being nearly blind, but to me it's a boring commonplace rather than a fascinating novelty and there are lots of other more interesting things to talk about. *Jane Copsey*

* People who have invited me for a meal make a big performance of cutting up my food without even asking me whether it is necessary – and mostly it isn't! *Tony Barringer*

* I tell people that I am partially sighted and they ask, 'Can't you get any glasses that would help?' *Cheryl Gabriel*

* When I ask someone to read the indicator board on a railway station they invariably ask me why I can't read it for myself. *Sarah Newman*

28.2 How to guide a blind person

All volunteers should familiarise themselves with the basic guiding techniques illustrated in this section. **The most important rule is always to let the blind person take the sighted guide's arm**. Visually impaired people may accept the fact that sighted people tend to grasp them by the arm but this is not the safest way to guide, because this position means that the sighted person is effectively pushing the blind person along and is not really able to give any support. If the blind person takes the sighted guide's arm then the guide can keep slightly ahead and have a clearer view of where they are going, and of any obstacles to be avoided. As illustrated in 28.1 the blind person should grip her guide's arm just above the elbow and walk about half a pace behind. If the guide keeps her arm close to her side then the blind person can feel the movements of her body and may not need constant instructions to 'turn left' or 'turn right'. In mobility jargon the guide's arm which is held by the blind person is known as the 'grip arm', and the blind person holds it with the 'grip hand'.

28.2.1 Showing someone to a seat

Another frequent manoeuvre which every helper needs to learn is how best to show a blind visitor to a seat. **It is bewildering for a blind person to be told to 'sit down' without any indication of where a seat is to be found, and frightening for a blind person to be physically pushed into a chair**. The best way is illustrated in 28.1. The sighted guide puts the hand of her 'grip arm' on the back of the chair. The blind person then slides her 'grip hand' down the guide's arm to locate the chair, and checks that there is nothing on the seat. Feeling the side of the chair with her leg, the blind person can usually sit down unaided, but the guide should say if there are any obstacles to avoid on either side of the chair.

28.2.2 Guiding on stairs or in crowded rooms

An inexperienced volunteer could be forgiven for thinking that all blind people want to do is to sit in a chair and perhaps have a cup of tea. It is not uncommon to see blind people sitting marooned in the midst of activity which they would enjoy if only someone would help them to get involved. It is not difficult or dangerous to help people with little or no sight to move about in a crowd, or up or down stairs, or through a narrow gap between tables at a reception, but there are simple techniques which make it safer and easier. Probably the most frightening situation is going down stairs. **The most common mistake that well-meaning sighted people make when guiding a blind friend is to say 'steps' without mentioning whether they are going up or down!** The hand and arm position is the same as for normal guiding (see 28.2), but when going up or down stairs the blind person is one full step behind and the 'grip hand' has therefore to stretch out a little further than on the level (see illustration in 28.1). Many blind people find it helpful to hold a banister or stair rail with their free hand, so it may be necessary for the guide to switch sides to enable this to be done. It is not necessary to count steps, but the guide should give a warning if the handrail ends before the last step. Once back on the level, the guide should say that was the last step, take one pace forward, pause briefly so that the blind person is also on the level and then move on. The best way to guide someone in a crowded situation is shown in 28.2. Here the sighted guide and his blind companion walk in single file. The guide's arm is still gripped in the usual way, but it is tucked behind his back so that the contact is easily maintained in a narrow space without knocking into anyone or anything.

Friendly ways of helping

If the day to day problems of blind people could be overcome only with the help of formal volunteers, life would be even more difficult. It is the friendly and unobtrusive help given by friends and neighbours or even a stranger in the street that can make all the difference. The passer-by who says to a blind person standing on the kerb, 'Hold your white stick where drivers can see it, then take my arm and we'll both get across!' has the right idea.

The guiding techniques which have been developed by mobility teachers over the years always stress that wherever possible blind people should be encouraged to be independent. When going through a door, for example, the guide should try to ensure that the blind person is on the hinge side, which means that after the guide has opened it they can go through together, and the blind person can use his free hand to shut the door behind them. All these techniques become easier with practice and some club organisers have successfully used experienced volunteers and blind members to demonstrate guiding techniques to new volunteers. And the best of them? **Remember to tell sighted newcomers not to put a cup of tea in front of a blind visitor without first explaining what they are doing!**

28.3 Advice for drivers

There is probably not a club in the United Kingdom which would not welcome an extra car driver. Arranging the transport of elderly frail people to and from the club's meeting place is every organiser's nightmare. Most pay the driving expenses of volunteers. Few volunteer drivers are likely to drive as much as 5000 miles a year, but those who clock up that impressive mileage should get hold of an Inland Revenue guidance note 'Volunteer Drivers and Tax' from their local tax office. Even the shortest journey with a blind passenger means that the driver needs to find the best way to get them in and out of the car. The photographs in the colour section describe a technique that enables a blind person to get safely into a car without being 'handled like a large parcel', as one blind man described a journey with a well-meaning but inexperienced driver.

A blind person who is reasonably mobile needs to be shown the handle of the car door and told which way the car is facing. Then, as the photographs show, it is not difficult for a blind person to protect themselves by placing their other hand on the roof of the car to ensure that they don't bang their head as they back into a seat. When a blind person is elderly and finds bending difficult, it is much easier to back into the front passenger seat and, once seated, swing the legs round into the car. It is also better to ask blind passengers if they need help with fastening the seat belt, than to assume that they cannot manage and buckle them in as though they were small children unable to cope.

28.4 Working alone

Not everyone enjoys working in a group and for some volunteers the possibility of working on a one-to-one basis is much more appealing. It is also potentially more challenging and it is probably best done by volunteers who have had some basic training, which increasingly is being offered by local societies. Some volunteers undertake the practical tasks which are difficult for many blind people who live alone to do for themselves. This may mean tackling minor household repair jobs – changing a light bulb, oiling a lock or mending a broken curtain rail. Others act as escorts on local shopping expeditions, or help blind talking book users by going through the catalogue and helping to compile a list of books. A volunteer whose knowledge of literature may not be as wide-ranging could also achieve the same result by taking a blind friend down to the local library where, by appointment, the librarian would probably be delighted to help make an appropriate selection from the Talking Book catalogue.

> A blind lady once told *In Touch*
> 'I can't stand people who say,
> 'Tell me if you want anything'.
> If only they would say 'I am
> going to X and Y shops.
> Can I get you anything
> while I'm there?'
> Then I would know that they
> really wanted to help and were
> not just saying it.'

28.4.1 Friendly visitors

A surprisingly large number (45%) of visually impaired people live on their own. 26% (90,000 people) living alone say that they are never visited by friends or neighbours and 11% say that they are never visited by a relative. In addition blind and partially sighted people living alone were visited no more frequently than people living with a sighted friend or relative. These data ... reveal the apparent absence of an informal support network of a vulnerable sector of society.
RNIB Needs Survey 1991

These statistics, which shocked the authors of the RNIB survey, underline the importance of the **friendly visitor service** which is being offered by an increasing number of voluntary societies. Someone who is able to be a reliable visitor, sensitive to the needs of the blind person, is a volunteer to be cherished. It does not always mean that the visitor has to sit and make conversation while sipping tea. One volunteer visitor has spent hours helping a partially sighted man who is a keen photographer to sort out his large collection of slides and prints. Another visitor has been teaching a blind lady to play a keyboard. A third, having discovered that the blind man he was asked to visit is keen on old time dancing, calls once a week to take him off to the local old time dance session and a visit to the pub afterwards! Volunteer visitors need to observe and listen carefully to assess what help is likely to be needed. It might be helpful for a first time visitor to come armed with a list of services that are being offered by the local society and ask whether any are of interest. To know that the local blind society has a list of reliable handymen who can undertake decorating jobs at reasonable rates or that there is an escort service for people wanting to go to the theatre or a concert may come as a pleasant surprise to a newly blind person, who thought that the only thing on offer locally was a bingo session at the blind club. One of the joys of retirement is to do things 'on the spur of the moment', a joy denied to many blind people who are forced to plan ahead. A phone call from a volunteer inviting them out for a drive can put some much appreciated spontaneity back into life.

28.4.2 How to be a good listener

But for many blind people who spend too much time on their own a visitor who will just sit and listen to them is really appreciated. It is not necessarily an easy thing to do. Most of us like to think of ourselves as good listeners. This may be quite easy if someone is telling us about a holiday, but it is not always easy to know how to react when someone is telling us about painful or upsetting experiences. People who have lost their sight are likely to experience grief, distress and anger and having a friendly visitor may be a welcome opportunity to express some of these feelings. It is sometimes difficult for the visitor to know what to say or do. The natural response for most people is to try to soothe an angry person or to cheer up someone who is upset. But these are very natural reactions to the loss of sight, and though it may be a painful experience for the listener, it is **usually more helpful to allow them to talk about their pain and grief than to try to distract them.**

People may say things like, 'I don't feel that life's worth living now I've lost my sight', or, 'I feel totally useless'. Try not to respond with a remark like, 'I know how you feel, Uncle George was just the same when he had his accident'. Find the words that will encourage them to talk more about their experience. Just saying, 'Tell me more about how you feel' may be all that is needed to allow them to unburden themselves. Someone visiting a blind person must also remember that **a smile may not be seen, but a friendly tone of voice, or a gentle touch on the arm will convey the message that you really are listening.** Many elderly people are very concerned not to be a nuisance, or take up too much time. One experienced visitor made a point of settling herself with a deep sigh into her chair as a signal that she was making herself comfortable and not intending to rush off to her next call.

As much as possible, listen without interrupting. Don't be frightened to sit in silence for a couple of minutes. If you feel that you must say something, don't pose questions that open up areas that have not been discussed. Say something that indicates that you have heard and understood what has been said. If someone has told you what a loss it is not to be able to read the daily newspaper, it may be tempting to respond that you feel the standards of journalism have sunk so low that papers are not worth reading nowadays. But someone who has lost the ability to read has also lost the ability to choose whether to buy a daily paper. They need to express their feelings about that loss – and it would be more helpful if their visitor said something like, 'It must be hard not to be able to read a newspaper like you used to do every day. What do you miss most?' **It is only after people have had a chance to talk about their feelings of loss, that they may feel able to accept the advice about**

Fred is 82, blind and has lived alone since his wife died. While he appreciated the kindness of his neighbour Mary who insisted on knocking at his door at 9 every morning to check that he was all right, he wanted to find some alternative way of letting her know if he really had a problem. Eventually he hit on a simple solution. Fred arranged that Mary's newspaper was delivered to his house, and he then went out to put it through her letter box by 9 o'clock. If by any chance he failed to do this then Mary would come round to see if he needed any help.

alternative ways to get the information previously obtained from the newspaper (see 26.7).

Most difficult of all is not to show any embarrassment if someone bursts into tears when relating their experiences. It is a very natural part of the grieving process and by allowing someone to show their feelings a sympathetic listener is helping a blind person to come to terms with their loss. Trying to distract attention from the grief, or attempting to cheer them up, is more likely to ensure that the distress remains bottled up and prolongs the despair and depression felt because no one appears to want to listen to their feelings. **A good listener needs only to listen, not to say or do anything to make things better.** Good listening may in itself enable the healing process to get under way.

The same guidelines apply if visiting someone who gets really angry over incidents or people considered to be responsible for their present situation. Visitors should not say anything which might indicate that they are taking sides in any disputes, whether it relates to an unsympathetic eye specialist or an unhelpful relative. They should not give advice, just respond with remarks that show that they are really paying attention.

It is worth emphasising to all visitors that nothing they can say will restore the sight that has been lost. But a good listener can, over a period of time, help a person come to terms with a new situation. People who have lost their sight in adult life say that it took about two years before they felt able to cope as before. **All too often a friendly visitor feels a sense of failure if after an hour's conversation with a newly blind person they seem to be as depressed or upset as before. No one can achieve a miracle in just one hour of listening,** but a regular visitor over a period of months should be able to see some changes. However if there is no sign of any reduction in the expressions of anger and resentment, it may be an indication that this is a person who might benefit from some sessions with a professional counsellor (see 14.3.1).

28.5 Helping in residential homes

It is not only the elderly blind people living in their own homes who may need a visitor; blind people in residential homes and nursing homes also welcome contact with someone from the 'outside world'. Working with blind people in these residential settings is a challenging task which demands a great deal of resilience and patience. Some volunteers act as the contact for all the blind people in a certain home, visit them regularly and act as a liaison between the staff, the local voluntary society for the blind and the social services department. It is not a commitment to be taken up lightly, since promised visits are eagerly anticipated by elderly residents who often have outlived all their friends and relations, and it is intensely disappointing if a promised visitor fails to arrive.

28.5.1 Advocacy services

An **advocacy** service for elderly people in residential care has been pioneered by Age Concern, Berkshire. Volunteer agents are appointed to help residents handle their financial affairs; the help given ranges from pension collection and payment of fees to shopping for personal items. Frail, blind people are among those who benefit from this scheme. Details from *Anne Snell, Age Concern, Berkshire, St Andrews House, Wilton Road, Reading RG30 2SS* ℘ 01734 594242. Sense has a pilot project in the Midlands, the South West and South East linking volunteer advocates with deafblind people in residential care. The advocate builds up a relationship with a deafblind person with communication difficulties. Advocates aim to give deafblind people more of a voice in how services are provided and to promote recognition of their rights, including their right to as full and normal a life as possible. Details from *Vanessa Davies, Sense Headquarters.*

No guessing

The myth that all blind people have perfect hearing leads too many sighted people to fall into the trap of thinking that they will always be recognised by a blind friend by merely saying hallo. The late David Scott Blackhall, who presented the **In Touch** programme from its inception in 1961 until 1981, summed up the reaction of visually impaired people to this infuriating habit by the following verse which he included in an *In Touch* pantomime:

> There'll be no Christmas kisses, for those who cry, 'you know who this is!'

28.6 Helping in hospitals

There are also increasing opportunities for volunteers to work in hospitals as supportive helpers when a blind patient is admitted into a ward where staff are busy and not used to dealing with someone who cannot see. The RNIB's leaflet **Helping Visually Impaired People in Hospital** can be a useful guide. An increasing number of voluntary societies are now running information desks in the eye clinics of their local hospitals, and helping to ensure that someone who is losing their sight is put in touch with all the services that are available. Here the need is for volunteers who have familiarised themselves with some of the basic pieces of equipment likely to be of use in everyday situations, as well as knowing where to go for help and advice on benefits, mobility training and all aspects of rehabilitation.

28.7 Training

There are as yet few opportunities for training volunteers to work with blind and partially sighted people. There is still a feeling that a kind heart and good intentions

Blind volunteers

Quite a number of volunteers are themselves visually impaired, and as well as helping or advising sighted volunteers they can provide an encouraging example for newly blind people of what can be achieved without sight. However, sighted volunteers can sometimes forget that the most confident and competent blind person does need a little help and consideration in order to participate fully in many activities. Jessica Finch, a totally blind woman who has done a lot of voluntary work, has the following wish list for sighted people on any committee with a blind member.

• Check in what format (large print, braille, tape, computer disk) information and committee minutes should be sent to a blind member, and ensure that it gets there at the same time as other people receive the print version.

• Make sure that transport to and from meetings is offered.

• Ensure that at the meeting people identify themselves when speaking, and that when there is a vote, it is done verbally with all giving their name and not by show of hands.

• Make sure that a blind person coming to the committee is introduced to the person sitting on either side of them. Remember to show them where to put their coat and the location of the toilet, and alert them to the tin of biscuits in the middle of the table!

are the only attributes that are needed by a volunteer, but it would be easier for both the volunteers and those they are trying to help, if the sighted volunteer had some basic knowledge of blind services and some idea of where to get information. Many of the local voluntary societies run short courses, and some social service departments recruit and train their own volunteers with a 'visual impairment' element in their courses. The advantage of joining such a course is that it gives a volunteer hoping to work with blind people an opportunity to find out about other services from which blind people might benefit. There is also much that a volunteer can learn by observing and talking to visually impaired people. Experienced blind people are generally very happy to share their expertise with a sighted person whose response is not, 'It's wonderful – the way you get into my car / find your way around this building', but 'Tell me how you manage to do this so easily so that I can help other people to do the same'.

28.8 Information for volunteers

There is no magazine produced specifically to meet the needs of volunteers working with blind people, but RNIB **Update** is an excellent monthly magazine which reflects the activities of local voluntary societies. It is a good source of information about new services, publications, courses or equipment that might be of use to voluntary societies and their volunteers. It is produced by the RNIB **Voluntary Agencies Link Unit**. There are also some useful audio visual aids which would serve volunteers as an introduction to the needs of blind people. **Seeing It Our Way** is a 17 minute Australian film in which blind people talk of the type of help they appreciate as well as the kind of help they would prefer not to have. Its message is equally relevant to British volunteers. Available from *Boulter-Hawker Films Ltd., 28 St George Street, Hadleigh, Ipswich IP7 5BG* ✆ 01473 822235, price £49 plus VAT, or can be hired for £9.78 a day.

There is also a British video **Look at it my way** which conveys a similar message. Available from *East Sussex Association for the Blind, 9 Sutton Road, Seaford BN25 1RU* ✆ 01323 898681, price £55, or can be hired for £13.50 for 7 days. The *In Touch* programme, though primarily made for blind people, is found to be helpful for many sighted listeners who not only want to keep up with relevant news and developments but also want to hear the viewpoint of blind and partially sighted people. The quarterly **In Touch Bulletin**, which summarises the programme information, is available on request. Print copies can be obtained by sending four large (A4) stamped, addressed envelopes to the *In Touch office, Broadcasting House, London W1A 1AA*. Braille, Moon and tape copies are also available: braille from *Scottish Braille Press*, Moon from *RNIB* and tape (£3 p.a.) from *Cadwell Recording Services*. The weekly **In Touch programme factsheets** are also available on request (send sae to *In Touch* office) and via the **In Touch Gateway**. Volunteers helping elderly blind people may also find it helpful to get copies of the two **In Touch Care Guides** which describe practical ways of coping with the most common sight problems in older people. **Waiting to See** (£2.50) is written for people with cataracts, and **Coping Again** (£3.50) has advice for people with macular disease. The latest Care Guide **101 Practical hints for living with poor sight** (£2.50) is full of suggestions for overcoming everyday problems. All Care Guides ⓛ ⓑ ⓣ are available from *In Touch Publishing*.

Many blind people have commented over the years that it is much more frustrating not to be able to find what one wants in one's own cupboard than not to be able to see the glory of the setting sun. **Volunteers who have familiarised themselves with some of the practical ideas passed on by more experienced blind people are likely to be more welcome than those who can express nothing more than sympathy**.

Reference J

J

29 Sources of information

For information on benefits, see 5.16

29.1 Where to buy equipment

All the following organisations and commercial companies supply goods by mail order and issue free catalogues on request. Some items can be VAT zero-rated when purchased by blind or partially sighted people. The catalogues give details.

APH Catalog of Instructional Aids, Tools and Supplies 1994-5, *American Printing House for the Blind, PO Box 6085, Louisville, Kentucky 40206-0085* ℘ 001 502 895 2405.

Consumer Products Catalog 🅛, *The Lighthouse Inc.*, 36-02 Northern Boulevard, Long Island City, NY 11101 1614 ℘ 001 718 937 6959.

Speechmaster catalogue, *Cobolt Systems Ltd.*, lists a range of talking watches and alarm clocks, personal and kitchen scales, as well as some mobility aids. Taped instructions supplied on request.

Brochure and **Catalogue** 🅛, *Partially Sighted Society*, lists large print goods, including calendars, diaries, playing cards, watches and clocks, plus a selection of task lights.

Product Guides 🅛 🅑 🅣 🅓: **Braille**, **Clocks and Watches**, **Daily Living**, **Games and Puzzles**, **Learning**, and **Mobility**. *Royal National Institute for the Blind, Customer Services*. Most equipment is supplied with instructions in large print. Braille and tape instructions are available on request. A subsidised price applies to blind and partially sighted people who live in the UK, voluntary societies for the blind and employers buying essential equipment for visually impaired employees. Further details in **Welcome to Shopping with RNIB** 🅛 🅑 🅣.

A number of mail order companies sell daily living equipment, some of which may be particularly helpful for visually impaired people who are frail or in poor health. Suppliers include: *Chester-Care, KeepAble*, and *Ways and Means, 17 Ludlow Hill Road, Nottingham NG2 6HD* ℘ 0115 945 2205. All branches of Boots can supply their **Independence in the Home** catalogue and accept orders for items; sometimes a home delivery service is possible. Many of their aids are stocked in the larger branches and can be bought over the counter.

Mail order companies stocking items for children with special needs include *Playring Ltd., Raven Educational, 13a Victoria Road, Wellingborough, Northamptonshire NN8 1HN* ℘ 01933 279108 (The Raven Collection: Toys to Encourage Child Development); *Rompa, Goyt Side Road, Chesterfield, Derbyshire S40 2PH* ℘ 01246 211777 and *Toys for the Handicapped*, (Fun and Achievement catalogue for children; Age Appropriate Resources for teenagers and adults with special needs).

Key to media of publication 🅟 clear print 🅛 large print 🅑 braille 🅣 tape 🅜 Moon 🅓 disk   **J**

Where a full address is not given in the text, see 32 (Useful addresses)

29.2 Training courses for work with visually impaired people

29.2.1 Care staff

RNIB Care Training Service offers training for care workers, support staff in education, and managers of residential units. Courses include a two-year certificated in-service course, an open learning training package and short courses. The Service is an NVQ Assessment Centre, approved by the Central Council for Education and Training in Social Work. Details from *RNIB Care Training School, Exhall Grange School, Wheelwright Lane, Ash Green, Coventry, CV7 9HP* ℘ 01203 366133.

29.2.2 Rehabilitation workers

The Guide Dogs for the Blind Association **School of Rehabilitation Studies** offers a Diploma of Higher Education in Rehabilitation Studies at Burghfield, Berkshire and Forfar, Scotland. The course is available in standard format, lasting 80 weeks, and accelerated, which takes 65 weeks. 'Top-up' and other short courses are also offered. A limited number of bursaries are available for students without funding. Details from *Simon Eamonson, School of Rehabilitation Studies, GDBA Headquarters*.

NEW **Henshaw's College** offers a full-time, 80 week Diploma in Rehabilitation Studies (Visual Impairment) course in Harrogate from June 1995. Details from *Lynne Weston.*

RNIB School of Rehabilitation Studies offers a one-year course leading to the Diploma in Higher Education, Rehabilitation, a five month mobility officer course and an orientation and mobility course for people working with visually impaired children. Details from *Patrick Heywood.*

29.2.3 Funding for training staff

Under the terms of the Social Services Training Support Programme, the Department of Health has set up a visual impairment sub-programme to encourage local authorities to provide resources for the training of staff working with visually impaired people.

The sub-programme consists of a specially reserved fund of £250,000 primarily intended for the training fees of rehabilitation workers, and also to allow mobility and technical officers to acquire through 'top-up' courses the additional skills to enable them to become rehabilitation officers. **Funds from the sub-programme may also be spent on courses directed towards staff who would benefit from an understanding of the needs of visually impaired people.**

NEW The Department of Health will receive bids for funds to cover part of the costs of course fees under this sub-programme from local authority social services departments in England, or from voluntary organisations where these organisations are formally contracted to provide services on behalf of a local authority in England. Voluntary organisations must apply through the social services department with

446

which they have a formal contract. The Department of Health will provide up to 70% of the course fees, subject to the availability of funds.

Local authority circular (95)3 gives full details of the programme and contains the official application form. A free booklet **Courses by Trainers in Visual Impairment** lists some of the organisations and individuals currently offering training. Both are available from *SC6A, Department of Health, Room 328, Wellington House, 133-135 Waterloo Road, London SE1 8UG.*

The Welsh, Scottish and Northern Ireland Offices have separate arrangements for funding training of rehabilitation workers.

29.2.4 Student nurses

NEW RNIB provides a national training programme for student nurses endorsed by the Royal College of Nursing and the English National Board for Nursing, Midwifery and Health Visiting. It consists of a ninety minute workshop, conducted by trainers with personal experience of visual impairment. The fee is £75 per workshop. Further details from *RNIB Community Education Office.*

29.2.5 Training for teachers

Six centres offer qualified teachers additional training to teach visually impaired children. Diploma courses vary: one year full-time, two years part-time or two years distance learning. Contact:

Birmingham University, *School of Education, Admissions Registry, Birmingham BI5 2TT* ℘ 0121 414 4887

Cambridge University, *Institute of Education, Admissions Registry, Cambridge CB2 2BX* ℘ 01223 69631

Heriot-Watt University, *Moray House Institute of Education, Professional Development Centre, Holyrood Road, Edinburgh EH8 8AQ* ℘ 0131 556 8455

London University, *Institute of Education, Olga Miller, Department of Educational Psychology and Special Educational Needs, 25 Woburn Square, London WC1H 0AA* ℘ 0171 612 6270

Manchester Metropolitan University, *Faculty of Community Studies, Law and Education, In-Service Office, 799 Wilmslow Road, Didsbury, Manchester M20 2RR* ℘ 0161 247 2011

University of Wales Swansea, *Department of Education, Administrator (Special Education), Hendrefoelan, Swansea SA2 7NB* ℘ 01792 201 231.

Birmingham University also offers:

- one year full-time Diploma or B.Phil (Ed) courses in the education of children with multi-sensory impairments to staff already working in that field
- distance learning Diploma, B.Phil (Ed) courses in Visual Impairment and also in Multi-Sensory Impairment
- one year part-time distance learning course leading to an Advanced Certificate in Education for teachers not working solely with deafblind children but who wish to know more about their education. Contact *Heather Murdoch or Angela Hall* ℘ 0121 414 4887

J

- one year distance education course leading to an Advanced Certificate in Education for staff in Further Education and Rehabilitation Services. Contact *Juliet Stone* ✆ 0121 414 4866.

  London University also accredits:

- an Advanced Course in Multi-Sensory Impairment which various institutions offer to professionals working in this field or teachers qualified in one or more of these areas: severe learning difficulties, visual or hearing impairment.

- **NEW** a joint London University, RNIB and Moorfields Eye Hospital Trust one year course (held at Moorfields): Assessing Children's Vision. Contact *Olga Miller* ✆ 0171 612 6270/0181 968 8600.

RNIB Education Centres, in collaboration with regional universities, are developing modular courses accredited towards diploma, first degree and masters qualifications. They also offer in-service short courses on mobility, low vision, technology, music, pre-school children etc. Some courses target particular groups such as educational psychologists, nursery nurses, classroom assistants. Contact the centres direct for their in-service training programmes.

RNIB Education Centre Wales offers Counselling Skills Training for professional and support staff working with families of visually impaired children or children with special needs. Consisting of 30 hours study and a course assignment it leads to a Higher Education Certificate in Further Professional Studies, accredited by Gwent College of Higher Education. Contact *Joyce Chatterton, RNIB Education Centre Wales, 4th Floor, 33-35 Cathedral Road, Cardiff CF1 2HB* ✆ 01222 668606.

RNIB and **Gwent College of Higher Education** jointly offer a two year part-time course leading to an Advanced Diploma in Special Education Needs. Contact *Jennie Sparks, Gwent College of Higher Education, Caerleon Campus, PO Box 179, Newport, Gwent NP6 1XJ* ✆ 01633 432217.

The Scottish Sensory Centre offers a postgraduate Diploma in Special Educational Needs course, via six specialist routes, including Visual Impairment. Contact *Marianna Buultjens, Scottish Sensory Centre, Moray House Institute of Education, Heriot-Watt University, Holyrood Road, Edinburgh EH8 8AQ* ✆ 0131 558 6501.

29.2.6 International training courses

NEW The **Stockholm Institute of Education** has developed international low vision therapy training in English. The first course starts in August 1995. Three independent modules (basic, advanced and more advanced) are planned, each lasting five months. They will be held partly in the student's prospective workplace. Students will be specialist teachers, ophthalmic nurses, orthoptists, occupational therapists and others holding equivalent qualifications. Details from *Orjan Backman, Director of Studies, Stockholm Institute of Education, Department of Special Education, PO Box 47308, S-100 74 Stockholm, Sweden* ✆ 00 46 8 737 9621.

29.2.7 Training packs

Eye to Eye. (£105. 1991. RNIB). This five part audio-visual programme takes viewers through the frustrations of everyday life experienced by partially sighted children.

With Support. (£56. 1990. RNIB). Designed to promote discussion of the issues involved when visually impaired children are integrated into mainstream education. Filmed in four LEAs.

(NEW) Reaching the Needs of People with Visual Disabilities. (£125. 1994. RNIB) Detailed training material, including slides, handouts and audio-cassettes, to enable staff in voluntary and statutory services to deliver 'in-house' visual disability training. The package is particularly helpful for people who are responsible for assessment under the NHS and Community Care Act 1990.

(NEW) **New Independence!** (£165. 1995. RNIB). A practically based training package for front-line care and nursing staff who work with older blind and partially sighted people in accommodation with care support. It provides an opportunity to acquire basic essential skills and knowledge, linked to hands-on activities.

Visual Handicap (Disabled Living Foundation. £22.50) is a distance learning pack to help physiotherapists, occupational therapists and other health care professionals who may work with patients who have visual problems.

(NEW) **One of the Family** (£110. 1995. RNIB). Four videos and booklets for staff working with blind children who have multiple disabilities.

29.3 Further reading

Perspective on Training: professional support for blind and partially sighted people in the community ❶❸❼ (Visual Handicap Group. RNIB. 1995. £9.95). This consultative report draws attention to limitations in the current quality of training, and to manpower and service problems. It sets out the essential information needed to shape future strategy.

29.4 Professional associations

The **Association for the Education and Welfare of the Visually Handicapped** (VIEW) is for professionals working with visually impaired people. Subscription (£25 p.a.) includes the British Journal of Visual Impairment and the Association's Bulletin. It entitles attendance at regional meetings and conferences. Three special interest Chapters are open to members: Social Care, Teachers, and Further Education. Details from the *VIEW Administrator* ✆ 01203 361127.

The **Association for the Development of Life Skills and Independence of the Visually Impaired** is a forum for teachers and others with a professional interest. Membership organisations (subscription £30 p.a.) can send as many representatives as they wish to meetings held in May and November or receive information and hand-outs. Details from *Stephanie Odams, West of England School, Topsham Road, Countess Wear, Exeter EX2 6HA* ✆ 01392 454200.

J

29.5 Sources of information

Useful local information sources include public libraries, talking newspapers, voluntary societies for the blind and the Citizens Advice Bureaux. Social services departments may provide guides to local services in braille, large print or on cassette.

Public utilities, government departments and agencies issue information in large print, braille and, more frequently, on cassette. Local talking newspapers sometimes keep a collection. The local public library should be able to find out whether, for example, a particular Charter is available on cassette.

Public library sources range from collections of large print and audio books, to closed circuit televisions and electronic scanners linked to a braille printer or speech synthesizer. Almost all public libraries employ a special services librarian who has a special responsibility for readers with disabilities, including visually impaired people. Increasingly public libraries provide information in large print, tape and braille about local events and services.

Share the Vision aims to improve library services for visually impaired people. A prototype national catalogue of reading materials in accessible formats is due to be ready in summer 1995, so libraries will be able to check whether a particular book is available in large print, braille, Moon or on tape. **STVnews** is a quarterly newsletter ⓑⓣⓓ available free to public libraries and similar services. Details from *Peter Craddock, Share the Vision, 36 Circular Road, Castlerock, Co. Londonderry BT51 4XA* ✆ 01265 848303.

Can every body reach you: library services for blind and partially sighted people ⓟⓑⓣ (Library Association, revised edition 1995) is a leaflet describing the services public libraries should aim to provide. Free from *Library Association, 7 Ridgmount Street, London WC1E 7AE* ✆ 0171 636 7543.

29.5.1 Specialist national information services

Action for Blind People (see 4.4.1). A mobile unit tours the country and visitors can access the same computer database as the London headquarters. Information can be provided in any format.

LOOK (National Federation of Families with Visually Impaired Children). See 31.2 (Parents support groups).

Royal National Institute for the Blind has information services covering education, benefits rights, advocacy and multiple disability based in London ✆ 0171 388 1266. An Information and Advocacy Officer (North) is based at Tate House, Harrogate ✆ 01423 880749.

RNIB Reference Library has the largest UK collection of material on blindness and partial sight. Anyone interested in visual impairment may use it. Closed circuit television and an Open Book scanner (see 20.13.7) available. Loan facilities.

VIS (Visual Impairment Service) has a database on visual impairment, especially on education. It aims to be accessible by Internet in late 1995. It is available in various formats including print and IBM compatible or Apple Mac disk. Details from *Liz Izatt, VIS Development Officer, Scottish Sensory Centre, Moray House Institute, Holyrood Road, Edinburgh EH8 8AQ* ✆ 0131 558 6501.

Wales Council for the Blind has a database of information on visual disability in Wales, residential accommodation, contact addresses, and aids and equipment. Information can be provided in large print, braille, on tape or on computer disk. Details from *Dylan Evans.*

29.6 Further Reading

Blind and Partially Sighted Adults in Britain: The RNIB Survey. Vol I. HMSO/RNIB, 1991. Bruce, Ian et al.

Blind and Partially Sighted Children in Britain: the RNIB Survey. Vol II. HMSO/RNIB 1992. Walker, Errol et al.

British Journal of Visual Impairment ❶ ❸ ❶❶ is published three times a year and is designed for anyone professionally concerned with visually impaired children or adults. Tape copies can be obtained by sending three C90 cassettes in a wallet with a return label to *Kent Association for the Blind, 72 College Road, Maidstone, Kent ME15 6SJ.* Annual subscription £28.00. For print copies, contact *British Journal of Visual Impairment.*

Grapevine: Information for Everyone ❶ ❸ ❶. A guide to good practice for information providers. 2nd ed. 1994. Free from *Lothian Disability Information Service, 8 Lochend Road, Edinburgh EH6 8BR* ✆ 0131 555 2151.

Innovations in Information ❶ (£10 p.a.) aims to improve the transmission of information to people with disabilities and reports initiatives from around the world. Three issues a year. Contact *The National Information Forum, Post Point 202c, BT Camelford House, 87 Albert Embankment, London, SE1 7TS* ✆ 0171 582 7003.

Introducing RNIB ❶ ❸ ❶. Free leaflet in English, Welsh, Greek, Turkish, Bengali, Gujerati, Hindi, Urdu, Punjabi and Chinese.

Your Guide to RNIB services: Services for visually impaired people, their families and professionals ❶ ❸ ❶ ❶ and Internet http://www.rnib.org.uk which is a free annual directory.

RNIB Publications is a free comprehensive, annually updated, catalogue of all RNIB booklets, service leaflets, magazines, posters and videos.

See it Right ❶ ❸ ❶ (RNIB. 1993. £3.50). Sets out ways in which government bodies and commercial companies can meet the needs of blind and partially sighted people.

UK Organisations for Blind and Partially Sighted People ❶ ❶ ❶ (£20. RNIB. 1994). A comprehensive listing of the main organisations.

You and Your Sight: living with a sight problem ❶ ❸ ❶ (HMSO. 1994. £4.95). Todd, Hilary and Wolf, Francesca. An easy to read booklet of practical advice and information.

Sight Problems? A short guide to sources of help. Free. RNIB 1994.

J

29.7 Films, videos and sight simulations

Some Films on Blindness (RNIB. May 1993). This is a select list of films and other audio-visual materials available in the UK.

Seeing Differently. A set of colour slides simulating various eye conditions. Based on the simulated views in the colour section of this Handbook. Details from *In Touch Publishing*.

Sense can supply a comprehensive list of films dealing with deafblind people.

Simulation Spectacles. A set of 10 goggles simulating the effects of various eye conditions. £105 or £115 if order is combined with **See What I mean**: a 7 minute video to introduce sighted people to some everyday problems of living with a visual impairment. Contact: *Visual Impairment North East, c/o Fred Hodson, 52 Linskill Terrace, North Shields, Tyne & Wear NE30 2EW* ℘ 0191 257 4388.

30 National grant making charities

A number of charities pay small pensions or make cash grants to blind people in particularly difficult circumstances and who live in a specific locality. Many of these are listed in RNIB's **Guide to UK Organisations for Visually Disabled People** and the **Charities Digest**, an annual publication found in the reference section of public libraries. They are able to consider helping after they are satisfied that applicants are receiving their full entitlement from State funds. They also want to be certain that, if a pension is granted, it will not adversely affect the person's income support, so pensions in excess of £10 per week are seldom possible.

People in real need of help can approach a charity direct but it is perhaps better to consult a social worker or a voluntary worker who can do it on their behalf. Sometimes a social worker will be able to suggest a local charity which might be prepared to help and will approach it for the blind person.

30.1 Charities

Blind Business Association Charitable Trust helps blind people who manage their own businesses. It helps with the provision of specialist computers and other business equipment, start-up grants or loans in special circumstances. Contact *Blind Business Association Charitable Trust, Queensgate Business Centre, Portcullis House, Cromwell Road, Peterborough PE1 2EB* ℘ 01733 68228.

Blindness: Research for Learning, Work and Leisure promotes research and study of the 'educational, psychological, vocational and social needs of people who are blind or who are substantially handicapped by defective vision, and to disseminate the findings of such research'. Contact *Peter Price, c/o 13 Streetsbrook Road, Solihull, West Midlands B90 3PA.*

Cecilia Charity for the Blind can make modest grants to individuals for special equipment or training not funded by statutory bodies, and to specialist organisations or clubs for the blind and partially sighted. Individuals must enclose an endorsement from social services or the local blind society and organisations must include their latest accounts. Contact *Peter S. Rust, 61 West Smithfield, London EC1A 9EA* ℘ 0171 606 5711.

Electronic Aids for the Blind co-ordinates appeals on behalf of children, students, unemployed people and people on low incomes who need specialist electronic equipment but are unable to obtain it from statutory sources or personal resources. In 1993/4 beneficiaries ranged in age from 21 months to 82 years. Contact *Jayne Payne, Suite 4B, 71-75 High Street, Chislehurst, Kent BR7 5AG* ℘ 0181 295 3636.

The **Sir Beachcroft Towse Ex-Service Fund** is administered by RNIB and is able to give small grants and pensions to ex-servicemen and women who are in special need. The charity is mainly financed by an annual grant of £1,000 given by St. Dunstan's from money raised by the Poppy Day appeal.

Gardner's Trust for the Blind distributes an income of just over £70,000, half in the form of small pensions and half in grants (maximum amount £300), to registered blind and partially sighted people living in England and Wales. Grants may help towards the cost of computer equipment, especially for students, or for house repairs or heating for older people. The Trust has a special interest in music. It cannot help with holidays, nursing home fees or debt arrears. Contact *The Secretary, Gardner's Trust, Suite 118, Canada House, 272 Field End Road, Eastcote, Middlesex HA4 9NA* ✆ 0181 866 4400.

The **James Powell UK Trust** helps disabled people by providing communication aids, equipment and related services. In the case of a visually impaired person, this might include a brailler, a television reading aid or computer technology. Help is given primarily to individuals and applications should be supported by a social worker or a doctor, with evidence that funding from a statutory source has not been possible. Help with telephone bills is excluded. Contact *The Secretary, James Powell UK Trust, c/o Disability Scotland, Princes House, 5 Shandwick Place, Edinburgh EH2 4RG* ✆ 0131 228 8800.

The **Royal Blind Pension Society** provides small weekly pensions, paid quarterly, to blind and partially sighted people of any age who are in special need. Administered by **Action for Blind People**, at present there are over 300 recipients and over £40,000 is given in grants and pensions.

Royal National Institute for the Blind administers a number of charities to help registered blind and partially sighted people. Grants may help meet the cost of closed circuit television, computer equipment, braillers and microwave ovens or help meet unexpected expenses such as house repairs. They must be for a specific need, related in some way to the applicant's visual disability. Help cannot normally be given for telephone installation and rental, nursing home fees, repeatedly accruing debts or fees/maintenance for educational courses.

The **Telephones for the Blind Fund** meets part of the cost of telephone installation and rental. It helps blind people of limited means who live alone, or are often alone, especially at night, or whose partner is also disabled by age or infirmity. The fund needs to be satisfied that applicants have been refused help from their local authority under the provisions of the Chronically Sick and Disabled Persons Act. Contact *Telephones for the Blind Fund, 7 Huntersfield Close, Reigate, Surrey RH2 0DX* ✆ 01737 248032.

The **Vision Charity** supports blind children with multiple handicaps and children suffering from dyslexia. It does not normally donate money, but uses its buying power to purchase equipment needed by schools, colleges, groups and, in exceptional circumstances, individuals. Since 1976 it has funded 40 guide dogs, 10 minibuses, numerous computers and CCTVs. Its latest project is the creation of a studio complex at the Royal National College to enable students to obtain work in radio and television. Contact *Gillian Fitzpatrick, PO Box 30, East Horsley, Surrey KT24 6JX* ✆ 01483 282580.

J

31 Support Groups for Parents

In recent years the number of self-help groups has increased enormously. National groups are focussed on eye conditions. Some are very small because the eye condition their children have in common is so rare but, just because of this, they are highly valued. Where no group is listed for a particular eye condition, **Contact a Family** has a **national telephone helpline** (✆ 0171 383 3555) for parents and professionals. It has details of over 300 national groups specialising in specific conditions and rare syndromes.

Over fifty local groups of parents are affiliated to **LOOK** (National Federation of Families with Visually Impaired Children). Most groups hold regular get-togethers, with outings and parties for the children, and have close contact with professional staff in their area. They can provide a very down-to-earth **users' guide to local help**.

31.1 Self-help groups linked to eye conditions

The **Albino Fellowship** offers advice, information and help to albino people, the parents of albino children and to doctors or anyone concerned in their care. A quarterly newsletter is issued. Annual subscription £5.00. Contact *Henry McDermott, 14 Powmill Gardens, Prestwick KA9 2NZ* ✆ *01292 470336.*

Tadpoles (**International Glaucoma Association**) is a support group for children with congenital glaucoma. Membership is free to IGA members. A booklet **Glaucoma in babies and children: a guide for parents** answers many of the questions that parents ask. Contact *Jackie Drewett, 65 Bush Barns, West Cheshunt, Hertfordshire EN7 6ED* ✆ *01992 627490.*

The **Laurence-Moon-Bardet-Biedl Society** offers advice, information and encouragement and the opportunity to meet with other families who have children with this syndrome. It issues **Introducing LMBBS** and regular newsletters. There are no membership fees. Contact *Mrs Chris Stoves, 23 Lodge Causeway, Fishponds, Bristol BS16 3JA* ✆ *0117 965 4154.*

The **Micro and Anophthalmic Children's Society** (MACS) can put families in touch with others who have similar problems and, in particular, support them through the emotionally and physically difficult period when their children are undergoing necessary cosmetic treatment. MACS circulates a newsletter and holds occasional family weekends. There are no membership fees. Contact *Mrs. Maggie Bourne, 1 Skyrmans Fee, Kirby Cross, Frinton-on-Sea, Essex CO13 0RN* ✆ *01255 677511.*

The **Nystagmus Action Group** supports research and provides help and information. A telephone helpline **Insight** ✆ 01392 72573 can put callers in touch with others with nystagmus and advise on services and equipment. Publications include a free factsheet and two bookets **Growing up with Nystagmus** ❶Ⓑ❶ and **Living with Nystagmus** ❶Ⓑ❶ (£2.19 each), a quarterly newsletter, information sheets for teachers and cassette recordings of talks given by education and health specialists at NAG meetings. Annual membership subscription, including one booklet, £7.00. Contact *Miss G. M. Holloway, 9 Calthorpe Road, Stoke Hill, Exeter EX4 7JS* ℘ 01392 72573 (helpline).

NEW **FROST (Friends of the Osteopetrosis Support Trust)** supports families with children who suffer from this rare bone disease which can cause blindness. Contact *Margaret Wright, 10 Cumberland Avenue, Fixby, Huddersfield HD2 2JJ* ℘ 01484 545974.

The **Retinoblastoma Society** has a network of regional co-ordinators, all of whom have first hand experience of the condition and are ready to befriend families, giving special help to those with children who have been newly diagnosed. A play specialist works one day a week at St. Bartholomew's Hospital. A newsletter is published three times a year. Contact *National Co-ordinator, c/o Academic Department of Paediatric Oncology, St Bartholomew's Hospital, London EC1A 7BE* ℘ 0171 600 3309 (Weds).

A **ROP (retinopathy of prematurity)** support group meets twice a year in Liverpool. The group is parent led, the parents deciding on topics and speakers. Parents from any part of the country are welcome, even if only on a 'one-off' basis. Contact *Christine Reid, c/o RNIB Education Information Service*.

The **NEW** **Stickler Syndrome Support Group** was launched in 1994 and is in contact with over 75 families. It aims to circulate a quarterly newsletter and is preparing factsheets for members. A **Youngster Network** links children and young adults. Membership is free. Contact *Co-ordinator Wendy Hughes, 27 Braycourt Avenue, Walton-on-Thames, Surrey KT12 2AZ* ℘ 01932 229421.

The **Young Usher Group** is a branch of **Sense** and has its own magazine – YUM. Members meet together in groups in various parts of the country. Contact *Jeremy Morgan, 84 Horn Lane, Woodford Green, Essex IG8 9AH.* ℘ 0181 504 8415 (Minicom).

NEW **Stargardt's Disease** (a form of juvenile macular dystrophy). A group is being formed at the time of writing. Contact *Mrs. Chait, 53 Cavendish Road, Salford, Manchester M7 4NQ* ℘ 0161 792 7392.

31.2 LOOK

The National and Edinburgh offices of LOOK provide information on education, ophthalmology, local contacts, leisure and training opportunities and issue a quarterly **newsletter**. A free **information pack** is available on request. Free membership is offered to families or people with parental care of visually impaired children, or young people aged 18 – 21.

As and when funds permit, LOOK is appointing **Regional Development Officers**. Already in post are:

London *Nick Gregory, c/o Royal London Society for the Blind, 105 Salusbury Road, London NW6 6RH* ✆ 0171 625 1570

South England *Lynda Henke, 2 Hook Cottages, Hook Lane, Aldingbourne, West Sussex PO20 6TB* ✆ 01243 542189

Midlands *Wendy Sainsbury, 185 Birches Road, Codsall, Wolverhampton WV8 2JW* ✆ 01902 847951

North England *Ruth Duff, c/o RNIB Education Support Services, Grosvenor House, Grosvenor Road, Headingley, Leeds LS6 2DZ* ✆ 0113 274 9949 or (home) ✆ 01942 674555

Scotland *Carolyn Finlayson, 10 Magdala Crescent, Edinburgh EH12 5BE* ✆ 0131 313 5711

Wales *Alastair Holbrook, 39 Downton View, Ludlow, Shropshire SY8 1JE* ✆ 01584 875439

LOOK Plus The national contact for parents of children with multiple disabilities is *LOOK Plus, Ms. C. Scott, 11 Haslemere Road, Windsor, Berkshire SL4 5ET* ✆ 01753 866854.

31.3 Parents' support groups

Avon **LOOK West**, *Mrs. A. Thompson, 67 Whitecroft Avenue, Whitchurch, Bristol BS4 9JF* ✆ 01272 832272

Berkshire **LOOK Berkshire**, *Elaine Wright, 5 Cody Close, Woodley, Reading RG5 4XN* ✆ 01734 690896

Buckinghamshire **Victa**, *Nina Holman, Fircombe Hall, North Street, Castlethorpe, Milton Keynes MK19 7EW* ✆ 01908 510860

Cambridgeshire **Parents for Parents**, *Mrs. Carol McGregor, 141 Hern Road, Ramsey St. Mary, Huntingdon PE17 1SY* ✆ 01733 844587

Cornwall **Patch**, *Helen Slevin, 3 Lynher Way, Callington PL17 7PN* ✆ 01579 82544
LOOK West, *Bryan Green, Tregoose House, Clodgey Lane, Helston TR13 8PJ* ✆ 01326 574502
Foresight, *Margaret Baillie, Gannel Building, The Old County Hall, Truro* ✆ 01872 3233438

Devon *Mrs Jenny Shorters, **West of England School**, Countess Wear, Exeter EX2 6HA* ✆ 01392 454200
Smiling Eyes, *Mrs. A. Knill, Waterworks Cottage, Hore Down, Ilfracombe EX34 8ND* ✆ 01271 864022
LOOK South Devon, *Pamela Sanders, 51 Spencer Road, Foxhole, Paignton TQ3 3SY* ✆ 01803 524227
See-Saw, *Yvonne Benwell (LOOK National Vice-Chairman), 19 Bowhays Walk, Eggbuckland, Plymouth PL6 5SH* ✆ 01752 770797

J

Gloucestershire **Parents Group**, Mark Geraghty, SENARC (Special Educational Needs Area Resource Centre), Churchdown Lane, Hucclecote, Gloucester GL3 3QN ✆ 01452 427257

Hampshire **LOOK Solent**, Carl Moore, 17 Salerno Road, Hilsea, Portsmouth PO2 9PP ✆ 01705 662036

Hertfordshire **See-Link**, Linda McLachlan, Education Officer, Hertfordshire Society for the Blind, Trinity Centre, Fanham's Hall Road, Ware SG12 7PS ✆ 01992 588145

Kent **Parent Support Group**, Janet John, 5 Plains Avenue, Maidstone ME15 7AT ✆ 01622 761082
Dorton House Parents Support Group, Mrs. Pauline Davies, Dorton House School, Seal, nr. Sevenoaks TN15 0ED ✆ 01732 761477

Greater London **LOOK London**, Tula Baxter (LOOK National Chairman), 25 Newlands Avenue, Thames Ditton KT7 0HD ✆ 0181 398 1208 or ✆ 0171 625 1570 (office hours)
Mike and Trisha Lancaster, 15 Second Avenue, Bush Hill Park, Enfield EN1 1BT ✆ 0181 366 8445
Ms Petra Smillie, Headteacher, Dysart School, Dukes Avenue, Kingston-upon-Thames KT2 5QY ✆ 0181 546 0610
Mary Riches, 98 Boxtree Lane, Harrow Weald, Middlesex HA3 6JE ✆ 0181 428 2512
Sunshine House Parent Group, Mrs Alison Harris, c/o 33 Dene Road, Northwood, Middlesex HA6 1DD ✆ 01753 887265 (home)
Southwark Family Group, Steve Lockett, 2 Davey Street, Peckham SE15 6LF ✆ 0181 858 0395 or 0171 701 1962 (office hours)
Vision, Jean Watkins, 52 Honister Heights, Purley CR8 1EU ✆ 0181 660 1767

Lancashire **Blackpool, Fylde and Wyre BOPS** (Blind or Partially Sighted), Pearl Grunshaw, 33 Larkholme Parade, Fleetwood FY7 8LL ✆ 01253 773581
Ruth Duff (LOOK North England Regional Development Officer), 129 Coronation Drive, Leigh WN7 2YZ ✆ 01942 674555 or (work) ✆ 0113 274 8855
LOOK Oldham, Mrs. Jean Prew, 398 Milnrow Road, Shaw, Oldham OL2 8BL ✆ 01706 843067

Leicestershire **Derek and Julie Brooks**, 29 Manor Drive, Loughborough LE11 2LR ✆ 01509 233466
David Mumford, Royal Leicester Society for the Blind, Gedding Road, Leicester LE5 5DU ✆ 0116 249 0909

Lincolnshire **VIPS** (Visually Impaired Parent's Support), Pamela Henderson, 36 Kingsway, Nettleham, Lincoln LN2 2QA ✆ 01522 754080

Merseyside **Mrs Harrison** ✆ 0151 280 2596
Parents' Group, Pat Clarke, Wirral Society of the Blind and Partially Sighted, Ashville Lodge, Ashville Road, Birkenhead L41 8AU ✆ 0151 652 8877
West Cheshire Eye, Mr. J.R. Coles, 12 Greenlea Close, Whitby, South Wirral L65 6QA ✆ 0151 356 1458

Nottinghamshire *LOOK Ahead*, Mrs. Fiona Towle, 25 Fox Covert, Colwick, Nottingham NG4 2DD ✆ 0115 940 1150

Oxfordshire *Pamela Crane*, Oxford Primary School, Ferry Hinksey Road, Oxford OX2 0BY ✆ 01865 792744

Suffolk *LOOK Suffolk*, Mrs. Des Shelley, 62 Onehouse Road, Stowmarket IP14 1QP ✆ 01449 675016

Surrey *LOOK South East Surrey*, Mrs. J. Freeborough, Bellis House, Midholmwood Lane, Dorking RH5 4HB ✆ 01306 876918
LOOK West Surrey, Mr. D. Tranter, 15 Snow Drop Way, Bisley, Woking GU24 9BL ✆ 01483 797002

Sussex *LOOK East Sussex*, Jackie Leroux, 2 Campbell Road, Brighton BN1 4QD ✆ 01273 687561
LOOK South East, Lynda Henke (LOOK South England Regional Development Officer, address above)
LOOK Sussex, Wendy Peek, 51 Western Road, Hurstpierpoint BN6 9SU ✆ 01273 832267

Tyne and Wear *Mrs. Y. Robinson*, Regional Service for VI, Silverhill Centre, Stocksfield Avenue, Newcastle-upon-Tyne NE5 2DX ✆ 0191 228 0030
Mr R. Bateman, Gosforth High School, Knightsbridge, Great North Road, Newcastle-upon-Tyne ✆ 0191 284 1082
Support Group for Visually Impaired Children, Mrs. M. Thompson, Belmont CE Junior School, Buckinghamshire Road, Belmont, Co. Durham ✆ 0191 384 4178
Out of Sight Carers Group, Sarah Potter, 47 Elmtree Gardens, Whitley Bay NE25 8XQ ✆ 0191 252 7674

Warwickshire *Blink*, Hazel Blatchly, 1 Hawthorn Road, Leamington Spa ✆ 01926 420178

West Midlands *Visually Impaired Children's Support Group*, Wendy Sainsbury (LOOK Midlands Regional Development Officer, address above)
Family Support Group, Roy Sutton, 78 Walsall Road, Walsall WS3 4DD ✆ 01922 693842
Peepers, Mrs. Gina Southey, 69 Cape Road, Warwick CV34 5AA ✆ 01926 491499

Wiltshire *Trellis House Group* (for children with any disability), Ms. Marion Lowe, 9 Sorrell Close, Trowbridge BA14 0XX ✆ 01225 777181

Worcestershire *Brenda Wornham*, Worcestershire Association for the Blind, 13 Wylds Lane, Worcester WR5 1DA ✆ 01905 351311
Miss Dina Murdie, RNIB New College, Whittington Road, Worcester WR5 2JX ✆ 01905 763933

Yorkshire *LOOK Bradford*, Mr Muhammed Saleem, 41 Stanmore Place, Bradford BD7 2EN ✆ 01274 521865
Calderdale Vision Service, Gordon Hewitt, ALSS Health Training & Development Centre, Free School Lane, Halifax ✆ 01422 364899

Foresight, Mrs. S. Tyers, 11 Helene Court, Salandine Nook, Huddersfield HD3 3WS ✆ 01484 648952

The Vision Group, Wendy Harrison, York Child Development Centre, York District Hospital, Wiggington Road, York YO3 7HE ✆ 01904 631313

NORTHERN IRELAND   Foyle Victa, Viola Kee, Sensory Support Service, 16 Bishop Street, Londonderry BT48 6PN ✆ 01504 374619

SCOTLAND   LOOK Lothian & Borders, Carolyn Finlayson (Scottish Regional Development Officer, address above)

Sight, Neil Farquharson, 18 Livingstone Terrace, Dundee DD3 8RJ ✆ 01382 827079

Parents Support Group, Linda Mooney, House G11, 643 Argyle Street, Glasgow G3 8UF ✆ 0141 248 3189

LOOK/Spovic, Sharon Tornow, 4 Ancaster Drive, Glasgow G13 1ND ✆ 0141 954 9904

Young Vision, Lorna Hall, Pre-5 Learning Support, Avon School, Carlisle Road, Hamilton ML3 7EW ✆ 01698 285444

Spovic, Isobel McNaught, 79 Munro Avenue, Kilmarnock KA1 2NA ✆ 01563 201382

WALES   Gwent Victa, Debbie Jones, 22 Myrtle Drive, Beavers Walk, Rogerstone, Newport, Gwent ✆ 01633 897155 or 01222 380280 (office hours)

Victa Taff Ely, Mrs P.J. Buglass, 30 Nantmelyn Terrace, Tonyrefail, near Porth, Mid Glamorgan CF39 8BA ✆ 01443 676724

Victa, Steve Andrews, c/o 18 Glen Road, Neath, West Glamorgan SA11 3DS ✆ 01639 632734

J

Useful addresses

Listed here are organisations and suppliers frequently referred to in this book. A comprehensive list of organisations of and for visually impaired people **UK Organizations for Visually Disabled People** is published by RNIB.

A

Action for Blind People Head office, 14/16 Verney Road, London
SE16 3DZ **0171 732 8771**

Advisory Centre for Education 1B Aberdeen Studios, 22-24
Highbury Grove, London N5 2EA **0171 354 8321**

Age Concern England Astral House, 1268 London Road, London
SW16 4ER.. **0181 679 8000**

AlphaVision Ltd. Seymore House, Copyground Lane,
High Wycombe, Bucks. HP12 3HE **01494 530555**

Aptech Ltd. Aptech House, Meadowfield, Ponteland,
Newcastle-upon-Tyne NE20 9SD **01661 860999**

B

Bible Society Stonehill Green, Westlea, Swindon SN5 7DG **01793 513713**

Birmingham Royal Institution for the Blind (BRIB)
48 Woodville Road, Harborne, Birmingham B17 9TG........... **0121 428 5000**

British Blind Sport (BBS) 67 Albert Street,
Rugby CV21 2SN.. **01788 536142**

Blind Spot (U.K.) Ltd. Priors House, 5-15 Beaumont Road, Plaistow,
London E13 8RG... **0181 472 9655**

British Computer Association of the Blind Steve Plumpton,
BCM Box 950, London WC1N 3XX............................ **01203 563111**

British Diabetic Association 10 Queen Anne Street,
London WIM 0BD.. **0171 323 1531**

British Journal of Visual Impairment c/o VIEW, York House,
Exhall Grange School, Wheelwright Lane, Coventry CV7 9HP **01203 361127**

British Retinitis Pigmentosa Society Hon. Sec. Lynda Cantor,
PO Box 350, Buckingham MK18 5EL......................... **01280 860363**

British Wireless for the Blind Fund Gabriel House, 34 New Road,
Chatham, Kent ME4 4QR................................... **01634 832501**

C

Cadwell Recording Services for the Blind 17 Trusthams,
Broadwindsor, Beaminster, Dorset DT8 3QB .... **01308 868500** or **868465**

Calibre Aylesbury, Bucks. HP22 5XQ .... **01296 432339** or **81211**

Carers National Association 20-25 Glasshouse Yard,
London EC1A 4JS **0171 490 8818**

Chester-care Low Moor Estate, Kirkby-in-Ashfield,
Nottinghamshire NG17 7JZ **01623 757955**

Chivers Press Publishers Windsor Bridge Road, Bath,
Avon BA2 3AX **01225 335336**

Clarke & Smith Melbourne House, Melbourne Road, Wallington,
Surrey SM6 8SD **0181 669 4411**

ClearVision Project Linden Lodge School, 61 Princes Way, London
SW19 6JB **0181 780 2712**

Cobolt Systems Ltd The Old Mill House, Mill Road, Reedham,
Norwich, Norfolk NR13 3HA **01493 700172**

Concept Systems 204-206 Queens Road, Beeston,
Nottingham NG9 2DB **0115 925 5988**

Confederation of Tape Information Services (COTIS) c/o RNIB
Express Reading Service, 79 High Street, Tarporley,
Cheshire CW6 0AB **01829 733351**

Counsel and Care Twyman House, 16 Bonny Street,
London NW1 9PG (10.30 a.m.–4 p.m.) **0171 485 1566**

D

Department for Education Publications Centre PO Box 6927,
London E3 3NZ **0171 510 0150**

Department of Transport 2 Marsham Street, London SW1P 3EB
Mobility Unit Room S10/20 .... **0171 276 5257**
Orange Badge Unit Room C10/02 .... **0171 276 6291**

Disability Alliance Educational and Research Association
1st Floor East, Universal House, 88-94 Wentworth Street,
London E1 7SA **0171 247 8776**

Disability Network 8 Wolverhampton House, 123 Church Street,
St. Helens, Merseyside WA9 1JS **01744 451215**

Disability Resource Team 3rd Floor Bedford House, 125-133
Camden High Street, London NW1 7JR **0171 482 5305**

Disabled Living Foundation 380-4 Harrow Road,
London W9 2HU **0171 289 6111**

Dixey of Wigmore Street 19 Wigmore Street,
London W1H 9LA .... **0171 491 2713** or **0171 935 4280**

Dolphin Systems for People with Disabilities Ltd
PO Box 83, Worcester WR3 8TU **01905 754577**

Dorton College of Further Education (Royal London Society for the Blind) Seal Drive, Seal, Sevenoaks, Kent TN15 0AH..... **01732 764123**

Dorton House School

Dorton IT Support Centre Seal, Near Sevenoaks, Kent TN15 0EB.. **01732 761477**

E

Electricity Association (publications) 30 Millbank, London SW1P 4RD... **0171 344 5766**

Electronic Aids for the Blind Suite 4B, 71-75 High Street, Chislehurst, Kent BR7 5AG................................. **0181 295 3636**

Eye Donor scheme – see UK Transplant Support Service

F

fingatip labels Unit 26A, Lenton Business Centre, Lenton Boulevard, Nottingham NG7 2BY..................... **0115 942 0941**

Foundation for Communication for the Disabled 25 High Street, Woking, Surrey GU21 1BW.......... **01483 727848** or **727844**

Further Education Funding Council Cheylesmore House, Quinton Road, Coventry CV1 2WT.......................... **01203 863000**

G

Gift of Thomas Pocklington 20 Lansdowne Road, London W11 3LL.. **0171 727 6426**

Guide Dogs for the Blind Association Hillfields, Burghfield, Reading, Berks. RG7 3YG.................................. **01734 835555**

H

Help the Aged St. James's Walk, London EC1R 0BE............. **0171 253 0253**

Henshaw's College Bogs Lane, Starbeck, Harrogate HG1 4ED ... **01423 886451**

Henshaw's Society for the Blind John Derby House, 88-92 Talbot Road, Old Trafford, Manchester M16 0GS......... **0161 872 1234**

Horizon CCTV 11/12 Lowman Units, Tiverton Business Park, Tiverton, Devon EX16 6SR **01884 254172**

I

International Glaucoma Association c/o Mrs Wright, King's College Hospital, Denmark Hill, London SE5 9RS **0171 737 3265**

In Touch Programme BBC, Broadcasting House, London W1A 1AA ....
Programme enquiries, weekly factsheets, quarterly bulletins – send s.a.e.

In Touch Publishing 37 Charles Street, Cardiff CF1 4EB **01222 222403**
.... **Fax 01222 222383**
In Touch Gateway 37 Charles Street, Cardiff CF1 4EB... **Modem 01222 222099**
Isis Large Print 7 Centremead, Osney Mead, Oxford OX2 0ES ... **01865 250333**

J

Jewish Care 221 Golders Green Road,
London NW11 9DQ **0181 458 3282**

K

Keep Able Ltd Fleming Close, Park Farm, Wellingborough,
Northants. NN8 3UF... **01933 679426**
Kent Association for the Blind 72 College Road,
Maidstone ME15 6SJ.. **01622 691357**

L

Linden Lodge School 61 Princes Way, Wimbledon Park,
London SW19 6JB **0181 788 0107**
Living Paintings Trust Silchester House, Silchester,
Berkshire RG7 2LT **01734 700766**
**LOOK (National Federation of Families with Visually Impaired
Children)** National office, c/o Queen Alexandra College,
Court Oak Road, Harborne, Birmingham B17 9TG **0121 428 5038**
LVA Ltd. 24 Regent Street, Nottingham NG1 5DH............... **0115 947 4011**

M

Macular Disease Society Central Office, PO Box 268, Weybridge,
Surrey KT13 0YW **01932 829331**
Magna Large Print Books Magna House, Long Preston,
nr. Skipton, North Yorks. BD23 4ND **01729 840225**
Master Transcriptions MT Studios on the Common, The Pantiles,
Tunbridge Wells, Kent TN2 5TE **01892 516157**
Monument Tape Services 20 Laburnum Road, Wellington,
Somerset TA21 8EL **01823 662104**

N

**National Association of Local Societies for the Visually
Impaired (NALSVI)** Administration Secretary Sue Ferguson,
21 Greencliffe Drive, York YO3 6NA............................ **01904 671921**
National Deafblind League 18 Rainbow Court, Paston Ridings,
Peterborough PE4 7UP............................... **(qwerty) 01733 321982**

National Federation of the Blind Unity House, Smyth Street,
Westgate, Wakefield, West Yorks. WF1 1ER **01924 291313**

National League of the Blind and Disabled 2 Tenterden Road,
London N17 8BE **0181 808 6030**

National Library for the Blind Cromwell Road, Bredbury,
Stockport SK6 2SG (24 hour answerphone) **0161 494 0217**

National Pre-School Learning Alliance 61-63 Kings Cross Road,
London WC1X 9LL **0171 833 0991**

The National Trust Valerie Wenham, Adviser, Facilities for Disabled
Visitors, 36 Queen Anne's Gate, London SW1H 9AS **0171 222 9251**

O

Opsis Secretary General, Sir Antony Walker, KCB, Gretton House,
43 Hatton Garden, London EC1N 8EE **0171 405 6697**

P

Papworth Ability Services Ltd. Unit D3A, Telford Road, Bicester,
Oxon. OX6 0TZ **01869 324414**

Partially Sighted Society
Registered office PO Box 322, Doncaster DN1 2NX **01302 323132**
General administration, printing, enlarging, mail order, membership, publications
Greater London Office 62 Salusbury Road, London NW6 6RH. **0171 372 1551**
General enquiries, Low Vision Adviser
Sight Centres at Exeter and Salisbury Details in 34
Low vision advice and training, information and counselling

Pathway Communications Berrows House, Bath Street,
Hereford HR1 2HF **01432 273311**

Pia 37 Charles Street, Cardiff CF1 4EB **01222 222782**
Dotline Braille and large print support line **01222 222456**
. . . . **Fax 01222 222383**
. . . . **ISDN 01222 221126**

Playback Service for the Blind 276 St Vincent Street,
Glasgow G2 5RP **0141 248 5811**

Playring Ltd. 53 Westbere Road, London NW2 3SP **0171 794 9497**

Portset Systems Shield House, Brook Street,
Bishops Waltham SO3 1AX **01489 896837**

Professional Vision Services Welbury House, 90 Walsworth Road,
Hitchin, Hertfordshire SG4 9SX **01462 420751**

Projects by the Blind Wandsworth 10-12 Yukon Road,
London SW12 9PU **0181 675 3900**

Pulse Data International (UK) Ltd. Greensbury Farm, Bolnhurst,
Bedford MK44 2ET **01234 376771**

465

Q

Queen Alexandra College (BRIB) 49 Court Oak Road, Harborne,
Birmingham B17 9TG... **0121 428 5050**

R

RADAR (Royal Association for Disability and Rehabilitation)
12 City Forum, 25 City Road, London EC1V 8AF................ **0171 250 3222**
.... **minicom 0171 250 4119**

REMAP (technical equipment for disabled people)
Mr. J. Wright, Hazeldene, Ightham, Sevenoaks, Kent TN15 9AD.. **01732 883818**

**Research Centre for the Education of the Visually
Handicapped (RCEVH)** University of Birmingham, School of
Education, Edgbaston, Birmingham B15 2TT.................... **0121 414 6733**

Research Institute for Consumer Affairs (RICA)
2 Marylebone Road, London NW1 4DF **0171 935 2460**

RNC Enterprises – see Royal National College

RNIB (Royal National Institute for the Blind)
Head office 224 Great Portland Street, London W1N 6AA **0171 388 1266**
*Benefit Rights and Information Team (including grants) • Community Education •
Community and Health Services (Community Care Direct Services) • Education Information
Service (under 16s; see also 8.6.2) • Employment and Student Support Network
(Employment Development and Technology Unit, Self Employment Development Unit, see
also 10.4.2) • Ethnic Minorities Development Officer • Health Services Development Unit (low
vision enhancement advisory service) • Information and Practice Development Service on
Multiple Disability • Leisure Service • Music Advisory Service • RNIB/GDBA Joint Mobility Unit
• Physiotherapy Support Service • Reference Library • Residential and Hotel Services • See It
Right Office • Social Services Development Unit • Technical Research • Voluntary Agencies
Link Unit*

Production and Distribution Centre PO Box 173,
Peterborough, Cambs. PE2 6WS. Direct line to Customer Services,
calls charged at local rate **0345 023153**
Answerphone after office hours **01733 370777**
*Cassette and Braille Libraries • Equipment and games • Production of braille,
Moon, tactile maps and diagrams • Recording Centre*

Accommodation with Care Support Service Tate House,
28 Wetherby Road, Harrogate, North Yorkshire HG2 7SA **01423 886927**

Employment Assessment and Rehabilitation Centres Manor
House, Middle Lincombe Road, Torquay, Devon TQ1 2NG...... **01803 214523**
Alwyn House, 3 Wemysshall Road, Ceres, Cupar, Fife KY15 5LX . **01334 82289**
Express Reading Service 79 High Street, Tarporley,
Cheshire CW6 0AB **01829 732115**
Housing Service Garrow House, 190 Kensal Road,
London W10 5BT... **0181 969 2380**

466

Multiple Disability Services 7 The Square, 111 Broad Street, Edgbaston, Birmingham B15 1AS............................. **0121 643 9912**

Training Service on Multiple Disability Springfield Centre, Springfield Road, Bishopbriggs, Glasgow G64 1PN **0141 772 5588**
   Consultancy on Multiple Disability, Scotland

Redhill College Philanthropic Road, Redhill, Surrey RH1 4DZ ... **01737 768935**

Resource centres Devon, Greater London, Somerset, Northern Ireland, Scotland, (details under Resource centres)

RNIB Scotland 10 Magdala Crescent, Edinburgh EH12 5BE.... **0131 313 1498**

School of Rehabilitation Studies University of Central England, Faculty of Health & Social Sciences, Cox Building, Perrybar, Birmingham B42 2SU **0121 331 5000**

Social Service Development Unit 7 The Square, 111 Broad Street, Edgbaston, Birmingham B15 1AS............ **0121 643 9912**

Talking Book Service Mount Pleasant, Wembley, Middx. HA0 1RR. Calls charged at local rate, answerphone service outside working hours.................................. **0345 626843**

Vocational College Radmoor Road, Loughborough, Leics. LE11 3BS **01509 611077**
   BESS • Outreach Service • Students Support Service

Royal Blind School PO Box 500, 50 Gillespie Crescent, Edinburgh EH10 4HZ...................................... **0131 229 1456**

Royal Leicestershire Society for the Blind Gedding Road, Leicester LE5 5DU **0116 249 0909**

Royal London Society for the Blind 105 Salusbury Road, London NW6 6RH.. **0171 624 8844**

Royal National College for the Blind
RNC Enterprises College Road, Hereford HR1 1EB.............. **01432 265725**

Royal National Institute for Deaf People (RNID) 105 Gower Street, London WC1E 6AH.................................... **0171 387 8033**

Royal School for the Blind Church Road North, Wavertree, Liverpool L15 6TQ.. **0151 733 1012**

S

St. Dunstan's Working for Men and Women blinded in the Services PO Box 4XB, 12-14 Harcourt Street, London W1A 4XB.. **0171 723 5021**

Scottish Braille Press Craigmillar Park, Edinburgh EH16 5NB... **0131 662 4445**

Scottish National Federation for the Welfare of the Blind PO Box 500, Gillespie Crescent, Edinburgh EH10 4HZ **0131 229 1456**

seeABILITY (Royal School for the Blind) Highlands Road, Leatherhead, Surrey KT22 8NR................................ **01372 373086**

Sense, the National Deafblind and Rubella Association)
11-13 Clifton Terrace, London N4 3SR........................... **0171 272 7774**

Sense Cymru Shand House, 20 Newport Road, Cardiff CF2 1YB .. **01222 457641**

Sense Northern Ireland Resource Centre, Graham House,
Knockbracken, Healthcare Park, Saintfield Road, Belfast BT8 8BH . **01232 705688**

Sense Scotland Unit 5/2, 8 Elliot Place, Glasgow G3 8EP........ **0141 221 7577**

Sensory Systems Ltd 1 Watling Gate, 297-303 Edgware Road,
London NW9 6NB... **0181 205 3002**

Sight & Sound Technology Qantel House, Anglia Way,
Moulton Park, Northampton NN6 1JA.......................... **01604 790969**

Skill: National Bureau for Students with Disabilities
336 Brixton Road, London SW9 7AA **0171 978 9890**

Society of Blind Lawyers Sec. John Wall, 20 Cleveland Road,
Worcester Park, Surrey KT4 7JH **0181 330 1290**

T

Talking Newspaper Association of the UK (TNAUK)
Talking Newspaper Enterprises Ltd. (TNEL)
National Recording Centre, Heathfield, E. Sussex TN21 8DB...... **01435 866102**

Tandy Bilston Road, Wednesbury, West Midlands WS10 7JN..... **0121 556 6429**

Techno-Vision Systems Ltd 76 Bunting Road Industrial Estate,
Northampton NN2 6EE **01604 792777**

Torch Trust for the Blind Torch House, Hallaton, Market
Harborough, Leics. LE16 8UJ.................................. **01858 555301**

Toys for the Handicapped (TFH) 76 Barracks Road, Sandy Lane
Industrial Estate, Stourport-on-Severn, Worcs. DY13 9QB........ **01299 827820**

U

UK Transplant Support Service Authority Fox Den Road,
Stoke Gifford, Bristol BS12 6RR................................ **0117 975 7575**

Ulverscroft Large-Print Books The Green, Bradgate Road, Anstey,
Leicester LE7 7FU.. **0116 236 4325**

Usher Services (Sense) Ashley House, 4 Church Road, Edgbaston,
Birmingham B15 3TD... **0121 456 1564**

V

VISAbility 5 Burnham Gardens, Cranford, Hounslow,
Middlesex TW4 6LS... **0181 897 8587**

Vision Aid 22A Chorley New Road, Bolton BL1 4AP **01204 31882**

Visually Impaired Musicians Association Secretary Julie
Smethurst, 79 Duncan Road, Crookes, Sheffield S10 1SN......... **01296 29529**

W

Wales Council for the Blind Shand House, 20 Newport Road,
Cardiff CF2 1YB **01222 473954**

Ways & Means (Nottingham Rehab) Ludlow Hill Road,
West Bridgford, Nottingham NG2 6HD **0115 936 0319**
24 hour answerphone **0115 945 2100**

West of England School for Children with Little or No Sight
Topsham Road, Countess Wear, Exeter,
Devon EX2 6HA **01392 454200/413333**

33 Transcription services

Agencies offering braille transcription include major braille producers, volunteers, prison braille units, and self-employed individuals operating on a commercial basis. The material they are prepared to handle varies from instruction leaflets for domestic equipment to full length books. Some transcribers still work with a manual brailler, but those who use computers are likely to offer a much quicker service. Transcribers can be approached direct, but it is advisable to check first with RNIB Customer Services to see if the material required is already available in braille, whether for sale or on loan, from RNIB or from another source in this country or overseas. Some services also produce large print and Moon transcripts. See also 19.6 (audio transcription).

LOCAL SERVICES are offered free, or with a charge for materials only, to visually impaired people by many of the **Resource Centres** listed at the end of the book, and by any public library which has the appropriate equipment. They may also have photocopy enlargers and sometimes a stereo photocopier to produce tactile copiers of simple maps, plans and diagrams.

NATIONAL SERVICES are listed here with the following details:
Approximate **time taken**, given average circumstances, to transcribe 2, 100 and 500 A4 pages of straightforward English **print** text into Grade 2 braille (assuming print is clear enough to capture by scanner, if used). Time taken to produce multiple copies not included. *Text on computer disk may be dealt with much more quickly, particularly longer documents.*

Approximate **charge** (if any) to business customers for transcribing 2, 100 and 500 A4 pages of straightforward English print text into Grade 2 braille (by computer, if applicable, where this is the cheaper option). Charge for multiple copies not included. 'Discounts' indicates concessionary rates for individual visually handicapped or other special customers. *Transcribing from disk may cost less than from print. Where there is no charge, or a charge for materials only, donations may be welcome.*

Method used for transcription (manual/computer, text keyed/scanned, type of computer disk and file format accepted).

Other material transcribed (e.g. technical, mathematical, foreign languages), **additional services** offered (binding, multiple copies, jumbo-sized braille, diagrams/maps, Moon, large print, dual media output – print with the equivalent braille embossed on the same sheet) and any **limitation on type of material** accepted.

The large variation in prices quoted here to some extent reflects the different style of services offered. When seeking a quotation it is worth checking the points that are important to you, for example: is the text processed unchanged, or is it edited for braille accuracy and style; is the text proofread in braille after translation; is a guaranteed completion date offered?

J

	Special terms	2 page
Access to print, Central Library, Princes Way, Bradford BD1 1NN. ℘ **01274 754681. Fax 01274 395108.**	Discounts	1 day £1.50
AIRS (Access to Information & Reading Services), The Central Library, Prince Consort Road, Gateshead NE8 4LN. ℘ **0191 477 3478. Fax 0191 477 7454.**		1 day £5
Blind Spot (UK) Ltd, Priors House, 5-15 Beaumont Road, Plaistow, London E13 8RJ. ℘ **0181 472 9655. Fax 0181 472 9691. Stephen Bourne**		1 day £10
Braille & Large Print Services, The Central Library, Calverley Street, Leeds LS1 3AB. ℘ **0113 247 8262. Fax 0113 247 8268.**	Free to Leeds individuals & community groups	1 day £1.40
Braille Bureau, County Hall, West Bridgford, Nottingham NG2 7QP. ℘ **0115 982 3823 ext 3157. Fax 0115 981 7153.**	Free to visually impaired	1 day £3
Braille Guild (Voluntary service), 26 Huntsmans Way, Badsworth, Pontefract, W Yorks. WF9 1BE. ℘ **01977 648882. Mr D J Downham**	Free to local visually impaired	1 week £5
Braille-Tran Services, The Lodge Bungalow, High Street, Baldock, Hertfordshire SG7 6BL. ℘ **01462 892365. Miss Ruth Bishop**		1 day £5
Braudio Transcriptions, 8 Morpeth Terrace, North Shields NE29 7AN. ℘ **0191 258 6324. Michael Gray**		2 days £3
Chester, Cheshire & Clwyd Society for the Blind, Vision Resource Centre, 67 Liverpool Road, Chester CH2 1AP. ℘ **01244 382222. Fax 01244 377482. Mrs Anne Roberts**	Charges by arrangement	1 day

0 pages	500 pages	
-3 weeks £65	1 month £320	▶ Computer, scanner/keying, IBM compatible disks, Wordperfect or ASCII ▶ Tech, ring binding, copying, LARGE PRINT
1 week £160	2-3 weeks £800	▶ Manual/computer, scanner/keying, IBM compatible disks, Apple ▶ Binding, copying, LARGE PRINT, distribution
3 days £150	1 week £650	▶ Manual/computer, scanner/keying, IBM compatible 3.5" disks, Wordperfect or ASCII ▶ Single or double sided braille, plastic comb or treasury tag binding, copying, distribution, plastic labels, LARGE PRINT, dual media, braille to print, transcription also made on waterproof embossable sheets.
-2 weeks £70	1 month £350	▶ Computer, scanner/keying, IBM compatible,3.5" or 5.25" disks, Wordperfect 5.1, or ASCII ▶ Maths (simple), binding, copying, Minolta 3D diagrams (simple), LARGE PRINT, no books
2 days £150	10 days £750	▶ Computer, keying ▶ Copying, LARGE PRINT
months £120	–	▶ Manual/computer, keying, IBM compatible 3.5" disks, ASCII ▶ Plastic ring binding, copying (limited), no long documents
-3 weeks £160	6 months £800	▶ Manual ▶ No handwritten material, treasury tag binding, braille to print
0 days £110	(from disk only) 1 week £550	▶ Manual/computer, keying, IBM compatible 3.5" or 5.25" disks Wordperfect or ASCII ▶ Charts/tables, maps/diagrams, treasury tag binding, copying, LARGE PRINT
2 weeks	1 month	▶ Computer, keying, IBM compatible 3.5" or 5.25" disks, Wordstar ▶ Treasury tag binding, copying, distribution, LARGE PRINT

J

	Special terms	2 page...
David Lee, 51 Farnway, Darley Abbey, Derby DE22 2BQ. ℘ **01332 559172.**		4-5 days £1.75
Derbyshire Centre for Integrated Living, Long Close, Ripley, Derbyshire DE5 3HY. ℘ **01773 740246. Fax 01773 570185. David Guy, Centre Manager**	Discounts. Free to local visually impaired	1 day £3
DRT (Disability Resource Team) Transcription Service, 3rd Floor Bedford House, 125-133 Camden High Street, London NW1 7JR. ℘ **0171 482 5305. Fax 0171 482 0796. Maurice Press**		1 day £10.50
Guild of Church Braillists, 321 Feltham Hill Road, Ashford, Middx. TW15 1LP. ℘ **01784 258040.**	No charges	1 week
Hampshire Braille Transcription Service (Voluntary service), 10 Crabwood Drive, Southampton SO3 3DX. ℘ **01703 477784. Mr D Roy Eklund**	Charges for materials/expenses only	2 weeks
Henshaw's Society for the Blind, John Derby House, 88-92 Talbot Road, Old Trafford M16 OGS. ℘ **0161 872 1234. Fax 0161 848 9889. Elizabeth Percy**		1 day £1.50
H.M. Prison Kingston, Milton Road, Portsmouth PO3 6AS. ℘ **01705 829561 ext. 269. Mrs. Lilliman**	Charges on application. Visually impaired charged for materials only.	1 day
H.M. Young Offenders Institution Aylesbury, 17 Bierton Road, Aylesbury, Bucks. HP20 1EH. ℘ **01296 24435. Braille Instructor**	Charges for materials only	1 week
H.M. Prison Dartmoor, Braille Unit, Princetown, Yelverton, Devon PL20 6RR. ℘ **01822 89261 ext 386. Braille Liaison Officer**	Charges for materials only	1 day
H.M. Prison Edinburgh, 33 Stenhouse Road, Edinburgh EH11 3LN. ℘ **0131 444 3000. Fax 0131 444 3045. Braille Co-ordinator**	No charge	1 week

J

0 pages	500 pages	
–	–	▶ Computer, keying ▶ Very short documents only
1 week £150	2-3 weeks £750	▶ Computer, scanner/keying, IBM compatible 3.5″ or 5.25″ disks, any major wordprocessors or ASCII ▶ Plastic ring binding, copying, distribution, LARGE PRINT
3-4 days £75	10 days £220	▶ Manual/computer, scanner/keying, IBM compatible disks, most WP packages, ASCII preferred ▶ Tech, German, French, spiral binding, multiple copying, LARGE PRINT
–	–	▶ Manual ▶ Christian material mainly, longer documents by arrangement
months	–	▶ Manual/computer, keying, IBM compatible 3.5″ & 5.25″ high/double density disks, ASCII ▶ Binding, short documents only
1 week £75	2 weeks £375	▶ Manual/computer, scanner/keying, IBM compatible 3.5″ disks, Wordperfect ▶ Tech, maths (from disk only), treasury tag binding, copying, LARGE PRINT
month	3 months	▶ Manual ▶ Children's story & school text books, French, Latin, Spanish, maths, diagrams, some technical material, copying, binding.
month	6 months	▶ Computer, keying, IBM compatible disks ▶ Binding, diagrams, copying, braille files embossed from disk, LARGE PRINT
3 weeks	8-10 weeks	▶ Manual ▶ English, French, limited maths, copying, diagrams, binding
5 weeks	–	▶ Computer, keying, IBM compatible 3.5″ disks Wordperfect, Wordstar, ASC11 ▶ French, Russian, Welsh, binding

J

	Special terms	2 page
H.M. Prison Maidstone, 36 County Road, Maidstone, Kent ME14 1UZ. ✆ **01622 755611. Mr D Mitchell, Contract services**	Charge for materials only	1 day
H.M. Prison Perth, 3 Edinburgh Road, Perth PH2 8AT. ✆ **01738 22293 ext 215. Activities Unit Manager**	Charges for materials only	2 days
H.M. Prison Wakefield, Love Lane, Wakefield, West Yorkshire WF2 9AG. ✆ **01924 378282. Education Officer**	Charge for materials only – or customers supply own	1 day
H.M. Prison Wayland, Thetford, Norfolk IP25 6RL. ✆ **01953 884103. Fax 01953 882248. Mrs W E Sargeant, Education Officer**	Charges for materials only	1 day
Huddersfield Library, Princess Alexandra Walk, Huddersfield HD1 2SU. ✆ **01484 424959. Fax 01484 531983. Mrs Eileen Cartmell**	Discounts. Charge for postage & packing	1 day £1.80
Jenni Fortescue, 3 King Dick Lane, St George, Bristol BS5 8HN. ✆ **0117 955 7992.**	Discounts available	1 day £5
Judith Furse, 23 Masefield Avenue, Upper Stratton, Swindon, Wilts. SN2 6HT. ✆ **01793 644346.**	Discounts available	1 day £3
Julie Smethurst, 79 Duncan Road, Crookes, Sheffield S10 1SN. ✆ **0114 268 5405.**		2 days £5
Leeds Braille Group (Voluntary service), 27 Nook Road, Scholes, Leeds LS15 4AX. ✆ **0113 273 4283. Mrs Margaret Taylor**	Binding charge only	1 week
Lin Berwick, 9 Hunter Drive, Hornchurch, Essex RM12 5TP. ✆ **01708 477582. Fax same number.**		1 day £5
Lisa Jayne Redford Enterprises, Park 5, Business Centre, Top Floor, Bradley House, Harrier Way, Sowton, Exeter EX2 7HU. ✆ **01392 445488. Fax same number.**		by arrangem £6

0 pages	500 pages	
2 weeks	2 months	▶ Manual ▶ Tech, maths, knitting patterns, French, German, binding, copying, diagrams, maps, cards
1 month	–	▶ Manual ▶ Tech, maths, French, Spanish, binding, copying, short documents only
6 weeks	3-4 months	▶ Manual ▶ Tech, maths, some foreign languages, binding, copying, diagrams
1 month	2 months	▶ Manual/computer, keying, IBM compatible 3.5" disks, WS2000 or ASCII ▶ Maths (limited), copying, maps, diagrams
by arrangement £90	by arrangement £450	▶ Computer, scanner/keying, IBM compatible 3.5" disks, MS Word, Works, Wordstar, Wordperfect or ASCII ▶ Binding, copying, maps/diagrams, LARGE PRINT
3-4 days £150	1 week £500 or on application	▶ Manual/computer, keying, IBM compatible 3.5" & 5.25" disks, Wordperfect, other WP packages or ASCII ▶ Tech, French, Spanish, copying, LARGE PRINT
10 days £150	1 month £750	▶ Manual/computer, keying, IBM compatible 3.5" disks, Wordperfect or ASCII ▶ Braille to print
3 months £180	6 months £900	▶ Manual, computer, Eureka A4 & IBM compatible disks, ASCII, audio tape ▶ Copying, diagrams
month	3 months	▶ Manual ▶ Tech, maths, French, German, Hebrew, binding, diagrams (limited)
4 weeks £160	–	▶ Computer, keying ▶ Treasury tag binding, no long documents
–	–	▶ Computer, scanner/keying, IBM & Eureka A4 compatible disks, audio tape ▶ Treasury tag binding, LARGE PRINT

J

	Special terms	2 page
MagRay Document Services, 178 Castle Road, Northolt, Middlesex UB5 4SG. ℘ **0181 864 7208. Ray Dawson**		1 day £5
Martin Freshwater, 34 Settles Street, London E1 1JP. ℘ **0171 247 2414.**		2 days £5
Mersey Braille, 63 Easton Road, New Ferry, Wirral, Merseyside L62 1DW. ℘ **0151 645 5712. Mrs E Kearns**		1 day £2
NOSITE Braille Transcription Service, Wallsend People's Centre, Frank St, Wallsend NE28 6RN. ℘ **0191 263 0005. Fax 0191 295 4691. Hugh Twiss**		1 day £1.60
Pia, 37 Charles Street, Cardiff CF1 4EB. ℘ **01222 222782. Fax 01222 222383. Modem 01222 222696. ISDN 01222 221126. Gail Chester and Paula Tooze**		1 day £10
Queen Alexandra College (BRIB), Court Oak Road, Harborne, Birmingham B17 9TG. ℘ **0121 428 5018. Fax 0121 428 5048. Keith Askew, Projects Manager, Business Centre**		2 days £14
Quickprint, 64 Haddon Drive, Boyatt Wood, Eastleigh, Hampshire SO5 4PF. ℘ **01703 616159. Mrs H Dickinson**		2 days £4.40
Rakaso Systems Ltd, PO Box 931, London N12 9XF. ℘ **0181 446 5555.**		1 day £20

0 pages	500 pages	
2-3 days £120	3 weeks £600	▶ Manual/computer, scanner/keying, IBM compatible 5.25" or 3.5" or BBC disks, WordPerfect or ASCII preferred ▶ French (manual braille only), treasury tag or plastic comb binding, multiple copies, LARGE PRINT, braille to print, double-sided braille
2 weeks £160	on application	▶ Manual, ▶ Maths, tech, maps & diagrams
2 weeks £100	on application	▶ Computer, keying, IBM compatible 3.5" disks, ASCII ▶ Knitting patterns, recipes
3 days £80	2 months £400	▶ Manual/computer, scanner/keying, IBM compatible/ Eureka A4 3.5" disks, ASCII ▶ Tech, binding, copying, JUMBO braille, MOON, LARGE PRINT
2 days £169	5 days £445	▶ Computer, scanner/keying, any disk format, many wordprocessor formats, modem, ISDN ▶ Long runs, distribution, interpoint, tech, maths (limited), Catalan, Spanish, French, Irish, Russian, Welsh, Wire-O-Binding, treasury tagging, plastic labels, copying, LARGE PRINT, dual media, braille-to-print
0 days 350; 50 pages maximum ccepted	–	▶ Manual/computer, scanner/keying, IBM compatible 3.5" or 5.25" disks, audio tape ▶ Binding, copying, distribution, short documents only, LARGE PRINT
5 days £200	7-10 days £750	▶ Manual/computer, scanner/keying, IBM compatible 3.5" & 5.25" disks, Wordperfect or ASCII ▶ Tech, maths, Welsh, computer print-outs split & attached with treasury tags, copying, LARGE PRINT, braille to print
eek; price on plication	2-4 weeks; price on application	▶ Computer, scanner/keying, IBM compatible 5.25" disks, ASCII preferred ▶ Tech, computer print-outs split & attached with treasury tags, copying, LARGE PRINT, dual media

J

	Special terms	2 page
RNIB, PO Box 173, Peterborough PE2 6WS. ℘ **0345 023153. Fax 01733 371555. Customer Services**	Free to visually impaired	details on applicatio
RNIB & Leeds University Brailling Service, 7 Springfield Mount, Leeds LS2 9NG. ℘ **0113 233 3928.**	Free to visually impaired	1 week £5
Roy Tysoe (Voluntary service), Salvation Army Hostel, 122/124 Spa Road, London SE16. ℘ **0171 237 1107 (after 5 pm).**	No charges	1 day
Scantran Services, PO Box 318, Northampton, NN3 9EY. ℘ **01604 785771. Andrew Wade**		2 days £2
Scottish Braille Press, Craigmillar Park, Edinburgh EH16 5NB. ℘ **0131 662 4445. Fax 0131 662 1968.**	Charges on application	1 day
Speedwell Transcribing Service, 2 Haines Close, Aylesbury, Bucks. HP19 3TS. ℘ **01296 29529. Mrs D Hayward**	Discounts	2 days £5
St Vincent's School for the Blind, Yew Tree Lane, Liverpool L12 9HN. ℘ **0151 228 9968. Fax 0151 252 0216.**		2-3 day £5
TABS (Tactile Audio Braille Services Ltd), YPI Buildings, 83-93 George Street, Hull HU1 3EN. ℘ **01482 585383.**	Discounts to visually impaired	2-3 days £5
Techno-Vision Braille Services Ltd., 76 Bunting Road, Northampton NN2 6EE. ℘ **01604 792777. Fax 01604 792726.**		1 day £1

J

480

pages	500 pages	
details on application	details on application	▶ Manual/computer, scanner/keying, most wp packages, ASCII preferred, modem ▶ Tech, maths, foreign languages, bank statements, binding, copying, diagrams/maps, JUMBO braille, MOON, LARGE PRINT, dual media, braille files embossed from disk
month £50	–	▶ Computer, scanner/keying, IBM compatible 3.5″ disks, Wordperfect or ASCII preferred ▶ Tech, elementary maths, binding, copying, diagrams, LARGE PRINT (single copies only), dual media, student work takes priority, no very long documents
5 weeks	20 weeks	▶ Manual ▶ India tag binding, mainly Christian material
3 weeks £100	4 weeks £230	▶ Manual/computer, scanner/keying, IBM compatible 3.5″ or Eureka A4 disks, audio tape, modem ▶ Tech, copying, braille files embossed from disk
1 week	3-4 weeks	▶ Manual/computer, keying, IBM compatible disks, ASCII preferred ▶ Tech, maths, foreign languages, signs, business cards, binding, copying, diagrams
1 week £250	1 month £1,250	▶ Manual/computer, keying, IBM compatible 5.25″ disks, ASCII files ▶ Copying
by arrangement	by arrangement	▶ Manual/computer, keying, IBM compatible 5.25″ disks, Wordperfect, Wordstar, ASCII ▶ Maths, diagrams, binding, copying, LARGE PRINT
10 days £100	4 weeks £650	▶ Manual/computer, scanner/keying, IBM compatible 3.5″ or 5.25″ disks, Wordperfect/ASCII preferred ▶ Binding, copying, LARGE PRINT, braille files embossed from disk, tactile & large print maps
1 day £50	1 day £250	▶ Computer, scanner/keying, IBM compatible 3.5″ & 5.25″ disks in various wp formats, Internet ▶ Tech, foreign languages, multiple braille copies (800 pages an hour double or single sided), binding (various methods), JUMBO BRAILLE, LARGE PRINT, dual media. No mathematical, musical or scientific braille.

J

481

	Special terms	2 pag
Teeside & District Society for the Blind, Stockton Road, Middlesborough TS5 4AH. *℘* **01642 247518. Sue Whelan**	Charges on application (min. £7.50)	1 day
Torch Trust, Torch House, Market Harborough LE16 8UJ. *℘* **01858 555301. Fax 01858 555371. Dr M Townsend**	Materials charge only	–
Trandat Services, 39 Lea Road, Harpenden, Herts. AL5 4PQ. *℘* **01582 767410. Fax same number. Martine Brooks**		1 day £3
Transcription & Copying Service, 52 West End, Cholsey OX10 9LW. *℘* **01491 651399. Mrs Linda Deacon**		1 day £5
Val Redford, 65 Castle Road, Newport, Isle of Wight PO30 1DT. *℘* **01983 526503.**		2 days £4
Voluntary Transcribers Group (Voluntary service), 8 Segbourne Road, Rubery, Birmingham B45 9SX. *℘* **0121 453 4268. Mrs W Batchelor**	No charges	1 day
Waltham Forest Transcription Service, Town Hall, Forest Road, Walthamstow, London E17 4JF. *℘* **0181 527 5544 ext 4854. Fax 0181 503 3988. Michael Flood, Media Resources Co-ordinator**	Discounts to local visually impaired	1 week £25
Windsor Howells (Voluntary service), 28 Elizabeth Way, Hanworth, Middlesex TW13 7PH. *℘* **0181 890 5669.**	Charge for materials only	1 day
Yorkshire Braille Service (Voluntary service), 49 Sandhill Oval, Leeds LS17 8EF. *℘* **0113 268 4863. Mrs Barbara Jackson**	Materials/expenses only	1 week

J

0 pages	500 pages	
1 week	2 weeks (from disk only)	▶ Manual/computer, keying, IBM compatible 3.5" & 5.25" disks, Wordperfect, ASCII ▶ Treasury tag binding, copying, LARGE PRINT
2 months	6 months	▶ Manual/computer, scanner/keying, IBM compatible disks, ASCII files ▶ Binding, copying, LARGE PRINT, dual media (if multiple copies), Christian material only, no very short documents
2 weeks £150	1 month £700	▶ Computer, scanner/keying, IBM compatible 3.5" disks, Wordperfect 5.1 & other major wp packages or ASCII ▶ French (including translation to & from), LARGE PRINT, text accepted on tape
1-2 weeks £250	2 weeks; by arrangement	▶ Manual/computer, keying, any format disk, ASCII preferred ▶ Tech, maths, some foreign languages, binding, copying
5 weeks £120	–	▶ Manual/computer, keying, IBM compatible 3.5" disks, Wordperfect or ASCII, Eureka disks ▶ Copying
1 month	5 months	▶ Manual ▶ Simple maths, binding, simple diagrams, novels, German, French, limited copying
1 month £200	–	▶ Computer, scanner/keying, IBM compatible 3.5" disks, Wordperfect ▶ Treasury tag or spring-clip binding, multiple copies, LARGE PRINT
1 month	3 months	▶ Computer, keying, IBM compatible 3.5" & 5.25" disks, ASCII preferred ▶ Tech, maths (limited), comb binding, no religious material
1 month	3 months	▶ Manual ▶ Tech/maths (limited), binding, copying (limited), prefer no political/religious material

J

34 Resource centres

Most places are now served by a local resource centre where blind and partially sighted people can obtain information, examine, and sometimes buy equipment suited to their needs. The number of such centres continues to rise – 188 are listed in this Handbook. They are mainly run by local voluntary agencies or social services. Public libraries are included where there is a unit specially for visually impaired people, with specialist staff and equipment.

Addresses of local disabled living centres, serving people with any kind of disability, can be obtained from the *Disabled Living Centres Council, 286 Camden Road, London N7 0BJ* ✆ 0171 700 1707 (moving summer 1995, calls and post will be redirected). The Guide Dogs for the Blind Association Training Centres (see 12.4) also have resource centres open to past and present guide dog owners, or to anyone considering training with a guide dog. See also national information services in 29.

As indicated in these charts, the facilities that centres provide vary widely. Where the need to make an appointment is not stipulated, it is worth checking if someone with the appropriate knowledge will be available to deal with particular enquiries or demonstrate specialist equipment.

34.1 Further reading

A new deal for blind and partially sighted people ❶❷❸. Visual Handicap Group (£9.95. 1993. RNIB). Argues the case for a national network of resource centres to provide focal points for integrated services for visually impaired people.

34.2 Key to tables

A	**visits by appointment** only (at times shown)
D	**open daily** Monday to Friday (hours of opening)
M Tu W Th F S	**other opening days**
RNIB	Equipment supplied by **RNIB**
Commercial	Daily living aids from **commercial sources**
Hi tech	**High technology** (e.g. electronic reading equipment described in 18.4, specialist computers in chapter 20, talking teletext in 19.8.3)
Low-vision aids	✇ hand-held/stand magnifiers
	⚬ specialist lighting
	⟨TV⟩ closed-circuit television magnifiers
	Ⓐ professional advice on choice/use of magnifiers – see 3.15
Teaching	(daily living/communication) provided/can be arranged
Enlarging copier	**enlarged** copies
Tactile copier	**tactile** copies
Transcription	❸ braille, ⓜ Moon, ❶ large print, ❸ tape
Other	mobile units etc

* The 188 UK resource centres are listed under **ENGLAND**, **SCOTLAND**, **NORTHERN IRELAND**, **ISLE OF MAN** and **WALES**.
* England is divided into regions, which are arranged geographically from **South east** to **North east**.
* In each section, centres are listed alphabetically by **town**.
* To find your way quickly to your region, check this map for the section number.

34.3 ENGLAND

KEY IN 34.2

Resource Centre address and telephone number

Opening days and times

34.3.1 South East

Resource Centre address and telephone number	Opening days and times
Social Service Department, Chantry House, Chantry Way, **Andover** SP10 1LP ✆ 01264 324173	F 9.30-1, first F morning each month
Brighton Society for the Blind, William Moon Lodge, The Linkway, Hollingdean, **Brighton** BN1 7EJ ✆ 01273 507251	D 9-4.30
West Sussex Association for the Blind, 38 South Street, **Chichester** PO19 1EL ✆ 01243 788333	D
Kent Association for the Blind, Bridge Court, Brent Way, **Dartford** ✆ 01322 229820	A
The Well Resource Centre, Winchelsea Street, **Dover** CT17 9ST ✆ 01304 241740	A, D 9-5
Eastbourne Blind Society, Longstone Road, **Eastbourne** BN22 8DA ✆ 01323 729511	M Tu Th F 9-4 W 9-2
Hampshire Association for the Care of the Blind, 25 Church Road, Bishopstoke, **Eastleigh** S05 6LB ✆ 01703 641244	M-Th 9-5 F 9-4.30
Dengate Resource Centre for Visually Impaired People, Avenue Road, **Erith**, Kent DA8 3AU ✆ 0181 303 7777 or 01322 350084/5	A
Surrey Voluntary Association for the Blind, Rentwood, School Lane, Fetcham, **Leatherhead** KT22 9JX ✆ 01372 377701	A, D 9-4.30
Kent Association for the Blind, 72 College Road, **Maidstone** ME15 6SJ ✆ 01622 691357	A, D 9-5
Crescent Resource Centre, Cocks Crescent, off Blagdon Road, **New Malden**, Surrey KT3 4TA ✆ 0181 949 1955	A
Frank Sorrell Centre, Prince Albert Road, Eastney, **Portsmouth** PO4 9HR ✆ 01705 737174/831214	A, M W F 10-3.00
Portsmouth Association for the Blind, 48 Stubbington Avenue, North End, **Portsmouth** PO2 0HY ✆ 01705 661717	D 8.30-4.30
Kent Association for the Blind, Rehabilitation & Resource Centre, 32 St Mildred's Road, **Ramsgate** CT11 0EG ✆ 01843 588733	A
Hastings & Rother Voluntary Association for the Blind, Carolyn House, 383 Battle Road, **St Leonards-on-Sea** TN37 7BE ✆ 01424 853711	D 9.30-1, 2-4.30
East Sussex Association for the Blind, 9 Sutton Road, **Seaford** BN25 1RU ✆ 01323 898681	D 9.30-1, 2-4.30
Southampton Society for the Blind, 3 Bassett Avenue, **Southampton** SO16 7DP ✆ 01703 769882	A, M-Th 9-1 2-4 F 9-1
Kent Association for the Blind, 27 Monson Terrace, off Monson Road, **Tunbridge Wells** TN1 1LS ✆ c/o 01732 362442	

J

RNIB	Commercial	Hi tech	Low vision aids	Low vision	Teaching	Enlarging copier	Tactile copier	Transcription	Other
✓	✓		💡 🅰/SDF	✓					
✓	✓	✓	🔍 💡 TV	incl. low vision	✓	✓		B T M	
✓	✓	✓	🔍 💡 TV		✓			L B T	Mobile unit
✓	✓		💡	✓	✓			L	Mobile unit
✓	✓	✓	TV	✓					Induction loops
✓	✓		🔍 TV	✓	✓			B T M	
✓	✓	✓	🔍 💡 TV	✓	✓			L B	
✓	✓	✓	🔍 💡 TV	✓					
✓	✓		🔍 💡 TV 🅰/SDF	✓	✓		✓	L B T M	
✓	✓		🔍 💡 TV 🅰/SDF	✓	✓			L B T	Induction loop. Mobile unit
✓	✓		🔍 💡 🅰/SDF	✓	✓			L B T	Induction loop
	✓	✓			✓	✓			
✓	✓		🔍 🅰/SDF	✓	✓			L B T	Fitted with induction loops
✓	✓		🔍 💡 TV 🅰/SDF	✓	✓			L B T	Mobile unit
✓	✓		🔍 💡 TV	✓				L B T	Mobile unit
✓	✓		💡 TV	✓	✓			L B T	
✓	✓				✓			L	
									Ring for up-to-date information

J

Resource Centre address and telephone number	Opening days and times

34.3.2 London

Resource Centre address and telephone number	Opening days and times
Projects by the Blind Wandsworth, 10-12 Yukon Road, **Balham**, London SW12 9PU ✆ 0181 675 3900	**D** 8.30-5.30 **S** 9-1
Merton Voluntary Association for the Blind, The Guardian Centre, 67 Clarendon Road, **Colliers Wood**, London SW19 2DX ✆ 0181 540 5446	**D** 9-5
Croydon Voluntary Association for the Blind, 72/74 Wellesley Road, **Croydon** CR0 2AR ✆ 0181 688 2486	**M-Th** 8.30-4.30 **F** 8.30-1
Resource Centre for the Visually Impaired, Rose Taylor Centre, 55b The Sunny Road, **Enfield** EN3 5EF **Telephone Monday mornings only** ✆ 0181 805 6666	**A, M** 9.30-12
Royal London Society for the Blind, Technology Centre, 105 Salusbury Road, **Kilburn**, London NW6 6RH ✆ 0171 624 8844	**D** 9-4
Lewisham Social Services, Laurence House, 1 Catford Road, **Lewisham**, London SE6 4SW ✆ 0181 695 6000 ext 8644	**A** or **Th** 9.30-12.30
In Touch Kitchen, c/o Disabled Living Foundation, 380-4 Harrow Road, **London** W9 2HU ✆ 0171 289 6111	**A, D** 10-5
RNIB, 224 Great Portland Street, **London** W1N 6AA ✆ 0171 388 1266	**M-Th** 9.30-5.15 **F** 9.30-5 **S** 9.30-12
Organisation of Blind African-Caribbeans, 24 Mayward House, Benhill Road, **Peckham**, London SE5 7NA ✆ 0171 703 3688	**D** 10-5
Near Vision Aids Assessment Unit, Stamford Hill Community Centre, 91-93 **Stamford Hill**, London N16 5TP ✆ 0181 800 5672	**A**
Haringey Phoenix Group, North Block, The Selby Centre, Selby Road, **Tottenham** N17 8JL ✆ 0181 885 4130	**D** 9.30-4.30

34.3.3 Wessex

Resource Centre address and telephone number	Opening days and times
Bath & Wansdyke Society for the Blind & Partially Sighted, 11 Manvers Street, **Bath** BA1 1JQ ✆ 01225 446555	**D** 10-12.30 1.30-4
Bournemouth Blind Aid Society Centre for the Visually Impaired, Victoria Park Road, **Bournemouth** BH9 2RB ✆ 01202 546644	**A** or **M-W** 10-4
Social Services Department, Boscombe Day Centre, Owls Road, Boscombe, **Bournemouth** BH15 1AA ✆ 01202 537997	**A** or **Tu** 10-4.00
BRSB (Bristol Royal Society for the Blind), Centre for People with a Visual Impairment, Stillhouse Lane, Bedminster, **Bristol** BS3 4EB ✆ 0117 953 7750	**A D** 10-4.30
RNIB Resource Centre, 6 Victoria Court, Victoria Street, **Burnham-on-Sea** TA8 1AL ✆ 01278 795634	**D** 9.15-4.00 **S** 10-12

RNIB	Commercial	Hi tech	Low vision aids	Teaching	Enlarging copier	Tactile copier	Transcription	Other
✓	✓	✓	🔍 💡 [TV] [A-SDF]	✓	✓	✓	L B T	
✓	✓		🔍 💡 [TV]	✓	✓		L B T	
✓	✓		🔍 💡 [TV] [A-SDF]	✓			L B T M	
✓	✓		🔍 💡 [TV]	✓				
✓		✓	🔍 💡 [TV] [A-SDF]	✓	✓		L T	Mobile unit
✓	✓	✓	🔍 💡 [TV]	✓	✓		L B T	Resource flat
								Ring for up-to-date information
✓	✓	✓	🔍 💡 [TV]	For hi-tech equip, by appt.				
✓	✓	✓	🔍 [TV]	✓			L B T	
✓	✓		🔍 💡 [TV] [A-SDF]	✓			B T	
✓	✓	✓	🔍 💡 [TV]	✓	✓		B T	
✓	✓	✓	🔍 💡 [TV]	✓	✓			
✓	✓		[TV]	✓			B T	
								Ring for up-to-date information
✓	✓	✓	🔍 💡 [TV]	✓	✓		L B T	
✓	✓		🔍 💡 [TV] [A-SDF]	✓			L B T M	

Resource Centre address and telephone number	Opening days and times

Wessex *continued*

Wiltshire Blind Association, St Lucy's, 1 Commercial Road, **Devizes** SN10 1EH ✆ 01380 723682	**D** 9-12.45, 2-5
Social Services Department, Sight & Sound Centre, Acland Road, **Dorchester** ✆ 01305 251414	**A** or **W** 10-4.00
Dorset County Association for the Blind, 220 Ashley Road, Parkstone, **Poole** BH14 9BY ✆ 01202 742421	**D** 9-4.30
Partially Sighted Society Sight Centre, Salisbury District Hospital, **Salisbury** SP2 8BJ ✆ 01722 336262 ext. 2175	**A, D** 9-5
Somerset County Association for the Blind, 10 Belvedere Road **Taunton** TA1 1BW ✆ 01823 333818	**A** or **M** 2-4
See-Here Centre, St. George's Hospital, **Trowbridge**. Contact Sensory Loss Team, Social Services, Southfield, Victoria Road, Devizes SN10 ✆ 01380 725201	**A, D** 9-5
Woodspring Association for the Blind, c/o The Lauriston Hotel, 6-12 Knightstone Road, **Weston-super-Mare** BS23 2AN ✆ 01934 419393	**D** 10-1, 2-4

34.3.4 South West

Devon County Association for the Blind, 16 York Road, **Exeter** EX4 6BA ✆ 01392 77196	**A** or **D** 9.30-1
Partially Sighted Society Sight Centre, Dean Clarke House, Southernhay East, **Exeter** EX1 1PE ✆ 01392 210656	**A, D** 9-5
RNIB Ivybridge Transcription Unit, 10 Erme Road, **Ivybridge** PL21 0AB ✆ 01752 690092	**M-Th** 9.30-12.30 **M** 6.30-8.30 **F** 9.30-11.30
Sight & Hearing Centre, Pounds House, Outland Road, Peverell, **Plymouth** PL2 3PX ✆ 01752 788999	**D** 9-1, 2-5
Devon County Council Social Services, Tavistock Sensory Advice Services, Harewood House, 66 Plymouth Road, **Tavistock** PL19 8BU ✆ 01822 612112	**A, W** 9.30-12.30
RNIB Manor House, Skills Development Centre, Middle Lincombe Road, **Torquay** TQ1 2NG ✆ 01803 214523	**A, D**
Cornwall County Association for the Blind, Sight Centre, Newham Quay, **Truro** TR1 2DP ✆ 01872 261110	**D** 9-5

J

RNIB	Commercial	Hi tech	Low vision aids	Teaching	Enlarging copier	Tactile copier	Transcription	Other
✓	✓	✓	🔍 💡 TV	✓	✓		Ⓑ Ⓣ	Mail order service
✓	✓		🔍 💡 TV [A/SDF]	✓				
✓	✓		💡 TV		✓		Ⓛ Ⓑ Ⓣ	
✓	✓	✓	🔍 💡 TV [A/SDF]	incl. low vision				
✓	✓	✓	🔍 💡 TV [A/SDF]	✓	✓		Ⓛ Ⓑ Ⓣ	
✓	✓	✓	🔍 💡 TV	✓	✓		Ⓛ Ⓑ Ⓣ	
✓	✓		TV	✓			Ⓣ	
✓	✓		💡		✓		Ⓛ Ⓣ	
	✓		🔍 💡 TV	low vision	✓			
					✓	✓	Ⓛ Ⓑ Ⓣ Ⓜ	
✓	✓	✓	💡 TV	✓	✓		Ⓛ Ⓑ Ⓣ	
✓	✓		💡 TV	✓	✓			
✓	✓	✓	🔍 💡 TV [A/SDF]	✓	✓	✓	Ⓛ Ⓑ Ⓣ Ⓜ	
✓	✓	✓	🔍 💡 TV [A/SDF]	✓	✓			

ENGLAND *continued*

Resource Centre address and telephone number	Opening days and times

34.3.5 East Anglia

Resource Centre address and telephone number	Opening days and times
Camsight (Cambridgeshire Society for the Blind & Partially Sighted), East View, 5 Coles Lane, Oakington, **Cambridge** CB4 5BA ℘ 01223 236868	**A**, **Tu-F** 10-4
Essex Voluntary Association for the Blind, 29 Moulsham Street, **Chelmsford** CM2 OHS ℘ 01245 352560	**D** 9-5
Harlow Library, The High, **Harlow** CM20 1HA ℘ 01279 413772 Textphone 01279 431723	**A**, **M Tu Th F** 9-7.30, **W S** 9-5
Huntingdonshire Society for the Blind, 8 St Mary's Street, **Huntingdon** PE18 6PE ℘ 01480 453438	**D** 10-3 **S** 10-1
Waveney Centre for Independent Living, 161 Rotterdam Road, **Lowestoft** NR32 2EZ ℘ 01502 538571	**A**, **M-Th** 9.30-4.30, **F** 9.30-3.30
Norfolk & Norwich Association for the Blind, Magpie Road, **Norwich** NR3 1JH ℘ 01603 629558	**A**, **D** 9.30-4
The National Deaf-Blind League, 18 Rainbow Court, Paston Ridings, **Peterborough** PE4 7UP ℘ 01733 573511, text 01733 321982	**A**, **M-Th** 9-5 **F** 9-4
Southend Library, Victoria Avenue, **Southend-on-Sea** SS2 6EX ℘ 01702 612621 Textphone 01702 600579	**A S** and evenings, **D** 9-5

34.3.6 South Midlands

Resource Centre address and telephone number	Opening days and times
Buckinghamshire Association for the Blind, 143 Meadowcroft, **Aylesbury** HP19 3HH ℘ 01296 87556	**A**, **D** 9-4
Sight Concern (North Bedfordshire), 6 St Paul's Square, **Bedford** MK40 1SQ ℘ 01234 354064	**D** 10-11.30
Enterprises by the Blind, 593 Hitchin Road, **Luton** LU2 7UN ℘ 01582 27588	**D** 9-4
South Bedfordshire Society for the Welfare of the Blind, 14 Stuart Street, **Luton** LU1 2SL ℘ 01582 20396	**D** 9-12
Northamptonshire Association for the Blind, Wardington Court, Welford Road, **Northampton** NN2 8AG ℘ 01604 791333	**D** 9-4
Oxfordshire Association for the Blind, 3 Enstone Road, Charlbury, **Oxford OX7 3QR** ℘ 01608 810329	**A**, **D** 9-4
Berkshire County Blind Society, Midleton House, 5 Erleigh Road, **Reading** RG1 5LR ℘ 01734 872803	**A**, **D** 9-4
Reading Association for the Blind, Walford Hall, Carey Street, **Reading** RG1 7JS ℘ 01734 572960	**Tu** & **F** 9.30-4.30 **W** 9.30-12.30
Wiltshire Blind Association, Thamesdown Branch, Craven House, 145 Victoria Road, **Swindon** ℘ 01793 523374	**A**, **T** 10-3 **S** 10-12.30
Hertfordshire Society for the Blind, Trinity Centre, Fanhams Hall Road, **Ware** SG12 7PS ℘ 01992 588145	**A**, **M-Th** 8.45-5 **F** 8.45-4.15

J

RNIB	Commercial	Hi tech	Low vision aids	Teaching	Enlarging copier	Tactile copier	Transcription	Other
✓	✓		🔍 💡 TV	✓	✓	✓	B T	
✓	✓		🔍 · A(SDF)	✓				
✓		✓	TV	✓				
✓				✓	✓		L B T	
✓	✓	✓	🔍 💡 A(SDF)	✓			L B T	Induction loops
✓	✓		🔍 💡 TV	✓	✓		B T M	
✓	✓			✓			L B M	
		✓	TV		✓		B	

RNIB	Commercial	Hi tech	Low vision aids	Teaching	Enlarging copier	Tactile copier	Transcription	Other
✓	✓	✓	🔍 💡 TV A(SDF)	✓	✓		L B T	
✓	✓		🔍 💡 TV	✓	✓		L B T	
✓	✓	✓	🔍 💡 TV	✓			L T	
✓	✓		🔍 💡	✓	✓		L B T M	
✓	✓	✓	🔍 💡 TV	✓	✓		L B T	Mobile unit
✓	✓		🔍 💡					
✓	✓	✓	💡 TV	✓	✓		B T	
✓			🔍 💡 TV A(SDF)	✓	✓		L B	
✓	✓		💡				T	
✓	✓	✓	🔍 💡 TV A(SDF)	✓	✓		L B T M	Mobile unit

J

Resource Centre address and telephone number

Opening days and times

34.3.7 West Midlands & Welsh Marches

Resource Centre address and telephone number	Opening days and times
Birmingham City Council Social Services, Rehabilitation Unit, 79-81 Duchess Rd, Edgbaston, **Birmingham** B16 8JD ✆ 0121 455 0045	A
Birmingham Royal Institution for the Blind (BRIB), Cowley Centre, 23 Gravelly Hill North, Erdington, **Birmingham** B23 6BT ✆ 0121 373 1336	D 9.30-4.30
Birmingham Royal Institution for the Blind (BRIB), Low Vision Centre, 62 Woodville Rd, Harborne, **Birmingham** B17 9AX ✆ 0121 428 5080	A, D 9-5
Birmingham Royal Institution for the Blind (BRIB), Resource Centre, 48 Woodville Rd, Harborne, **Birmingham** B17 9TG ✆ 0121 428 5055	D 9-5
Central Library, Chamberlain Square, **Birmingham** B3 3HQ ✆ 0121 235 4545	D 9-8 S 9-5
Forest of Dean Association for the Visually Impaired, Foxes Bridge Day Centre, Valley Road, **Cinderford** GL14 2LJ ✆ 01594 827711	A
Coventry Society for the Blind Resource Centre, 3 Earlsdon Avenue South, **Coventry** CV5 6DR ✆ 01203 717522	D 9-5
Hatherley Day Centre, Hatherley Road, **Gloucester** GL1 4PW ✆ 01452 311628 (answerphone)	A, D 9-4
Rikenel Day Centre for the Blind, Montpellier, **Gloucester** ✆ 01452 426000 ext 6102	A
Herefordshire Association for the Blind, 9A Mortimer Road, **Hereford** HR4 9SP ✆ 01432 352297	D 9-12
Royal National College for the Blind, Flexible Learning Centre, College Road, **Hereford** HR1 1EB ✆ 01432 265725	A, D during term time 9-5, 7-9 weekends by arrangement
Shropshire Disability Resource Centre, Lancaster Road, Harlescott **Shrewsbury** SY1 3NJ ✆ 01743 444599	A, M-Th 8.45-5 F 8.45-4
Plantsbrook School, Upper Holland Road, **Sutton Coldfield** B72 1RB ✆ 0121 355 5626 ext 22	A, D 2.15-3.30
The Disabled Living Centre, Services for People with a Visual Impairment, The Shrubbery, The Crescent, **Walsall** WS1 2DE ✆ 01922 721159	A, M-Th 9-5 F 9-4.30
Walsall Society for the Blind, Hawley House, 11 Hatherton Road, **Walsall** WS1 1XS ✆ 01922 27638	D 9-4.30
Warwickshire Association for the Blind, The George Marshall Centre, Puckering's Lane, **Warwick** CV34 4UH ✆ 01926 494129	M-Th 9-5.30 F 9-5
Crest Assessment & Rehabilitation Unit, 107 All Saints Way, **West Bromwich** ✆ 0121 588 2509	A, M-Th 9-5.30 F 9-5
Beacon Centre, Wolverhampton Road East, **Wolverhampton** WV4 6AZ ✆ 01902 880111	T-Th 11-4
Worcestershire Association for the Blind, 13 Wylds Lane, **Worcester** WR5 1DA ✆ 01905 351311	A, M-Th 9.30-3.30 F 9.30-12.30

J

RNIB	Commercial	Hi tech	Low vision aids	Teaching	Enlarging copier	Tactile copier	Transcription	Other
✓	✓	✓	🔍 💡 (TV)	✓	✓			
✓	✓		🔍	✓	✓		Ⓛ Ⓑ Ⓣ	
			(TV) 🅰SDF					
✓	✓	✓	💡 (TV)	✓	✓	✓	Ⓛ Ⓑ Ⓣ	Mobile unit
	✓	✓	(TV)		✓			
✓	✓	✓	🔍 💡 (TV)	✓	✓		Ⓛ Ⓑ Ⓣ	
✓	✓	✓	💡 (TV)	✓	✓		Ⓛ Ⓑ Ⓣ	
	✓		🔍 💡 (TV) 🅰SDF	✓	✓			
✓	✓		(TV)	✓			Ⓑ Ⓣ	
✓	✓		🔍 💡 (TV)	✓	✓			
✓		✓	🔍 💡 (TV)					
✓	✓	✓	🔍 💡 (TV)	✓	✓	✓	Ⓛ Ⓑ Ⓣ	Induction loop. Mobile unit
	✓	✓	🔍 💡 (TV)	✓				
✓	✓		🔍 💡 🅰SDF	✓				Induction loops
✓	✓	✓	💡 (TV)	✓	✓			
✓	✓	✓	🔍 💡 (TV)	✓	✓		Ⓛ Ⓑ Ⓣ	
✓	✓	✓	🔍 💡 (TV)	✓	✓			
✓	✓	✓	🔍 💡 (TV)	✓	✓		Ⓛ Ⓑ Ⓣ	
✓	✓		💡 (TV) 🅰SDF	✓	✓	✓	Ⓑ Ⓣ	

Resource Centre address and telephone number

34.3.8 North Midlands

Resource Centre address and telephone number	Opening days and times
Central Library, New Beetwell Street, **Chesterfield** S40 1QN ℘ 01246 209292	**A, D** 9.30-7 **S** 9.30-1
The Lindsey Blind Society, Melbourne House, 15 Highgate, **Cleethorpes** DN15 6QS ℘ 01472 695771, 01507 603824	**A**
Derbyshire Association for the Blind, 65 Nottingham Road, **Derby** DE1 3QS ℘ 01332 292262	**D** 9-5
The Lindsey Blind Society, The Lucy Mumby Centre, 5 Spital Terrace, **Gainsborough** DN21 2HD ℘ 01427 810791, 01507 605604	**A**
Royal Leicestershire Society for the Blind, Gedding Road, **Leicester** LE5 5DU ℘ 0116 249 0909	**M-Th** 9.30-4 **F** 9.30-3.30
The Lindsey Blind Society, Ramsgate House, Pleasant Place, **Louth** LN11 0NA ℘ 01507 605604	**A**
Nottinghamshire Royal Society for the Blind, Chaucer House, 13 Layton Avenue, **Mansfield** ℘ 01623 23292	**A**
The Independent Living Centre, The Arts Centre, The Brampton, **Newcastle-under-Lyme** ST5 0QP ℘ 01782 634949	**M-W** 10-3 **Th** 10-12.30
Nottinghamshire Royal Society for the Blind, Ortzen Street, Radford, **Nottingham** NG7 4BN ℘ 0115 970 6806	**D** 9-5
Central Library, Carlton Street, **Scunthorpe** DN15 6XT ℘ 01724 860161	**A, M-Th** 9.30-5 **F** 9.30-4.30
The Lindsey Blind Society, 12 Cole Street, **Scunthorpe** DN15 6QS ℘ 01724 840456, 01507 603824/605604	**A, Tu W F** 9.30-4 **Th** 9.30-12
The Lindsey Blind Society, The Lumley Centre for the Blind, 7 Lumley Avenue, **Skegness** PE25 2AH ℘ 01754 760656, 01507 605604	**Tu W Th F** 10-4
Staffordshire Association for the Welfare of the Blind, North Walls, **Stafford** ST16 3AD ℘ 01785 54572	**A, D** 9-1
P.A.B. Potteries Association for the Blind, Elsing Street, off City Road, Fenton, **Stoke-on-Trent** ST4 2PR ℘ 01782 846194	**D** 9-4

J

RNIB	Commercial	Hi tech	Low vision aids		Teaching	Enlarging copier	Tactile copier	Transcription	Other
	✓	✓	📺			✓		L B T	
✓	✓				✓				
✓	✓	✓	💡📺		✓	✓		L B T	
✓	✓				✓				
✓	✓	✓	💡📺 ⒶSDF		✓	✓		L B T M	Induction loops. Mobile Unit
✓	✓				✓	✓			
✓	✓		🔍						
✓	✓	✓	🔍💡📺		✓	✓		L B T M	Mobile unit
		✓				✓		L B T	
✓	✓	✓	📺 ⒶSDF		✓	✓		L B T	
✓	✓	✓			✓	✓			
✓	✓		🔍💡📺		✓	✓		L B T M	
✓	✓				✓	✓		L B M	

Resource Centre address and telephone number

Opening days and times

34.3.9 Yorkshire

Resource Centre address and telephone number	Opening days and times
Central Library, Prince's Way, **Bradford** BD1 1NN ℘ 01274 754681/753675	**A** or **D** 9-5
Centre for the Visually Impaired, 124 Morley Street, **Bradford** BD7 1BB ℘ 01274 726205	**M** to **Th** 8.30-5 **F** 8.30-4.30
Doncaster & District Association for the Blind, Clark Memorial Hall, Town Fields, Bennetthorpe, **Doncaster** DN1 2JQ ℘ 01302 326397	**M & F** 9-4 **W** 1-6
Partially Sighted Society Sight Centre, **Doncaster**. To be opened later in 1995. Enquiries to PO Box 322, DN1 2XA ℘ 01302 323132	
Reading Aids Unit, Central Library, Waterdale, **Doncaster** DN1 3JE ℘ 01302 735391	**D** 9-5
Halifax Society for the Blind, 3 Wards End, **Halifax** HX1 1DD ℘ 01422 352383	**M W Th** 9-3
Harrogate & District Society for the Blind, Russell Sergeant House, 23 East Parade, **Harrogate** HG1 5LF ℘ 01423 565915	**D** 9.30-4.30
Henshaw's Outreach, Bogs Lane, **Harrogate** HG1 4ED ℘ 01423 886451	**A, D** 9-5
Huddersfield Library, Princess Alexandra Walk, **Huddersfield** HD1 2SU ℘ 01484 424959	**D** 9-5
Hull & East Riding Institute for the Blind, Beech Holme, Beverley Road, **Hull** HU5 1NF ℘ 01482 342297	**D, M F** 9-5
Humberside Libraries, Stock Services, St. Andrews, Baker Street, **Hull** HU2 8HQ ℘ 01482 883060	**A, M-Th** 9.30-5 **F** 9.30-4.30
Central Library, Braille & Large Print Services, Calverly Street, **Leeds** LS1 3AB ℘ 0113 247 8262	**M Tu W F** 9-4.30 **Th** 9.30-4.30
William Merritt Disabled Living Centre, St. Mary's Hospital, Green Hill Road, Armley, **Leeds** LS12 3QE ℘ 0113 279 3140	**A, M-Th** 9-4.30 **F** 9-4
Vis-Ability, Rotherham's Disability Information Service, Central Library, Walker Place **Rotherham** S65 1JH ℘ 01709 373658	**D** 10-12, 1-4
Scarborough Blind & Partially Sighted Society, 33A Scalby Road, **Scarborough** YO12 5PZ ℘ 01723 354417	**D** 10-4
Royal Sheffield Institution for the Blind, 5 Mappin Street, **Sheffield** S1 4DT ℘ 0114 272 2757	**D** 8.30-4
Sheffield VIP Group, Unit 21, Cooper Building, Sheffield Science Park, Arundel Street, **Sheffield** S1 2NS ℘ 0114 272 4140	**A, M-Th** 10-2
York Blind & Partially Sighted Society, Bootham House, 61 Bootham, **York** YO3 7BT ℘ 01904 636269	**D** 10-2

J

RNIB	Commercial	Hi tech	Low vision aids	Teaching	Enlarging copier	Tactile copier	Transcription	Other
		✓	TV	✓			(L)(B)(T)	
✓	✓	✓	🔍 💡 TV [A/SDF chart]	✓	✓	✓	(B) (M)	
✓	✓		🔍	✓				
								Ring for up-to-date information
	✓	✓	🔍 TV	✓			(L)(B)(T)	
✓	✓		🔍 💡 TV				(B)(T)	
✓	✓	✓	🔍 💡 TV	✓			(B)(T)(M)	
✓	✓	✓	🔍 💡 TV	✓	✓	✓	(L)(B)(T)	
	✓			✓	✓		(L)(B)(T)	
✓	✓		🔍 💡 TV	✓			(L)(B)(T)	
	✓		TV	✓			(L)(B)(T)	
	✓		🔍 💡 TV	✓	✓		(L)(B)(T)	
✓	✓		🔍 [A/SDF chart]	✓	✓			
	✓		🔍 TV	✓			(L)(B)(T)	
✓	✓	✓	🔍 💡 TV incl. computers	✓	✓		(L)(B)(T)(M)	Mobile unit
✓	✓		🔍 💡 TV	✓	✓		(L)(B)(T)	
	✓	✓	🔍 TV				(L)(B)	
✓	✓	✓	🔍 💡 TV	✓			(L)(B)(T)(M)	

J

Resource Centre address and telephone number

Opening days and times

34.3.10 North West

Resource Centre address and telephone number	Opening days and times
Accrington & District Society of the Blind, 32 Bank Street, **Accrington** BB5 1HP ✆ 01254 233332	**M Tu Th F** 9.15-5
Wirral Society of the Blind & Partially Sighted, Ashville Lodge, Ashville Road **Birkenhead** L41 8AU ✆ 0151 652 8877	**D** 9-1
Blackburn & Darwen Society for the Blind, 1/2 Thwaites House, Railway Road, **Blackburn** BB1 5AX ✆ 01254 54143	**W & F** 9-3.30 **S** 10-12, by arrangement
Central Library, Town Hall Street, **Blackburn** BB2 1AG ✆ 01254 661221	**D** 9.30-4
Blackpool, Fylde & Wyre Society for the Blind, 25 Squires Gate Lane, **Blackpool** FY4 1SH ✆ 01253 345255	**A**
Central Library, Le Mans Crescent, **Bolton** BL1 1SE ✆ 01204 522311 ext 2176	**A, M Tu Th F** 9.30-5 alternate **S** 9.30-5 alternate **W** 9.30-1
Burnley Central Library, Hargreaves Street, **Burnley** BB11 2BD ✆ 01282 37115	**D** 9.30-5 **S** 9.30-12.30
Carlisle Society for the Blind, 11 Finkle Street, **Carlisle** CA3 8UU ✆ 01228 593104	**Tu-F** 10-12, 1-4
Chester, Cheshire & Clwyd Society for the Blind Vision Resource Centre, 67 Liverpool Road, **Chester** CH2 1AP ✆ 01244 382222	**M-Th** 9-4 **F** 9-3
The IRIS Centre, 14 Chapel Street, **Crewe** CW2 7DQ ✆ 01270 250316	**M** (alternate) **Tu** 11-2.30 **Th** by appointment
Centre for the Visually Impaired, Wellington Parade, King Street, **Dukinfield** SK16 4LE ✆ 0161 330 0014	**M Th F** 2-4.30 **W** 10-1 2-4.30 **S** 10-1
Tameside Blind Association, 4 Wellington Parade, **Dukinfield** SK16 4LE ✆ 0161 330 7778	**D** 9.30-3.30
Salford Social Services, Sensory Disability Team, Irwell Place, **Eccles** ✆ 0161 789 7331	**D** 8.30-4.30
South Lakeland Voluntary Society for the Blind, Stricklandgate House, 92 Stricklandgate, **Kendal** LA9 4PU ✆ 01539 726613	**W-F** 9.30-4
Central Library, William Brown Street, **Liverpool** L3 8EW ✆ 0151 225 5470	**M-Th** 9-7.30 **F S** 9-5
Christopher Grange, Rehabilitation Centre for the Visually Impaired (Catholic Blind Institute), Youens Way, East Prescot Road, **Liverpool** L14 2EW ✆ 0151 220 2525	**A, D** 9-5
Liverpool Voluntary Society for the Blind, Lime Court Day Centre, Upper Baker Street, **Liverpool** L6 1ND ✆ 0151 263 8360	**D** 9-4
Merseyside Regional Resource Centre, Henshaw's Society for the Blind, 7 The Strand, **Liverpool** L2 0PP ✆ 0151 227 1226	**D** 9-4.30
Macclesfield Society for the Blind, 15 Queen Victoria Street **Macclesfield** SK11 6LP ✆ 01625 422602	**D** 9.30-12

J

RNIB	Commercial	Hi tech	Low vision aids	Teaching	Enlarging copier	Tactile copier	Transcription	Other
✓	✓		🔍 💡 TV				B T	
✓	✓	✓	🔍 💡 TV A/SDF	✓	✓		B T	Advocacy service
✓	✓	✓	🔍 TV	✓			B T M	
		✓					L B T	
✓	✓	✓	🔍 💡 TV	✓			L B T	
✓	✓	✓	🔍 TV		✓		L B T	
✓	✓	✓	💡 TV		✓		L B T	
✓		✓	🔍 TV		✓		L B T	
✓	✓		💡 TV A/SDF	✓	✓		L B	
✓	✓		🔍 💡 TV	✓				
✓	✓	✓	🔍 💡 TV A/SDF		✓		L B T	
✓	✓	✓	🔍 💡	✓	✓		L B T M	
✓	✓		💡 TV	✓	✓		L B M	Induction loops
✓	✓		🔍 💡 TV A/SDF	✓	✓			
✓	✓	✓	TV	✓			L B T	
✓	✓	✓	🔍 💡 TV	✓	✓			
✓	✓	✓	🔍 💡 TV	✓	✓		L B T	
✓	✓	✓	🔍 💡 TV A/SDF	✓	✓		L B T	Mobile unit. Light room
✓	✓		💡	✓			T	

Resource Centre address and telephone number	Opening days and times

North West *continued*

Central Library, St Peter's Square, **Manchester** M2 5PD. Also by appointment at **Crumpsall**, **Gorton**, & **Wythenshawe** Libraries ✆ 0161 234 1989	**A, M Tu Th F S** 10-1 2-5, **W** 10-8
Disabled Living, Redbank House, 4 St. Chad's Street, Cheetham, **Manchester** M8 8QA ✆ 0161 832 3678	**D** 9-4.30
Greater Manchester Regional Resource Centre, Henshaw's Society for the Blind, John Derby House, 88-92 Talbot Road, Old Trafford, **Manchester** M16 OGS ✆ 0161 872 1234	**D** 9-4.30
Preston & N Lancashire Blind Welfare Society, Beechwood Centre for the Blind, 91 Balmoral Road, **Morecambe** LA3 1SS ✆ 01524 414846	**A, Tu F**
Sensory Services Team, Social Services Department, New Vale House, Greaves Street, **Oldham** OL1 1DW ✆ 0161 628 6882 Minicom 0161 633 0110	**D** 9-5
Harris (Central) Library, Market Square, **Preston** PR1 2PP ✆ 01772 253191	**A**
Preston & N Lancashire Blind Welfare Society, Howick House, Howick Park Avenue, Penwortham, **Preston** PR1 OLS ✆ 01772 744148	**D** 9-4
Chester, Cheshire & Clwyd Society for the Blind Vision Resource Centre, 57 Church Street, **Runcorn** WA7 1LG ✆ 01928 560205	**M-Th** 9-4 **F** 9-3
DASH (Disability Advice & Information St Helens), Central Library, Victoria Square, **St Helens** WA10 1DY ✆ 01744 453053	**D** 10-4
Stockport Institute for the Blind Resource Centre, Walthew House, 122 Shaw Heath, **Stockport** SK2 6QS ✆ 0161 480 2616	**A, D** 9-3
DIAL Trafford, Crossford, Highfield Close, **Stretford** M32 8NE ✆ 0161 864 2262	**A, D** 10-4
Rex Furness Centre, Warrington, Widnes & District Society for the Blind, 14 Museum Street, **Warrington** WA1 1HU ✆ 01925 632700	**T, Th 10-5** alternate **W 10-3**

34.3.11 North East

South Durham Society for the Blind and Visually Handicapped, West Lodge, West Crescent, **Darlington** DFL3 7PS ✆ 01325 483344	**M-F** 9-5
Hartlepool Blind Welfare Association, Avenue Road, **Hartlepool** TS24 8BB ✆ 01429 272494	**M-Th** 9-5 **F** 9-4
Northumberland Association for Visual Handicap, 20a Shaftoe Leazes, **Hexham** NE46 3DW ✆ 01434 600860	**A, D** 9-5
Teesside & District Society for the Blind, Stockton Road, **Middlesbrough** TS5 4AH ✆ 01642 247518	**A, D** 10-4.30

J

RNIB	Commercial	Hi tech	Low vision aids	Teaching	Enlarging copier	Tactile copier	Transcription	Other
		✓	🔍 💡 TV	✓	✓		(L)(B)(T)	
✓	✓		🔍 💡	✓				Induction loops
✓	✓	✓	🔍 💡 TV	✓	✓		(L)(B)(T)	Mobile unit. Sensory room (see chapter 7)
✓	✓		🔍 💡 TV				(L)(B)(T)(M)	
✓	✓		💡	✓	✓		(L)(B)(T)	Induction loops
	✓	✓	TV		✓		(L)(B)(T)	
✓	✓		🔍 TV	✓	✓		(L)(B)(T)(M)	
✓	✓		💡 A/SDF	✓			(L)(B)	
		✓	TV		✓		(L)(B)	
✓			TV				(L)(B)(T)	
✓	✓		🔍 💡 A/SDF		✓			Induction loops
✓	✓		TV A/SDF		✓			

RNIB	Commercial	Hi tech	Low vision aids	Teaching	Enlarging copier	Tactile copier	Transcription	Other
✓	✓			✓	✓		(L)(B)	
✓	✓		TV	✓			(L)(B)(T)	
✓	✓		🔍	✓	✓		(L) (T)	
✓	✓	✓	🔍 TV	✓	✓		(L)(B)(T)	

Resource Centre address and telephone number	Opening days and times

North East *continued*

Disability North, The Dene Centre, Castles Farm Road, **Newcastle-upon-Tyne** NE3 1PH ✆ 0191 284 0480	A, D 9-5
Newcastle-upon-Tyne Voluntary Society for the Blind, Mea House, Ellison Place, **Newcastle-upon-Tyne** NE1 8XS ✆ 0191 232 7292	A, M-Th 10-4
Sensory Support Team, Social Services Dept., Civic Centre, **Newcastle-upon-Tyne** NE1 8PA ✆ 0191 232 8520 ext 6325/6334	A, D 9-5
Tynemouth Blind Welfare Society, Pearey House, Preston Park, **North Shields** NE29 9JR ✆ 0191 257 4388	M Tu W F 8.30-5 Th 8.30-6.30

34.4 SCOTLAND

Grampian Society for the Blind, 21 John Street, **Aberdeen** AB1 1BT ✆ 01224 625622	D 10-4
Dumfries & Galloway Regional Council, 24 Catherine Street, **Dumfries** DG1 1DZ ✆ 01387 53927	D 9-12.30, 1.30-5
Dundee Society for Visually Impaired People, 35 Yeaman Shore, **Dundee** DD1 4BU ✆ 01382 227101	A, D 10-4
Central Library, George IV Bridge, **Edinburgh** EH1 1EG ✆ 0131 225 5584 ext 232	A, D 9-9 S 9-1
Society for the Welfare & Teaching of the Blind, 4 Coates Crescent, **Edinburgh** EH3 7AP ✆ 0131 225 6381	M-Th 10-4, F 10-3
Glasgow & West of Scotland Society for the Blind, 2 Queen's Crescent, St. George's Cross, **Glasgow** G4 9BW ✆ 0141 332 4632	D 9-5
Mitchell Library, North Street, **Glasgow** G3 7DN ✆ 0141 305 2920	D 9-9 & S 9-5
Resource Centre for the Blind, 276 St Vincent Street, .**Glasgow** G2 5RP ✆ 0141 248 5811	M-Th 8.45-4.45 F 8.45-3.55 2nd S in month 9.30-1.30
Highland Vision Services, 38 Ardconnel Street, **Inverness** IV2 3EX ✆ 01463 233663	D 9-5
Fife Society for the Blind, 1 Townsend Place, **Kirkcaldy** KY1 1HB ✆ 01592 260761	D 9-12, 2-5
Perth & Kinross Society for the Blind, 8 St Leonard's Bank, **Perth** PH2 8EB ✆ 01738 26969	M-Th 9-5, F 9-4.30
RNIB Resource Centre, 9 Viewfield Place, **Stirling** FK8 1NL ✆ 01786 451752	D 10-4

J

RNIB	Commercial	Hi tech	Low vision aids	Teaching	Enlarging copier	Tactile copier	Transcription	Other
✓	✓		🔍		✓			
✓	✓	✓	🔍 [TV]	✓			L B T	
✓	✓			✓	✓		L B T	Mobile unit. Induction loops
✓	✓		🔍 ☼ [TV]	✓			L B T	
✓	✓	✓	🔍 ☼ [TV]	✓	✓		L B T M	
✓	✓		🔍	✓			L B T	
✓	✓	✓	🔍 ☼ [TV] [A]	✓	✓		L B T	
		✓	🔍 [TV]		✓		L B T	
✓	✓		🔍 ☼ [TV]	✓			B T	
✓	✓	✓	🔍 ☼ [TV]	✓	✓		L B T	
		✓	🔍 [TV]				B T	
✓	✓	✓	🔍 ☼ [TV] [A]	✓	✓		L B T	2 mobile units
✓	✓	✓	🔍 ☼ [TV]	✓	✓		L B T M	
✓	✓	✓	🔍 ☼ [TV] [A]	✓	✓	✓	L B T	
✓	✓	✓	🔍 [TV]	✓	✓		L B T	
✓	✓		🔍 [TV]	✓	✓		B	

NORTHERN IRELAND, ISLE OF MAN | KEY IN 34.2

Resource Centre address and telephone number

Opening days and times

34.5 NORTHERN IRELAND

Resource Centre address and telephone number	Opening days and times
Blind Centre for Northern Ireland, 70 North Road, **Belfast** BT5 5NJ ✆ 01232 654366	**D** 9.30-5
Parkmount, Parkmount Day Centre, Shore Road, **Belfast** ✆ c/o 01232 391691 (social services office)	**A**
RNIB Northern Ireland Service Bureau, Unit B, 40 Linenhall Street, **Belfast** BT2 8BG ✆ 01232 329373	**D** 10-4
Blind Centre for Northern Ireland, 5 Long Commons, **Coleraine**, Co. Londonderry ✆ 01265 320333	**D** 9.30-5
Brookgreen Resource Centre, 11 Brook Street, **Coleraine** BT52 1PP ✆ 01265 55112	**A**
RNIB Resource Centre, Sensory Support Service, 16 Bishop Street, **Londonderry** BT48 6PW ✆ 01504 374619	**M- Th** 9-5 **F** 9-4.30
Magherafelt Social Services, 60 Hospital Road, **Magherafelt** BT45 5EG ✆ 01648 32703	**A, D** 9-5
Southern Health & Social Services Board; Moy Resource Centre, Dungannon Road, **Moy** BT71 7SN ✆ 01868 784832	**M-Th** 9-5.15 **F** 9-4.15
Conifers Resource Centre, Newry & Mourne Health & Social Services Trust, Dromalane Road, **Newry** BT35 8AP ✆ 01693 250800	**A, D** 9-5
Sight & Hearing Information Service, Health & Care Centre, 23-25 Regent Street, **Newtownards** BT23 4RU ✆ 01247 822944	**Tu & Th**, 2-4
Craigavon & Banbridge Health & Social Services Community Trust, Cherrytrees Resource Centre,1a Edenderry Gardens, **Portadown** BT63 5EA ✆ 01762 394088	**A, D** 9-1, 1.45-5

34.6 ISLE OF MAN

Resource Centre address and telephone number	Opening days and times
Manx Blind Welfare Society, 35 Derby Square, **Douglas** ✆ 0624 674727	**D** 9-4.30 (office) **T-Th** 2-4.30 (day centres)

J

506

RNIB	Commercial	Hi tech	Low vision aids	Teaching	Enlarging copier	Tactile copier	Transcription	Other
		✓	📺	✓	✓		❶ ❷ ❸ (L B T)	Mobile unit: tactile kit
✓	✓	✓	🔍 💡	✓				Induction loops
✓	✓	✓	🔍 💡 📺	✓	✓		❶ ❷ (L B)	Mobile unit
		✓	📺	✓				
✓	✓	✓	🔍 💡 📺 ▦(A/SDF)	✓				Induction loops. Mobile unit
✓	✓		🔍		✓			
✓			🔍					
✓	✓	✓	🔍 💡 📺	✓	✓		❶ ❷ ❸ (L B T)	
✓	✓		🔍 💡 📺	✓	✓			
✓	✓	✓	🔍 💡 📺 ▦(A/SDF)	✓			❶ ❷ ❸ (L B T)	
✓	✓		🔍 💡 📺 ▦(A/SDF)	✓	✓	✓		Induction loops
✓		✓	🔍 💡 📺	✓	✓		❸ (T)	

WALES

Resource Centre address and telephone number	Opening days and times

34.7 WALES

Resource Centre address and telephone number	Opening days and times
North Wales Society for the Blind, 325 High Street, **Bangor**, Gwynedd LL57 1YB ✆ 01248 353604	**D** 9-5, **S** by appointment
The Barry Blind Club, The Vale Resource Centre, Hen Goleg, College Fields Close, **Barry** CF62 8LF ✆ 01446 730402	**A, M & Th** 10-12, **Tu** 1.30-3.30
Cardiff Institute for the Blind, Shand House, 20 Newport Road, **Cardiff** CF2 1YB ✆ 01222 485414	**M-Th** 8.45-4.45 **F** 9-3.45
Resource Centre for the Visually Handicapped, 125 Cathedral Road, **Cardiff** CF1 9PH ✆ 01222 225810	**A, M-Th** 9.30-4.30 **F** 9.30-4
Spoilt for Choice, 89/90 Pontmorlais, **Merthyr Tydfil** CF47 8UH ✆ 01685 370072	**D & S** 9-5
Chester, Cheshire & Clwyd Society for the Blind, N.E. Wales Vision Resource Centre, Llys Alun Resource Centre, Clayton Road, **Mold** CH7 1ST ✆ 01352 757277	**D** 10-3
Gwent Association for the Blind, Torfaen Business Centre, Panteg Way, New Inn, **Pontypool** ✆ 01495 763650	**A, Tu & Th** mornings
Resource & Rehabilitation Centre for Visually Impaired People, 1 Heol-y-Gog, Gowerton, **Swansea** SA4 3BX ✆ 01792 872375	**A, D** 8.30-4

RNIB	Commercial	Hi tech	Low vision aids	Teaching	Enlarging copier	Tactile copier	Transcription	Other
✓	✓	✓	🔍 💡 [TV]	✓	✓		L B T	
✓			🔍 💡 [A-SDF]					
✓	✓	✓	🔍 💡 [TV]	✓	✓		L B T	
✓	✓		🔍 💡 [TV]	✓	✓			
✓	✓		🔍		✓			
✓	✓		💡 [A-SDF]	✓			L B	
✓	✓	✓	🔍 💡 [TV] [A-SDF]	✓	✓		L B T M	Induction loops
✓	✓	✓	🔍 💡 [TV]	✓	✓		L B T	

Index

Commercial firms are mostly excluded, as are italicised addresses in the text, resource centres listed in chapter 34, and holiday accommodation listed in chapter 22. Phrases such as 'of the blind' are sometimes omitted. See also **How to use this book** in the Directory. The letters **yp** before a page number indicate that it will be found in the yellow pages at the front of the book

J

J

J

J

J

J

J

J

J

I

J

J

J

J

J

J

J

J

J

J

Sight simulation quiz

Answers to the quiz on page 32

1 True.

2 Shielding her eyes from glare: glare is a nuisance if you are normal sighted, but disabling if you have many visual impairments – see 3.12.

3 Two. When seen from unusual angles, familiar objects can easily become unrecognisable, whether you have normal or impaired vision – see 3.14.

4 Teddy, laundry bag. Ability to see colour depends on the cone cells of the retina, which are more closely grouped in the centre of the retina at the rear of the eye. The rod cells give us sideways vision, and also resolve objects in poor light and in the dark. If the cone cells are damaged, monochrome and peripheral vision may survive, or vice versa. See 2.3.3, 2.3.4, 3.1.

5 The man's lunch? Or the dog's? The slightest visual hints can help us to 'read' the world about us. Noticing the dog gazing intently across our line of vision at a food bag might just alert you to avoid the dog as he leaps across your path. But the visual world of people with a sight impairment loses much of this secondary information which sighted people take for granted when anticipating many contingencies. See 3.14.

6 Yes, you might, if you had learnt how to use your remaining peripheral vision – see 2.3.3, 3.9.1.

7 Yes, you might, so long as you realise that there is something more to see by looking left – see 23.7.

8 Contrast! A bright yellow collar perhaps. Or changing the breed to a Dalmatian – see 3.14.1.

9 An optical device to broaden your remaining field of vision – see 3.3, 3.9.2.

10 Wear a wide-brimmed hat or an eyeshade, or walk on the shady side of the street – see 3.12.1.

J